THE FLIRT

BY THE SAME AUTHOR

THE GENTLEMAN FROM INDIANA

THE GUEST OF QUESNAY

MONSIEUR BEAUCAIRE

THE BEAUTIFUL LADY

THE TWO VANREVELS

HIS OWN PEOPLE

IN THE ARENA

“You darling!”

THE FLIRT

BY

BOOTH TARKINGTON

Author of "His Own People," "The Guest of Quesnay," "The Beautiful Lady," "In the Arena," "The Two Vanrevels," "Monsieur Beaucaire," "The Gentleman from Indiana," etc.

ILLUSTRATIONS BY
CLARENCE F. UNDERWOOD

GARDEN CITY NEW YORK
DOUBLEDAY, PAGE & COMPANY
1913

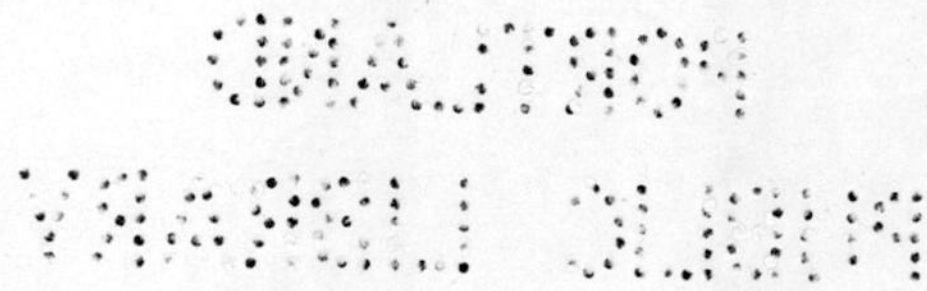

To

SUSANAH

ILLUSTRATIONS

THE FLIRT

THE FLIRT

CHAPTER ONE

VALENTINE CORLISS walked up Corliss Street the hottest afternoon of that hot August, a year ago, wearing a suit of white serge which attracted a little attention from those observers who were able to observe anything except the heat. The coat was shaped delicately; it outlined the wearer, and, fitting him as women's clothes fit women, suggested an effeminacy not an attribute of the tall Corliss. The effeminacy belonged all to the tailor, an artist plying far from Corliss Street, for the coat would have encountered a hundred of its fellows at Trouville or Ostende this very day. Corliss Street is the Avenue du Bois de Boulogne, the Park Lanc, the Fifth Avenue, of Capitol City, that smoky illuminant of our great central levels, but although it esteems itself an established cosmopolitan thoroughfare, it is still provincial enough to be watchful; and even in its torrid languor took some note of the alien garment.

Mr. Corliss, treading for the first time in seventeen years the pavements of this namesake of his grandfather, mildly repaid its interest in himself. The street, once the most peaceful in the world, he thought, had changed. It was still long and straight, still shaded by trees so noble that they were betrothed, here and there, high over the wide white roadway, the shimmering tunnels thus contrived shot with gold and blue; but its pristine complete restfulness was departed: gasoline had arrived, and a pedestrian, even this August day of heat, must glance two ways before crossing.

Architectural transformations, as vital, staggered the returned native. In his boyhood that posthumously libelled sovereign lady, Anne, had terribly prevailed among the dwellings on this highway; now, however, there was little left of the jig-saw's hare-brained ministrations; but the growing pains of the adolescent city had wrought some madness here. There had been a revolution which was a riot; and, plainly incited by a new outbreak of the colonies, the Goth, the Tudor, and the Tuscan had harried the upper reaches to a turmoil attaining its climax in a howl or two from the Spanish Moor.

Yet it was a pleasant street in spite of its improvements; in spite, too, of a long, gray smoke-plume crossing the summer sky and dropping an occasional atomy of coal upon Mr. Corliss's white coat. The green continuous masses of tree-foliage, lawn, and shrubbery were splendidly asserted; there was a faint wholesome odour from the fine block pavement of the roadway, white, save where the snailish water-wagon laid its long strips of steaming brown. Locusts, serenaders of the heat, invisible among the branches, rasped their interminable cadences, competing bitterly with the monotonous chattering of lawn-mowers propelled by glistening black men over the level swards beneath. And though porch and terrace were left to vacant wicker chairs and swinging-seats, and to flowers and plants in jars and green boxes, and the people sat unseen — and, it might be guessed, unclad for exhibition, in the dimmer recesses of their houses — nevertheless, a summery girl under an alluring parasol now and then prettily trod the sidewalks, and did not altogether suppress an ample consciousness of the white pedestrian's stalwart grace; nor was his quick glance too distressingly modest to be aware of these faint but attractive perturbations.

A few of the oldest houses remained as he remembered them, and there were two or three relics of mansard and cupola days; but the herd of cast-iron deer that once guarded these lawns, standing sentinel to all true gentry: Whither were they fled? In his boyhood, one specimen betokened a family of position and affluence; two, one on each side of the front walk, spoke of a noble opulence; two and a fountain were overwhelming. He wondered in what obscure thickets that once proud herd now grazed; and then he smiled, as through a leafy opening of shrubbery he caught a glimpse of a last survivor, still loyally alert, the haughty head thrown back in everlasting challenge and one foreleg lifted, standing in a vast and shadowy backyard with a clothesline fastened to its antlers.

Mr. Corliss remembered that backyard very well: it was an old battlefield whereon he had conquered; and he wondered if "the Lindley boys" still lived there, and if Richard Lindley would hate him now as implacably as then.

A hundred yards farther on, he paused before a house more familiar to him than any other, and gave it a moment's whimsical attention, without emotion.

It was a shabby old brick structure, and it stood among the gayest, the most flamboyant dwellings of all Corliss Street like a bewildered tramp surrounded by carnival maskers. It held place full in the course of the fury for demolition and rebuilding, but remained unaltered — even unrepaired, one might have thought — since the early seventies, when it was built. There was a sagging cornice, and the nauseous brown which the walls had years ago been painted was sooted to a repellent dinge, so cracked and peeled that the haggard red bricks were exposed, like a beggar through the holes in his coat. It was one of those houses which are large without being commodious; its very tall, very narrow windows, with their attenuated, rusty inside shutters, boasting to the passerby of high ceilings but betraying the miserly floor spaces. At each side of the front door was a high and cramped bay-window, one of them insanely culminating in a little six-sided tower of slate, and both of them girdled above the basement windows by a narrow porch, which ran across the front of the house and gave access to the shallow vestibule. However, a pleasant circumstance modified the gloom of this edifice and assured it a remnant of reserve and dignity in its ill-considered old age: it stood back a fine hundred feet from the highway, and was shielded in part by a friendly group of maple trees and one glorious elm, hoary, robust, and majestic, a veteran of the days when this was forest ground.

Mr. Corliss concluded his momentary pause by walking up the broken cement path, which was hard beset by plantain-weed and the long grass of the ill-kept lawn. Ascending the steps, he was assailed by an odour as of vehement bananas, a diffusion from some painful little chairs standing in the long, high, dim, rather sorrowful hall disclosed beyond the open double doors. They were stiff little chairs of an inconsequent, mongrel pattern; armless, with perforated wooden seats; legs tortured by the lathe to a semblance of buttons strung on a rod; and they had that day received a streaky coat of a gilding preparation which exhaled the olfactory vehemence mentioned. Their present station was temporary, their purpose, as obviously, to dry; and they were doing some incidental gilding on their own account, leaving blots and splashes and sporadic little round footprints on the hardwood floor.

The old-fashioned brass bell-handle upon the caller's right drooped from its socket in a dead fag, but after comprehensive manipulation on the part of the young man, and equal complaint on its own, it was constrained to permit a dim tinkle remotely. Somewhere in the interior a woman's voice, not young, sang a repeated fragment of "Lead, Kindly Light," to the accompaniment of a flapping dust-cloth, sounds which ceased upon a second successful encounter with the bell. Ensued a silence, probably to be interpreted as a period of whispered consultation out of range; a younger voice called softly and urgently, "Laura!" and a dark-eyed, dark-haired girl of something over twenty made her appearance to Mr. Corliss.

At sight of her he instantly restored a thin gold card-case to the pocket whence he was in the act of removing it. She looked at him with only grave, impersonal inquiry; no appreciative invoice of him was to be detected in her quiet eyes, which may have surprised him, possibly the more because he was aware there was plenty of appreciation in his own kindling glance. She was very white and black, this lady. Tall, trim, clear, she looked cool in spite of the black winter skirt she wore, an effect helped somewhat, perhaps, by the crisp freshness of her white waist, with its masculine collar and slim black tie, and undoubtedly by the even and lustreless light ivory of her skin, against which the strong black eyebrows and undulated black hair were lined with attractive precision; but, most of all, that coolness was the emanation of her undisturbed and tranquil eyes. They were not phlegmatic: a continuing spark glowed far within them, not ardently, but steadily and inscrutably, like the fixed stars in winter.

Mr. Valentine Corliss, of Paris and Naples, removed his white-ribboned straw hat and bowed as no one had ever bowed in that doorway. This most vivid salutation — accomplished by adding something to a rather quick inclination of the body from the hips, with the back and neck held straight — expressed deference without affecting or inviting cordiality. It was an elaborate little formality of a kind fancifully called "foreign," and evidently habitual to the performer.

It produced no outward effect upon the recipient. Such self-control is unusual.

"Is Mr. Madison at home? My name is Valentine Corliss."

"He is at home." She indicated an open doorway upon her right. "Will you wait in there?"

"Thank you," said Mr. Corliss, passing within. "I shall be ——" He left the sentence unfinished, for he was already alone, and at liberty to reflect upon the extraordinary coolness of this cool young woman.

The room, with its closed blinds, was soothingly dark after the riotous sun without, a grateful obscurity which was one of two attractions discovered in it by Mr. Corliss while he waited. It was a depressing little chamber, disproportionately high, uncheered by seven chairs (each of a different family, but all belonging to the same knobby species, and all upholstered a repellent blue), a scratched "inlaid table," likewise knobby, and a dangerous looking small sofa — turbulent furniture, warmly harmonious, however, in a common challenge to the visitor to take comfort in any of it. A once-gilt gas chandelier hung from the distant ceiling, with three globes of frosted glass, but undeniable evidence that five were intended; and two of the three had been severely bitten. There was a hostile little coal-grate, making a mouth under a mantel of imitation black marble, behind an old blue-satin fire-screen upon which red cat-tails and an owl over a pond had been roughly embroidered in high relief, this owl motive being the inspiration of innumerable other owls reflected in innumerable other ponds in the formerly silver moonlight with which the walls were papered. Corliss thought he remembered that in his boyhood, when it was known as "the parlour" (though he guessed that the Madison family called it "the reception room," now) this was the place where his aunt received callers who, she justifiably hoped, would not linger. Altogether, it struck him that it might be a good test-room for an alienist: no incipient lunacy would remain incipient here.

There was one incongruity which surprised him — a wicker waste-paper basket, so nonsensically out of place in this arid cell, where not the wildest hare-brain could picture any one coming to read or write, that he bestowed upon it a particular, frowning attention, and so discovered the second attractive possession of the room. A fresh and lovely pink rose, just opening full from the bud, lay in the bottom of the basket.

There was a rustling somewhere in the house and a murmur, above which a boy's voice became audible in emphatic but undistinguishable complaint. A whispering followed, and a woman exclaimed protestingly, "Cora!" And then a startlingly pretty girl came carelessly into the room through the open door.

She was humming "Quand l' Amour Meurt" in a

gay preoccupation, and evidently sought something upon the table in the centre of the room, for she continued her progress toward it several steps before realizing the presence of a visitor. She was a year or so younger than the girl who had admitted him, fairer and obviously more plastic, more expressive, more perishable, a great deal more insistently feminine; though it was to be seen that they were sisters. This one had eyes almost as dark as the other's, but these were not cool; they were sweet, unrestful, and seeking; brilliant with a vivacious hunger: and not Diana but huntresses more ardent have such eyes. Her hair was much lighter than her sister's; it was the colour of dry corn-silk in the sun; and she was the shorter by a head, rounder everywhere and not so slender; but no dumpling: she was exquisitely made. There was a softness about her: something of velvet, nothing of mush. She diffused with her entrance a radiance of gayety and of gentleness; sunlight ran with her. She seemed the incarnation of a caressing smile.

She was point-device. Her close, white skirt hung from a plainly embroidered white waist to a silken instep; and from the crown of her charming head to the tall heels of her graceful white suède slippers, heels of a sweeter curve than the waist of a violin, she was as modern and lovely as this dingy old house was belated and hideous.

Mr. Valentine Corliss spared the fraction of a second for another glance at the rose in the waste-basket.

The girl saw him before she reached the table, gave a little gasp of surprise, and halted with one hand carried prettily to her breast.

"Oh!" she said impulsively; "I *beg* your pardon. I didn't know there was —— I was looking for a book I thought I ——"

She stopped, whelmed with a breath-taking shyness, her eyes, after one quick but condensed encounter with those of Mr. Corliss, falling beneath exquisite lashes. Her voice was one to stir all men: it needs not many words for a supremely beautiful "speaking-voice" to be recognized for what it is; and this girl's was like herself, hauntingly lovely. The intelligent young man immediately realized that no one who heard it could ever forget it.

"I see," she faltered, turning to leave the room; "it isn't here — the book."

"There's something else of yours here," said Corliss.

"Is there?" She paused, hesitating at the door, looking at him over her shoulder uncertainly.

"You dropped this rose." He lifted the rose from the waste-basket and repeated the bow he had made at the front door. This time it was not altogether wasted.

"I?"

"Yes. You lost it. It belongs to you."

"Yes — it does. How curious!" she said slowly. "How curious it happened to be *there!*" She stepped to take it from him, her eyes upon his in charming astonishment. "And how odd that ——" She stopped; then said quickly:

"How did you know it was *my* rose?"

"Any one would know!"

Her expression of surprise was instantaneously merged in a flash of honest pleasure and admiration, such as only an artist may feel in the presence of a little masterpiece by a fellow-craftsman.

Happily, anticlimax was spared them by the arrival of the person for whom the visitor had asked at the door, and the young man retained the rose in his hand.

Mr. Madison, a shapeless hillock with a large, harassed, red face, evidently suffered from the heat: his gray hair was rumpled back from a damp forehead; the sleeves of his black alpaca coat were pulled up to the elbow above his uncuffed white shirt-sleeves; and he carried in one mottled hand the ruins of a palm-leaf fan, in the other a balled wet handkerchief which released an aroma of camphor upon the banana-burdened air. He bore evidences of inadequate adjustment after a disturbed siesta, but, exercising a mechanical cordiality, preceded himself into the room by a genial half-cough and a hearty, "Well-well-well," as if wishing to indicate a spirit of polite, even excited, hospitality.

"I expected you might be turning up, after your letter," he said, shaking hands. "Well, well, well! I remember you as a boy. Wouldn't have known you, of course; but I expect you'll find the town about as much changed as you are."

With a father's blindness to all that is really vital, he concluded his greeting inconsequently: "Oh, this is my little girl Cora."

"Run along, little girl," said the fat father.

His little girl's radiant glance at the alert visitor imparted her thorough comprehension of all the old man's absurdities, which had reached their climax in her dismissal. Her parting look, falling from Corliss's face to the waste-basket at his feet, just touched the rose in his hand as she passed through the door.

CHAPTER TWO

CORA paused in the hall at a point about twenty feet from the door, a girlish stratagem frequently of surprising advantage to the practitioner; but the two men had begun to speak of the weather. Suffering a momentary disappointment, she went on, stepping silently, and passed through a door at the end of the hall into a large and barren looking dining-room, stiffly and skimpily furnished, but well-lighted, owing to the fact that one end of it had been transformed into a narrow "conservatory," a glass alcove now tenanted by two dried palms and a number of vacant jars and earthen crocks.

Here her sister sat by an open window, repairing masculine underwear; and a handsome, shabby, dirty boy of about thirteen sprawled on the floor of the "conservatory" unloosing upon its innocent, cracked, old black and white tiles a ghastly family of snakes, owls, and visaged crescent moons, in orange, green, and other loathsome chalks. As Cora entered from the hall, a woman of fifty came in at a door opposite, and, a dust-cloth retained under her left arm, an unsheathed weapon ready for emergency, leaned sociably against the door-casing and continued to polish a tablespoon with a bit of powdered chamois-skin. She was tall and slightly bent; and, like the flat, old, silver spoon in her hand, seemed to have been worn thin by use; yet it was plain that the three young people in the room "got their looks" from her. Her eyes, if tired, were tolerant and fond; and her voice held its youth and something of the music of Cora's.

"What is he like?" She addressed the daughter by the window.

"Why don't you ask Coralie?" suggested the sprawling artist, relaxing his hideous labour. He pronounced his sister's name with intense bitterness. He called it "Cora-*lee*," with an implication far from subtle that his sister had at some time thus Gallicized herself, presumably for masculine favour; and he was pleased to receive tribute to his satire in a flash of dislike from her lovely eyes.

"I ask Laura because it was Laura who went to the door," Mrs. Madison answered. "I do not ask

Cora because Cora hasn't seen him. Do I satisfy you, Hedrick?"

"'Cora hasn't seen him!'" the boy hooted mockingly. "She hasn't? She was peeking out of the library shutters when he came up the front walk, and she wouldn't let me go to the door; she told Laura to go, but first she took the library waste-basket and laid one o' them roses ——"

"*Those* roses," said Cora sharply. "He *will* hang around the neighbours' stables. I think you ought to do something about it, mother."

"*Them* roses!" repeated Hedrick fiercely. "One o' them roses Dick Lindley sent her this morning. Laid it in the waste-basket and sneaked it into the reception room for an excuse to go galloping in and ——"

"'Galloping'?" said Mrs. Madison gravely.

"It was a pretty bum excuse," continued the unaffected youth, "but you bet your life you'll never beat our Cora-*lee* when there's a person in pants on the premises! It's sickening." He rose, and performed something like a toe-dance, a supposed imitation of his sister's mincing approach to the visitor. "Oh, dear, I *am* such a little sweety! Here I am all alone just reeking with Browning-and-

I never thought there was a man here!"

Tennyson and thinking to myself about such lovely things, and walking around looking for my nice pretty rose. Where can it be? Oh heavens, Mister, are *you* here? Oh my, I never, never thought that there was a *man* here! How you frighten me! See what a shy little thing I am? You *do* see, *don't* you, old sweeticums? Ta, ta, here's papa. Remember me by that rose, 'cause it's just like me. Me and it's twins, you see, cutie-sugar!" The diabolical boy then concluded with a reversion to the severity of his own manner: "If she was *my* daughter I'd whip her!"

His indignation was left in the air, for the three ladies had instinctively united against him, treacherously including his private feud in the sex-war of the ages: Cora jumped lightly upon the table and sat whistling and polishing the nails of one hand upon the palm of another; Laura continued to sew without looking up, and Mrs. Madison, conquering a tendency to laugh, preserved a serene countenance and said ruminatively:

"They were all rather queer, the Corlisses."

Hedrick stared incredulously, baffled; but men must expect these things, and this was no doubt a helpful item in his education.

"I wonder if he wants to sell the house," said Mrs. Madison.

"I wish he would. Anything that would make father get out of it!" Cora exclaimed. "I hope Mr. Corliss will burn it if he doesn't sell it."

"He might want to live here himself."

"He!" Cora emitted a derisive outcry.

Her mother gave her a quick, odd look, in which there was a real alarm. "What is he like, Cora?"

"Awfully foreign and distinguished!"

This brought Hedrick to confront her with a leap as of some wild animal under a lash. He landed close to her; his face awful.

"Princely, I should call him," said Cora, her enthusiasm undaunted. "Distinctly princely!"

"Princely," moaned Hedrick. "Pe-rin-sley!"

"Hedrick!" Mrs. Madison reproved him automatically. "In what way is he 'foreign,' Cora?"

"Oh, every way." Cora let her glance rest dreamily upon the goaded boy. "He has a splendid head set upon a magnificent torso ——"

"*Torso!*" Hedrick whispered hoarsely.

"Tall, a glorious figure — like a young guardsman's." Madness was gathering in her brother's eyes; and observing it with quiet pleasure, she added: "One sees immediately he has the grand manner, the *bel air*."

Hedrick exploded. "'*Bel air'!*" he screamed, and began to jump up and down, tossing his arms frantically, and gasping with emotion. "Oh, bel air! Oh, blah! 'Henry Esmond!' Been readin' 'Henry Esmond!' Oh, you be-yoo-tiful Cora-Beatrix-a-*lee!* Magganifisent torso! Gull*o*-rious figgi-your! Bel air! Oh, slush! Oh, luv-a-ly slush!" He cast himself convulsively upon the floor, full length. "Luv-a-ly, *luv*-a-ly slush!"

"He is thirty, I should say," continued Cora, thoughtfully. "Yes — about thirty. A strong, keen face, rather tanned. He's between fair and dark ——"

Hedrick raised himself to the attitude of the "Dying Gaul." "And with 'hair slightly silvered at the temples!' *Ain't* his hair slightly silvered at the temples?" he cried imploringly. "Oh, sister, in pity's name let his hair be slightly silvered at the temples? Only three grains of corn, your Grace; my children are starving!"

He collapsed again, laid his face upon his extended arms, and writhed.

"He has rather wonderful eyes," said Cora. "They seem to look right through you."

"Slush, slush, luv-a-ly slush," came in muffled tones from the floor.

"And he wears his clothes so well — so differently! You feel at once that he's not a person, but a personage."

Hedrick sat up, his eyes closed, his features contorted as with agony, and chanted, impromptu:

"Slush, slush, luv-a-ly, slush!
Le'ss all go a-swimmin' in a dollar's worth o' mush.
Slush in the morning, slush at night,
If I don't get my slush I'm bound to get tight!"

"Hedrick!" said his mother.

"Altogether I should say that Mr. Valentine Corliss looks as if he lived up to his name," Cora went on tranquilly. "Valentine Corliss of Corliss Street — I think I rather like the sound of that name." She let her beautiful voice linger upon it caressingly. "Valentine Corliss."

Hedrick opened his eyes, allowed his countenance to resume its ordinary proportions, and spoke another name slowly and with honeyed thoughtfulness:

"Ray Vilas."

This was the shot that told. Cora sprang down from the table with an exclamation.

Hedrick, subduing elation, added gently, in a mournful whisper:

"*Poor* old Dick Lindley!"

His efforts to sting his sister were completely successful at last: Cora was visibly agitated, and appealed hotly to her mother. "Am I to bear this kind of thing all my life? Aren't you *ever* going to punish his insolence?"

"Hedrick, Hedrick!" said Mrs. Madison sadly.

Cora turned to the girl by the window with a pathetic gesture. "Laura —— " she said, and hesitated.

Laura Madison looked up into her sister's troubled eyes.

"I feel so morbid," said Cora, flushing a little and glancing away. "I wish —— " She stopped.

The silent Laura set aside her work, rose and went out of the room. Her cheeks, too, had reddened faintly, a circumstance sharply noted by the terrible boy. He sat where he was, asprawl, propped by his arms behind him, watching with acute concentration the injured departure of Cora, following her sister. At the door, Cora, without pausing, threw him a look over her shoulder: a full-eyed shot of frankest hatred.

A few moments later, magnificent chords sounded through the house. The piano was old, but tuned to the middle of the note, and the keys were swept by a master hand. The wires were not hammered; they were touched knowingly as by the player's own fingers, and so they sang — and from out among the chords there stole an errant melody. This was not "piano-playing" and not a pianist's triumphant nimbleness — it was music. Art is the language of a heart that knows how to speak, and a heart that knew how was speaking here. What it told was something immeasurably wistful, something that might have welled up in the breast of a young girl standing at twilight in an April orchard. It was the inexpressible made into sound, an improvisation by a master player.

"You hear what she's up to?" said Hedrick, turning his head at last. But his mother had departed.

He again extended himself flat upon the floor, face downward, this time as a necessary preliminary to rising after a manner of his own invention. Mysteriously he became higher in the middle, his body slowly forming first a round and then a pointed arch, with forehead, knees, and elbows touching the floor. A brilliantly executed manœuvre closed his Gothic period, set him upright and upon his feet; then, without ostentation, he proceeded to the kitchen, where he found his mother polishing a sugar-bowl.

He challenged her with a damnatory gesture in the direction of the music. "You hear what Cora's up to?"

Mrs. Madison's expression was disturbed; she gave her son a look almost of appeal, and said, gently:

"I believe there's nothing precisely criminal in her getting Laura to play for her. Laura's playing always soothes her when she feels out of sorts — and — you weren't very considerate of her, Hedrick. You upset her."

"Mentioning Ray Vilas, you mean?" he demanded.

"You weren't kind."

"She deserves it. Look at her! *You* know why she's got Laura at the piano now."

"It's — it's because you worried her," his mother faltered evasively. "Besides, it is very hot, and Cora isn't as strong as she looks. She said she felt morbid and —— "

"Morbid? Blah!" interrupted the direct boy. "She's started after this Corliss man just like she did for Vilas. If I was Dick Lindley I wouldn't stand for Cora's —— "

"Hedrick!" His mother checked his outburst pleadingly. "Cora has so much harder time than the other girls; they're all so much better off. They seem to get everything they want, just by asking: nice clothes and jewellery — and automobiles. That seems to make a great difference nowadays; they all seem to have automobiles. We're so dreadfully poor, and Cora has to struggle so for what good times she —— "

"Her?" the boy jibed bitterly. "I don't see her doing any particular struggling." He waved his hand in a wide gesture. "She takes it *all!*"

"There, there!" the mother said, and, as if feeling the need of placating this harsh judge, continued gently: "Cora isn't strong, Hedrick, and she does have a hard time. Almost every one of the other girls in her set is at the seashore or somewhere having a gay summer. You don't realize, but it's mortifying to have to be the only one to stay at home, with everybody knowing it's because your father can't afford to send her. And this house is so hopeless,"

Mrs. Madison went on, extending her plea hopefully; "it's impossible to make it attractive, but Cora keeps trying and trying: she was all morning on her knees gilding those chairs for the music-room, poor child, and —— "

"'Music-room'!" sneered the boy. "Gilt chairs! All show-off! That's all she ever thinks about. It's all there is to Cora, just show-off, so she'll get a string o' fellows chasin' after her. She's started for this Corliss just exactly the way she did for Ray Vilas!"

"Hedrick!"

"Just look at her!" he cried vehemently. "Don't you know she's tryin' to make this Corliss think it's *her* playin' the piano right now?"

"Oh, no —— "

"Didn't she do that with Ray Vilas?" he demanded quickly. "Wasn't that exactly what she did the first time he ever came here — got Laura to play and made him think it was *her?* Didn't she?"

"Oh — just in fun." Mrs. Madison's tone lacked conviction; she turned, a little confusedly, from the glaring boy and fumbled among the silver on the kitchen table. "Besides — she told him afterward that it was Laura."

"He walked in on her one day when she was battin' away at the piano herself with her back to the door. Then she pretended it had been a joke, and he was so far gone by that time he didn't care. He's crazy, anyway," added the youth, casually. "Who is this Corliss?"

"He owns this house. His family were early settlers and used to be very prominent, but they're all dead except this one. His mother was a widow; she went abroad to live and took him with her when he was about your age, and I don't think he's ever been back since."

"Did he use to live in this house?"

"No; an aunt of his did. She left it to him when she died, two years ago. Your father was agent for her."

"You think this Corliss wants to sell it?"

"It's been for sale all the time he's owned it. That's why we moved here; it made the rent low."

"Is he rich?"

"They used to have money, but maybe it's all spent. It seemed to me he might want to raise money on the house, because I don't see any other reason that could bring him back here. He's already mortgaged it pretty heavily, your father told me. I don't —— " Mrs. Madison paused abruptly, her eyes widening at a dismaying thought. "Oh, I do hope your father will know better than to ask him to stay to dinner!"

Hedrick's expression became cryptic. "Father won't ask him," he said. "But I'll bet you a thousand dollars he stays!"

The mother followed her son's thought and did not seek to elicit verbal explanation of the certainty which justified so large a venture. "Oh, I hope not," she said. "Sarah's threatening to leave, anyway; and she gets so cross if there's extra cooking on wash-days."

"Well, Sarah'll have to get cross," said the boy grimly; "and *I*'ll have to plug out and go for a quart of brick ice-cream and carry it home in all this heat; and Laura and you'll have to stand over the stove with Sarah; and father'll have to change his shirt; and we'll all have to toil and moil and sweat and suffer while Cora-lee sits out on the front porch and talks toodle-do-dums to her new duke. And then she'll have *you* go out and kid him along while ——"

"*Hedrick!*"

"Yes, you will! — while she gets herself all dressed

and powdered up again. After that, she'll do her share of the work: she'll strain her poor back carryin' Dick Lindley's flowers down the back stairs and stickin' 'em in a vase over a hole in the tablecloth that Laura hasn't had time to sew up. You wait and see!"

The gloomy realism of this prophecy was not without effect upon the seer's mother. "Oh, no!" she exclaimed, protestingly. "We really can't manage it. I'm sure Cora won't want to ask him —— "

"You'll see!"

"No; I'm sure she wouldn't think of it, but if she does I'll tell her we can't. We really can't, to-day."

Her son looked pityingly upon her. "She ought to be *my* daughter," he said, the sinister implication all too plain; — "just about five minutes!"

With that, he effectively closed the interview and left her.

He returned to his abandoned art labours in the "conservatory," and meditatively perpetrated monstrosities upon the tiles for the next half-hour, at the end of which he concealed his box of chalks, with an anxiety possibly not unwarranted, beneath the sideboard; and made his way toward the front door, first glancing, unseen, into the kitchen where his mother still pursued the silver. He walked through the hall on tiptoe, taking care to step upon the much stained and worn strip of "Turkish" carpet, and not upon the more resonant wooden floor. The music had ceased long since.

The open doorway was like a brilliantly painted picture hung upon the darkness of the hall, though its human centre of interest was no startling bit of work, consisting of Mr. Madison pottering aimlessly about the sun-flooded, unkempt lawn, fanning himself, and now and then stooping to pull up one of the thousands of plantain-weeds that beset the grass. With him the little spy had no concern; but from a part of the porch out of sight from the hall came Cora's exquisite voice and the light and pleasant baritone of the visitor. Hedrick flattened himself in a corner just inside the door.

"I should break any engagement whatsoever if I had one," Mr. Corliss was saying with what the eavesdropper considered an offensively "foreign" accent and an equally unjustifiable gallantry; "but of course I haven't: I am so utterly a stranger here. Your mother is immensely hospitable to wish you to ask me, and I'll be only too glad to stay.

Perhaps after dinner you'll be very, very kind and play again? Of course you know how remarkable such —— "

"Oh, just improvising," Cora tossed off, carelessly, with a deprecatory ripple of laughter. "It's purely with the mood, you see. I can't make myself do things. No; I fancy I shall not play again today."

There was a moment's silence.

"Shan't I fasten that in your buttonhole for you," said Cora.

"You see how patiently I've been awaiting the offer!"

There was another little silence; and the listener was able to construct a picture (possibly in part from an active memory) of Cora's delicate hands uplifted to the gentleman's lapel and Cora's eyes for a moment likewise uplifted.

"Yes, one has moods," she said, dreamily. "I am *all* moods. I think you are too, Mr. Corliss. You *look* moody. Aren't you?"

A horrible grin might have been seen to disfigure the shadow in the corner just within the doorway.

"You look moody. Aren't you?"

CHAPTER THREE

IT WAS cooler outdoors, after dinner, in the dusk of that evening; nevertheless three members of the Madison family denied themselves the breeze, and, as by a tacitly recognized and habitual house-rule, so disposed themselves as to afford the most agreeable isolation for the younger daughter and the guest, who occupied wicker chairs upon the porch. The mother and father sat beneath a hot, gas droplight in the small "library"; Mrs. Madison with an evening newspaper, her husband with "King Solomon's Mines"; and Laura, after crisply declining an urgent request from Hedrick to play, had disappeared upstairs. The inimical lad alone was inspired for the ungrateful rôle of duenna.

He sat upon the topmost of the porch steps with the air of being permanently implanted; leaning forward, elbows on knees, cheeks on palms, in a treacherous affectation of profound reverie; and his back (all of him that was plainly visible in the hall light) tauntingly close to a delicate foot which would, God wot! willingly have launched him into the darkness beyond. It was his dreadful pleasure to understand wholly the itching of that shapely silk and satin foot.

The gas-light from the hall laid a broad orange path to the steps — Cora and her companion sat just beyond it, his whiteness gray, and she a pale ethereality in the shadow. She wore an evening gown that revealed a vague lilac through white, and shimmered upon her like a vapour. She was very quiet; and there was a wan sweetness about her, an exhalation of wistfulness. Cora, in the evening, was more like a rose than ever. She was fragrant in the dusk. The spell she cast was an Undine's: it was not to be thought so exquisite a thing as she could last. And who may know how she managed to say what she did in the silence and darkness? For it was said — without words, without touch, even without a look — as plainly as if she had spoken or written the message: "If I am a rose, I am one to be worn and borne away. Are you the man?"

With the fall of night, the street they faced had become still, save for an infrequent squawk of irritation on the part of one of the passing automobiles, gadding for the most part silently, like fireflies. But after a time a strolling trio of negroes came singing along the sidewalk.

> "In the evening, by the moonlight, you could hear
> those banjos ringing;
> In the evening, by the moonlight, you could hear
> those darkies singing.
> How the ole folks would injoy it; they would sit
> all night an' lis-sun,
> As we sang *i-i-n* the evening *by-y-y* the moonlight.'

"Ah, *that* takes me back!" exclaimed Corliss. "That's as it used to be. I might be a boy again."

"And I suppose this old house has many memories for you?" said Cora, softly.

"Not very many. My old-maid aunt didn't like me overmuch, I believe; and I wasn't here often. My mother and I lived far down the street. A big apartment-house stands there now, I noticed as I was walking out here this afternoon — the 'Verema,' it is called, absurdly enough!"

"Ray Vilas lives there," volunteered Hedrick, not altering his position.

"Vilas?" said the visitor politely, with a casual recollection that the name had been once or twice emphasized by the youth at dinner. "I don't remember Vilas among the old names here."

"It wasn't, I guess," said Hedrick. "Ray Vilas has only been here about two years. He came from Kentucky."

"A great friend of yours, I suppose."

'He ain't a boy," said Hedrick, and returned to silence without further explanation.

"How cool and kind the stars are to-night," said Cora, very gently.

She leaned forward from her chair, extending a white arm along the iron railing of the porch; bending toward Corliss, and speaking toward him and away from Hedrick in as low a voice as possible, probably entertaining a reasonable hope of not being overheard.

"I love things that are cool and kind," she said. "I love things that are cool and strong. I love iron." She moved her arm caressingly upon the railing. "I love its cool, smooth touch. Any strong life must have iron in it. I like iron in men." She leaned a very little closer to him.

"Have you iron in you, Mr. Corliss?" she asked.

At these words the frayed edge of Hedrick's broad white collar was lifted perceptibly from his coat, as if by a shudder passing over the back and shoulders beneath.

"If I have not," answered Corliss in a low voice, "I will have — now!"

"Tell me about yourself," she said.

"Dear lady," he began — and it was an effective beginning, for a sigh of pleasure parted her lips as he spoke — "there is nothing interesting to tell. I have spent a very commonplace life."

"I think not. You shouldn't call any life commonplace that has escaped *this!*" The lovely voice was all the richer for the pain that shook it now. "This monotony, this unending desert of ashes, this death in life!"

"This town, you mean?"

"This prison, I mean! Everything. Tell me what lies outside of it. You can."

"What makes you think I can?"

"I don't need to answer that. You understand perfectly."

Valentine Corliss drew in his breath with a sound murmurous of delight, and for a time they did not speak.

"Yes," he said, finally, "I think I do."

"There are meetings in the desert," he went on,

slowly. "A lonely traveller finds another at a spring, sometimes."

"And sometimes they find that they speak the same language?"

His answer came, almost in a whisper:

"'Even as you and I.'"

"'Even as you and I,'" she echoed, even more faintly.

"Yes."

Cora breathed rapidly in the silence that followed; she had every appearance of a woman deeply and mysteriously stirred. Her companion watched her keenly in the dusk, and whatever the reciprocal symptoms of emotion he may have exhibited, they were far from tumultuous, bearing more likeness to the quiet satisfaction of a good card-player taking what may prove to be a decisive trick.

After a time she leaned back in her chair again, and began to fan herself slowly.

"You have lived in the Orient, haven't you, Mr. Corliss?" she said in an ordinary tone.

"Not lived. I've been East once or twice. I spend a greater part of the year at Posilipo."

"Where is that?"

"On the fringe of Naples."

"Do you live in a hotel?"

"No." A slight surprise sounded in his voice. "I have a villa there."

"Do you know what that seems to me?" Cora asked gravely, after a pause; then answered herself, after another: "Like magic. Like a strange, beautiful dream."

"Yes, it is beautiful," he said.

"Then tell me: What do you do there?"

"I spend a lot of time on the water in a boat."

"Sailing?"

"On sapphires and emeralds and turquoises and rubies, melted and blown into waves."

"And you go yachting over that glory?"

"Fishing with my crew — and loafing."

"But your boat is really a yacht, isn't it?"

"Oh, it might be called anything," he laughed.

"And your sailors are Italian fishermen?"

Hedrick slew a mosquito upon his temple, smiting himself hard. "No, they're Chinese!" he muttered hoarsely.

"They're Neapolitans," said Corliss.

"Do they wear red sashes and earrings?" asked Cora.

"One of them wears earrings and a derby hat!"

"Ah!" she protested, turning to him again. "You don't tell me. You let me cross-question you, but you don't tell me things! Don't you see? I want to know what *life* is! I want to know of strange seas, of strange people, of pain and of danger, of great music, of curious thoughts! What are the Neapolitan women like?"

"They fade early."

She leaned closer to him. "Before the fading have you — have you loved — many?"

"All the pretty ones I ever saw," he answered gayly, but with something in his tone (as there was in hers) which implied that all the time they were really talking of things other than those spoken. Yet here this secret subject seemed to come near the surface.

She let him hear a genuine little snap of her teeth. "I *thought* you were like that!"

He laughed. "Ah, but you were sure to see it!"

"You could 'a' seen a Neapolitan woman yesterday, Cora," said Hedrick, obligingly, "if you'd looked out the front window. She was working a hurdy-gurdy up and down this neighbourhood all afternoon." He turned genially to face his sister, and added: "Ray Vilas used to say there were lots of pretty girls in Lexington."

Cora sprang to her feet. "You're not smoking," she said to Corliss hurriedly, as upon a sudden discovery. "Let me get you some matches."

She had entered the house before he could protest, and Hedrick, looking down the hall, was acutely aware that she dived desperately into the library. But, however tragic the cry for justice she uttered there, it certainly was not prolonged; and the almost instantaneous quickness of her reappearance upon the porch, with matches in her hand, made this one of the occasions when her brother had to admit that in her own line Cora was a miracle.

"So thoughtless of me," she said cheerfully, resuming her seat. She dropped the matches into Mr. Corliss's hand with a fleeting touch of her finger-tips upon his palm. "Of course you wanted to smoke. I can't think why I didn't realize it before. I must have —— "

A voice called from within, commanding in no uncertain tones.

"Hedrick! I should like to see you!"

Hedrick rose, and, looking neither to the right nor

to the left, went stonily into the house, and appeared before the powers.

"Call me?" he inquired with the air of cheerful readiness to proceed upon any errand, no matter how difficult.

Mr. Madison countered diplomacy with gloom. "I don't know what to do with you. Why can't you let your sister alone?"

"Has Laura been complaining of me?"

"Oh, Hedrick!" said Mrs. Madison.

Hedrick himself felt the justice of her reproof: his reference to Laura was poor work, he knew. He hung his head and began to scrape the carpet with the side of his shoe.

"Well, what'd Cora say I been doing to her?"

"You know perfectly well what you've been doing," said Mr. Madison sharply.

"Nothing at all; just sitting on the steps. What'd she *say?*"

His father evidently considered it wiser not to repeat the text of accusation. "You know what you did," he said heavily.

"Oho!" Hedrick's eyes became severe, and his sire's evasively shifted from them.

"You keep away from the porch," said the father, uneasily.

"You mean what I said about Ray Vilas?" asked the boy.

Both parents looked uncomfortable, and Mr. Madison, turning a leaf in his book, gave a mediocre imitation of an austere person resuming his reading after an impertinent interruption.

"That's what you mean," said the boy accusingly. "Ray Vilas!"

"Just you keep away from that porch."

"Because I happened to mention Ray Vilas?" demanded Hedrick.

"You let your sister alone."

"I got a right to know what she said, haven't I?"

There was no response, which appeared to satisfy Hedrick perfectly. Neither parent met his glance; the mother troubled and the father dogged, while the boy rejoiced sternly in some occult triumph. He inflated his scant chest in pomp and hurled at the defeated pair the well-known words:

"I wish she was *my* daughter — about five minutes!"

New sounds from without — men's voices in greeting, and a ripple of response from Cora somewhat lacking in enthusiasm — afforded Mr. Madison unmistakable relief, and an errand upon which to send his deadly offspring.

Hedrick, after a reconnaissance in the hall, obeyed at leisure. Closing the library door nonchalantly behind him, he found himself at the foot of a flight of unillumined back stairs, where his manner underwent a swift alteration, for here was an adventure to be gone about with ceremony. "Ventre St. Gris!" he muttered hoarsely, and loosened the long rapier in the shabby sheath at his side. For, with the closing of the door, he had become a Huguenot gentleman, over forty and a little grizzled perhaps, but modest and unassuming; wiry, alert, lightning-quick, with a wrist of steel and a heart of gold; and he was about to ascend the stairs of an unknown house at Blois in total darkness. He went up, crouching, ready for anything, without a footfall, not even causing a hideous creak; and gained the top in safety. Here he turned into an obscure passage, and at the end of it beheld, through an open door, a little room in which a dark-eyed lady sat writing in a book by the light of an oil lamp.

The wary Huguenot remained in the shadow and observed her.

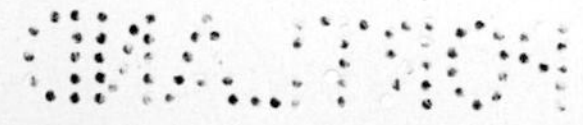

Laura was writing in an old ledger she had found in the attic, blank and unused. She had rebound it herself in heavy gray leather; and fitted it with a tiny padlock and key. She wore the key under her dress upon a very thin silver chain round her neck. Upon the first page of the book was written a date, now more than a year past, the month was June — and beneath it:

"Love came to me to-day."

Nothing more was written upon that page.

CHAPTER FOUR

LAURA, at this writing, looked piquantly unfamiliar to her brother: her eyes were moist and bright; her cheeks were flushed, and as she bent low, intently close to the book, a loosened wavy strand of her dark hair almost touched the page. Hedrick had never before seen her wearing an expression so "becoming" as the eager and tremulous warmth of this; though sometimes, at the piano, she would play in a reverie which wrought such glamour about her that even a brother was obliged to consider her rather handsome. She looked more than handsome now, so strangely lovely, in fact, that his eyes watered painfully with the protracted struggle to read a little of the writing in her book before she discovered him.

He gave it up at last, and lounged forward blinking, with the air of finding it sweet to do nothing.

"Whatch' writin'?" he asked in simple carelessness.

At the first sound of his movement she closed the

book in a flash; then, with a startled, protective gesture, extended her arms over it, covering it.

"What is it, Hedrick?" she asked, breathlessly.

"What's the padlock for?"

"Nothing," she panted. "What is it you want?"

"You writin' poetry?"

Laura's eyes dilated; she looked dangerous.

"Oh, I don't care about your old book," said Hedrick, with an amused nonchalance Talleyrand might have admired. "There's callers, and you have to come down."

"Who sent you?"

"A man I've often noticed around the house," he replied blightingly. "You may have seen him — I think his name's Madison. His wife and he both sent for you."

One of Laura's hands instinctively began to arrange her hair, but the other remained upon the book. "Who is it calling?"

"Richard Lindley and that Wade Trumble."

Laura rose, standing between her brother and the table. "Tell mother I will come down."

Hedrick moved a little nearer, whereupon, observing his eye, she put her right hand behind her upon the book. She was not deceived, and boys are not only superb strategic actors sometimes, but calamitously quick. Appearing to be unaware of her careful defence, he leaned against the wall and crossed his feet in an original and interesting manner.

"Of course *you* understand," he said cosily. "Cora wants to keep this Corliss in a corner of the porch where she can coo at him; so you and mother 'll have to raise a ballyhoo for Dick Lindley and that Wade Trumble. It'd been funny if Dick hadn't noticed anybody was there and kissed her. What on earth does he want to stay engaged to her for, anyway?"

"You don't know that she is engaged to Mr. Lindley, Hedrick."

"Get out!" he hooted. "What's the use talking like that to me? A blind mackerel could see she's let poor old Lindley think he's High Man with her these last few months; but he'll have to hit the pike now, I reckon, 'cause this Corliss is altogether too pe-rin-sley for Dick's class. Lee roy est mort. Vive lee roy!"

"Hedrick, won't you please run along? I want to change my dress."

"What for? There was company for dinner and you didn't change then."

Laura's flushed cheeks flushed deeper, and in her confusion she answered too quickly. "I only have one evening gown. I — of course I can't wear it every night."

"Well, then," he returned triumphantly, "what do you want to put it on now for?"

"*Please* run along, Hedrick," she pleaded.

"You didn't for this Corliss," he persisted sharply. "You know Dick Lindley couldn't see anybody but Cora to save his life, and I don't suppose there's a girl on earth fool enough to dress up for that Wade Trum —— "

"Hedrick!" Laura's voice rang with a warning which he remembered to have heard upon a few previous occasions when she had easily proved herself physically stronger than he. "Go and tell mother I'm coming," she said.

He began to whistle "Beulah Land" as he went, but, with the swift closing of the door behind him, abandoned that pathetically optimistic hymn prematurely, after the third bar.

Twenty minutes later, when Laura came out and went downstairs, a fine straight figure in her black evening gown, the Sieur de Marsac — that hard-bitten Huguenot, whose middle-aged shabbiness was but the outward and deceptive seeming of the longest head and the best sword in France — emerged cautiously from the passageway and stood listening until her footsteps were heard descending the front stairs. Nevertheless, the most painstaking search of her room, a search as systematic as it was feverish, failed to reveal where she had hidden the book.

He returned wearily to the porch.

A prophet has always been supposed to take some pleasure, perhaps morbid, in seeing his predictions fulfilled; and it may have been a consolation to the gloomy heart of Hedrick, sorely injured by Laura's offensive care of her treasure, to find the grouping upon the porch as he had foretold: Cora and Mr. Corliss sitting a little aloof from the others, far enough to permit their holding an indistinct and murmurous conversation of their own. Their sequestration, even by so short a distance, gave them an appearance of intimacy which probably accounted for the rather absent greeting bestowed by Mr. Lindley upon the son of the house, who met him with some favour.

This Richard Lindley was a thin, friendly looking young man with a pleasing, old-fashioned face which suggested that if he were minded to be portrayed it should be by the daguerreotype, and that a high, black stock would have been more suitable to him than his businesslike, modern neck-gear. He had fine eyes, which seemed habitually concerned with faraway things, though when he looked at Cora they sparkled; however, it cannot be said that the sparkling continued at its brightest when his glance wandered (as it not infrequently did this evening) from her lovely head to the rose in Mr. Corliss's white coat.

Hedrick, resuming a position upon the top step between the two groups, found the conversation of the larger annoying because it prevented him from hearing that of the smaller. It was carried on for the greater part by his mother and Mr. Trumble; Laura sat silent between these two; and Lindley's mood was obviously contemplative. Mr. Wade Trumble, twenty-six, small, earnest, and already beginning to lose his hair, was talkative enough.

He was one of those people who are so continuously aggressive that they are negligible. "What's the matter here? Nobody pays any attention to me. *I'm* important!" He might have had that legend engraved on his card, it spoke from everything else that was his: face, voice, gesture — even from his clothes, for they also clamoured for attention without receiving it. Worn by another man, their extravagance of shape and shade might have advertised a self-sacrificing effort for the picturesque; but upon Mr. Trumble they paradoxically confirmed an impression that he was well off and close. Certainly this was the impression confirmed in the mind of the shrewdest and most experienced observer on that veranda. The accomplished Valentine Corliss was quite able to share Cora's detachment satisfactorily, and be very actively aware of other things at the same time. For instance: Richard Lindley's preoccupation had neither escaped him nor remained unconnected in his mind with that gentleman's somewhat attentive notice of the present position of a certain rose.

Mr. Trumble took up Mrs. Madison's placid weather talk as if it had been a flaunting challenge; he made it a matter of conscience and for argument; for he was a doughty champion, it appeared, when nothings were in question, one of those stern men who will have accuracy in the banal, insisting upon portent in talk meant to be slid over as mere courteous sound.

"I don't know about that, now," he said with severe emphasis. "I don't know about that at all. I can't say I agree with you. In fact, I do not agree with you: it was hotter in the early part of July, year before last, than it has been at any time this summer. Several degrees hotter — several degrees."

"I fear I must beg to differ with you," he said, catching the poor lady again, a moment later. "I beg to differ decidedly. Other places get a great deal more heat. Look at Egypt."

"Permit me to disagree," he interrupted her at once, when she pathetically squirmed to another subject. "There's more than one side to this matter. You are looking at this matter from a totally wrong angle. . . . Let me inform you that statistics. . . ." Mrs. Madison's gentle voice was no more than just audible in the short intervals he permitted; a blind listener would have thought Mr. Trumble at the telephone. Hedrick was thankful when his mother finally gave up altogether the display of her ignorance, inaccuracy, and general misinformation, and Trumble talked alone. That must have been the young man's object; certainly he had struggled for it; and so it must have pleased him. He talked on and on and on; he passed from one topic to another with no pause; swinging over the gaps with a "Now you take," or, "And that reminds me," filling many a vacancy with "So-and-so and so-and-so," and other stencils, while casting about for material to continue. Everything was italicized, the significant and the trivial, to the same monotone of emphasis. Death and shoe-laces were all the same to him.

Anything was all the same to him so long as he talked.

Hedrick's irritation was gradually dispelled; and, becoming used to the sound, he found it lulling; relaxed his attitude and drowsed; Mr. Lindley was obviously lost in a reverie; Mrs. Madison, her hand shading her eyes, went over her market-list for the morrow and otherwise set her house in order; Laura alone sat straight in her chair; and her face was toward the vocalist, but as she was in deep shadow her expression could not be guessed. However, one person in that group must have listened with genuine pleasure — else why did he talk?

It was the returned native whose departure at last rang the curtain on the monologue. The end of the long sheltered seclusion of Cora and her companion was a whispered word. He spoke it first:

"To-morrow?"

"To-morrow."

Cora gave a keen, quick, indrawn sigh — not of sorrow — and sank back in her chair, as he touched her hand in farewell and rose to go. She remained where she was, motionless and silent in the dark, while he crossed to Mrs. Madison, and prefaced a leave-taking unusually formal for these precincts with his mannered bow. He shook hands with Richard Lindley, asking genially:

"Do you still live where you did — just below here?"

"Yes."

"When I passed by there this afternoon," said Corliss, "it recalled a stupendous conflict we had, once upon a time; but I couldn't remember the cause."

"I remember the cause," said Mr. Lindley, but, stopping rather short, omitted to state it.

"At all events, it was settled."

"Yes," said the other quietly. "You whipped me."

"Did I so?" Corliss laughed gayly. "We mustn't let it happen again!"

Mr. Trumble joined the parting guest, making simultaneous adieus with unmistakable elation. Mr. Trumble's dreadful entertainment had made it a happy evening for him.

As they went down the steps together, the top of his head just above the level of his companion's shoulder, he lifted to Corliss a searching gaze like an actor's hopeful scrutiny of a new acquaintance; and before they reached the street his bark rang eagerly on the stilly night: "Now *there* is a point on which I beg to differ with you. . . ."

Mrs. Madison gave Lindley her hand. "I think I'll go in. Good-night, Richard. Come, Hedrick!"

Hedrick rose, groaning, and batted his eyes painfully as he faced the hall light. "What'd you and this Corliss fight about?" he asked, sleepily.

"Nothing," said Lindley.

"You said you remembered."

"Oh, I remember a lot of useless things."

"Well, what was it? I want to know what you fought about."

"Come, Hedrick," repeated his mother, setting a gently urgent hand on his shoulder."

"I won't," said the boy impatiently, shaking her off and growing suddenly very wideawake and determined. "I won't move a step till he tells me what they fought about. Not a step!"

"Well — it was about a 'show.' We were only boys, you know — younger than you, perhaps."

"A circus?"

"A boy-circus he and my brother got up in our yard. I wasn't in it."

"Well, what did you fight about?"

"I thought Val Corliss wasn't quite fair to my brother. That's all."

"No, it isn't! How wasn't he fair?"

"They sold tickets to the other boys; and I thought my brother didn't get his share."

"This Corliss kept it all?"

"Oh, something like that," said Lindley, laughing. "Probably I was in the wrong."

"And he licked you?"

"All over the place!"

"I wish I'd seen it," said Hedrick, not unsympathetically, but as a sportsman. And he consented to be led away.

Laura had been standing at the top of the steps looking down the street, where Corliss and his brisk companion had emerged momentarily from deep shadows under the trees into the illumination of a swinging arc-lamp at the corner. They disappeared; and she turned, and, smiling, gave the delaying guest her hand in good-night.

His expression, which was somewhat troubled, changed to one of surprise as her face came into the light, for it was transfigured. Deeply flushed, her eyes luminous, she wore that shining look Hedrick had seen as she wrote in her secret book.

"Why, Laura!" said Lindley, wondering.

She said good-night again, and went in slowly. As she reached the foot of the stairs, she heard him moving a chair upon the porch, and Cora speaking sharply:

"Please don't sit close to me!" There was a sudden shrillness in the voice of honey, and the six words were run so rapidly together they seemed to form but one. After a moment Cora added, with a deprecatory ripple of laughter not quite free from the same shrillness:

"You see, Richard, it's so — it's so hot, to-night."

CHAPTER FIVE

HALF an hour later, when Lindley had gone, Cora closed the front doors in a manner which drew an immediate cry of agony from the room where her father was trying to sleep. She stood on tiptoe to turn out the gas-light in the hall; but for a time the key resisted the insufficient pressure of her finger-tips: the little orange flame, with its black-green crescent over the armature, so maliciously like the "eye" of a peacock feather, limned the exquisite planes of the upturned face; modelled them with soft and regular shadows; painted a sullen loveliness. The key turned a little, but not enough; and she whispered to herself a monosyllable not usually attributed to the vocabulary of a damsel of rank. Next moment, her expression flashed in a brilliant change, like that of a pouting child suddenly remembering that to-morrow is Christmas. The key surrendered instantly, and she ran gayly up the familiar stairs in the darkness.

The transom of Laura's door shone brightly; but the knob, turning uselessly in Cora's hand, proved the door itself not so hospitable. There was a brief rustling within the room; the bolt snapped, and Laura opened the door.

"Why, Laura," said Cora, observing her sister with transient curiosity, "you haven't undressed. What have you been doing? Something's the matter with you. I know what it is," she added, laughing, as she seated herself on the edge of the old black-walnut bed. "You're in love with Wade Trumble!"

"He's a strong man," observed Laura. "A remarkable throat."

"Horrible little person!" said Cora, forgetting what she owed the unfortunate Mr. Trumble for the vocal wall which had so effectively sheltered her earlier in the evening. "He's like one of those booming June-bugs, batting against the walls, falling into lamp-chimneys —— '

"He doesn't get very near the light he wants," said Laura.

"Me? Yes, he would like to, the rat! But he's consoled when he can get any one to listen to his awful chatter. He makes up to himself among women for the way he gets sat on at the club. But he has his use: he shows off the other men so, by contrast. Oh, Laura!" She lifted both hands to her cheeks, which were beautiful with a quick suffusion of high colour. "Isn't he gorgeous!"

"Yes," said Laura gently, "I've always thought so."

"Now what's the use of that?" asked Cora peevishly, "with *me?* I didn't mean Richard Lindley. You *know* what I mean."

"Yes — of course — I do," Laura said.

Cora gave her a long look in which a childlike pleading mingled with a faint, strange trouble; then this glance wandered moodily from the face of her sister to her own slippers, which she elevated to meet her descending line of vision.

"And you know I can't help it," she said, shifting quickly to the rôle of accuser. "So what's the use of behaving like the Pest?" She let her feet drop to the floor again, and her voice trembled a little as she went on: "Laura, you don't know what I had to endure from him to-night. I really don't think I can stand it to live in the same house any longer with that frightful little devil. He's been throwing Ray Vilas's name at me until — oh, it was ghastly to-night! And then — then ——" Her tremulousness increased. "I haven't said anything about it all day, but I *met* him on the street downtown, this morning ——"

"You met Vilas?" Laura looked startled. "Did he speak to you?"

"'Speak to me!'" Cora's exclamation shook with a half-laugh of hysteria. "He made an awful *scene!* He came out of the Richfield Hotel barroom on Main Street just as I was going into the jeweller's next door, and he stopped and bowed like a monkey, square in front of me, and — and he took off his hat and set it on the pavement at my feet and told me to kick it into the gutter! Everybody stopped and stared; and I couldn't get by him. And he said — he said I'd kicked his heart into the gutter and he didn't want it to catch cold without a hat! And wouldn't I please be so kind as to kick ——" She choked with angry mortification. "It was horrible! People were stopping and laughing, and a rowdy began to make fun of Ray, and pushed him, and they got into a scuffle, and I ran into the jeweller's and almost fainted."

"He is insane!" said Laura, aghast.

"He's nothing of the kind; he's just a brute. He does it to make people say I'm the cause of his drinking; and everybody in this gossipy old town *does* say it—just because I got bored to death with his everlasting do-you-love-me-to-day-as-well-as-yesterday style of torment, and couldn't help liking Richard better. Yes, every old cat in town says I ruined him, and that's what he wants them to say. It's so unmanly! I wish he'd die! Yes, I *do* wish he would! Why doesn't he kill himself?"

"Ah, don't say that," protested Laura.

"Why not? He's threatened to enough. And I'm afraid to go out of the house because I can't tell when I'll meet him or what he'll do. I was almost sick in that jeweller's shop, this morning, and so upset I came away without getting my pendant. There's *another* thing I've got to go through, I suppose!" She pounded the yielding pillow desperately. "Oh, oh, oh! Life isn't worth living—it seems to me sometimes as if everybody in the world spent his time trying to think up ways to make it harder for me! I couldn't have worn the pendant, though, even if I'd got it," she went on, becoming thoughtful. "It's Richard's silly old engagement ring, you know," she explained, lightly. "I had it made up into a pendant, and heaven knows how I'm going to get Richard to see it the right way. He was so unreasonable to-night."

"Was he cross about Mr. Corliss monopolizing you?"

"Oh, you know how he is," said Cora. "He didn't speak of it exactly. But after you'd gone, he asked me —— " She stopped with a little gulp, an expression of keen distaste about her mouth.

"Oh, he wants me to wear my ring," she continued, with sudden rapidity: "and how the dickens *can* I when I can't even tell him it's been made into a pendant! He wants to speak to father; he wants to *announce* it. He's sold out his business for what he thinks is a good deal of money, and he wants me to marry him next month and take some miserable little trip, I don't know where, for a few weeks, before he invests what he's made in another business. Oh!" she cried. "It's a *horrible* thing to ask a girl to do: to settle down — just housekeeping, housekeeping, housekeeping forever in this stupid, stupid town! It's so unfair! Men are just possessive;

they think it's *loving* you to want to possess you themselves. A beautiful 'love'! It's so mean! Men!" She sprang up and threw out both arms in a vehement gesture of revolt. "Damn 'em, I wish they'd let me *alone!*"

Laura's eyes had lost their quiet; they showed a glint of tears, and she was breathing quickly. In this crisis of emotion the two girls went to each other silently; Cora turned, and Laura began to unfasten Cora's dress in the back.

"Poor Richard!" said Laura presently, putting into her mouth a tiny pearl button which had detached itself at her touch. "This was his first evening in the overflow. No wonder he was troubled!"

"Pooh!" said Cora. "As if you and mamma weren't good enough for him to talk to! He's spoiled. He's so used to being called 'the most popular man in town' and knowing that every girl on Corliss Street wanted to marry him —— " She broke off, and exclaimed sharply: "I wish they would!"

"Cora!"

"Oh, I suppose you mean that's the reason *I* went in for him?"

"No, no," explained Laura hurriedly. "I only meant, stand still."

"Well, it was!" And Cora's abrupt laugh had the glad, free ring fancy attaches to the merry confidences of a buccaneer in trusted company.

Laura knelt to continue unfastening the dress; and when it was finished she extended three of the tiny buttons in her hand. "They're always loose on a new dress," she said. "I'll sew them all on tight, to-morrow."

Cora smiled lovingly. "You good old thing," she said. "You looked pretty to-night."

"That's nice!" Laura laughed, as she dropped the buttons into a little drawer of her bureau. It was an ugly, cheap, old bureau, its veneer loosened and peeling, the mirror small and flawed — a piece of furniture in keeping with the room, which was small, plain and hot, its only ornamental adjunct being a silver-framed photograph of Mrs. Madison with Cora, as a child of seven or eight, upon her lap.

"You really do look ever so pretty," asserted Cora.

"I wonder if I look as well as I did the last time I heard I was pretty," said the other. "That was at the Assembly in March. Coming down the stairs, I heard a man from out of town say, 'That black-haired Miss Madison is a pretty girl.' And some one with him said, 'Yes; you'll think so until you meet her sister!'"

"You are an old dear!" Cora enfolded her delightedly; then, drawing back, exclaimed: "You *know* he's gorgeous!" And with a feverish little ripple of laughter, caught her dress together in the back and sped through the hall to her own room.

This was a very different affair from Laura's, much cooler and larger; occupying half the width of the house; and a rather expensive struggle had made it pretty and even luxurious. The window curtains and the wall-paper were fresh, and of a quiet blue; there was a large divan of the same colour; a light desk, prettily equipped, occupied a corner; and between two gilt gas-brackets, whose patent burners were shielded by fringed silk shades, stood a cheval-glass six feet high. The door of a very large clothes-pantry stood open, showing a fine company of dresses, suspended from forms in an orderly manner; near by, a rosewood cabinet exhibited a delicate collection of shoes and slippers upon its four shelves. A dressing-table, charmingly littered with everything, took the place of a bureau;

and upon it, in a massive silver frame, was a large photograph of Mr. Richard Lindley. The frame was handsome, but somewhat battered: it had seen service. However, the photograph was quite new.

There were photographs everywhere: photographs framed and unframed; photographs large and photographs small, the fresh and the faded; tintypes, kodaks, "full lengths," "cabinets," groups — every kind of photograph; and among them were several of Cora herself, one of her mother, one of Laura, and two others of girls. All the rest were sterner. Two or three were seamed across with cracks, hastily recalled sentences to destruction; and here and there remained tokens of a draughtsman's over-generous struggle to confer upon some of the smooth-shaven faces additional manliness in the shape of sweeping moustaches, long beards, goatees, mutton-chops, and, in the case of one gentleman of a blond, delicate and tenor-like beauty, neck-whiskers; — decorations in many instances so deeply and damply pencilled that subsequent attempts at erasure had failed of great success. Certainly, Hedrick had his own way of relieving dull times.

Cora turned up the lights at the sides of the

cheval-glass, looked at herself earnestly, then absently, and began to loosen her hair. Her lifted hands hesitated; she re-arranged the slight displacement of her hair already effected; set two chairs before the mirror, seated herself in one; pulled up her dress, where it was slipping from her shoulder, rested an arm upon the back of the other chair as, earlier in the evening, she had rested it upon the iron railing of the porch, and, leaning forward, assumed as exactly as possible the attitude in which she had sat so long beside Valentine Corliss. She leaned very slowly closer and yet closer to the mirror; a rich colour spread over her; her eyes, gazing into themselves, became dreamy, inexpressibly wistful, cloudily sweet; her breath was tumultuous.

"'Even as you and I'?" she whispered.

Then, in the final moment of this after-the-fact rehearsal, as her face almost touched the glass, she forgot how and what she had looked to Corliss; she forgot him; she forgot him utterly: she leaped to her feet and kissed the mirrored lips with a sort of passion.

"You *darling!*" she cried.

Cora's christening had been unimaginative, for the

name means only, "maiden." She should have been called Narcissa.

The rhapsody was over instantly, leaving an emotional vacuum like a silence at the dentist's. Cora yawned, and resumed the loosening of her hair.

When she had put on her nightgown, she went from one window to another, closing the shutters against the coming of the morning light to wake her. As she reached the last window, a sudden high wind rushed among the trees outside; a white flare leaped at her face, startling her; there was a boom and rattle as of the brasses, cymbals, and kettle-drums of some fatal orchestra; and almost at once it began to rain.

And with that, from the distance came a voice, singing; and at the first sound of it, though it was far away and almost indistinguishable, Cora started more violently than at the lightning; she sprang to the mirror lights, put them out; threw herself upon the bed, and huddled there in the darkness.

The wind passed; the heart of the storm was miles away; this was only its fringe; but the rain pattered sharply upon the thick foliage outside her windows; and the singing voice came slowly up the street.

It was a strange voice: high-pitched and hoarse — and not quite human, so utter was the animal abandon of it.

"I love a lassie, a bonnie, bonnie lassie," it wailed and piped, coming nearer; and the gay little air—wrought to a grotesque of itself by this wild, high voice in the rain — might have been a banshee's love-song.

> "I love a lassie, a bonnie, bonnie lassie.
> She's as pure as the lily in the dell ——"

The voice grew louder; came in front of the house; came into the yard; came and sang just under Cora's window. There it fell silent a moment; then was lifted in a long peal of imbecile laughter, and sang again:

> "Then slowly, slowly rase she up
> And slowly she came nigh him,
> And when she drew the curtain by —
> 'Young man I think you're dyin'.' "

Cora's door opened and closed softly, and Laura, barefooted, stole to the bed and put an arm about the shaking form of her sister.

"The drunken beast!" sobbed Cora. "It's to disgrace me! That's what he wants. He'd like nothing better than headlines in the papers: 'Ray Vilas arrested at the Madison residence'!" She choked with anger and mortification. "The neighbours ——"

"They're nearly all away," whispered Laura. "You needn't fear ——"

"Hark!"

The voice stopped singing, and began to mumble incoherently; then it rose again in a lamentable outcry:

"Oh, God of the fallen, be Thou merciful to me! Be Thou merciful — merciful — *merciful*" . . .

"*Merciful, merciful, merciful!*" it shrieked, over and over, with increasing loudness, and to such nerve-racking effect that Cora, gasping, beat the bedclothes frantically with her hands at each iteration.

The transom over the door became luminous; some one had lighted the gas in the upper hall. Both girls jumped from the bed, ran to the door, and opened it. Their mother, wearing a red wrapper, was standing at the head of the stairs, which Mr. Madison, in his night-shirt and slippers, was slowly and heavily descending.

Before he reached the front door, the voice outside ceased its dreadful plaint with the abrupt anticlimax of a phonograph stopped in the middle of a record. There was the sound of a struggle and wrestling, a turmoil in the wet shrubberies, branches cracking.

"Let me go, da—— " cried the voice, drowned again at half a word, as by a powerful hand upon a screaming mouth.

The old man opened the front door, stepped out, closing it behind him; and the three women looked at each other wanly during a hushed interval like that in a sleeping-car at night when the train stops. Presently he came in again, and started up the stairs, heavily and slowly, as he had gone down.

"Richard Lindley stopped him," he said, sighing with the ascent, and not looking up. "He heard him as he came along the street, and dressed as quick as he could, and ran up and got him. Richard's taken him away."

He went to his own room, panting, mopping his damp gray hair with his fat wrist, and looking at no one.

Cora began to cry again. It was an hour before any of this family had recovered sufficient poise to realize, with the shuddering gratitude of adventurers spared from the abyss, that, under Providence, Hedrick had not wakened!

CHAPTER SIX

MUCH light shatters much loveliness; but a pretty girl who looks pretty outdoors on a dazzling hot summer morning is prettier then than ever. Cora knew it; of course she knew it; she knew exactly how she looked, as she left the concrete bridge behind her at the upper end of Corliss Street and turned into a shrub-bordered bypath of the river park. In imagination she stood at the turn of the path just ahead, watching her own approach: she saw herself as a picture — the white-domed parasol, with its cheerful pale-green lining, a background for her white hat, her corn-silk hair, and her delicately flushed face. She saw her pale, live arms through their thin sleeves, and the light grasp of her gloved fingers upon the glistening stick of the parasol; she saw the long, simple lines of her close white dress and their graceful interchanging movements with the alternate advance of her white shoes over the fine gravel path; she saw the dazzling splashes of sunshine playing upon her through the changeful branches overhead. Cora never lacked a gallery: she sat there herself.

She refreshed the eyes of a respectable burgess of sixty, a person so colourless that no one, after passing him, could have remembered anything about him except that he wore glasses and some sort of moustache; and to Cora's vision he was as near transparent as any man could be, yet she did not miss the almost imperceptible signs of his approval, as they met and continued on their opposite ways. She did not glance round, nor did he pause in his slow walk; neither was she clairvoyant; none the less, she knew that he turned his head and looked back at her.

The path led away from the drives and more public walks of the park, to a low hill, thoughtfully untouched by the gardener and left to the shadowy thickets and good-smelling underbrush of its rich native woodland. And here, by a brown bench, waited a tall gentleman in white.

They touched hands and sat without speaking. For several moments they continued the silence, then turned slowly and looked at each other; then looked slowly and gravely away, as if to an audience in front of them. They knew how to do it; but probably a critic in the first row would have concluded that Cora felt it even more than Valentine Corliss enjoyed it.

"I suppose this is very clandestine," she said, after a deep breath. "I don't think I care, though."

"I hope you do," he smiled, "so that I could think your coming means more."

"Then I'll care," she said, and looked at him again.

"You dear!" he exclaimed deliberately.

She bit her lip and looked down, but not before he had seen the quick dilation of her ardent eyes. "I wanted to be out of doors," she said. "I'm afraid there's one thing of yours I don't like, Mr. Corliss."

"I'll throw it away, then. Tell me."

"Your house. I don't like living in it, very much. I'm sorry you *can't* throw it away."

"I'm thinking of doing that very thing," he laughed. "But I'm glad I found the rose in that queer old waste-basket first."

"Not too much like a rose, sometimes," she said. "I think this morning I'm a little like some of the old doors up on the third floor: I feel rather unhinged, Mr. Corliss."

"You don't look it, Miss Madison!"

"I didn't sleep very well." She bestowed upon him a glance which transmuted her actual explanation into, "I couldn't sleep for thinking of you." It was perfectly definite; but the acute gentleman laughed genially.

"Go on with you!" he said.

Her eyes sparkled, and she joined laughter with him. "But it's true: you did keep me awake. Besides, I had a serenade."

"Serenade? I had an idea they didn't do that any more over here. I remember the young men going about at night with an orchestra sometimes when I was a boy, but I supposed ——"

"Oh, it wasn't much like that," she interrupted, carelessly. "I don't think that sort of thing has been done for years and years. It wasn't an orchestra — just a man singing under my window."

"With a guitar?'

"No." She laughed a little. "Just singing."

"But it rained last night," said Corliss, puzzled.

"Oh, *he* wouldn't mind that!"

"How stupid of me! Of course, he wouldn't. Was it Richard Lindley?"

"Never!"

"I see. Yes, that was a bad guess: I'm sure Lindley's just the same steady-going, sober, plodding old horse he was as a boy. His picture doesn't fit a romantic frame — singing under a lady's window in a thunderstorm! Your serenader must have been very young.'

"He is," said Cora. "I suppose he's about twenty-three; just a boy — and a very annoying one, too!"

Her companion looked at her narrowly. "By any chance, is he the person your little brother seemed so fond of mentioning — Mr. Vilas?"

Cora gave a genuine start. "Good heavens! What makes you think that?" she cried, but she was sufficiently disconcerted to confirm his amused suspicion.

"So it was Mr. Vilas," he said. "He's one of the jilted, of course."

"Oh, 'jilted'!" she exclaimed. "All the wild boys that a girl can't make herself like aren't 'jilted,' are they?"

"I believe I should say — yes," he returned. "Yes, in this instance, just about all of them."

"Is every woman a target for you, Mr. Corliss? I suppose you know that you have a most uncomfortable way of shooting up the landscape." She stirred uneasily, and moved away from him to the other end of the bench.

"I didn't miss that time," he laughed.

"Don't you ever miss?"

He leaned quickly toward her and answered in a low voice: "You can be sure I'm not going to miss anything about *you*."

It was as if his bending near her had been to rouge her. But it cannot be said that she disliked his effect upon her; for the deep breath she drew in audibly, through her shut teeth, was a signal of delight; and then followed one of those fraught silences not uncharacteristic of dialogues with Cora.

Presently, she gracefully and uselessly smoothed her hair from the left temple with the backs of her fingers, of course finishing the gesture prettily by tucking in a hairpin tighter above the nape of her neck. Then, with recovered coolness, she asked:

"Did you come all the way from Italy just to sell our old house, Mr. Corliss?"

"Perhaps that was part of why I came," he said, gayly. "I need a great deal of money, Miss Cora Madison."

"For your villa and your yacht?"

"No; I'm a magician, dear lady —— "

"Yes," she said, almost angrily. "Of course you know it!"

"You mock me! No; I'm going to make everybody rich who will trust me. I have a secret, and it's worth a mountain of gold. I've put all I have into it, and will put in everything else I can get for myself, but it's going to take a great deal more than that. And everybody who goes into it will come out on Monte Cristo's island."

"Then I'm sorry papa hasn't anything to put in," she said.

"But he has: his experience in business and his integrity. I want him to be secretary of my company. Will you help me to get him?" he laughed.

"Do you want me to?" she asked with a quick, serious glance straight in his eyes, one which he met admirably.

"I have an extremely definite impression," he said lightly, "that you can make anybody you know do just what you want him to."

"And I have another that you have still another 'extremely definite impression' that takes rank over that," she said, but not with his lightness, for her tone was faintly rueful. "It is that you can make *me* do just what you want me to."

Mr. Valentine Corliss threw himself back on the bench and laughed aloud. "What a girl!" he cried. Then for a fraction of a second he set his hand over hers, an evanescent touch at which her whole body started and visibly thrilled.

She lifted her gloved hand and looked at it with an odd wonder; her alert emotions, always too ready, flinging their banners to her cheeks again.

"Oh, I don't think it's soiled," he said, a speech which she punished with a look of starry contempt. For an instant she made him afraid that something had gone wrong with his measuring tape; but with a slow movement she set her hand softly against her hot cheek; and he was reassured: it was not his touching her that had offended her, but the allusion to it.

"Thanks," he said, very softly.

She dropped her hand to her parasol, and began, musingly, to dig little holes in the gravel of the path. "Richard Lindley is looking for investments," she said.

"I'm glad to hear he's been so successful," returned Corliss.

"He might like a share in your gold-mine."

"Thank heaven it isn't literally a gold-mine," he exclaimed. "There have been so many crooked ones exploited I don't believe you could get anybody nowadays to come in on a real one. But I think you'd make an excellent partner for an adventurer who had discovered hidden treasure; and I'm that particular kind of adventurer. I think I'll take you in."

"Do you?"

"How would you like to save a man from being ruined?"

"Ruined? You don't mean it literally?"

"Literally!" He laughed gayly. "If I don't 'land' this I'm gone, smashed, finished — quite ended! Don't bother, I'm going to 'land' it. And it's rather a serious compliment I'm paying you, thinking you can help me. I'd like to see a woman — just once in the world — who could manage a thing like this." He became suddenly very grave. "Good God! wouldn't I be at her feet!"

Her eyes became even more eager. "You think I — I *might* be a woman who could?"

"Who knows, Miss Madison? I believe —— "

He stopped abruptly, then in a lowered, graver voice asked: "Doesn't it somehow seem a little queer to you when we call each other, 'Miss Madison' and 'Mr. Corliss'?"

"Yes," she answered slowly; "it does."

"Doesn't it seem to you," he went on, in the same tone, "that we only 'Miss' and 'Mister' each other in fun? That though you never saw me until yesterday, we've gone pretty far beyond mere surfaces? That we did in our talk, last night?"

"Yes," she repeated; "it does."

He let a pause follow, and then said huskily:

"How far are we going?"

"I don't know." She was barely audible; but she turned deliberately, and there took place an eager exchange of looks which continued a long while. At last, and without ending this serious encounter, she whispered:

"How far do *you* think?"

Mr. Corliss did not answer, and a peculiar phenomenon became vaguely evident to the girl facing him: his eyes were still fixed full upon hers, but he was not actually looking at her; nevertheless, and with an extraordinarily acute attention, he was unquestionably looking at something. The direct front of pupil and iris did not waver from her; but for the time he was not aware of her; had not even heard her question. Something in the outer field of his vision had suddenly and completely engrossed him; something in that nebulous and hazy background which we see, as we say, with the white of the eye. Cora instinctively turned and looked behind her, down the path.

There was no one in sight except a little girl and the elderly burgess who had glanced over his shoulder at Cora as she entered the park; and he was, in face, mien, and attire, so thoroughly the unnoticeable, average man-on-the-street that she did not even recall him as the looker-round of a little while ago. He was strolling benevolently, the little girl clinging to one of his hands, the other holding an apple; and a composite photograph of a thousand grandfathers might have resulted in this man's picture.

As the man and little girl came slowly up the walk toward the couple on the bench there was a faint tinkle at Cora's feet: her companion's scarf-pin, which had fallen from his tie. He was maladroit about picking it up, trying with thumb and forefinger to seize the pin itself, instead of the more readily grasped design of small pearls at the top, so that he pushed it a little deeper into the gravel; and then occurred a tiny coincidence: the elderly man, passing, let fall the apple from his hand, and it rolled toward the pin just as Corliss managed to secure the latter. For an instant, though the situation was so absolutely commonplace, so casual, Cora had a wandering consciousness of some mysterious tensity; a feeling like the premonition of a crisis very near at hand. This sensation was the more curious because nothing whatever happened. The man got his apple, joined in the child's laughter, and went on.

"What was it you asked me?" said Corliss, lifting his head again and restoring the pin to his tie. He gazed carelessly at the back of the grandsire, disappearing beyond a bush at a bend in the path.

"Who was that man?" said Cora with some curiosity.

"That old fellow? I haven't an idea. You see I've been away from here so many years I remember almost no one. Why?"

"I don't know, unless it was because I had an idea

you were thinking of him instead of me. You didn't listen to what I said."

"That was because I was thinking so intensely of you," he began instantly. "A startlingly vivid thought of you came to me just then. Didn't I look like a man in a trance?"

"What was the thought?"

"It was a picture: I saw you standing under a great bulging sail, and the water flying by in moonlight; oh, a moon and a night such as you have never seen! and a big blue headland looming up against the moon, and crowned with lemon groves and vineyards, all sparkling with fireflies — old watch-towers and the roofs of white villas gleaming among olive orchards on the slopes — the sound of mandolins —— "

"Ah!" she sighed, the elderly man, his grandchild, and his apple well-forgotten.

"Do you think it was a prophecy?" he asked.

"What do *you* think?" she breathed. "That was really what I asked you before."

"I think," he said slowly, "that I'm in danger of forgetting that my 'hidden treasure' is the most important thing in the world."

"In great danger?" The words were not vocal.

He moved close to her; their eyes met again, with increased eagerness, and held fast; she was trembling, visibly; and her lips — parted with her tumultuous breathing — were not far from his.

"Isn't any man in great danger," he said, "if he falls in love with you?"

"Well?"

CHAPTER SEVEN

TOWARD four o'clock that afternoon, a very thin, fair young man shakily heaved himself into a hammock under the trees in that broad backyard wherein, as Valentine Corliss had yesterday noticed, the last iron monarch of the herd, with unabated arrogance, had entered domestic service as a clothes-prop. The young man, who was of delicate appearance and unhumanly pale, stretched himself at full length on his back, closed his eyes, moaned feebly, cursed the heat in a stricken whisper. Then, as a locust directly overhead violently shattered the silence, and seemed like to continue the outrage forever, the shaken lounger stopped his ears with his fingers and addressed the insect in old Saxon.

A white jacketed mulatto came from the house bearing something on a silver tray.

"Julip, Mist' Vilas?" he said sympathetically.

Ray Vilas rustily manœuvred into a sitting position; and, with eyes still closed, made shift to accept the julep in both hands, drained half of it, opened his eyes, and thanked the cup-bearer feebly, in a voice and accent reminiscent of the melodious South.

"And I wonder," he added, "if you can tell me —— "

"I'm Miz William Lindley's house-man, Joe Vardens," said the mulatto, in the tone of an indulgent nurse. "You in Miz Lindley's backyard right now, sittin' in a hammick."

"I seem to gather almost that much for myself," returned the patient. "But I should like to know how I got here."

"Jes' come out the front door an' walk' aroun' the house an' set down. Mist' Richard had to go downtown; tole me not to wake you; but I heerd you splashin' in the bath an' you tole me you din' want no breakfuss —— "

"Yes, Joe, I'm aware of what's occurred since I woke," said Vilas, and, throwing away the straws, finished the julep at one draught. "What I want to know is how I happened to be here at Mr. Lindley's."

"Mist' Richard brought you las' night, suh. I don' know where he got you, but I heered a considerable thrashum aroun', up an' down the house, an' so I come help him git you to bed in one vem spare-rooms." Joe chuckled ingratiatingly. "Lord name! You cert'n'y wasn't askin' fer no *bed!*"

He took the glass, and the young man reclined again in the hammock, a hot blush vanquishing his pallor. "Was I — was I very bad, Joe?"

"Oh, you was all *right,*" Joe hastened to reassure him. "You was jes' on'y a little bit tight."

"Did it really seem only a little?" the other asked hopefully.

"Yessuh," said Joe promptly. "Nothin' at all. You jes' wanted to rare roun' little bit. Mist' Richard took gun away from you —— "

"What?"

"Oh, I tole him you wasn' goin' use it!" Joe laughed. "But you so wile he din' know what you do. You cert'n'y was drunkes' man *I* see in *long* while," he said admiringly. "You pert near had us bofe wore out 'fore you give up, an' Mist' Richard an' me, we *use'* to han'lin' drunkum man, too — use' to have big times week-in, week-out 'ith Mist' Will — at's Mist' Richard's brother, you know, suh, what died o' whiskey." He laughed again in high good-humour. "You cert'n'y laid it all over any vem ole times we had 'ith Mist' Will!"

Mr. Vilas shifted his position in the hammock uneasily; Joe's honest intentions to be of cheer to the sufferer were not wholly successful.

"I tole Mist' Richard," the kindly servitor continued, "it was a mighty good thing his ma gone up Norf endurin' the hot spell. Sence Mist' Will die she can't hardly bear to see drunkum man aroun' the house. Mist' Richard hardly ever tech nothin' himself no more. You goin' feel better, suh, out in the f'esh air," he concluded, comfortingly as he moved away.

"Joe!"

"Yessuh."

Mr. Vilas pulled himself upright for a moment. "What use in the world do you reckon one julep is to me?"

"Mist' Richard say to give you one drink ef you ask' for it, suh," answered Joe, looking troubled.

"Well, you've told me enough now about last night to make any man hang himself, and I'm beginning to remember enough more —— "

"Pshaw, Mist' Vilas," the coloured man interrupted, deprecatingly, "you din' broke nothin'!

You on'y had couple glass' wine too much. You din' make no trouble at all; jes' went right off to bed. You ought seen some vem ole times me an Mist' Richard use to have 'ith Mist' Will —— "

"Joe!"

"Yessuh."

"I want three more juleps and I want them right away."

The troubled expression upon the coloured man's face deepened. "Mist' Richard say jes' one, suh," he said reluctantly. "I'm afraid —— "

"Joe."

"Yessuh."

"I don't know," said Ray Vilas slowly, "whether or not you ever heard that I was born and raised in Kentucky."

"Yessuh," returned Joe humbly. "I heerd so."

"Well, then," said the young man in a quiet voice, "you go and get me three juleps. I'll settle it with Mr. Richard."

"Yessuh."

But it was with a fifth of these renovators that Lindley found his guest occupied, an hour later, while upon a small table nearby a sixth, untouched, awaited disposal beside an emptied coffee-cup.

Also, Mr. Vilas was smoking a cigarette with unshadowed pleasure; his eye was bright, his expression care-free; and he was sitting up in the hammock, swinging cheerfully, and singing the "Marseillaise." Richard approached through the yard, coming from the street without entering the house; and anxiety was manifest in the glance he threw at the green-topped glass upon the table, and in his greeting.

"Hail, gloom!" returned Mr. Vilas, cordially, and, observing the anxious glance, he swiftly removed the untouched goblet from the table to his own immediate possession. "Two simultaneous juleps will enhance the higher welfare," he explained airily. "Sir, your Mr. Varden was induced to place a somewhat larger order with us than he protested to be your intention. Trusting you to exonerate him from all so-and-so and that these few words, etcetera!" He depleted the elder glass of its liquor, waved it in the air, cried, "Health, host!" and set it upon the table. "I believe I do not err in assuming my cup-bearer's name to be Varden, although he himself, in his simple Americo-Africanism, is pleased to pluralize it. Do I fret you, host?"

"Not in the least," said Richard, dropping upon

a rustic bench, and beginning to fan himself with his straw hat. "What's the use of fretting about a boy who hasn't sense enough to fret about himself?"

"'Boy?'" Mr. Vilas affected puzzlement. "Do I hear aright? Sir, do you boy me? Bethink you, I am now the shell of five mint-juleps plus, and am pot-valiant. And is this mere capacity itself to be lightly *boyed?* Again, do I not wear a man's garment, a man's garnitures? Heed your answer; for this serge, these flannels, and these silks are yours, and though I may not fill them to the utmost, I do to the longmost, precisely. I am the stature of a man; had it not been for your razor I should wear the beard of a man; therefore I'll not be boyed. What have you to say in defence?"

"Hadn't you better let me get Joe to bring you something to eat?" asked Richard.

"Eat?" Mr. Vilas disposed of the suggestion with mournful hauteur. "There! For the once I forgive you. Let the subject never be mentioned between us again. We will tactfully turn to a topic of interest. My memories of last evening, at first hazy and somewhat disconcerting, now merely amuse me. Following the pleasant Spanish custom,

I went a-serenading, but was kidnapped from beneath the precious casement by — by a zealous arrival. Host, 'zealous arrival' is not the julep in action: it is a triumph of paraphrase."

"I wish you'd let Joe take you back to bed," said Richard.

"Always bent on thoughts of the flesh," observed the other sadly. "Beds are for bodies, and I am become a thing of spirit. My soul is grateful a little for your care of its casing. You behold, I am generous: I am able to thank my successor to Carmen!"

Lindley's back stiffened. "Vilas!"

"Spare me your protests." The younger man waved his hand languidly. "You wish not to confer upon this subject —— "

"It's a subject we'll omit," said Richard.

His companion stopped swinging, allowed the hammock to come to rest; his air of badinage fell from him; for the moment he seemed entirely sober; and he spoke with gentleness. "Mr. Lindley, if you please, I am still a gentleman — at times."

"I beg your pardon," said Richard quickly.

"No need of that!" The speaker's former careless and boisterous manner instantly resumed possession.

"You must permit me to speak of a wholly fictitious lady, a creature of my wanton fancy, sir, whom I call Carmen. It will enable me to relieve my burdened soul of some remarks I have long wished to address to your excellent self."

"Oh, all right," muttered Richard, much annoyed.

"Let us imagine," continued Mr. Vilas, beginning to swing again, "that I thought I had won this Carmen —— "

Lindley uttered an exclamation, shifted his position in his chair, and fixed a bored attention upon the passing vehicles in the glimpse of the street afforded between the house and the shrubberies along the side fence. The other, without appearing to note his annoyance, went on, cheerfully:

"She was a precocious huntress: early in youth she passed through the accumulator stage, leaving it to the crude or village belle to rejoice in numbers and the excitement of teasing cubs in the bear-pit. It is the nature of this imagined Carmen to play fiercely with one imitation of love after another: a man thinks he wins her, but it is merely that she has chosen him — for a while. And Carmen can have what she chooses; if the man exists who could show her that she cannot, she would follow him through the devil's dance; but neither you nor I would be that man, my dear sir. We assume that Carmen's eyes have been mine — her heart is another matter — and that she has grown weary of my somewhat Sicilian manner of looking into them, and, following her nature and the law of periodicity which Carmens must bow to, she seeks a cooler gaze and calls Mr. Richard Lindley to come and take a turn at looking. Now, Mr. Richard Lindley is straight as a die: he will not even show that he hears the call until he is sure that I have been dismissed: therefore, I have no quarrel with him. Also, I cannot even hate him, for in my clearer julep vision I see that he is but an interregnum. Let me not offend my friend: chagrin is to be his as it is mine. I was a strong draught, he but the quieting potion our Carmen took to settle it. We shall be brothers in woe some day. Nothing in the universe lasts except Hell: Life is running water; Love, a looking-glass; Death, an empty theatre! That reminds me: as you are not listening I will sing."

He finished his drink and lifted his voice hilariously:

"The heavenly stars far above her,
The wind of the infinite sea,
Who know all her perfidy, love her,
So why call it madness in me?
Ah, why call it madness ——"

He set his glass with a crash upon the table, sta ing over his companion's shoulder.

"*What*, if you please, is the royal exile who thu seeks refuge in our hermitage?"

His host had already observed the approachin visitor with some surprise, and none too graciousl It was Valentine Corliss: he had turned in from th street and was crossing the lawn to join the tw young men. Lindley rose, and, greeting him wit sufficient cordiality, introduced Mr. Vilas, wh bestowed upon the newcomer a very lively interest.

"You are as welcome, Mr. Corliss," said th previous guest, earnestly, "as if these sylvan shad were mine. I hail you, not only for your own sak but because your presence encourages a hope th our host may offer refreshment to the entire con pany."

Corliss smilingly declined to be a party to th diplomacy, and seated himself beside Richa Lindley on the bench.

"Then I relapse!" exclaimed Mr. Vilas, throwi

ıimself back full-length in the hammock. "I am ıot replete, but content. I shall meditate. Gen-lemen, speak on!"

He waved his hand in a gracious gesture, indicat-ıg his intention to remain silent, and lay quiet, his yes fixed steadfastly upon Corliss.

"I was coming to call on you," said the latter to ındley, "but I saw you from the street and thought ou mightn't mind my being as informal as I used ɔ be, so many years ago."

"Of course," said Richard.

"I have a sinister purpose in coming," Mr. Corliss ıughingly went on. "I want to bore you a little rst, and then make your fortune. No doubt ıat's an old story to you, but I happen to be one of ıe adventurers whose argosies are laden with real ırgoes. Nobody knows who has or hasn't money ɔ invest nowadays, and of course I've no means f knowing whether *you* have or not — you see hat a direct chap I am — but if you have, or can y hold of some, I can show you how to make it ring you an immense deal more."

"Naturally," said Richard pleasantly, "I shall e glad if you can do that."

"Then I'll come to the point. It is exceedingly

simple; that's certainly one attractive thing about it." Corliss took some papers and unmounted photographs from his pocket, and began to spread them open on the bench between himself and Richard. "No doubt you know Southern Italy as well as I do."

"Oh, I don't 'know' it. I've been to Naples; down to Paestum; drove from Salerno to Sorrento by Amalfi; but that was years ago."

"Here's a large scale map that will refresh your memory." He unfolded it and laid it across their knees; it was frayed with wear along the folds, and had been heavily marked and dotted with red and blue pencillings. "My millions are in this large irregular section," he continued. "It's the ankle bone and instep of Italy's boot; this sizable province called Basilicata, east of Salerno, north of Calabria. And I'll not hang fire on the point, Lindley. What I've got there is oil."

"Olives?" asked Richard, puzzled.

"Hardly!" Corliss laughed. "Though of course one doesn't connect petroleum with the thought of Italy, and of all Italy, Southern Italy. But in spite of the years I've lived there, I've discovered myself to be so essentially American and commercial that I want to drench the surface of that antique soil with the brown, bad-smelling crude oil that lies so deep beneath it. Basilicata is the coming great oil-field of the world — and that's my secret. I dare to tell it here, as I shouldn't dare in Naples."

"Shouldn't 'dare'?" Richard repeated, with growing interest, and no doubt having some vague expectation of a tale of the Camorra. To him Naples had always seemed of all cities the most elusive and incomprehensible, a laughing, thieving, begging, mandolin-playing, music-and-murder haunted metropolis, about which anything was plausible; and this impression was not unique, as no inconsiderable proportion of Mr. Lindley's fellow-countrymen share it, a fact thoroughly comprehended by the returned native.

"It isn't a case of not daring on account of any bodily danger," explained Corliss.

"No," Richard smiled reminiscently. "I don't believe that would have much weight with you if it were. You certainly showed no symptoms of that sort in your extreme youth. I remember you had the name of being about the most daring and foolhardy boy in town."

"I grew up to be cautious enough in business,

though,"said the other, shaking his head gravely "I haven't been able to afford not being careful." He adjusted the map — a prefatory gesture. "Now I'll make this whole affair perfectly clear to you It's a simple matter, as are most big things. I'l begin by telling you of Moliterno — he's been m most intimate friend in that part of the continen for a great many years; since I went there as a boy in fact."

He sketched a portrait of his friend, Prince Mol terno, bachelor chief of a historic house, the sou of honour, "land-poor"; owning leagues and league of land, hills and mountains, broken towers an ruins, in central Basilicata, a province described a wild country and rough, off the rails and not eas to reach. Moliterno and the narrator had gone the to shoot; Corliss had seen "surface oil" upon th streams and pools; he recalled the discovery of o near his own boyhood home in America; had talke of it to Moliterno, and both men had become mo and more interested, then excited. They decide to sink a well.

Corliss described picturesquely the difficulties this enterprise, the hardships and disappointment how they dragged the big tools over the mountai by mule power; how they had kept it all secret; how he and Moliterno had done everything with the help of peasant labourers and one experienced man, who had "seen service in the Persian oil-fields."

He gave the business reality, colouring it with details relevant and irrelevant, anecdotes and way-side incidents: he was fluent, elaborate, explicit throughout. They sank five wells, he said, "at the angles of this irregular pentagon you see here on the map, outlined in blue. These red circles are the wells." Four of the wells "came in tremendous," but they had managed to get them sealed after wasting — he was "sorry to think how many thousand barrels of oil." The fifth well was so enormous that they had not been able to seal it at the time of the speaker's departure for America.

"But I had a cablegram this morning," he added, "letting me know they've managed to do it at last. Here is the cablegram." He handed Richard a form signed "Antonio Moliterno."

"Now, to go back to what I said about not 'daring' to speak of this in Naples," he continued, smiling. "The fear is financial, not physical."

The knowledge of the lucky strike, he explained, must be kept from the "Neapolitan money-sharks."

A third of the land so rich in oil already belonged to the Moliterno estates, but it was necessary to obtain possession of the other two thirds "before the secret leaks into Naples." So far, it was safe, the peasants of Basilicata being "as medieval a lot as one could wish." He related that these peasants thought that the devils hiding inside the mountains had been stabbed by the drills, and that the oil was devils' blood.

"You can see some of the country people hanging about, staring at a well, in this kodak, though it's not a very good one." He put into Richard's hand a small, blurred photograph showing a spouting well with an indistinct crowd standing in an irregula semicircle before it.

"Is this the Basilicatan peasant costume?" asked Richard, indicating a figure in the foreground the only one revealed at all definitely. "It look more oriental. Isn't the man wearing a fez?"

"Let me see," responded Mr. Corliss very quickly "Perhaps I gave you the wrong picture. Oh, no, he laughed easily, holding the kodak closer to his eyes; "that's all right: it is a fez. That's old Sal viati, our engineer, the man I spoke of who'd worke in Persia, you know; he's always worn a fez sinc then. Got in the habit of it out there and says he'll never give it up. Moliterno's always chaffing him about it. He's a faithful old chap, Salviati."

"I see." Lindley looked thoughtfully at the picture, which the other carelessly returned to his hand. "There seems to be a lot of oil there."

"It's one of the smaller wells at that. And you can see from the kodak that it's just 'blowing' — not an eruption from being 'shot,' or the people wouldn't stand so near. Yes; there's an ocean of oil under that whole province; but we want a lot of money to get at it. It's mountain country; our wells will all have to go over fifteen-hundred feet, and that's expensive. We want to pipe the oil to Salerno, where the Standard's ships will take it from us, and it will need a great deal for that. But most of all we want money to get hold of the land; we must control the whole field, and it's big!"

"How did you happen to come here to finance it?"

"I was getting to that. Moliterno himself is as honourable a man as breathes God's air. But my experience has been that Neapolitan capitalists are about the cleverest and slipperiest financiers in the world. We could have financed it twenty times over in Naples in a day, but neither Moliterno nor I was willing to trust them. The thing is enormous, you see — a really colossal fortune — and Italian law is full of ins and outs, and the first man we talked to confidentially would have given us his word to play straight, and, the instant we left him, would have flown post-haste for Basilicata and grabbed for himself the two thirds of the field not yet in our hands. Moliterno and I talked it over many, many times; we thought of going to Rome for the money, to Paris, to London, to New York; but I happened to remember the old house here that my aunt had left me — I wanted to sell it, to add whatever it brought to the money I've already put in — and then it struck me I might raise the rest here as well as anywhere else."

The other nodded. "I understand."

"I suppose you'll think me rather sentimental," Corliss went on, with a laugh which unexpectedly betrayed a little shyness. "I've never forgotten that I was born here — was a boy here. In all my wanderings I've always really thought of this as home."

His voice trembled slightly and his face flushed; he smiled deprecatingly as though in apology for these symptoms of emotion; and at that both listeners felt (perhaps with surprise) the man's strong attraction. There was something very engaging about him: in the frankness of his look and in the slight tremor in his voice; there was something appealing and yet manly in the confession, by this thoroughgoing cosmopolite, of his real feeling for the home-town.

"Of course I know how very few people, even among the 'old citizens,' would have any recollection whatever of *me*," he went on; "but that doesn't make any difference in my sentiment for the place and its people. That street out yonder was named for my grandfather: there's a statue of my great uncle in the State House yard; all my own blood belonged here, and though I have been a wanderer and may not be remembered — naturally am *not* remembered — yet the name is honoured here, and I — I ——" He faltered again, then concluded with quiet earnestness: "I thought that if my good luck was destined to bring fortunes to others, it might as well be to my own kind — that at least I'd offer them the chance before I offered it to any one else." He turned and looked Richard in the face. "That's why I'm here, Mr. Lindley."

The other impulsively put out his hand. "I understand," he said heartily.

"Thank you." Corliss changed his tone for one less serious. "You've listened very patiently and I hope you'll be rewarded for it. Certainly you will if you decide to come in with us. May I leave the maps and descriptions with you?"

"Yes, indeed. I'll look them over carefully and have another talk with you about it."

"Thank heaven, *that's* over!" exclaimed the lounger in the hammock, who had not once removed his fascinated stare from the expressive face of Valentine Corliss. "If you have now concluded with dull care, allow me to put a vital question: Mr. Corliss, do you sing?"

The gentleman addressed favoured him with a quizzical glance from between half-closed lids, and probably checking an impulse to remark that he happened to know that his questioner sometimes sang, replied merely, "No."

"It is a pity."

"Why?"

"Nothing," returned the other, inconsequently. "It just struck me that you ought to sing the Toreador song."

Richard Lindley, placing the notes and maps in his pocket, dropped them, and, stooping, began to gather the scattered papers with a very red face. Corliss, however, laughed good-naturedly.

"That's most flattering," he said; "though there are other things in 'Carmen' I prefer — probably because one doesn't hear them so eternally."

Vilas pulled himself up to a sitting position and began to swing again. "Observe our host, Mr. Corliss," he commanded gayly. "He is a kind old Dobbin, much beloved, but cares damn little to hear you or me speak of music. He'd even rather discuss your oil business than listen to us talk of women, whereas nothing except women ever really interests *you*, my dear sir. He's not our kind of man," he concluded, mournfully; "not at all our kind of man!"

"I hope," Corliss suggested, "he's going to be my kind of man in the development of these oil-fields."

"How ridic" — Mr. Vilas triumphed over the word after a slight struggle — "ulous! I shall review that: ridiculous of you to pretend to be interested in oil-fields. You are not that sort of person whatever. Nothing could be clearer than that you would never waste the time demanded by fields of oil. Groundlings call this 'the mechanical age' — a vulgar error. My dear sir, you and I know that it is the age of Woman! Even poets have begun to see that she is alive. Formerly we did not speak of her at all, but of late years she has become such a scandal that she is getting talked about. Even our dramas, which used to be all blood, have become all flesh. I wish I were dead — but will continue my harangue because the thought is pellucid. Women selecting men to mate with are of only two kinds, just as there are but two kinds of children in a toy-shop. One child sets its fancy on one partic" — the orator paused, then continued — "on one certain toy and will make a distressing scene if she doesn't get it: she will have that one; she will go straight to it, clasp it and keep it; she won't have any other. The other kind of woman is to be understood if you will make the experiment of taking the other kind of child to a toy-shop and telling her you will buy her any toy in the place, but that you will buy her only one. If you do this in the morning, she will still be in the shop when it is closing for the night, because, though she runs to each toy in turn with excitement and delight, she sees another over her shoulder, and the one she has not touched is always her choice — until she has touched it! Some get broken in the handling. For my part, my wires are working rather rustily, but I must obey the Stage-Manager. For my requiem I wish somebody would ask them to play Gounod's masterpiece."

"What's that?" asked Corliss, amused.

"'The Funeral March of a Marionette!'"

"I suppose you mean that for a cheerful way of announcing that you are a fatalist."

"Fatalism? That is only a word," declared Mr. Vilas gravely. "If I am not a puppet then I am a god. Somehow, I do not seem to be a god. If a god is a god, one thinks he would know it himself. I now yield the floor. Thanking you cordially, I believe there is a lady walking yonder who commands salutation."

He rose to his feet, bowing profoundly. Cora Madison was passing, strolling rather briskly down the street, not in the direction of her home. She waved her parasol with careless gayety to the trio under the trees, and, going on, was lost to their sight.

"Hello!" exclaimed Corliss, looking at his watch

with a start of surprise. "I have two letters to write for the evening mail. I must be off."

At this, Ray Vilas's eyes — still fixed upon him, as they had been throughout the visit — opened to their fullest capacity, in a gaze of only partially alcoholic wildness.

Entirely aware of this singular glare, but not in the least disconcerted by it, the recipient proffered his easy farewells. "I had no idea it was so late. Good afternoon. Mr. Vilas, I have been delighted with your diagnosis. Lindley, I'm at your disposal when you've looked over my data. My very warm thanks for your patience, and — addio!"

Lindley looked after him as he strode quickly away across the green lawn, turning, at the street, in the direction Cora had taken; and the troubled Richard felt his heart sink with vague but miserable apprehension. There was a gasp of desperation beside him, and the sound of Ray Vilas's lips parting and closing with little noises of pain.

"So he knows her," said the boy, his thin body shaking. "Look at him, damn him! See his deep chest, that conqueror's walk, the easy, confident, male pride of him: a true-born, natural rake — the Toreador all over!"

His agitation passed suddenly; he broke into a loud laugh, and flung a reckless hand to his companion's shoulder.

"You good old fool," he cried. "*You'll* never play Don José!"

CHAPTER EIGHT

HEDRICK MADISON, like too many other people, had never thought seriously about the moon; nor ever had he encouraged it to become his familiar; and he underwent his first experience of its incomparable betrayals one brilliant night during the last week of that hot month. The preface to this romantic evening was substantial and prosaic: four times during dinner was he copiously replenished with hash, which occasioned so rich a surfeit within him that, upon the conclusion of the meal, he found himself in no condition to retort appropriately to a solicitous warning from Cora to keep away from the cat. Indeed, it was half an hour later, and he was sitting — to his own consciousness too heavily — upon the back fence, when belated inspiration arrived. But there is no sound where there is no ear to hear, and no repartee, alas! when the wretch who said the first part has gone, so that Cora remained unscathed as from his alley solitude Hedrick hurled in the teeth of the rising moon these bitter words:

"Oh, no; *our* cat only eats *soft* meat!"

He renewed a morbid silence, and the moon, with its customary deliberation, swung clear of a sweeping branch of the big elm in the front yard and shone full upon him. Nothing warned the fated youth not to sit there; no shadow of imminent catastrophe tinted that brightness: no angel whisper came to him, bidding him begone — and to go in a hurry and as far as possible. No; he sat upon the fence an inoffensive lad, and — except for still feeling his hash somewhat, and a gradually dispersing rancour concerning the cat — at peace. It is for such lulled mortals that the ever-lurking Furies save their most hideous surprises.

Chin on palms, he looked idly at the moon, and the moon inscrutably returned his stare. Plausible, bright, bland, it gave no sign that it was at its awful work. For the bride of night is like a card-dealer whose fingers move so swiftly through the pack the trickery goes unseen.

This moon upon which he was placidly gazing, because he had nothing else to do, betokened nought to Hedrick: to him it was the moon of any other night, the old moon; certainly no moon of his delight. Withal, it may never be gazed upon so fixedly and so protractedly — no matter how languidly — with entire impunity. That light breeds a bug in the brain. Who can deny how the moon wrought this thing under the hair of unconscious Hedrick, or doubt its responsibility for the thing that happened?

"*Little boy!*"

It was a very soft, small voice, silky and queer; and at first Hedrick had little suspicion that it could be addressing him: the most rigid self-analysis could have revealed to him no possibility of his fitting so ignominious a description.

"Oh, little boy!"

He looked over his shoulder and saw, standing in the alley behind him, a girl of about his own age. She was daintily dressed and had beautiful hair which was all shining in pale gold.

"Little boy!"

She was smiling up at him, and once more she used that wantonly inaccurate vocative:

"Little boy!"

Hedrick grunted unencouragingly. "Who you callin' 'little boy'?"

For reply she began to climb the fence. It was

high, but the young lady was astonishingly agile, and not even to be deterred by several faint wails from tearing and ripping fabrics — casualties which appeared to be entirely beneath her notice. Arriving at the top rather dishevelled, and with irregular pennons here and there flung to the breeze from her attire, she seated herself cosily beside the dumbfounded Hedrick.

She turned her face to him and smiled — and there was something about her smile which Hedrick did not like. It discomforted him; nothing more. In sunlight he would have had the better chance to comprehend; but, unhappily, this was moonshine.

"Kiss me, little boy!" she said.

"I won't!" exclaimed the shocked and indignant Hedrick, edging uneasily away from her.

"Let's play," she said cheerfully.

"Play what?"

"I like chickens. Did you know I like chickens?"

The rather singular lack of connection in her remarks struck him as a misplaced effort at humour.

"You're having lots of fun with me, aren't you?" he growled.

She instantly moved close to him and lifted her face to his.

"Kiss me, darling little boy!" she said.

There was something more than uncommonly queer about this stranger, an unearthliness of which he was confusedly perceptive, but she was not without a curious kind of prettiness, and her pale gold hair was beautiful. The doomed lad saw the moon shining through it.

"Kiss me, darling little boy!" she repeated.

His head whirled; for the moment she seemed divine.

George Washington used profanity at the Battle of Monmouth. Hedrick kissed her.

He instantly pushed her away with strong distaste. "There!" he said angrily. "I hope that'll satisfy you!" He belonged to his sex.

"Kiss me some more, darling little boy!" she cried, and flung her arms about him.

With a smothered shout of dismay he tried to push her off, and they fell from the fence together, into the yard, at the cost of further and almost fatal injuries to the lady's apparel.

Hedrick was first upon his feet. "Haven't you got *any* sense?" he demanded.

She smiled unwaveringly, rose (without assistance) and repeated: "Kiss me some more, darling little boy!"

"No, I won't! I wouldn't for a thousand dollars!"

Apparently, she did not consider this discouraging. She began to advance endearingly, while he retreated backward. "Kiss me some ——"

"I won't, I tell you!" Hedrick kept stepping away, moving in a desperate circle. He resorted to a brutal formula: "You make me sick!"

"Kiss me some more, darling lit ——"

"I won't!" he bellowed. "And if you say that again I'll ——"

"Kiss me some more, darling little boy!" She flung herself at him, and with a yell of terror he turned and ran at top-speed.

She pursued, laughing sweetly, and calling loudly as she ran, "Kiss me some more, darling little boy! Kiss me some more, darling little boy!"

The stricken Hedrick knew not whither to direct his flight: he dared not dash for the street with this imminent tattered incubus — she was almost upon him — and he frantically made for the kitchen door, only to swerve with a gasp of despair as his foot touched the step, for she was at his heels, and he was sickeningly assured she would cheerfully follow him through the house, shouting that damning refrain for all ears. A strangling fear took him by the throat — if Cora should come to be a spectator of this unspeakable flight, if Cora should hear that horrid plea for love! Then farewell peace; indeed, farewell all joy in life forever!

Panting sobbingly, he ducked under the amorous vampire's arm and fled on. He zigzagged desperately to and fro across the broad, empty backyard, a small hand ever and anon managing to clutch his shoulder, the awful petition in his ears:

"Kiss me some more, darling little boy!"

"*Hedrick!*"

Emerging from the kitchen door, Laura stood and gazed in wonder as the two eerie figures sped by her, circled, ducked, dodged, flew madly on. This commonplace purlieu was become the scene of a witch-chase; the moonlight fell upon the ghastly flitting face of the pursued, uplifted in agony, white, wet, with fay eyes; also it illumined the unreal elf following close, a breeze-blown fantasy in rags.

"Kiss me some more, darling little boy!"

"Kiss me some more, darl——"

Laura uttered a sharp exclamation. "Stand still, Hedrick!" she called. "You must!"

Hedrick made a piteous effort to increase his speed.

"It's Lolita Martin," called Laura. "She must have her way or nothing can be done with her. Stand *still!*"

Hedrick had never heard of Lolita Martin, but the added information concerning her was not ineffective: it operated as a spur; and Laura joined the hunt.

"Stand still!" she cried to the wretched quarry. "She's run away. She must be taken home. Stop, Hedrick! You *must* stop!"

Hedrick had no intention of stopping, but Laura was a runner, and, as he dodged the other, caught and held him fast. The next instant, Lolita, laughing happily, flung her arms round his neck from behind.

"Lemme go!" shuddered Hedrick. "Lemme go!"

"Kiss me again, darl ——"

"I — woof!" He became inarticulate.

"She isn't quite right," his sister whispered hurriedly in his ear. "She has spells when she's weak mentally. You must be kind to her. She only wants you to ——"

"'*Only*'!" he echoed hoarsely. "I won't ki ——" He was unable to finish the word.

"We must get her home," said Laura anxiously. "Will you come with me, Lolita, dear?"

Apparently Lolita had no consciousness whatever of Laura's presence. Instead of replying, she tightened her grasp upon Hedrick and warmly reiterated her request.

"Shut up, you parrot!" hissed the goaded boy.

"Perhaps she'll go if you let her walk with her arms round your neck," suggested Laura.

"If I *what?*"

"Let's try it. We've got to get her home; her mother must be frantic about her. Come, let's see if she'll go with us that way."

With convincing earnestness, Hedrick refused to make the experiment until Laura suggested that he remain with Lolita while she summoned assistance; then, as no alternative appeared, his spirit broke utterly, and he consented to the trial, stipulating with a last burst of vehemence that the progress of the unthinkable pageant should be through the alley.

"Come, Lolita," said Laura coaxingly. "We're going for a nice walk." At the adjective, Hedrick's burdened shoulders were racked with a brief spasm, which recurred as his sister added: "Your darling little boy will let you keep hold of him."

Lolita seemed content. Laughing gayly, she offered no opposition, but, maintaining her embrace with both arms and walking somewhat sidewise, went willingly enough; and the three slowly crossed the yard, passed through the empty stable and out into the alley. When they reached the cross-street at the alley's upper end, Hedrick balked flatly.

Laura expostulated, then entreated. Hedrick refused with sincere loathing to be seen upon the street occupying his present position in the group. Laura assured him that there was no one to see; he replied that the moon was bright and the evening early; he would die, and readily, but he would not set foot in the street. Unfortunately, he had selected an unfavourable spot for argument: they were already within a yard or two of the street; and a strange boy, passing, stopped and observed, and whistled discourteously.

"Ain't he the spooner!" remarked this unknown with hideous admiration.

"I'll thank you," returned Hedrick haughtily, "to go on about your own business."

"Kiss me some more, darling little boy!" said Lolita.

The strange boy squawked, wailed, screamed with laughter, howled the loving petition in a dozen keys of mockery, while Hedrick writhed and Lolita clung. Enriched by a new and great experience, the torturer trotted on, leaving viperish cachinnations in his wake.

But the martyrdom was at an end. A woman, hurrying past, bareheaded, was greeted by a cry of delight from Lolita, who released Hedrick and ran to her with outstretched arms.

"We were bringing her home, Mrs. Martin," said Laura, reassuringly. "She's all right; nothing's the matter except that her dress got torn. We found her playing in our yard."

"I thank you a thousand times, Miss Madison," cried Lolita's mother, and flutteringly plunged into a description of her anxiety, her search for Lolita, and concluded with renewed expressions of gratitude for the child's safe return, an outpouring of thankfulness and joy wholly incomprehensible to Hedrick.

"Not at all," said Laura cheerfully. "Come, Hedrick. We'll go home by the street, I think." She touched his shoulder, and he went with her in stunned obedience. He was not able to face the incredible thing that had happened to him: he walked in a trance of horror.

"Poor little girl!" said Laura gently, with what seemed to her brother an indefensibly misplaced compassion. "Usually they have her live in an institution for people afflicted as she is, but they brought her home for a visit last week, I believe. Of course you didn't understand, but I think you should have been more thoughtful. Really, you shouldn't have flirted with her."

Hedrick stopped short.

"'*Flirted'!*" His voice was beginning to show symptoms of changing, this year; it rose to a falsetto wail, flickered and went out.

With the departure of Lolita in safety, what had seemed bizarre and piteous became obscured, and another aspect of the adventure was presented to Laura. The sufferings of the arrogant are not wholly depressing to the spectator; and of arrogance Hedrick had ever been a master. She began to shake; a convulsion took her, and suddenly she sat upon the curbstone without dignity, and laughed as he had never seen her.

A horrid distrust of her rose within him: he

began to realize in what plight he stood, what terrors o'erhung.

"Look here," he said miserably, "are you — you aren't — you don't have to go and — and *talk* about this, do you?"

"No, Hedrick," she responded, rising and controlling herself somewhat. "Not so long as you're good."

This was no reassuring answer.

"And politer to Cora," she added.

Seemingly he heard the lash of a slave-whip crack in the air. The future grew dark.

"I know you'll try" — she said; and the unhappy lad felt that her assurance was justified; but she had not concluded the sentence — "darling little boy," she capped it, choking slightly.

"No other little girl ever fell in love with you, did there, Hedrick?" she asked, and, receiving an incoherent but furious reply, she was again overcome, so that she must lean against the fence to recover. "It seems — so — so *curious*," she explained, gasping, "that the first one — the — the only one — should be an — a — an ——" She was unable to continue.

Hedrick's distrust became painfully increased: he began to feel that he disliked Laura.

She was still wiping her eyes and subject to recurrent outbursts when they reached their own abode; and as he bitterly flung himself into a chair upon the vacant front porch, he heard her stifling an attack as she mounted the stairs to her own room. He swung the chair about, with its back to the street, and sat facing the wall. He saw nothing. There are profundities in the abyss which reveal no glimpse of the sky.

Presently he heard his father coughing near by; and the sound was hateful, because it seemed secure and unshamed. It was a cough of moral superiority; and just then the son would have liked to believe that his parent's boyhood had been one of degradation as complete as his own; but no one with this comfortable cough could ever have plumbed such depths: his imagination refused the picture — he was bitterly certain that Mr. Madison had never kissed an idiot.

Hedrick had a dread that his father might speak to him; he was in no condition for light conversation. But Mr. Madison was unaware of his son's near presence, and continued upon his purposeless way. He was smoking his one nightly cigar and enjoying the moonlight. He drifted out toward the sidewalk and was accosted by a passing acquaintance, a comfortable burgess of sixty, leading a child of six or seven, by the hand.

"Out taking the air, are you, Mr. Madison?" said the pedestrian, pausing.

"Yes; just trying to cool off," returned the other. "How are you, Pryor, anyway? I haven't seen you for a long time."

"Not since last summer," said Pryor. "I only get here once or twice a year, to see my married daughter. I always try to spend August with her if I can. She's still living in that little house, over on the next street, I bought for her through your real-estate company. I suppose you're still in the same business?"

"Yes. Pretty slack, these days."

"I suppose so, I suppose so," responded Mr. Pryor, nodding. "Summer, I suppose it usually is. Well, I don't know when I'll be going out on the road again myself. Business is pretty slack all over the country this year."

"Let's see—I've forgotten," said Madison ruminatively. "You travel, don't you?"

"For a New York house," affirmed Mr. Pryor. He did not, however, mention his "line." "Yes-sir," he added, merely as a decoration, and then said briskly: "I see you have a fine family, Mr. Madison; yes-sir, a fine family; I've passed here several times lately and I've noticed 'em: fine family. Let's see, you've got four, haven't you?"

"Three," said Madison. "Two girls and a boy."

"Well, sir, that's mighty nice," observed Mr. Pryor; "*mighty* nice! I only have my one daughter, and of course me living in New York when I'm at home, and her here, why, I don't get to see much of her. You got both your daughters living with you, haven't you?"

"Yes, right here at home."

"Let's see: neither of 'em's married, I believe?"

"No; not yet."

"Seems to me now," said Pryor, taking off his glasses and wiping them, "seems to me I did hear somebody say one of 'em was going to be married — engaged, maybe."

"No," said Madison. "Not that I know of."

"Well, I suppose you'd be the first to know! Yes-sir." And both men laughed their appreciation of this folly. "They're mighty good-looking girls, *that's* certain," continued Mr. Pryor. "And one of 'em's as fine a dresser as you'll meet this side the Rue de la Paix.

"You mean in Paris?" asked Madison, slightly surprised at this allusion. "You've been over there, Pryor?"

"Oh, sometimes," was the response. "My business takes me over, now and then. "I *think* it's one of your daughters I've noticed dresses so well. Isn't one of 'em a mighty pretty girl about twenty-one or two, with a fine head of hair sort of lightish brown, beautiful figure, and carries a white parasol with a green lining sometimes?"

"Yes, that's Cora, I guess."

"Pretty name, too," said Pryor approvingly. "Yes-sir. I saw her going into a florist's, down-town, the other day, with a fine-looking young fellow — I can't think of his name. Let's see: my daughter was with me, and she'd heard his name — said his family used to be big people in this town and ——"

"Oh," said Madison, "young Corliss."

"Corliss!" exclaimed Mr. Pryor, with satisfaction. "That's it, Corliss. Well, sir," he chuckled, "from the way he was looking at your Miss Cora it struck me he seemed kind of anxious for her name to be Corliss, too."

"Well, hardly I expect," said the other. "They just barely know each other: he's only been here a few weeks; they haven't had time to get much acquainted, you see."

"I suppose not," agreed Mr. Pryor, with perfect readiness. "I suppose not. "I'll bet *he* tries all he can to get acquainted though; he looked pretty smart to me. Doesn't he come about as often as the law allows?"

"I shouldn't be surprised," said Madison indifferently. "He doesn't know many people about here any more, and it's lonesome for him at the hotel. But I guess he comes to see the whole family; I left him in the library a little while ago, talking to my wife."

"That's the way! Get around the old folks first!" Mr. Pryor chuckled cordially; then in a mildly inquisitive tone he said: "Seems to be a fine, square young fellow, I expect?"

"Yes, I think so."

"Pretty name, 'Cora'," said Pryor.

"What's this little girl's name?" Mr. Madison indicated the child, who had stood with heroic patience throughout the incomprehensible dialogue.

"Lottie, for her mother. She's a good little girl."

"She is *so!* I've got a young son she ought to know," remarked Mr. Madison serenely, with an elderly father's total unconsciousness of the bridgeless gap between seven and thirteen. "He'd like to play with her. I'll call him."

"I expect we better be getting on," said Pryor. "It's near Lottie's bedtime; we just came out for our evening walk."

"Well, he can come and shake hands with her anyway," urged Hedrick's father. "Then they'll know each other, and they can play some other time." He turned toward the house and called loudly:

"Hedrick!"

There was no response. Behind the back of his chair Hedrick could not be seen. He was still sitting immovable, his eyes torpidly fixed upon the wall.

"Hed-*rick!*"

Silence.

"Oh, *Hed*-rick!" shouted his father. "Come *out* here! I want you to meet a little girl! Come and see a nice little girl!"

Mr. Pryor's grandchild was denied the pleasure At the ghastly words "*little girl,*" Hedrick dropped from his chair flat upon the floor, crawled to the end of the porch, wriggled through the railing, and immersed himself in deep shadow against the side of the house.

Here he removed his shoes, noiselessly mounted to the sill of one of the library windows, then reconnoitred through a slit in the blinds before entering.

The gas burned low in the "drop-light" — almost too dimly to reveal the two people upon a sofa across the room. It was a faint murmur from one of them that caused Hedrick to pause and peer more sharply. They were Cora and Corliss; he was bending close to her; her face was lifting to his.

"Ah, kiss me! Kiss me!" she whispered.

Hedrick dropped from the sill, climbed through a window of the kitchen, hurried up the back-stairs, and reached his own apartment in time to be violently ill in seclusion.

CHAPTER NINE

VILLAGES are scattered plentifully over the unstable buttresses of Vesuvius, and the inhabitants sleep o' nights: Why not? Quite unaware that he was much of their condition, Mr. Madison bade his incidental gossip and the tiny Lottie good-night, and sought his early bed. He maintained in good faith that Saturday night was "a great night to sleep," because of the later hour for rising; probably having also some factitious conviction that there prevailed a hush preparative of the Sabbath. As a matter of fact, in summer, the other members of his family always looked uncommonly haggard at the Sunday breakfast-table. Accepting without question his preposterous legend of additional matutinal slumber, they postponed retiring to a late hour, and were awakened — simultaneously with thousands of fellow-sufferers — at about half-after five on Sunday morning, by a journalistic uprising. Over the town, in these early hours, rampaged the small vendors of the manifold sheets: local papers and papers from greater cities, hawker succeeding hawker with yell upon yell and brain-piercing shrillings in unbearable cadences. No good burgher ever complained: the people bore it, as in winter they bore the smoke that injured their health, ruined their linen, spoiled their complexions, forbade all hope of beauty and comfort in their city, and destroyed the sweetness of their homes and of their wives. It is an incredibly patient citizenry and exalts its persecutors.

Of the Madison family, Cora probably suffered most; and this was the time when it was no advantage to have the front bedroom. She had not slept until close upon dawn, and the hawkers woke her irreparably; she could but rage upon her hot pillow. By and by, there came a token that another anguish kept company with hers. She had left her door open for a better circulation of the warm and languid air, and from Hedrick's room issued an "*oof!*" of agonized disgust. Cora little suspected that the youth recked not of newsboys: Hedrick's miseries were introspective.

The cries from the street were interminable; each howler in turn heard faintly in the distance, then in crescendo until he had passed and another succeeded him, and all the while Cora lay tossing and whispering between clenched teeth. Having ample reason, that morning, to prefer sleep to thinking, sleep was impossible. But she fought for it: she did not easily surrender what she wanted; and she struggled on, with closed eyes, long after she had heard the others go down to breakfast.

About a hundred yards from her windows, to the rear, were the open windows of a church which fronted the next street, and stood dos-à-dos to the dwelling of the Madisons. The Sunday-school hour had been advanced for the hot weather, and, partly on this account, and partly because of the summer absence of many families, the attendants were few. But the young voices were conducted, rather than accompanied, in pious melody by a cornetist who worthily thought to amend, in his single person, what lack of volume this paucity occasioned. He was a slender young man in hot black clothes; he wore the unfaçaded collar fatally and unanimously adopted by all adam's-apple men of morals; he was washed, fair, flat-skulled, clean-minded, and industrious; and the only noise of any kind he ever made in the world was on Sunday.

"Prashus joowuls, sweet joowuls, *thee* jams off iz crowowun," sang the little voices feebly. They were almost unheard; but the young man helped them out: figuratively, he put them out. And the cornet was heard: it was heard for blocks and blocks; it was heard over all that part of the town — in the vicinity of the church it was the only thing that could be heard. In his daily walk this cornetist had no enemies: he was kind-hearted; he would not have shot a mad dog; he gladly nursed the sick. He sat upon the platform before the children; he swelled, perspired and blew, and felt that it was a good blowing. If other thoughts vapoured upon the borders of his mind, they were of the dinner he would eat, soon after noon, at the house of one of the frilled, white-muslin teachers. He was serene. His eyes were not blasted; his heart was not instantly withered; his thin, bluish hair did not fall from his head; his limbs were not detached from his torso — yet these misfortunes had been desired for him, with comprehension and sincerity, at the first flat blat of his brassy horn.

It is impossible to imagine the state of mind of this young cornetist, could he have known that he had caused the prettiest girl in town to jump violently out of bed with what petitions upon her lips regarding his present whereabouts and future detention! It happened that during the course of his Sunday walk on Corliss Street, that very afternoon, he saw her — was hard-smitten by her beauty, and for weeks thereafter laid unsuccessful plans to "meet" her. Her image was imprinted: he talked about her to his boarding-house friends and office acquaintances, his favourite description being, "the sweetest-looking lady I ever laid eyes on."

Cora, descending to the breakfast-table rather white herself, was not unpleasantly shocked by the haggard aspect of Hedrick, who, with Laura and Mrs. Madison, still lingered.

"Good-morning, Cora," he said politely, and while she stared, in suspicious surprise, he passed her a plate of toast with ostentatious courtesy; but before she could take one of the slices, "Wait," he said; "it's very nice toast, but I'm afraid it isn't hot. I'll take it to the kitchen and have it warmed for you." And he took the plate and went out, walking softly.

Cora turned to her mother, appalled. "He'll be sick!" she said.

Mrs. Madison shook her head and smiled sadly.

"He helped to wait on all of us: he must have been doing something awful."

"More likely he wants permission to do something awful."

Laura looked out of the window.

"There, Cora," said Hedrick kindly, when he brought the toast; "you'll find that nice and hot."

She regarded him steadfastly, but with modesty he avoided her eye. "You wouldn't make such a radical change in your nature, Hedrick," she said, with a puzzled frown, "just to get out of going to church, would you?"

"I don't want to get out of going to church," he said. He gulped slightly. "I like church."

And church-time found him marching decorously beside his father, the three ladies forming a rear rank; a small company in the very thin procession of fanning women and mopping men whose destination was the gray stone church at the foot of Corliss Street. The locusts railed overhead: Hedrick looked neither to the right nor to the left.

They passed a club, of which a lower window was vacated simultaneously with their coming into view; and a small but ornate figure in pale gray crash hurried down the steps and attached itself to the second row of Madisons. "Good-morning," said Mr. Wade Trumble. "Thought I'd take a look-in at church this morning myself."

Care of this encumbrance was usually expected of Laura and Mrs. Madison, but to their surprise Cora offered a sprightly rejoinder and presently dropped behind them with Mr. Trumble. Mr. Trumble was also surprised and, as naïvely, pleased.

"What's happened?" he asked with cheerful frankness. "You haven't given me a chance to talk to you for a long while."

"Haven't I?" she smiled enigmatically. "I don't think you've tried very hard."

This was too careless; it did not quite serve, even for Trumble. "What's up?" he asked, not without shrewdness. "Is Richard Lindley out of town?"

"I don't know."

"I see. Perhaps it's this new chap, Corliss? Has he left?"

"What nonsense! What have they got to do with my being nice to you?" She gave him a dangerous smile, and it wrought upon him visibly.

"Don't you ever be nice to me unless you mean it," he said feebly.

Cora looked grave and sweet; she seemed mysteriously moved. "I never do anything I don't mean," she said in a low voice which thrilled the little man. This was machine-work, easy and accurate.

"Cora ——" he began, breathlessly.

"There!" she exclaimed, shifting on the instant to a lively brusqueness. "That's enough for you just *now*. We're on our way to church!"

Trumble felt almost that she had accepted him.

"Have you got your penny for the contribution box?" she smiled. "I suppose you really give a great deal to the church. I hear you're richer and richer."

"I do pretty well," he returned, coolly. "You can know just how well, if you like."

"Not on Sunday," she laughed; then went on, admiringly, "I hear you're very dashing in your speculations."

"Then you've heard wrong, because I don't speculate," he returned. "I'm not a gambler — except on certainties. I guess I disappointed a friend of yours the other day because I wouldn't back him on a thousand-to-one shot."

"Who was that?" she asked, with an expression entirely veiled.

"Corliss. He came to see me; wanted me to put real money into an oil scheme. Too thin!"

"Why is it 'too thin'?" she asked carelessly.

"Too far away, for one thing — somewhere in Italy. Anybody who put up his cash would have to do it on Corliss's bare word that he's struck oil."

"Well?" She turned her face to him, and a faint perturbation was manifest in her tone. "Isn't Mr. Corliss's 'bare word' supposed to be perfectly good?"

"Oh, I suppose so, but I don't know. He isn't known here: nobody really knows anything about him except that he was born here. Besides, I wouldn't make an investment on my own father's bare word, if he happened to be alive."

"Perhaps not!" Cora spoke impulsively, a sudden anger getting the better of her, but she controlled it immediately. "Of course I don't mean that," she laughed, sweetly. "But *I* happen to think Mr. Corliss's scheme a very handsome one, and I want my friends to make their fortunes, of course. Richard Lindley and papa are going into it."

"I'll bet they don't," said Trumble promptly. "Lindley told me he'd looked it over and couldn't see his way to."

"He did?" Cora stiffened perceptibly and bit her lip.

Trumble began to laugh. "This is funny: *you* trying to talk business! So Corliss has been telling you about it?"

"Yes, he has; and I understand it perfectly. I think there's an enormous fortune in it, and you'd better not laugh at me: a woman's instinct about such things is better than a man's experience sometimes."

"You'll find neither Lindley nor your father are going to think so," he returned skeptically.

She gave him a deep, sweet look. "But I mustn't be disappointed in you," she said, with the suggestion of a tremor in her voice, "whatever *they* do! You'll take my advice, won't you — Wade?"

"I'll take your advice in anything but business." He shook his head ominously.

"And wouldn't you take my advice in business," — she asked very slowly and significantly — "under *any* circumstances?"

"You mean," he said huskily, "if you were my — wife?"

She looked away, and slightly inclined her head.

"No," he answered doggedly, "I wouldn't. You

know mighty well that's what I want you to be, and I'd give my soul for the tip of your shoe, but business is an entirely different matter, and I ——"

"*Wade!*" she said, with wonderful and thrilling sweetness. They had reached the church; Hedrick and his father had entered; Mrs. Madison and Laura were waiting on the steps. Cora and Trumble came to a stop some yards away. "Wade, I — I *want* you to go into this."

"Can't do it," he said stubbornly. "If you ever make up your mind to marry me, I'll spend all the money you like on *you*, but you'll have to keep to the woman's side of the house."

"You make it pretty hard for me to be nice to you," she returned, and the tremor now more evident in her voice was perfectly genuine. "You positively refuse to do this — for me?"

"Yes I do. I wouldn't buy sight-unseen to please God 'lmighty, Cora Madison." He looked at her shrewdly, struck by a sudden thought. "Did Corliss ask you to try and get me in?"

"He did not," she responded, icily. "Your refusal is final?"

"Certainly!" He struck the pavement a smart rap with his walking-stick. "By George, I believe he *did* ask you! That spoils church for me this morning; I'll not go in. When you quit playing games, let me know. You needn't try to work me any more, because I won't stand for it, but if you ever get tired of playing, come and tell me so." He uttered a bark of rueful laughter. "Ha! I must say that gentleman has an interesting way of combining business with pleasure!"

Under favourable circumstances the blow Cora dealt him might have been physically more violent. "Good-morning," she laughed, gayly. "I'm not bothering much about Mr. Corliss's oil in Italy. I had a bet with Laura I could keep you from saying 'I beg to differ,' or talking about the weather for five minutes. She'll have to pay me!"

Then, still laughing, she lowered her parasol, and with superb impudence, brushed it smartly across his face; turned on her heel, and, red with fury, joined her mother and sister, and went into the church.

The service failed to occupy her attention: she had much in her thoughts to distract her. Nevertheless, she bestowed some wonderment upon the devotion with which her brother observed each ceremonial rite. He joined in prayer with real fervour; he sang earnestly and loudly; a great appeal sounded in his changing voice; and during the sermon he sat with his eyes upon the minister in a stricken fixity. All this was so remarkable that Cora could not choose but ponder upon it, and, observing Hedrick furtively, she caught, if not a clue itself, at least a glimpse of one. She saw Laura's clear profile becoming subtly agitated; then noticed a shimmer of Laura's dark eye as it wandered to Hedrick and so swiftly away it seemed not to dare to remain. Cora was quick: she perceived that Laura was repressing a constant desire to laugh and that she feared to look at Hedrick lest it overwhelm her. So Laura knew what had wrought the miracle. Cora made up her mind to explore this secret passage.

When the service was over and the people were placidly buzzing their way up the aisles, Cora felt herself drawn to look across the church, and following the telepathic impulse, turned her head to encounter the gaze of Ray Vilas. He was ascending the opposite aisle, walking beside Richard Lindley. He looked less pale than usual, though his thinness was so extreme it was like emaciation; but his eyes were clear and quiet, and the look he gave her was strangely gentle. Cora frowned and turned away her head with an air of annoyance. They came near each other in the convergence at the doors; but he made no effort to address her, and, moving away through the crowd as quickly as possible, disappeared.

Valentine Corliss was disclosed in the vestibule. He reached her an instant in advance of Mr. Lindley, who had suffered himself to be impeded; and Cora quickly handed the former her parasol, lightly taking his arm. Thus the slow Richard found himself walking beside Laura in a scattered group, its detached portion consisting of his near-betrothed and Corliss; for although the dexterous pair were first to leave the church, they contrived to be passed almost at once, and, assuming the position of trailers, lagged far behind on the homeward way.

Laura and Richard walked in the unmitigated glare of the sun; he had taken her black umbrella and conscientiously held it aloft, but over nobody. They walked in silence: they were quiet people, both of them; and Richard, not "talkative" under any circumstances, never had anything whatever to say to Laura Madison. He had known her for many years, ever since her childhood; seldom indeed formulating or expressing a definite thought about her, though sometimes it was vaguely of his consciousness that she played the piano nicely, and even then her music had taken its place as but a colour of Cora's background. For to him, as to every one else (including Laura), Laura was in nothing her sister's competitor. She was a neutral-tinted figure, taken-for-granted, obscured, and so near being nobody at all, that, as Richard Lindley walked beside her this morning, he glanced back at the lagging couple and uttered a long and almost sonorous sigh, which he would have been ashamed for anybody to hear; and then actually proceeded on his way without the slightest realization that anybody had heard it.

She understood. And she did not disturb the trance; she did nothing to make him observe that she was there. She walked on with head, shoulders, and back scorching in the fierce sun, and allowed him to continue shading the pavement before them with her umbrella. When they reached the house she gently took the umbrella from him and thanked him; and he mechanically raised his hat.

They had walked more than a mile together; he had not spoken a word, and he did not even know it.

CHAPTER TEN

DINNER on Sunday, the most elaborate feast of the week for the Madisons, was always set for one o'clock in the afternoon, and sometimes began before two, but not to-day: the escorts of both daughters remained, and a change of costume by Cora occasioned a long postponement. Justice demands the admission that her reappearance in a glamour of lilac was reward for the delay; nothing more ravishing was ever seen, she was warrantably informed by the quicker of the two guests, in a moment's whispered tête-à-tête across the banisters as she descended. Another wait followed while she prettily arranged upon the table some dozens of asters from a small garden-bed, tilled, planted, and tended by Laura. Meanwhile, Mrs. Madison constantly turned the other cheek to the cook. Laura assisted in the pacification; Hedrick froze the ice-cream to an impenetrable solidity; and the nominal head of the family sat upon the front porch with the two young men, and wiped his wrists and rambled politically till they were summoned to the dining-room.

Cora did the talking for the table, She was in high spirits; no trace remained of a haggard night: there was a bloom upon her — she was radiant. Her gayety may have had some inspiration in her daring, for round her throat she wore a miraculously slender chain of gold and enamel, with a pendant of minute pale sapphires scrolled about a rather large and very white diamond. Laura started when she saw it, and involuntarily threw a glance almost of terror at Richard Lindley. But that melancholy and absent-minded gentleman observed neither the glance nor the jewel. He saw Cora's eyes when they were vouchsafed to his vision, and when they were not he apparently saw nothing at all.

With the general exodus from the table, Cora asked Laura to come to the piano and play, a request which brought a snort from Hedrick, who was taken off his guard. Catching Laura's eye he applied a handkerchief with renewed presenc of mind, affecting to have sneezed, and stare searchingly over it at Corliss. He perceived tha the man remained unmoved, evidently already in formed that it was Laura who was the musicia

Cora must be going it pretty fast this time: such was the form of her brother's deduction.

When Laura opened the piano, Richard had taken a seat beside Cora, and Corliss stood leaning in the doorway. The player lost herself in a wandering medley, echoes from "Bohême" and "Pagliacci"; then drifted into improvisation and played her heart into it magnificently — a heart released to happiness. The still air of the room filled with wonderful, golden sound: a song like the song of a mother flying from earth to a child in the stars, a torrential tenderness, unpent and glorying in freedom. The flooding, triumphant chords rose, crashed — stopped with a shattering abruptness. Laura's hands fell to her sides, then were raised to her glowing face and concealed it for a moment. She shivered; a quick, deep sigh heaved her breast; and she came back to herself like a prisoner leaving a window at the warden's voice.

She turned. Cora and Corliss had left the room. Richard was sitting beside a vacant chair, staring helplessly at the open door.

If he had been vaguely conscious of Laura's playing, which is possible, certainly he was unaware that it had ceased.

"The others have gone out to the porch," she said composedly, and rose. "Shan't we join them?"

"What?" he returned, blankly. "I beg your pardon ——"

"Let's go out on the porch with the others."

"No, I ——" He got to his feet confusedly. "I was thinking —— I believe I'd best be going home."

"Not 'best,' I think," she said. "Not even better!"

"I don't see," he said, his perplexity only increased.

"Mr. Corliss would," she retorted quickly. "Come on: we'll go and sit with them." And she compelled his obedience by preceding him with such a confident assumption that he would follow that he did.

The fugitive pair were not upon the porch, however; they were discovered in the shade of a tree behind the house, seated upon a rug, and occupied in a conversation which would not have disturbed a sick-room. The pursuers came upon them, boldly sat beside them; and Laura began to talk with unwonted fluency to Corliss, but within five minutes found herself alone with Richard Lindley upon the rug. Cora had promised to show Mr. Corliss an "old print" in the library — so Cora said.

Lindley gave the remaining lady a desolate and faintly reproachful look. He was kind, but he was a man; and Laura saw that this last abandonment was being attributed in part to her.

She reddened, and, being not an angel, observed with crispness: "Certainly. You're quite right: it's my fault!"

"What did you say?" he asked vacantly.

She looked at him rather fixedly; his own gaze had returned to the angle of the house beyond which the other couple had just disappeared. "I said," she answered, slowly, "I thought it wouldn't rain this afternoon."

His wistful eyes absently swept the serene sky which had been cloudless for several days. "No, I suppose not," he murmured.

"Richard," she said with a little sharpness, "will you please listen to me for a moment?"

"Oh — what?" He was like a diver coming up out of deep water. "What did you say?" He laughed apologetically. "Wasn't I listening? I beg your pardon. What is it, Laura?"

"Why do you let Mr. Corliss take Cora away from you like that?" she asked gravely.

"He doesn't," the young man returned with a rueful shake of the head. "Don't you see? It's Cora that goes."

"Why do you let her, then?"

He sighed. "I don't seem to be able to keep up with Cora, especially when she's punishing me. I couldn't do something she asked me to, last night ——"

"Invest with Mr. Corliss?" asked Laura quickly.

"Yes. It seemed to trouble her that I couldn't. She's convinced it's a good thing: she thinks it would make a great fortune for us ——"

"'Us'?" repeated Laura gently. "You mean for you and her? When you're ——"

"When we're married. Yes," he said thoughtfully, "that's the way she stated it. She wanted me to put in all I have ——"

"Don't do it!" said Laura decidedly.

He glanced at her with sharp inquiry. "Do you mean you would distrust Mr. Corliss?'

"I wasn't thinking of that: I don't know whether I'd trust him or not — I think I wouldn't; there's something veiled about him, and I don't believe he is an easy man to know. What I meant was that I don't believe it would really be a good thing for you with Cora."

"It would please her, of course — thinking I deferred so much to her judgment."

"Don't do it!" she said again, impulsively.

"I don't see how I can," he returned sorrowfully. "It's my work for all the years since I got out of college, and if I lost it I'd have to begin all over again. It would mean postponing everything. Cora isn't a girl you can ask to share a little salary, and if it were a question of years, perhaps — perhaps Cora might not feel she could wait for me, you see."

He made this explanation with plaintive and boyish sincerity, hesitatingly, and as if pleading a cause. And Laura, after a long look at him, turned away, and in her eyes were actual tears of compassion for the incredible simpleton.

"I see," she said. "Perhaps she might not."

"Of course," he went on, "she's fond of having nice things, and she thinks this is a great chance for us to be millionaires; and then, too, I think she may feel that it would please Mr. Corliss and help to save him from disappointment. She seems to have taken a great fancy to him."

Laura glanced at him, but did not speak.

"He *is* attractive," continued Richard feebly. "I think he has a great deal of what people call 'magnetism': he's the kind of man who somehow makes you want to do what he wants you to. He seems a manly, straightforward sort, too — so far as one can tell — and when he came to me with his scheme I was strongly inclined to go into it. But it is too big a gamble, and I can't, though I was sorry to disappoint him myself. He was perfectly cheerful about it and so pleasant it made me feel small. I don't wonder at all that Cora likes him so much. Besides, he seems to understand her."

Laura looked very grave. "I think he does," she said slowly.

"And then he's 'different,'" said Richard. "He's more a 'man of the world' than most of us here: she never saw anything just like him before, and she's seen *us* all her life. She likes change, of course. That's natural," he said gently. "Poor Vilas says she wants a man to be different every day, and if he isn't, then she wants a different man every day."

"You've rather taken Ray Vilas under your wing, haven't you?" asked Laura.

"Oh, no," he answered deprecatingly. "I only

try to keep him with me so he'll stay away from downtown as much as possible."

"Does he talk much of Cora?"

"All the time. There's no stopping him. I suppose he can't help it, because he thinks of nothing else."

"Isn't that rather — rather queer for you?"

"'Queer'?" he repeated.

"No, I suppose not!" She laughed impatiently. "And probably you don't think it's 'queer' of you to sit here helplessly, and let another man take your place ——"

"But I don't 'let' him, Laura," he protested.

"No, he just does it!"

"Well," he smiled, "you must admit my efforts to supplant him haven't ——"

"It won't take any effort now," she said, rising quickly. Valentine Corliss came into their view upon the sidewalk in front, taking his departure. Seeing that they observed him, he lifted his hat to Laura and nodded a cordial good-day to Lindley. Then he went on.

Just before he reached the corner of the lot, he encountered upon the pavement a citizen of elderly and plain appearance, strolling with a grandchild.

The two men met and passed, each upon his opposite way, without pausing and without salutation, and neither Richard nor Laura, whose eyes were upon the meeting, perceived that they had taken cognizance of each other. But one had asked a question and the other had answered.

Mr. Pryor spoke in a low monotone, with a rapidity as singular as the restrained but perceptible emphasis he put upon one word of his question.

"I got you in the park," he said; and it is to be deduced that "got" was argot. "You're not *doing* anything here, are you?"

"No!" answered Corliss with condensed venom, his back already to the other. He fanned himself with his hat as he went on. Mr. Pryor strolled up the street with imperturbable benevolence.

"Your coast is cleared," said Laura, "since you wouldn't clear it yourself."

"Wish me luck," said Richard as he left her.

She nodded brightly.

Before he disappeared, he looked back to her again (which profoundly surprised her) and smiled rather disconsolately, shaking his head as in prophecy of no very encouraging reception indoors. The manner of this glance recalled to Laura what his mother had once said of him. "Richard is one of those sweet, helpless men that some women adore and others despise. They fall in love with the ones that despise them."

An ostentatious cough made her face about, being obviously designed to that effect; and she beheld her brother in the act of walking slowly across the yard with his back to her. He halted upon the border of her small garden of asters, regarded it anxiously, then spread his handkerchief upon the ground, knelt upon it, and with thoughtful care uprooted a few weeds which were beginning to sprout, and also such vagrant blades of grass as encroached upon the floral territory. He had the air of a virtuous man performing a good action which would never become known. Plainly, he thought himself in solitude and all unobserved.

It was a touching picture, pious and humble. Done into coloured glass, the kneeling boy and the asters — submerged in ardent sunshine — would have appropriately enriched a cathedral: Boyhood of Saint Florus the Gardener.

Laura heartlessly turned her back, and, affecting an interest in her sleeve, very soon experienced the sensation of being stared at with some poignancy from behind. Unchanged in attitude, she unravelled an imaginary thread, whereupon the cough reached her again, shrill and loud, its insistence not lacking in pathos.

She approached him, driftingly. No sign that he was aware came from the busied boy, though he coughed again, hollowly now — a proof that he was an artist. "All right, Hedrick," she said kindly. "I heard you the first time."

He looked up with utter incomprehension. "I'm afraid I've caught cold," he said, simply. "I got a good many weeds out before breakfast, and the ground was damp."

Hedrick was of the New School: everything direct, real, no striving for effect, no pressure on the stroke. He did his work: you could take it or leave it.

"You mustn't strain so, dear," returned his sister, shaking her head. "It won't last if you do. You see this is only the first day."

Struck to the heart by so brutal a misconception, he put all his wrongs into one look, rose in manly dignity, picked up his handkerchief, and left her.

Her eyes followed him, not without remorse: it was an exit which would have moved the bassviolist of a theatre orchestra. Sighing, she went to her own room by way of the kitchen and the back-stairs, and, having locked her door, brought the padlocked book from its hiding-place.

"I think I should not have played as I did, an hour ago," she wrote. "It stirs me too greatly and I am afraid it makes me inclined to self-pity afterward, and I must never let myself feel *that!* If I once begin to feel sorry for myself. . . . But I *will* not! No. You are here in the world. You exist. You *are*! That is the great thing to know and it must be enough for me. It is. I played to You. I played *just love* to you — all the yearning tenderness — all the supreme kindness I want to give you. Isn't love really just glorified kindness? No, there is something more. . . . I feel it, though I do not know how to say it. But it was in my playing — I played it and played it. Suddenly I felt that in my playing I had shouted it from the housetops, that I had told the secret to all the world and *everybody* knew. I stopped, and for a moment it seemed to me that I was dying of shame. But no one understood. No one had even listened. . . . Sometimes it seems to me that I am like Cora, that I am very deeply her sister in some things. My heart goes all to You — my revelation of it, my release of it, my outlet of it is all here in these pages (except when I play as I did to-day and as I shall not play again) and perhaps the writing keeps me quiet. Cora scatters her own releasings: she is looking for the You she may never find; and perhaps the penalty for scattering is never finding. Sometimes I think the seeking has reacted and that now she seeks only what will make her feel. I hope she has not found it: I am afraid of this new man — not only for your sake, dear. I felt repelled by his glance at me the first time I saw him. I did not like it — I cannot say just why, unless that it seemed too intimate. I am afraid of him for her, which is a queer sort of feeling because she has alw ——"

Laura's writing stopped there, for that day, interrupted by a hurried rapping upon the door and her mother's voice calling her with stress and urgency.

The opening of the door revealed Mrs. Madison in a state of anxious perturbation, and admitted the sound of loud weeping and agitated voices from below.

"Please go down," implored the mother. "You can do more with her than I can. She and your father have been having a terrible scene since Richard went home."

Laura hurried down to the library.

CHAPTER ELEVEN

"OH, *come* in, Laura!" cried her sister, as Laura appeared in the doorway. "Don't *stand* there! Come in if you want to take part in a grand old family row!" With a furious and tear-stained face, she was confronting her father who stood before her in a resolute attitude and a profuse perspiration. "Shut the door!" shouted Cora violently, adding, as Laura obeyed, "Do you want that little Pest in here? Probably he's eavesdropping anyway. But what difference does it make? I don't care. Let him hear! Let anybody hear that wants to! They can hear how I'm tortured if they like. I didn't close my eyes last night, and now I'm being tortured. Papa!" She stamped her foot. "Are you going to take back that insult to me?"

"'Insult'?" repeated her father, in angry astonishment.

"Pshaw," said Laura, laughing soothingly and coming to her. "You know that's nonsense, Cora.

Kind old papa couldn't do that if he tried. Dear, you know he never insulted anybody in his ——"

"Don't touch me!" screamed Cora, repulsing her. "Listen, if you've got to, but let me alone. He did too! He did! He *knows* what he said!"

"I do not!"

"He does! He does!" cried Cora. "He said that I was — I was too much 'interested' in Mr. Corliss."

"Is that an 'insult'?" the father demanded sharply.

"It was the way he said it," Cora protested, sobbing. "He meant something he didn't *say*. He did! He did! He *meant* to insult me!"

"I did nothing of the kind," shouted the old man. "I don't know what you're talking about. I said I couldn't understand your getting so excited about the fellow's affairs and that you seemed to take a mighty sudden interest in him."

"Well, what if I *do?*" she screamed. "Haven't I a right to be interested in what I choose? I've got to be interested in *something*, haven't I? *You* don't make life very interesting, do you? Do you think it's interesting to spend the summer in this horrible old house with the paper falling off the walls and our rotten old furniture that I work my hands off trying to make look decent and can't, and every other girl I know at the seashore with motor-cars and motor-boats, or getting a trip abroad and buying her clothes in Paris? What do *you* offer to interest me?"

The unfortunate man hung his head. "I don't see what all that has to do with it ——"

She seemed to leap at him. "You *don't?* You *don't?*"

"No, I don't. And I don't see why you're so crazy to please young Corliss about this business unless you're infatuated with him. I had an idea — and I was pleased with it, too, because Richard's a steady fellow — that you were just about engaged to Richard Lindley, and ——"

"Engaged!" she cried, repeating the word with bitter contempt. "Engaged! You don't suppose I'll marry him unless I want to, do you? I will if it suits me. I won't if it suits me not to; understand that! I don't consider myself engaged to anybody, and you needn't either. What on earth has that got to do with your keeping Richard Lindley from doing what Mr. Corliss wants him to?"

"*Engaged!*"

"I'm not keeping him from anything. He didn't say ——"

"He did!" stormed Cora. "He said he would if you went into it. He told me this afternoon, an hour ago ——"

"Now wait," said Madison. "I talked this over with Richard two days ago ——"

Cora stamped her foot again in frantic exasperation. "I'm talking about this afternoon!"

"Two days ago," he repeated doggedly; "and we came to the same conclusion: it won't do. He said he couldn't go into it unless he went over there — to Italy — and saw for himself just what he was putting his money into, and Corliss had told him that it couldn't be done; that there wasn't time, and showed him a cablegram from his Italian partner saying the secret had leaked out and that they'd have to form the company in Naples and sell the stock over there if it couldn't be done here within the next week. Corliss said he had to ask for an immediate answer, and so Richard told him no, yesterday."

"Oh, my God!" groaned Cora. "What has that got to do with *your* going into it? You're not going to risk any money! I don't ask you to *spend* anything, do I? You haven't got it if I did. All Mr. Corliss wants is your name. Can't you give even *that?* What importance is it?"

"Well, if it isn't important, what difference does it make whether I give it or not?"

She flung up her arms as in despairing appeal for patience. "It *is* important to *him!* Richard will do it if you will be secretary of the company: he promised me. Mr. Corliss told me your name was worth everything here: that men said down-town you could have been rich long ago if you hadn't been so square. Richard trusts you; he says you're the most trusted man in town ——"

"That's why I can't do it," he interrupted.

"No!" Her vehemence increased suddenly to its utmost. "No! Don't you say that, because it's a lie. That isn't the reason you won't do it. You won't do it because you think it would please *me!* You're afraid it might make me *happy!* Happy — happy — *happy!*" She beat her breast and cast herself headlong upon the sofa, sobbing wildly. "Don't come near me!" she screamed at Laura, and sprang to her feet again, dishevelled and frantic. "Oh, Christ in heaven! is there such a thing as happiness in this beast of a world? I want to leave it. I want to go away: I want *so* to die: Why can't I? Why can't I! Why can't I! Oh, God, why *can't* I die? Why can't ——"

Her passion culminated in a shriek: she gasped, was convulsed from head to foot for a dreadful moment, tore at the bosom of her dress with rigid bent fingers, swayed; then collapsed all at once. Laura caught her, and got her upon the sofa. In the hall, Mrs. Madison could be heard running and screaming to Hedrick to go for the doctor. Next instant, she burst into the room with brandy and camphor.

"I could only find these; the ammonia bottle's empty," she panted; and the miserable father started hatless, for the drug-store, a faint, choked wail from the stricken girl sounding in his ears: "It's — it's my heart, mamma."

It was four blocks to the nearest pharmacy; he made what haste he could in the great heat, but to himself he seemed double his usual weight; and the more he tried to hurry, the less speed appeared obtainable from his heavy legs. When he reached the place at last, he found it crowded with noisy customers about the "soda-fount"; and the clerks were stonily slow: they seemed to know that they were "already in eternity." He got very short of breath on the way home; he ceased to perspire and became unnaturally dry; the air was aflame and the sun shot fire upon his bare head. His feet inclined to strange disobediences: he walked the last block waveringly. A solemn Hedrick met him at the door.

"They've got her to bed," announced the boy. "The doctor's up there."

"Take this ammonia up," said Madison huskily, and sat down upon a lower step of the stairway with a jolt, closing his eyes.

"You sick, too?" asked Hedrick.

"No. Run along with that ammonia."

It seemed to Madison a long time that he sat there alone, and he felt very dizzy. Once he tried to rise, but had to give it up and remain sitting with his eyes shut. At last he heard Cora's door open and close; and his wife and the doctor came slowly down the stairs, Mrs. Madison talking in the anxious yet relieved voice of one who leaves a sick-room wherein the physician pronounces progress encouraging.

"And you're *sure* her heart trouble isn't organic?" she asked.

"Her heart is all right," her companion assured her. "There's nothing serious; the trouble is nervous. I think you'll find she'll be better after a good sleep. Just keep her quiet. Hadn't she been in a state of considerable excitement?"

"Ye-es — she ——"

"Ah! A little upset on account of opposition to a plan she'd formed, perhaps?"

"Well — partly," assented the mother.

"I see," he returned, adding with some dryness: "I thought it just possible."

Madison got to his feet, and stepped down from the stairs for them to pass him. He leaned heavily against the wall.

"You think she's going to be all right, Sloane?" he asked with an effort.

"No cause to worry," returned the physician. "You can let her stay in bed to-day if she wants to but ——" He broke off, looking keenly at Madison's face, which was the colour of poppies. "Hello! what's up with *you?*"

"I'm all — right."

"Oh, you are?" retorted Sloane with sarcasm. "Sit down," he commanded. "Sit right where you are — on the stairs, here," and, having enforced the order, took a stethoscope from his pocket. "Get him a glass of water," he said to Hedrick, who was at his elbow.

"Doctor!" exclaimed Mrs. Madison. "*He* isn't going to be sick, is he? You don't think he's sick *now?*"

"I shouldn't call him very well," answered the physician rather grimly, placing his stethoscope upon Madison's breast. "Get his room ready for him." She gave him a piteous look, struck with fear; then obeyed a gesture and ran flutteringly up the stairs.

"I'm all right now," panted Madison, drinking the water Hedrick brought him.

"You're not so darned all right," said Sloane coolly, as he pocketed his stethoscope. "Come, let me help you up. We're going to get you to bed."

There was an effort at protest, but the physician had his way, and the two ascended the stairs slowly, Sloane's arm round his new patient. At Cora's door, the latter paused.

"What's the matter?"

"I want," said Madison thickly — "I want — to speak to Cora."

"We'll pass that up just now," returned the other

brusquely, and led him on. Madison was almost helpless: he murmured in a husky, uncertain voice, and suffered himself to be put to bed. There, the doctor "worked" with him; cold "applications" were ordered; Laura was summoned from the other sick-bed; Hedrick sent flying with prescriptions, then to telephone for a nurse. The two women attempted questions at intervals, but Sloane replied with orders, and kept them busy.

"Do you — think I'm a — a pretty sick man, Sloane?" asked Madison after a long silence, speaking with difficulty.

"Oh, you're sick, all right," the doctor conceded.

"I — I want to speak to Jennie."

His wife rushed to the bed, and knelt beside it.

"Don't you go to confessing your sins," said Doctor Sloane crossly. "You're coming out of the woods all right, and you'll be sorry if you tell her too much. I'll begin a little flirtation with you, Miss Laura, if you please." And he motioned to her to follow him into the hall.

"Your father *is* pretty sick," he told her, "and he may be sicker before we get him into shape again. But you needn't be worried right now; I think he's not in immediate danger." He turned at the sound of Mrs. Madison's step, behind him, and repeated to her what he had just said to Laura. "I hope your husband didn't give himself away enough to be punished when we get him on his feet again," he concluded cheerfully.

She shook her head, tried to smile through tears, and, crossing the hall, entered Cora's room. She came back after a moment, and, rejoining the other two at her husband's bedside, found the sick man in a stertorous sleep. Presently the nurse arrived, and upon the physician's pointed intimation that there were "too many people around," Laura went to Cora's room. She halted on the threshold in surprise. Cora was dressing.

"Mamma says the doctor says he's all right," said Cora lightly, "and I'm feeling so much better myself I thought I'd put on something loose and go downstairs. I think there's more air down there."

"Papa isn't all right, dear," said Laura, staring perplexedly at Cora's idea of "something loose," an equipment inclusive of something particularly close. "The doctor says he is very sick."

"I don't believe it," returned Cora promptly. "Old Sloane never did know anything. Besides, mamma told me he said papa isn't in any danger."

"No 'immediate' danger," corrected Laura. "And besides, Doctor Sloane said you were to stay in bed until to-morrow."

"I can't help that." Cora went on with her lacing impatiently. "I'm not going to lie and stifle in this heat when I feel perfectly well again — not for an old idiot like Sloane! He didn't even have sense enough to give me any medicine." She laughed. "Lucky thing he didn't: I'd have thrown it out of the window. Kick that slipper to me, will you, dear?"

Laura knelt and put the slipper on her sister's foot. "Cora, dear," she said, "you're just going to put on a negligée and go down and sit in the library, aren't you?"

"Laura!" The tone was more than impatient. "I wish I could be let alone for five whole minutes some time in my life! Don't you think I've stood enough for one day? I can't bear to be questioned, questioned, questioned! What do you do it for? Don't you see I can't stand anything more? If you can't let me alone I do wish you'd keep out of my room."

Laura rose and went out; but as she left the door,

Cora called after her with a rueful laugh: "Laura, I know I'm a little devil!"

Half an hour later, Laura, suffering because she had made no reply to this peace-offering, and wishing to atone, sought Cora downstairs and found no one. She decided that Cora must still be in her own room; she would go to her there. But as she passed the open front door, she saw Cora upon the sidewalk in front of the house. She wore a new and elaborate motoring costume, charmingly becoming, and was in the act of mounting to a seat beside Valentine Corliss in a long, powerful-looking, white "roadster" automobile. The engine burst into staccato thunder, sobered down; the wheels began to move — both Cora and Corliss were laughing and there was an air of triumph about them — Cora's veil streamed and fluttered: and in a flash they were gone.

Laura stared at the suddenly vacated space where they had been. At a thought she started. Then she rushed upstairs to her mother, who was sitting in the hall near her husband's door.

"Mamma," whispered Laura, flinging herself upon her knees beside her, "when papa wanted to speak to you, was it a message to Cora?"

"Yes, dear. He told me to tell her he was sorry

he'd made her sick, and that if he got well he'd try to do what she asked him to."

Laura nodded cheerfully. "And he *will* get well, darling mother," she said, as she rose. "I'll come back in a minute and sit with you."

Her return was not so quick as she promised, for she lay a long time weeping upon her pillow, whispering over and over:

"Oh, poor, poor papa! Oh, poor, poor Richard!"

CHAPTER TWELVE

WITHIN a week Mr. Madison's illness was a settled institution in the household; the presence of the nurse lost novelty, even to Hedrick, and became a part of life; the day was measured by the three regular visits of the doctor. To the younger members of the family it seemed already that their father had always been sick, and that he always would be; indeed, to Cora and Hedrick he had become only a weak and querulous voice beyond a closed door. Doctor Sloane was serious but reassuring, his daily announcement being that his patient was in "no immediate danger."

Mrs. Madison did not share her children's sanguine adaptability; and, of the three, Cora was the greatest solace to the mother's troubled heart, though Mrs. Madison never recognized this without a sense of injustice to Laura, for Laura now was housewife and housekeeper — that is, she did all the work except the cooking, and on "wash-day" she did that. But Cora's help was to the very spirit itself, for she was sprightly in these hours of trial: with indomitable gayety she cheered her mother, inspiring in her a firmer confidence, and, most stimulating of all, Cora steadfastly refused to consider her father's condition as serious, or its outcome as doubtful.

Old Sloane exaggerated, she said; and she made fun of his gravity, his clothes and his walk, which she mimicked till she drew a reluctant and protesting laugh from even her mother. Mrs. Madison was sure she "couldn't get through" this experience save for Cora, who was indeed the light of the threatened house.

Strange perversities of this world: Cora's gayety was almost unbearable to her brother. Not because he thought it either unfeeling or out of place under the circumstances (an aspect he failed to consider), but because years of warfare had so frequently made him connect cheerfulness on her part with some unworthily won triumph over himself that habit prevailed, and he could not be a witness of her high spirits without a strong sense of injury. Additionally, he was subject to a deeply implanted suspicion of any appearance of unusual happiness in her as having source, if not in his own defeat, then in something vaguely "soft" and wholly distasteful. She grated upon him; he chafed, and his sufferings reached the surface. Finally, in a reckless moment, one evening at dinner, he broke out with a shout and hurled a newly devised couplet concerning luv-a-ly slush at his sister's head. The nurse was present: Cora left the table; and Hedrick later received a serious warning from Laura. She suggested that it might become expedient to place him in Cora's power.

"Cora knows perfectly well that something peculiar happened to you," she advised him. "And she knows that I know what it was; and she says it isn't very sisterly of me not to tell her. Now, Hedrick, there was no secret about it; you didn't *confide* your — your trouble to me, and it would be perfectly honourable of me to tell it. I won't unless you make me, but if you can't be polite and keep peace with Cora — at least while papa is sick — I think it may be necessary. I believe," she finished with imperfect gravity, "that it — it would keep things quieter."

The thoughts of a boy may be long, long thoughts, but he cannot persistently remember to fear a threatened catastrophe. Youth is too quickly intimate with peril. Hedrick had become familiar vith his own, had grown so accustomed to it he was n danger of forgetting it altogether; therefore it vas out of perspective. The episode of Lolita had begun to appear as a thing of the distant and clouded oast: time is so long at thirteen. Added to this, is late immaculate deportment had been, as Laura uggested, a severe strain; the machinery of his ature was out of adjustment and demanded a violent reaction before it could get to running again t average speed. Also, it is evident that his lestruction had been planned on high, for he was nad enough to answer flippantly:

"Tell her! Go on and tell her — *I* give you leaf! *That* wasn't anything anyway — just helped you et a little idiot girl home. What is there to that? never saw her before; never saw her again; didn't ave half as much to do with her as you did yourself. he was a lot more *your* friend than mine; I didn't ven know her. I guess you'll have to get something better on me than that, before you try to oss *this* ranch, Laura Madison!"

That night, in bed, he wondered if he had not een perhaps a trifle rash; but the day was bright vhen he awoke, and no apprehension shadowed is morning face as he appeared at the breakfast table. On the contrary, a great weight had lifted from him; clearly his defiance had been the proper thing; he had shown Laura that her power over him was but imaginary. Hypnotized by his own words to her, he believed them; and his previous terrors became gossamer; nay, they were now merely laughable. His own remorse and shame were wholly blotted from memory, and he could not understand why in the world he had been so afraid nor why he had felt it so necessary to placate Laura She looked very meek this morning. *That* showed The strong hand was the right policy in dealing with women. He was tempted to insane daring: the rash unfortunate child waltzed on the lip of the crater.

"Told Cora yet?" he asked, with scornful laughter

"Told me what?" Cora looked quickly up from her plate.

"Oh, nothing about this Corliss," he returned scathingly. "Don't get excited."

"Hedrick!" remonstrated his mother, out of habit

"She never thinks of anything else these days," he retorted. "Rides with him every evening in his pe-rin-sley hired machine, doesn't she?'

"Really, you should be more careful about the way you handle a spoon, Hedrick," said Cora languidly, and with at least a foundation of fact. "It is not the proper implement for decorating the cheeks. We all need nourishment, but it is *so* difficult when one sees a deposit of breakfast-food in the ear of one's vis-a-vis."

Hedrick too impulsively felt of his ears and was but the worse stung to find them immaculate and the latter half of the indictment unjustified.

"Spoon!" he cried. "I wouldn't talk about spoons if I were you, Cora-lee! After what I saw in the library the other night, believe *me*, you're the one of this family that better be careful how you 'handle a spoon'!"

Cora had a moment of panic. She let the cup she was lifting drop noisily upon its saucer, and gazed whitely at the boy, her mouth opening wide.

"Oh, no!" he went on, with a dreadful laugh. "I didn't hear you asking this Corliss to kiss you! Oh, no!"

At this, though her mother and Laura both started, a faint, odd relief showed itself in Cora's expression. She recovered herself.

"You little liar!" she flashed, and, with a single quick look at her mother, as of one too proud to appeal, left the room.

"Hedrick, Hedrick, Hedrick!" wailed Mrs. Madison. "And she told me you drove her from the table last night too, right before Miss Peirce!" Miss Peirce was the nurse, fortunately at this moment in the sick-room.

"I *did* hear her ask him that," he insisted, sullenly. "Don't you believe it?"

"Certainly not!"

Burning with outrage, he also left his meal unfinished and departed in high dignity. He passed through the kitchen, however, on his way out of the house; but, finding an unusual politeness to the cook nothing except its own reward, went on his way with a bitter perception of the emptiness of the world and other places.

"Your father managed to talk more last night," said Mrs. Madison pathetically to Laura. "He made me understand that he was fretting about how little we'd been able to give our children; so few advantages; it's always troubled him terribly. But sometimes I wonder if we've done right: we've neither of us ever exercised any discipline. We just couldn't bear to. You see, not having any money, or the things money could buy, to give, I think we've instinctively tried to make up for it by indulgence in other ways, and perhaps it's been a bad thing. Not," she added hastily, "not that you aren't all three the best children any mother and father ever had! *He* said so. He said the only trouble was that our children were too good for us." She shook her head remorsefully throughout Laura's natural reply to this; was silent a while; then, as she rose, she said timidly, not looking at her daughter: "Of course Hedrick didn't mean to tell an outright lie. They were just talking, and perhaps he—perhaps he heard something that made him think what he *did*. People are so often mistaken in what they hear, even when they're talking right to each other, and ——"

"Isn't it more likely," said Laura, gravely, "that Cora was telling some story or incident, and that Hedrick overheard that part of it, and thought she was speaking directly to Mr. Corliss?"

"Of course!" cried the mother with instant and buoyant relief; and when the three ladies convened, a little later, Cora (unquestioned) not only confirmed this explanation, but repeated in detail the story she had related to Mr. Corliss. Laura had been quick.

Hedrick passed a variegated morning among

comrades. He obtained prestige as having a father like-to-die, but another boy turned up who had learned to chew tobacco. Then Hedrick was pronounced inferior to others in turning "cart-wheels," but succeeded in a wrestling match for an apple, which he needed. Later, he was chased empty-handed from the rear of an ice-wagon, but greatly admired for his retorts to the vociferous chaser: the other boys rightly considered that what he said to the ice-man was much more horrible than what the ice-man said to him. The ice-man had a fair vocabulary, but it lacked pliancy; seemed stiff and fastidious compared with the flexible Saxon in which Hedrick sketched a family tree lacking, perhaps, some plausibility as having produced even an ice-man, but curiously interesting zoölogically.

He came home at noon with the flush of this victory new upon his brow. He felt equal to anything, and upon Cora's appearing at lunch with a blithe, bright air and a new arrangement of her hair, he opened a fresh campaign with ill-omened bravado.

"Ear-muffs in style for September, are they?" he inquired in allusion to a symmetrical and becoming undulation upon each side of her head. "Too bad Ray Vilas can't come any more; he'd like those, I know he would."

Cora, who was talking jauntily to her mother, went on without heeding. She affected her enunciation at times with a slight lisp; spoke preciously and over-exquisitely, purposely mincing the letter R, at the same time assuming a manner of artificial distinction and conscious elegance which never failed to produce in her brother the last stage of exasperation. She did this now. "Charming woman, that dear Mrs. Villard," she prattled. "I met her downtown this morning. Dear mamma, you should but have seen her delight when she saw *me*. She was but just returned from Bar Harbor —— "

"'Baw-hawbaw'!" Poor Hedrick was successfully infuriated immediately. "What in thunder is 'Baw-hawbaw'? Mrs. Villawd! Baw-hawbaw! Oh, maw!"

"She had no idea she should find *me* in town, she said," Cora ran on, happily. "She came back early on account of the children having to be sent to school. She has such adorable children — beautiful, dimpled babes —— "

"*Slush! Slush! Luv-a-ly slush!*"

"—And her dear son, Egerton Villard, he's grown to be such a comely lad, and he has the most charming courtly manners: he helped his mother out of her carriage with all the air of a man of the world, and bowed to me as to a duchess. I think he might be a great influence for good if the dear Villards would but sometimes let him associate a little with our unfortunate Hedrick. Egerton Villard is really distingué; he has a beautiful head; and if he could be induced but to let Hedrick follow him about but a little —— "

"I'll beat his beautiful head off for him if he but butts in on me but a little!" Hedrick promised earnestly. "Idiot!"

Cora turned toward him innocently. "What did you say, Hedrick?"

"I said 'Idiot'!"

"You mean Egerton Villard?"

"Both of you!"

"You think I'm an idiot, Hedrick?" Her tone was calm, merely inquisitive.

"Yes, I do!"

"Oh, no," she said pleasantly. "Don't you think if I were *really* an idiot I'd be even fonder of you than I am?"

It took his breath. In a panic he sat waiting he knew not what; but Cora blandly resumed her interrupted remarks to her mother, beginning a description of Mrs. Villard's dress; Laura was talking unconcernedly to Miss Peirce; no one appeared to be aware that anything unusual had been said. His breath came back, and, summoning his presence of mind, he found himself able to consider his position with some degree of assurance. Perhaps, after all, Cora's retort had been merely a coincidence. He went over and over it in his mind, making a pretence, meanwhile, to be busy with his plate. "If I were *really* an idiot." . . . It was the "*really*" that troubled him. But for that one word, he could have decided that her remark was a coincidence; but "*really*" was ominous; had a sinister ring. "If I were *really* an idiot!" Suddenly the pleasant clouds that had obscured his memory of the fatal evening were swept away as by a monstrous Hand: it all came back to him with sickening clearness. So is it always with the sinner with his sin and its threatened discovery. Again, in his miserable mind, he sat beside Lolita on the fence, with the moon shining through her hair; and he knew — for he had often read it — that a man could be punished his whole life through for a single moment's weakness. A man might become rich, great, honoured, and have a large family, but his one soft sin would follow him, hunt him out and pull him down at last. "*Really* an idiot!" Did that relentless Comanche, Cora, know this Thing? He shuddered. Then he fell back upon his faith in Providence. It *could* not be that she knew! Ah, no! Heaven would not let the world be so bad as that! And yet it did sometimes become negligent — he remembered the case of a baby-girl cousin who fell into the bath-tub and was drowned. Providence had allowed that: What assurance had he that it would not go a step farther?

"Why, Hedrick," said Cora, turning toward him cheerfully, "you're not really eating anything; you're only pretending to." His heart sank with apprehension. Was it coming? "You really must eat," she went on. "School begins so soon, you must be strong, you know. How we shall miss you here at home during your hours of work!"

With that, the burden fell from his shoulders, his increasing terrors took wing. If Laura had told his ghastly secret to Cora, the latter would not have had recourse to such weak satire as this. Cora was not the kind of person to try a popgun on an enemy when she had a thirteen-inch gun at her disposal; so he reasoned; and in the gush of his relief and happiness, responded:

"You're a little too cocky lately, Cora-lee: I wish you were *my* daughter — just about five minutes!"

Cora looked upon him fondly. "What would you do to me," she inquired with a terrible sweetness "— darling little boy?"

Hedrick's head swam. The blow was square in the face; it jarred every bone; the world seemed to topple. His mother, rising from her chair, choked slightly, and hurried to join the nurse, who was already on her way upstairs. Cora sent an affectionate laugh across the table to her stunned antagonist.

"You wouldn't beat me, would you, dear?" she murmured. "I'm almost sure you wouldn't; not if I asked you to kiss me some *more!*"

All doubt was gone, the last hope fled! The worst had arrived. A vision of the awful future flamed across his staggered mind. The doors to the arena were flung open: the wild beasts howled for hunger of him; the spectators waited.

Cora began lightly to sing:

> . . . "Dear,
> Would thou wert near
> To hear me tell how fair thou art!
> Since thou art gone I mourn all alone,
> Oh, my Lolita ——"

She broke off to explain: "It's one of those passionate little Spanish serenades, Hedrick. I'll sing it for your boy-friends next time they come to play in the yard. I think they'd like it. When they know why you like it so much, I'm sure they will. Of course you *do* like it — you roguish little lover!" A spasm rewarded this demoniacal phrase. "Darling little boy, the serenade goes on like this:

> "Oh, my Lolita, come to my heart:
> Oh, come beloved, love let me press thee,
> While I caress thee
> In one long kiss, Lolita!
> Lolita come! Let me ——"

Hedrick sprang to his feet with a yell of agony. "Laura Madison, you tattle-tale," he bellowed, "I'll never forgive you as long as I live! I'll get even with you if it takes a thousand years!"

With that, and pausing merely to kick a rung out of a chair which happened to be in his way, he rushed from the room.

His sisters had risen to go, and Cora flung her arms round Laura in ecstacy. "You mean old viper!" she cried. "You could have told me days ago! It's almost too good to be true: it's the first time in my whole life I've felt safe from the Pest for a moment!"

Laura shook her head. "My conscience troubles me; it did seem as if I ought to tell you — and mamma thought so, too; and I gave him warning, but now that I have done it, it seems rather mean and ——"

"No!" exclaimed Cora. "You just gave me a chance to protect myself for once, thank heaven!" And she picked up her skirts and danced her way into the front hall.

"I'm afraid," said Laura, following, "I shouldn't have done it."

"Oh, Laura," cried the younger girl, "I *am* having the best time, these days! This just caps it." She lowered her voice, but her eyes grew even brighter. "I think I've shown a certain gentleman a few things he didn't understand!"

"Who, dear?"

"Val," returned Cora lightly; "Valentine Corliss. I think he knows a little more about women than he did when he first came here."

"You've had a difference with him?" asked Laura with eager hopefulness. "You've broken with him?"

"Oh, Lord, no! Nothing like that." Cora leaned to her confidentially. "He told me, once, he'd be at the feet of any woman that could help put through an affair like his oil scheme, and I decided I'd just show him what I could do. He'd talk about it to me; then he'd laugh at me. That very Sunday when I got papa to go in —— "

"But he didn't," said Laura helplessly. "He only said he'd try to —— when he gets well."

"It's all the same — and it'll be a great thing for him, too," said Cora, gayly. "Well, that very afternoon before Val left, he practically told me I was no good. Of course he didn't use just those words — that isn't his way — but he laughed at me. And haven't I shown him! I sent Richard a note that very night saying papa had consented to be secretary of the company, and Richard had said he'd go in if papa did that, and he couldn't break his word —— "

"I know," said Laura, sighing. "I know."

"Laura" — Cora spoke with sudden gravity — "did you ever know anybody like me? I'm almost getting superstitious about it, because it seems to me I *always* get just what I set out to get. I believe I could have anything in the world if I tried for it."

"I hope so, if you tried for something good for you," said Laura sadly. "Cora, dear, you will — you will be a little easy on Hedrick, won't you?"

Cora leaned against the newel and laughed till she was exhausted.

CHAPTER THIRTEEN

MR. TRUMBLE'S offices were heralded by a neat blazon upon the principal door, "Wade J. Trumble, Mortgages and Loans"; and the gentleman thus comfortably, proclaimed, emerging from that door upon a September noontide, burlesqued a start of surprise at sight of a figure unlocking an opposite door which exhibited the name, "Ray Vilas," and below it, the cryptic phrase, "Probate Law."

"Water!" murmured Mr. Trumble, affecting to faint. "You ain't going in *there*, are you, Ray?" He followed the other into the office, and stood leaning against a bookcase, with his hands in his pockets, while Vilas raised the two windows, which were obscured by a film of smoke-deposit: there was a thin coat of fine sifted dust over everything. "Better not sit down, Ray," continued Trumble, warningly. "You'll spoil your clothes and you might get a client. That word 'Probate' on the door ain't going to keep 'em out forever. You recognize the old place, I s'pose? You must have been here at least twice since you moved in. What's the matter? Dick Lindley hasn't missionaried you into any idea of *working*, has he? Oh, no, *I* see: the Richfield Hotel bar has closed — you've managed to drink it all at last!"

"Have you heard how old man Madison is to-day?" asked Ray, dusting his fingers with a handkerchief.

"Somebody told me yesterday he was about the same. He's not going to get well."

"How do you know?" Ray spoke quickly.

"Stroke too severe. People never recover —— "

"Oh, yes, they do, too."

Trumble began hotly: "I beg to dif —— " but checked himself, manifesting a slight confusion. "That is, I know they don't. Old Madison may live a while, if you call that getting well; but he'll never be the same man he was. Doctor Sloane says it was a bad stroke. Says it was 'induced by heat prostration and excitement.' 'Excitement!'" he repeated with a sour laugh. "Yep, I expect a man could get all the excitement he wanted in *that* house, especially if he was her daddy. Poor old man, I don't believe he's got five thousand dollars in the world, and look how she dresses!"

Ray opened a compartment beneath one of the bookcases, and found a bottle and some glasses. "Aha," he muttered, "our janitor doesn't drink, I perceive. Join me?" Mr. Trumble accepted, and Ray explained, cheerfully: "Richard Lindley's got me so cowed I'm afraid to go near any of my old joints. You see, he trails me; the scoundrel has kept me sober for whole days at a time, and I've been mortified, having old friends see me in that condition; so I have to sneak up here to my own office to drink to Cora, now and then. You mustn't tell him. What's she been doing to *you*, lately?"

The little man addressed grew red with the sharp, resentful memory. "Oh, nothing! Just struck me in the face with her parasol on the public street, that's all!" He gave an account of his walk to church with Cora. "I'm through with that girl!" he exclaimed vindictively, in conclusion. "It was the damnedest thing you ever saw in your life: right in broad daylight, in front of the church. And she laughed when she did it; you'd have thought she was knocking a puppy out of her way. She can't do that to me twice, I tell you. What the devil do you see to laugh at?"

"You'll be around," returned his companion, refilling the glasses, "asking for more, the first chance she gives you. Here's her health!"

"I don't drink it!" cried Mr. Trumble angrily. "And I'm through with her for good, I tell you! I'm not your kind: I don't let a girl like that upset me till I can't think of anything else, and go making such an ass of myself that the whole town gabbles about it. Cora Madison's seen the last of me, I'll thank you to notice. She's never been half-decent to me; cut dances with me all last winter; kept me hanging round the outskirts of every crowd she was in; stuck me with Laura and her mother every time she had a chance; then has the nerve to try to use me, so's she can make a bigger hit with a new man! You can bet your head I'm through! She'll get paid though! Oh, she'll get paid for it!"

"How?" laughed Ray.

It was a difficult question. "You wait and see," responded the threatener, feebly. "Just wait and see. She's wild about this Corliss, I tell you," he continued, with renewed vehemence. "She's crazy about him; she's lost her head at last —— "

"You mean he's going to avenge you?"

"No, I don't, though he might, if she decided to marry him."

"Do you know," said Ray slowly, glancing over his glass at his nervous companion, "it doesn't strike me that Mr. Valentine Corliss has much the air of a marrying man."

"He has the air to *me*," observed Mr. Trumble, "of a darned bad lot! But I have to hand it to him: he's a wizard. He's got something besides his good looks — a man that could get Cora Madison interested in 'business'! In *oil!* Cora Madison! How do you suppose —— "

His companion began to laugh again. "You don't really suppose he talked his oil business to her, do you, Trumble?"

"He must have. Else how could she —— "

"Oh, no, Cora herself never talks upon any subject but one; she never listens to any other either."

"Then how in thunder did he —— "

"If Cora asks you if you think it will rain," interrupted Vilas, "doesn't she really seem to be asking: 'Do you love me? How much?' Suppose Mr. Corliss is an expert in the same line. Of course he can talk about oil!"

"He strikes me," said Trumble, "as just about

the slickest customer that ever hit this town. I like Richard Lindley, and I hope he'll see his fifty thousand dollars again. *I* wouldn't have given Corliss thirty cents."

"Why do you think he's a crook?"

"I don't say that," returned Trumble. "All *I* know about him is that he's done some of the finest work to get fifty thousand dollars put in his hands that I ever heard of. And all anybody knows about him is that he lived here seventeen years ago, and comes back claiming to know where there's oil in Italy. He shows some maps and papers and gets cablegrams signed 'Moliterno.' Then he talks about selling the old Corliss house here, where the Madisons live, and putting the money into his oil company: he does that to sound plausible, but I have good reason to know that house was mortgaged to its full value within a month after his aunt left it to him. He'll not get a cent if it's sold. That's all. And he's got Cora Madison so crazy over him that she makes life a hell for poor old Lindley until he puts all he's saved into the bubble. The scheme may be all right. How do *I* know? There's no way to tell, without going over there, and Corliss won't let anybody do that — oh, he's got a plausible excuse for it! But I'm sorry for Lindley: he's so crazy about Cora, he's soft. And she's so crazy about Corliss *she's* soft! Well, I used to be crazy about her myself, but I'm not soft — I'm not the Lindley kind of loon, thank heaven!"

"What kind are you, Trumble?" asked Ray, mildly.

"Not your kind either," retorted the other going to the door. "She cut me on the street the other day; she's quit speaking to me. If you've got any money, why don't you take it over to the hotel and give it to Corliss? She might start speaking to *you* again. I'm going to lunch!" He slammed the door behind him.

Ray Vilas, left alone, elevated his heels to the sill, and stared out of the window a long time at a gravelled roof which presented little of interest. He replenished his glass and his imagination frequently, the latter being so stirred that when, about three o'clock, he noticed the inroads he had made upon the bottle, tears of self-pity came to his eyes. "Poor little drunkard!" he said aloud. "Go ahead and do it. Isn't anything *you* won't do!" And, having washed his face at a basin in a corner, he set his hat slightly upon one side, picked up a walking stick and departed jauntily, and, to the outward eye, presentably sober.

Mr. Valentine Corliss would be glad to see him, the clerk at the Richfield Hotel reported, after sending up a card, and upon Ray's following the card, Mr. Valentine Corliss in person confirmed the message with considerable amusement and a cordiality in which there was some mixture of the quizzical. He was the taller; and the robust manliness of his appearance, his splendid health and boxer's figure offered a sharp contrast to the superlatively lean tippler. Corliss was humorously aware of his advantage: his greeting seemed really to say, "Hello, my funny bug, here you are again!" though the words of his salutation were entirely courteous; and he followed it with a hospitable offer.

"No," said Vilas; "I won't drink with you." He spoke so gently that the form of his refusal, usually interpreted as truculent, escaped the other's notice. He also declined a cigar, apologetically asking permission to light one of his own cigarettes; then, as he sank into a velour-covered chair, apologized again for the particular attention he was bestowing upon the apartment, which he recognized as one of the "*suites de luxe*" of the hotel.

"'Parlour, bedroom, and bath,'" he continued, with a melancholy smile; "and 'Lachrymae,' and 'A Reading from Homer.' Sometimes they have 'The Music Lesson,' or 'Winter Scene' or 'A Neapolitan Fisher Lad' instead of 'Lachrymae,' but they always have 'A Reading from Homer.' When you opened the door, a moment ago, I had a very strong impression that something extraordinary would some time happen to me in this room."

"Well," suggested Corliss, "you refused a drink in it."

"Even more wonderful than that," said Ray, glancing about the place curiously. "It may be a sense of something painful that already has happened here — perhaps long ago, before your occupancy. It has a pathos."

"Most hotel rooms have had something happen in them," said Corliss lightly. "I believe the managers usually change the door numbers if what happens is especially unpleasant. Probably they change some of the rugs, also."

"I feel —— " Ray paused, frowning. "I feel as if some one had killed himself here."

"Then no doubt some of the rugs *have* been changed."

"No doubt." The caller laughed and waved his hand in dismissal of the topic. "Well, Mr. Corliss," he went on, shifting to a brisker tone, "I have come to make my fortune, too. You are Midas. Am I of sufficient importance to be touched?"

Valentine Corliss gave him sidelong an almost imperceptibly brief glance of sharpest scrutiny — it was like the wink of a camera shutter — but laughed in the same instant. "Which way do you mean that?"

"You have been quick," returned the visitor, repaying that glance with equal swiftness, "to seize upon the American idiom. I mean: How small a contribution would you be willing to receive toward your support!"

Corliss did not glance again at Ray; instead, he looked interested in the smoke of his cigar. "'Contribution,'" he repeated, with no inflection whatever. "'Toward my support.'"

"I mean, of course, how small an investment in your oil company."

"Oh, anything, anything," returned the promoter, with quick amiability. "We need to sell all the stock we can."

"All the money you can get?"

"Precisely. It's really a colossal proposition, Mr. Vilas." Corliss spoke with brisk enthusiasm. "It's a perfectly certain enormous profit upon everything that goes in. Prince Moliterno cables me later investigations show that the oil-field is more than twice as large as we thought when I left Naples. He's on the ground now, buying up what he can, secretly."

"I had an impression from Richard Lindley that the secret had been discovered."

"Oh, yes; but only by a few, and those are trying to keep it quiet from the others, of course."

"I see. Does your partner know of your success in raising a large investment?"

"You mean Lindley's? Certainly." Corliss waved his hand in light deprecation. "Of course that's something, but Moliterno would hardly be apt to think of it as very large! You see he's putting in about five times that much, himself, and I've already turned over to him double it for myself. Still, it counts — certainly; and of course it will be a great thing for Lindley."

"I fear," Ray said hesitatingly, "you won't be much interested in my drop for your bucket. I have twelve hundred dollars in the world; and it is in the bank — I stopped there on my way here. To be exact, I have twelve hundred and forty-seven dollars and fifty-one cents. My dear sir, will you allow me to purchase one thousand dollars' worth of stock? I will keep the two hundred and forty-seven dollars and fifty-one cents to live on — I may need an egg while waiting for you to make me rich. Will you accept so small an investment?"

"Certainly," said Corliss, laughing. "Why not? You may as well profit by the chance as any one. I'll send you the stock certificates — we put them at par. I'm attending to that myself, as our secretary, Mr. Madison, is unable to take up his duties."

Vilas took a cheque-book and a fountain-pen from his pocket.

"Oh, any time, any time," said Corliss cheerfully, observing the new investor's movement.

"Now, I think," returned Vilas quietly. "How shall I make it out?"

"Oh, to me, I suppose," answered Corliss indifferently. "That will save a little trouble, and I can turn it over to Moliterno, by cable, as I did Lindley's. I'll give you a receipt —— "

"You need not mind that," said Ray. "Really it is of no importance."

"Of course the cheque itself is a receipt," remarked Corliss, tossing it carelessly upon a desk. "You'll have some handsome returns for that slip of paper, Mr. Vilas."

"In that blithe hope I came," said Ray airily. "I am confident of it. I have my own ways of divination, Mr. Corliss. I have gleams." He rose as if to go, but stood looking thoughtfully about the apartment again. "Singular impression," he murmured. "Not exactly as if I'd seen it in a dream; and yet — and yet —— "

"You have symptoms of clairvoyance at times, I take it." The conscious, smooth superiority of the dexterous man playing with an inconsequent opponent resounded in this speech, clear as the humming of a struck bell; and Vilas shot him a single open glance of fire from hectic eyes. For that instant, the frailer buck trumpeted challenge. Corliss — broad-shouldered, supple of waist, graceful and strong — smiled down negligently; yet the very air between the two men seemed charged with an invisible explosive. Ray laughed quickly, as in undisturbed good nature; then, flourishing his stick, turned toward the door.

"Oh, no, it isn't clairvoyance — no more than

when I told you that your only real interest is women. He paused, his hand upon the door-knob. "I'm a quaint mixture, however: perhaps I should be handled with care."

"Very good of you," laughed Corliss — "this warning. The afternoon I had the pleasure of meeting you I think I remember your implying that you were a mere marionette."

"A haggard harlequin!" snapped Vilas, waving his hand to a mirror across the room. "Don't I look it?" And the phrase fitted him with tragic accuracy. "You see? What a merry wedding-guest I'll be! I invite you to join me on the nuptial eve."

"Thanks. Who's getting married: when the nuptial eve?"

Ray opened the door, and, turning, rolled his eyes fantastically. "Haven't you heard?" he cried. "When Hecate marries John Barleycorn!" He bowed low. "Mr. Midas, adieu."

Corliss stood in the doorway and watched him walk down the long hall to the elevator. There, Ray turned and waved his hand, the other responding with gayety which was not assumed: Vilas might be insane, or drunk, or both, but the signature upon his cheque was unassailable.

Corliss closed the door and began to pace his apartment thoughtfully. His expression manifested a peculiar phenomenon. In company, or upon the street, or when he talked with men, the open look and frank eyes of this stalwart young man were disarming and his most winning assets. But now, as he paced alone in his apartment, now that he was not upon exhibition, now when there was no eye to behold him, and there was no reason to dissimulate or veil a single thought or feeling, his look was anything but open; the last trace of frankness disappeared; the muscles at mouth and eyes shifted; lines and planes intermingled and altered subtly; there was a moment of misty transformation — and the face of another man emerged. It was the face of a man uninstructed in mercy; it was a shrewd and planning face: alert, resourceful, elaborately perceptive, and flawlessly hard. But, beyond all, it was the face of a man perpetually on guard.

He had the air of debating a question, his hands in his pockets, his handsome forehead lined with a temporary indecision. His sentry-go extended the length of his two rooms, and each time he came back into his bedroom his glance fell consideringly upon a steamer-trunk of the largest size, at the foot of his bed. The trunk was partially packed as if for departure. And, indeed, it was the question of departure which he was debating.

He was a man of varied dexterities, and he had one faculty of high value, which had often saved him, had never betrayed him; it was intuitive and equal to a sixth sense: he always knew when it was time to go. An inner voice warned him; he trusted to it and obeyed it. And it had spoken now, and there was his trunk half-packed in answer. But he had stopped midway in his packing, because he had never yet failed to make a clean sweep where there was the slightest chance for one; he hated to leave a big job before it was completely finished — and Mr. Wade Trumble had refused to invest in the oil-fields of Basilicata.

Corliss paused beside the trunk, stood a moment immersed in thought; then nodded once, decisively, and, turning to a dressing-table, began to place some silver-mounted brushes and bottles in a leather travelling-case.

There was a knock at the outer door. He frowned, set down what he had in his hands, went to the door and opened it to find Mr. Pryor, that plain citizen, awaiting entrance.

Corliss remained motionless in an arrested attitude, his hand upon the knob of the opened door. His position did not alter; he became almost unnaturally still, a rigidity which seemed to increase. Then he looked quickly behind him, over his shoulder, and back again, with a swift movement of the head.

"No," said Pryor, at that. "I don't want you. I just thought I'd have two minutes' talk with you. All right?"

"All right," said Corliss quietly. "Come in." He turned carelessly, and walked away from the door, keeping between his guest and the desk. When he reached the desk, he turned again and leaned against it, his back to it, but in the action of turning his hand had swept a sheet of note-paper over Ray Vilas's cheque — a too conspicuous oblong of pale blue. Pryor had come in and closed the door.

"I don't know," he began, regarding the other through his glasses, with steady eyes, "that I'm going to interfere with you at all, Corliss. I just happened to strike you — I wasn't looking for you. I'm on vacation, visiting my married daughter that lives here, and I don't want to mix in if I can help it."

Corliss laughed, easily. "There's nothing for you to mix in. You couldn't if you wanted to."

"Well, I hope that's true," said Pryor, with an air of indulgence, curiously like that of a teacher for a pupil who promises improvement. "I do indeed. There isn't anybody I'd like to see turn straight more than you. You're educated and cultured, and refined, and smarter than all hell. It would be a big thing. That's one reason I'm taking the trouble to talk to you."

"I told you I wasn't doing anything," said Corliss with a petulance as oddly like that of a pupil as the other's indulgence was like that of a tutor. "This is my own town; I own property here, and I came here to sell it. I can prove it in half-a-minute's telephoning. Where do you come in?"

"Easy, easy," said Pryor, soothingly. "I've just told you I don't want to come in at all."

"Then what do you want?"

"I came to tell you just one thing: to go easy up there at Mr. Madison's house."

Corliss laughed contemptuously. "It's *my* house. I own it. That's the property I came here to sell."

"Oh, I know," responded Pryor. "That part of it's all right. But I've seen you several times with that young lady, and you looked pretty thick, to me. You know you haven't got any business doing such things, Corliss. I know your record from Buda Pesth to Copenhagen and —— "

"See here, my friend," said the younger man, angrily, "you may be a tiptop spotter for the government when it comes to running down some poor old lady that's bought a string of pearls in the Rue de la Paix —— "

"I've been in the service twenty-eight years," remarked Pryor, mildly.

"All right," said the other with a gesture of impatience; "and you got me once, all right. Well, that's over, isn't it? Have I tried anything since?"

"Not in that line," said Pryor.

"Well, what business have you with any other line?" demanded Corliss angrily. "Who made *you* general supervisor of public morals? I want to know —— "

"Now, what's the use your getting excited? I'm just here to tell you that I'm going to keep an eye on you. I don't know many people here, and I haven't taken any particular pains to look you up. For all I know, you're only here to sell your house, as you say. But I know old man Madison a little, and I kind of took a fancy to him; he's a mighty nice old man, and he's got a nice family. He's sick and it won't do to trouble him; but — honest, Corliss — if you don't slack off in that neighbourhood a little, I'll have to have a talk with the young lady herself."

A derisory light showed faintly in the younger man's eyes as he inquired, softly: "That all, Mr. Pryor?"

"No. Don't try anything on out here. Not in *any* of your lines."

"I don't mean to."

"That's right. Sell your house and clear out. You'll find it healthy." He went to the door. "So far as I can see," he observed, ruminatively, "you haven't brought any of that Moliterno crowd you used to work with over to this side with you."

"I haven't seen Moliterno for two years," said Corliss, sharply.

"Well, I've said my say." Pryor gave him a last word as he went out. "You keep away from that little girl."

"Ass!" exclaimed Corliss, as the door closed. He exhaled a deep breath sharply, and broke into a laugh. Then he went quickly into his bedroom and began to throw the things out of his trunk.

CHAPTER FOURTEEN

HEDRICK MADISON'S eyes were not of marble; his heart was not flint nor his skin steel plate: he was flesh and tender; he was a vulnerable, breathing boy, with highly developed capacities for pain which were now being taxed to their utmost. Once he had loved to run, to leap, to disport himself in the sun, to drink deep of the free air; he had loved life and one or two of his fellow-men. He had borne himself buoyantly, with jaunty self-confidence, even with some intolerance toward the weaknesses of others, not infrequently displaying merriment over their mischances; but his time had found him at last; the evil day had come. Indian Summer was Indian for him, indeed: sweet death were welcome; no charity was left in him. He leaped no more, but walked broodingly and sought the dark places. And yet it could not be said that times were dull for him: the luckless picket who finds himself in an open eighty-acre field, under the eye of a sharpshooter up a tree, would not be apt to describe the experience as dull. And Cora never missed a shot; she loved the work; her pleasure in it was almost as agonizing for the target as was the accuracy of her fire.

She was ingenious: the horrible facts at her disposal were damaging enough in all conscience: but they did not content her. She invented a love-story, assuming that Hedrick was living it: he was supposed to be pining for Lolita, to be fading, day-by-day, because of enforced separation; and she contrived this to such an effect of reality, and with such a diabolical affectation of delicacy in referring to it, that the mere remark, with gentle sympathy, "I think poor Hedrick is looking a little better to-day," infallibly produced something closely resembling a spasm. She formed the habit of never mentioning her brother in his presence except as "poor Hedrick," a too obvious commiseration of his pretended attachment — which met with like success. Most dreadful of all, she invented romantic phrases and expressions assumed to have been spoken or written by Hedrick in reference to his unhappiness; and she repeated them so persistently, yet always with such apparent sincerity of belief that they were quotations from him, and not her inventions, that the driven youth knew a fear, sometimes, that the horrid things were actually of his own perpetration.

The most withering of these was, "Torn from her I love by the ruthless hand of a parent. . . ." It was not completed; Cora never got any further with it, nor was there need: a howl of fury invariably assured her of an effect as satisfactory as could possibly have been obtained by an effort less impressionistic. Life became a series of easy victories for Cora, and she made them somehow the more deadly for Hedrick by not seeming to look at him in his affliction, nor even to be aiming his way: he never could tell when the next shot was coming. At the table, the ladies of his family might be deep in dress, or discussing Mr. Madison's slowly improving condition, when Cora, with utter irrelevance, would sigh, and, looking sadly into her coffee, murmur, "Ah, *fond* mem'ries!" or, "*Why* am I haunted by the dead past?" or, the dreadful, "Torn from her I love by the ruthless hand of a parent. . . ."

There was compassion in Laura's eyes and in his mother's, but Cora was irresistible, and they always ended by laughing in spite of themselves; and though they pleaded for Hedrick in private, their remonstrances proved strikingly ineffective. Hedrick was the only person who had ever used the high hand with Cora: she found repayment too congenial. In the daytime he could not go in the front yard, but Cora's window would open and a tenderly smiling Cora lean out to call affectionately, "Don't walk on the grass — darling little boy!" Or, she would nod happily to him and begin to sing:

"Oh come beloved, love let me press thee,
While I caress thee
" In one long kiss, Lolita. . . . "

One terror still hung over him. If it fell — as it might at any fatal moment — then the utmost were indeed done upon him; and this apprehension bathed his soul in night. In his own circle of congenial age and sex he was, by virtue of superior bitterness and precocity of speech, a chief — a moral castigator, a satirist of manners, a creator of stinging nicknames; and many nourished unhealed grievances which they had little hope of satisfying against him; those who attempted it invariably departing with more to avenge than they had brought with them. Let these once know what Cora knew. . . . The vision was unthinkable!

It was Cora's patent desire to release the hideous item, to spread the scandal broadcast among his fellows — to ring it from the school-bells, to send it winging on the hot winds of Hades! The boys had always liked his yard and the empty stable to play in, and the devices he now employed to divert their activities elsewhere were worthy of a great strategist. His energy and an abnormal ingenuity accomplished incredible things: school had been in session several weeks and only one boy had come within conversational distance of Cora; — him Hedrick bore away bodily, in simulation of resistless high spirits, a brilliant exhibition of stagecraft.

And then Cora's friend, Mrs. Villard, removed her son Egerton from the private school he had hitherto attended, and he made his appearance in Hedrick's class, one morning at the public school. Hedrick's eye lighted with a savage gleam; timidly the first joy he had known for a thousand years crept into his grim heart. After school, Egerton expiated a part of Cora's cruelty. It was a very small part, and the exploit no more than infinitesimally soothing to the conqueror, but when Egerton finally got home he was no sight for a mother.

Thus Hedrick wrought his own doom: Mrs. Villard telephoned to Cora, and Cora went immediately to see her.

It happened to Hedrick that he was late leaving home the next morning. His entrance into his classroom was an undeniable sensation, and within ten minutes the teacher had lost all control of the school. It became necessary to send for the principal. Recess was a frantic nightmare for Hedrick, and his homeward progress at noon a procession of such uproarious screamers as were his equals in speed. The nethermost depths were reached when an ignoble pigtailed person he had always trodden upon flat-footed screamed across the fence from next door, as he reached fancied sanctuary in his own back-yard:

"Kiss me some *more*, darling little boy!"

This worm, established upon the fence opposite the conservatory windows, and in direct view from the table in the dining-room, shrieked the accursed request at short intervals throughout the luncheon hour. The humour of childhood is sometimes almost intrusive.

And now began a life for Hedrick which may be rather painfully but truthfully likened to a prolongation of the experiences of a rat that finds itself in the middle of a crowded street in daylight: there is plenty of excitement but no pleasure. He was pursued, harried, hounded from early morning till nightfall, and even in his bed would hear shrill shouts go down the sidewalk from the throats of juvenile fly-by-nights: "Oh dar-ling lit-oh darling lit-oh *lit*-tle boy, *lit*-tle boy, kiss me some *more*!" And one day he overheard a remark which strengthened his growing conviction that the cataclysm had affected the whole United States: it was a teacher who spoke, explaining to another a disturbance in the hall of the school. She said, behind her hand:

"*He kissed an idiot.*"

Laura had not even remotely foreseen the consequences of her revelation, nor, indeed, did she now properly estimate their effect upon Hedrick. She and her mother were both sorry for him, and did what they could to alleviate his misfortunes, but there was an inevitable remnant of amusement in their sympathy. Youth, at war, affects stoicism but not resignation: in truth, resignation was not much in Hedrick's line, and it would be far from the fact to say that he was softened by his sufferings. He brooded profoundly and his brightest thought was revenge. It was not upon Cora that his chief bitterness turned. Cora had always been the constant, open enemy: warfare between them was a regular condition of life; and unconsciously, and without "thinking it out," he recognized the naturalness of her seizing upon the deadliest weapon against him that came to her hand. There was nothing unexpected in that: no, the treachery, to his mind, lay in the act of Laura, that non-combatant, who had furnished the natural and habitual enemy with this scourge. At all times, and with or without cause, he ever stood ready to do anything possible for the reduction of Cora's cockiness, but now it was for the taking-down of Laura and the repayment of her uncalled-for and overwhelming assistance to the opposite camp that he lay awake nights and kept his imagination hot. Laura was a serene person, so neutral — outwardly, at least — and so little concerned for herself in any matter he could bring to mind, that for purposes of revenge she was a difficult proposition. And then, in a desperate hour, he remembered her book.

Only once had he glimpsed it, but she had shown unmistakable agitation of a mysterious sort as she wrote in it, and, upon observing his presence, a prompt determination to prevent his reading a word of what she had written. Therefore, it was something peculiarly sacred and intimate. This deduction was proved by the care she exercised in keeping the book concealed from all eyes. A slow satisfaction began to permeate him: he made up his mind to find that padlocked ledger.

He determined with devoted ardour that when he found it he would make the worst possible use of it: the worst, that is, for Laura. As for consequences to himself, he was beyond them. There is an Irish play in which an old woman finds that she no longer fears the sea when it has drowned the last of her sons; it can do nothing more to her. Hedrick no longer feared anything.

The book was somewhere in Laura's room, he knew that; and there were enough opportunities to search, though Laura had a way of coming in unexpectedly which was embarrassing; and he suffered from a sense of inadequacy when — on the occasion of his first new attempt — he answered the casual inquiry as to his presence by saying that he "had a headache." He felt there was something indirect in the reply; but Laura was unsuspicious and showed no disposition to be analytical. After this, he took the precaution to bring a school-book with him and she often found the boy seated quietly by her west window immersed in study: he said he thought his headaches came from his eyes and that the west light "sort of eased them a little."

The ledger remained undiscovered, although probably there has never been a room more thoroughly and painstakingly searched, without its floor being taken up and its walls torn down. The most mysterious, and, at the same time, the most maddening thing about it was the apparent simplicity of the task. He was certain that the room contained the book: listening, barefooted, outside the door at night, he had heard the pen scratching. The room was as plain as a room can be, and small. There was a scantily filled clothes-press; he had explored every cubic inch of it. There was the small writing table with one drawer; it held only some note-paper and a box of pen-points. There was a bureau; to his certain knowledge it contained no secret whatever. There were a few giltless chairs, and a white "wash-stand," a mere basin and slab with exposed plumbing. Lastly, there was the bed, a very large and ugly "Eastlake" contrivance; he had acquired a close acquaintance with all of it except the interior of the huge mattress itself, and here, he finally concluded, must of necessity be the solution. The surface of the mattress he knew to be unbroken;

nevertheless the book was there. He had recently stimulated his deductive powers with a narrative of French journalistic sagacity in a similar case; and he applied French reasoning. The ledger existed. It was somewhere in the room. He had searched everything except the interior of the mattress. The ledger was in that interior.

The exploration thus become necessary presented some difficulties. Detection in the act would involve explanations hard to invent; it would not do to say he was looking for his knife; and he could not think of any excuse altogether free from a flavour of insincerity. A lameness beset them all and made them liable to suspicion; and Laura, once suspicious, might be petty enough to destroy the book, and so put it out of his power forever. He must await the right opportunity, and, after a racking exercise of patience, at last he saw it coming.

Doctor Sloane had permitted his patient to come down stairs for an increasing interval each day. Mr. Madison crept, rather than walked, leaning upon his wife and closely attended by Miss Peirce. He spoke with difficulty and not clearly; still, there was a perceptible improvement, and his family were falling into the habit of speaking of him as "almost well." On that account, Mrs. Madison urged her daughters to accept an invitation from the mother of the once courtly Egerton Villard. It was at breakfast that the matter was discussed.

"Of course Cora must go," Laura began, "but ——"

"But nothing!" interrupted Cora. "How would it look if I went and you didn't? Everybody knows papa's almost well, and they'd think it silly for us to give up the first real dance since last spring on that account; yet they're just spiteful enough, if I went and you stayed home, to call me a 'girl of no heart.' Besides," she added sweetly, "we ought to go to show Mrs. Villard we aren't hurt because Egerton takes so little notice of poor Hedrick."

Hedrick's lips moved silently, as in prayer.

"I'd rather not," said Laura. "I doubt if I'd have a very good time."

"You would, too," returned her sister, decidedly. "The men like to dance with you; you dance every bit as well as I do, and that black lace is the most becoming dress you ever had. Nobody ever remembers a black dress, anyway, unless it's cut very conspicuously, and yours isn't. I can't go without you; they love to say nasty things about me, and you're too good a sister to give 'em this chance, you old dear." She laughed and nodded affectionately across the table at Laura. "You've got to go!"

"Yes, it would be nicer," said the mother. And so it was settled. It was simultaneously settled in Hedrick's mind that the night of the dance should mark his discovery of the ledger. He would have some industrious hours alone with the mysterious mattress, safe from intrusion.

Meekly he lifted his eyes from his plate. "I'm glad you're going, sister Laura," he said in a gentle voice. "I think a change will do you good."

"Isn't it wonderful," exclaimed Cora, appealing to the others to observe him, "what an improvement a disappointment in love can make in deportment?"

For once, Hedrick only smiled.

CHAPTER FIFTEEN

LAURA had spent some thoughtful hours upon her black lace dress with results that astonished her family: it became a ball-gown — and a splendidly effective one. She arranged her dark hair in a more elaborate fashion than ever before, in a close coronal of faintly lustrous braids; she had no jewellery and obviously needed none. Her last action but one before she left her room was to dispose of the slender chain and key she always wore round her neck; then her final glance at the mirror — which fairly revealed a lovely woman — ended in a deprecatory little "face" she made at herself. It meant: "Yes, old lady, you fancy yourself very passable in here all by yourself, don't you? Just wait: you'll be standing beside Cora in a moment!"

And when she did stand beside Cora, in the latter's room, a moment later, her thought seemed warranted. Cora, radiant-eyed, in high bloom, and exquisite from head to foot in a shimmering white dancing-dress, a glittering crescent fastening the silver fillet that bound her vivid hair, was a flame of enchantment. Mrs. Madison, almost weeping with delight, led her daughters proudly, an arm round the waist of each, into her husband's room. Propped with pillows, he reclined in an armchair while Miss Peirce prepared his bed, an occupation she gave over upon this dazzling entrance, departing tactfully.

"Look at these," cried the mother; "— from our garden, Jim, dear! Don't we feel rich, you and I?"

"And — and — Laura," said the sick man, with the slow and imperfect enunication caused by his disease; "Laura looks pretty — too."

"Isn't she adorable!" Cora exclaimed warmly. "She decided to be the portrait of a young duchess, you see, all stately splendour — made of snow and midnight!"

"Hear! hear!" laughed Laura; but she blushed with pleasure, and taking Cora's hand in hers lifted it to her lips.

"And do you see Cora's crescent?" demanded Mrs. Madison. "What do you think of *that* for magnificence? She went down town this morning with seven dollars, and came back with that and her party gloves and a dollar in change! Isn't she a bargainer? Even for rhinestones they are the cheapest things you ever heard of. They look precisely like stones of the very finest water." They did — so precisely, indeed, that if the resemblance did not amount to actual identity, then had a jeweller of the town been able to deceive the eye of Valentine Corliss, which was an eye singularly learned in such matters.

"They're — both smart girls," said Madison, "both of them. And they look — beautiful, to-night — both. Laura is — amazing!"

When they had gone, Mrs. Madison returned from the stairway, and, kneeling beside her husband, put her arms round him gently: she had seen the tear that was marking its irregular pathway down his flaccid, gray cheek, and she understood.

"Don't. Don't worry, Jim," she whispered. "Those bright, beautiful things! — aren't they treasures?"

"It's — it's Laura," he said. "Cora will be all — right. She looks out for — herself. I'm — I'm afraid for — Laura. Aren't you?"

"No, no," she protested. "I'm not afraid for either of them." But she was: the mother had always been afraid for Cora.

. . . . . At the dance, the two girls, attended up the stairway to the ballroom by a chattering covey of black-coats, made a sensational entrance to a gallant fanfare of music, an effect which may have been timed to the premonitory tuning of instruments heard during the ascent; at all events, it was a great success; and Cora, standing revealed under the wide gilt archway, might have been a lithe and shining figure from the year eighteen-hundred-and-one, about to dance at the Luxembourg. She placed her hand upon the sleeve of Richard Lindley, and, glancing intelligently over his shoulder into the eyes of Valentine Corliss, glided rhythmically away.

People looked at her; they always did. Not only the non-dancers watched her; eyes everywhere were upon her, even though the owners gyrated, glided and dipped on distant orbits. The other girls watched her, as a rule, with a profound, an almost passionate curiosity; and they were prompt to speak well of her to men, except in trustworthy intimacy, because they did not enjoy being wrongfully thought jealous. Many of them kept somewhat aloof from her; but none of them ever nowadays showed "superiority" in her presence, or snubbed her: that had been tried and proved disastrous in rebound. Cora never failed to pay her score — and with a terrifying interest added, her native tendency being to take two eyes for an eye and the whole jaw for a tooth. They let her alone, though they asked and asked among themselves the never-monotonous question: "Why do men fall in love with girls like that?" a riddle which, solved, makes wives condescending to their husbands.

Most of the people at this dance had known one another as friends, or antagonists, or indifferent acquaintances, for years, and in such an assembly there are always two worlds, that of the women and that of the men. Each has its own vision, radically different from that of the other; but the greatest difference is that the men are unaware of the other world, only a few of them — usually queer ones like Ray Vilas — vaguely perceiving that there are two visions, while all the women understand both perfectly. The men splash about on the surface; the women keep their eyes open under water. Or, the life of the assembly is like a bright tapestry: the men take it as a picture and are not troubled to know how it is produced; but women are weavers. There was a Beauty of far-flung renown at Mrs. Villard's to-night: Mary Kane, a creature so made and coloured that young men at sight of her became as water and older men were apt to wonder regretfully why all women could not have been made like Mary. She was a kindly soul, and never intentionally outshone her sisters; but the perfect sumptuousness of her had sometimes tried the amiability of Cora Madison, to whom such success without effort and without spark seemed unfair, as well as bovine. Miss Kane was a central figure at the dance, shining tranquilly in a new triumph: that day her engagement had been announced to Mr. George Wattling, a young man of no special attainments, but desirable in his possessions and suitable to his happiness. The pair radiated the pardonable, gay importance of newly engaged people, and Cora, who had never before bestowed any notice upon Mr. Wattling, now examined him with thoughtful attention.

Finding him at her elbow in a group about a punch bowl, between dances, she offered warm felicitations. "But I don't suppose you care whether *I* care for you to be happy or not," she added, with a little plaintive laugh; — "you've always hated me so!"

Mr. Wattling was startled: never before had he imagined that Cora Madison had given him a thought; but there was not only thought, there was feeling, in this speech. She seemed to be concealing with bravery an even deeper feeling than the one inadvertently expressed. "Why, what on earth makes you think that?" he exclaimed.

"Think it? I *know* it!" She gave him a strange look, luminous yet mysterious, a curtain withdrawn only to show a shining mist with something undefined but dazzling beyond. "I've always known it!" And she turned away from him abruptly.

He sprang after her. "But you're wrong. I've never ——"

"Oh, yes, you have." They began to discuss it, and for better consideration of the theme it became necessary for Cora to "cut" the next dance, promised to another, and to give it to Mr. Wattling. They danced several times together, and Mr. Wattling's expression was serious. The weavers of the tapestry smiled and whispered things the men would not have understood — nor believed.

Ray Vilas, seated alone in a recessed and softly lighted gallery, did not once lose sight of the flitting sorceress. With his elbows on the railing, he leaned out, his head swaying slowly and mechanically as she swept up and down the tumultuously moving room, his passionate eyes gaunt and brilliant with his hunger. And something very like a general thrill passed over the assembly when, a little later, it was seen that he was dancing with her. Laura, catching a glimpse of this couple, started and looked profoundly disturbed.

The extravagance of Vilas's passion and the depths he sounded, in his absurd despair when discarded, had been matters of almost public gossip; he was accounted a somewhat scandalous and unbalanced but picturesque figure; and for the lady whose light hand had wrought such havoc upon him to be seen dancing with him was sufficiently startling to elicit the universal remark — evidently considered superlative—that it was "just like Cora Madison!" Cora usually perceived, with an admirably clear head, all that went on about her; and she was conscious of increasing the sensation, when after a few turns round the room, she allowed her partner to conduct her to a secluding grove of palms in the gallery. She sank into the chair he offered, and, fixing her eyes upon a small lamp of coloured glass which hung overhead, ostentatiously looked bored.

"At your feet, Cora," he said, seating himself upon a stool, and leaning toward her. "Isn't it appropriate that we should talk to music — we two? It shouldn't be that quick step though — not dance-music — should it?"

"Don't know 'm sure," murmured Cora.

"You werekind to dance with me," he said huskily. "I dared to speak to you ——"

She did not change her attitude nor the direction of her glance. "I couldn't cut you very well with the whole town looking on. I'm tired of being talked about. Besides, I don't care much who I dance with — so he doesn't step on me."

"Cora," he said, "it is the prelude to 'L'Arlesienne' that they should play for you and me. Yes, I think it should be that."

"Never heard of it."

"It's just a rustic tragedy, the story of a boy in the south of France who lets love become his whole life, and then — it kills him."

"Sounds very stupid," she commented languidly.

"People do sometimes die of love, even nowadays," he said, tremulously — "in the South."

She let her eyes drift indifferently to him and perceived that he was trembling from head to foot; that his hands and knees shook piteously; that his lips quivered and twitched; and, at sight of this agitation, an expression of strong distaste came to her face.

"I see." Her eyes returned to the lamp. "You're from the South, and of course it's going to kill you."

"You didn't speak the exact words you had in your mind.'"

"Oh, what words did I have 'in my mind'?" she asked impatiently.

"What you really meant was: 'If it does kill you, what of it?'"

She laughed, and sighed as for release.

"Cora," he said huskily, "I understand you a little because you possess me. I've never — literally never — had another thought since the first time I saw you: nothing but you. I think of you actually every moment. Drunk or sober, asleep or awake, it's nothing but you, you, *you!* It will never be different: I don't know why I can't get over it — I only know I can't. You own me; you burn like a hot coal in my heart. You're through with me, I know. You drained me dry. You're like a child who eats so heartily of what he likes that he never touches it again. And I'm a dish you're sick of. Oh, it's all plain enough, I can tell you. I'm not exciting any more — no, just a nauseous slave!"

"Drunk or sober . . . it's nothing but you!"

"Do you want people to hear you?" she inquired angrily, for his voice had risen.

He tempered his tone. "Cora, when you liked me you went a pretty clipping gait with me," he said, trembling even more than before. "But you're infinitely more infatuated with this Toreador of a Corliss than you were with me; you're lost in him; you're slaving for him as I would for you. How far are you going with ——"

"Do you want me to walk away and leave you?" she asked, suddenly sitting up straight and looking at him with dilating eyes. "If you want a 'scene'——"

"It's over," he said, more calmly. "I know now how dangerous the man is. Of course you will tell him I said that." He laughed quietly. "Well — between a dangerous chap and a desperate one, we may look for some lively times! Do you know, I believe I think about as continuously of him, lately, as I do of you. That's why I put almost my last cent into his oil company, and got what may be almost my last dance with you!"

"I wouldn't call it 'almost' your last dance with me!" she returned icily. "Not after what you've said. I had a foolish idea you could behave — well, at least decently."

"Did Corliss tell you that I insulted him in his rooms at the hotel?"

"You!" She laughed, genuinely. "I see him letting you!"

"He did, however. By manner and in speech I purposely and deliberately insulted him. You'll tell him every word of this, of course, and he'll laugh at it, but I give myself the pleasure of telling you. I put the proposition of an 'investment' to him in a way nobody not a crook would have allowed to be smoothed over — and he allowed it to be smoothed over. He ate it! I felt he was a swindler when he was showing Richard Lindley his maps and papers, and now I've proved it to myself, and it's worth the price." Often, when they had danced, and often during this interview, his eyes lifted curiously to the white flaming crescent in her hair; now they fixed themselves upon it, and in a flash of divination he cried: "You wear it for me!"

She did not understand. "Finished raving?" she inquired.

"I gave Corliss a thousand dollars," he said, slowly. "Considering the fact that it was my last, I flatter myself it was not unhandsomely done — though I may never need it. It has struck me that the sum was about what a man who had just cleaned up fifty thousand might regard as a sort of 'extra'— 'for lagniappe' — and that he might have thought it an appropriate amount to invest in a present— some jewels perhaps — to place in the hair of a pretty friend!"

She sprang to her feet, furious, but he stood in front of her and was able to bar the way for a moment.

"Cora, I'll have a last word with you if I have to hold you," he said with great rapidity and in a voice which shook with the intense repression he was putting upon himself. "We do one thing in the South, where I came from. We protect our women ——"

"This looks like it! Keeping me when ——"

"I love you," he said, his face whiter than she had ever seen it. "I love you! I'm your dog! You take care of yourself if you want to take care of anybody else! As sure as ——"

"My dance, Miss Madison." A young gentleman on vacation from the navy had approached, and, with perfect unconsciousness of what he was interrupting, but with well-founded certainty that he was welcome to the lady, urged his claim in a confident voice. "I thought it would never come, you know; but it's here at last and so am I." He laughed propitiatingly.

Ray yielded now at once. She moved hima side with her gloved forearm as if he were merely an awkward stranger who unwittingly stood between her and the claiming partner. Carrying the gesture farther, she took the latter's arm, and smilingly, and without a backward glance, passed onward and left the gallery. The lieutenant, who had met her once or twice before, was her partner for the succeeding dance as well, and, having noted the advantages of the place where he had discovered her, persuaded her to return there to sit through the second. Then without any fatiguing preamble, he proposed marriage. Cora did not accept, but effected a compromise, which, for the present, was to consist of an exchange of photographs (his to be in uniform) and letters.

She was having an evening to her heart. Ray's attack on Corliss had no dimming effect; her thought of it being that she was "used to his raving"; it meant nothing; and since Ray had prophesied she would tell Corliss about it, she decided not to do so.

The naval young gentleman and Valentine Corliss were the greatest of all the lions among ladies that night; she had easily annexed the lieutenant, and Corliss was hers already; though, for a purpose, she had not yet been seen in company with him. He was visibly "making an impression." His name, as he had said to Richard Lindley, was held in honour in the town; and there was a flavour of fancied romance in his absence since boyhood in unknown parts, and his return now with a 'foreign air' and a bow that almost took the breath of some of the younger recipients. He was, too, in his way, the handsomest man in the room; and the smiling, open frankness of his look, the ready cordiality of his manner, were found very winning. He caused plenty of flutter.

Cora waited till the evening was half over before she gave him any visible attention. Then, during a silence of the music, between two dances, she made him a negligent sign with her hand, the gesture of one indifferently beckoning a creature who is certain to come, and went on talking casually to the man who was with her. Corliss was the length of the room from her, chatting gayly with a large group of girls and women; but he immediately nodded to her, made his bow to individuals of the group, and crossed the vacant, glistening floor to her. Cora gave him no greeting whatever; she dismissed her former partner and carelessly turned away with Corliss to some chairs in a corner.

"Do you see that?" asked Vilas, leaning over the balcony railing with Richard Lindley. "Look! She's showing the other girls — don't you see? He's the New Man; she let 'em hope she wasn't going in for him; a lot of them probably didn't even know that she knew him. She sent him out on parade till they're all excited about him; now she shows 'em he's entirely her property — and does it so matter-of-factly that it's rubbed in twice as hard as if she seemed to take some pains about it. He doesn't dance: she'll sit out with him now, till they all read the tag she's put on him. She says she hates being talked about. She lives on it! — so long as it's envious. And did you see her with that chap from the navy? Neptune thinks he's dallying with Venus perhaps, but he'll get ——"

Lindley looked at him commiseratingly. "I think I never saw prettier decorations. Have you noticed Ray? Must have used a thousand chrysanthemums."

"Toreador!" whispered the other between his teeth, looking at Corliss; then, turning to his companion, he asked: "Has it occurred to you to get any information about Basilicata, or about the ancestral domain of the Moliterni, from our consul-general at Naples?"

Richard hesitated. "Well — yes. Yes, I did think of that. Yes, I thought of it."

"But you didn't do it."

"No. That is, I haven't yet. You see, Corliss explained to me that ——"

His friend interrupted him with a sour laugh. "Oh, certainly! He's one of the greatest explainers ever welcomed to our city!"

Richard said mildly: "And then, Ray, once I've gone into a thing I — I don't like to seem suspicious."

"Poor old Dick!" returned Vilas compassionately. "You kind, easy, sincere men are so conscientiously untruthful with yourselves. You know in your heart that Cora would be furious with you if you seemed suspicious, and she's been so nice to you since you put in your savings to please her, that you can't bear to risk offending her. She's twisted you around her little finger, and the unnamed fear that haunts you is that you won't be allowed to stay there — even twisted!"

"Pretty decorations, Ray," said Richard; but he grew very red.

"Do you know what you'll do," asked Ray, regarding him keenly, "if this Don Giovanni from Sunny It' is shown up as a plain get-rich-quick swindler?"

"I haven't considered ——"

"You would do precisely," said Ray, "nothing! Cora'd see to that. You'd sigh and go to work again, beginning at the beginning where you were years ago, and doing it all over. Admirable resignation, but not for me! I'm a stockholder in his company and in shape to 'take steps'! I don't know if I'd be patient enough to make them legal — perhaps I should. He may be safe on the legal side. I'll know more about that when I find out if there is a Prince Moliterno in Naples who owns land in Basilicata."

"You don't doubt it?"

"I doubt everything! In this particular matter I'll have less to doubt when I get an answer from the consul-general. *I*'ve written, you see."

Lindley looked disturbed. "You have?"

Vilas read him at a glance. "You're afraid to find out!" he cried. Then he set his hand on the other's shoulder. "If there ever was a God's fool, it's you, Dick Lindley. Really, I wonder the world hasn't kicked you around more than it has; you'd never kick back! You're as easy as an old shoe. Cora makes you unhappy," he went on, and with the very mention of her name, his voice shook with passion,— "but on my soul I don't believe you know what jealousy means: you don't even understand hate; you don't eat your heart ——"

"Let's go and eat something better," suggested Richard, laughing. "There's a continuous supper downstairs and I hear it's very good."

Ray smiled, rescued for a second from himself. "There isn't anything better than your heart, you old window-pane, and I'm glad you don't eat it. And if I ever mix it up with Don Giovanni T. Corliss — 'T' stands for Toreador — I do believe it'll be partly on your ——" He paused, leaving the sentence unfinished, as his attention was caught by the abysmal attitude of a figure in another part of the gallery: Mr. Wade Trumble, alone in a corner, sitting upon the small of his small back, munching at an unlighted cigar and otherwise manifesting a biting gloom. Ray drew Lindley's attention to this tableau of pain. "Here's a three of us!" he said.

He turned to look down into the rhythmic kaleidoscope of dancers. "And there goes the girl we all *ought* to be morbid about."

"Who is that?"

"Laura Madison. Why aren't we? What a self-respecting creature she is, with that cool, sweet steadiness of hers — she's like a mountain lake. She's lovely and she plays like an angel, but so far as anybody's ever thinking about her is concerned she might almost as well not exist. Yet she's really beautiful to-night, if you can manage to think of her except as a sort of retinue for Cora."

"She *is* rather beautiful to-night. Laura's always a very nice-looking girl," said Richard, and with the advent of an idea, he added: "I think one reason she isn't more conspicuous and thought about is that she is so quiet," and, upon his companion's greeting this inspiration with a burst of laughter, "Yes, that was a brilliant deduction," he said; "but I do think she's about the quietest person I ever knew. I've noticed there are times when she'll scarcely speak at all for half an hour, or even more."

"You're not precisely noisy yourself," said Ray. "Have you danced with her this evening?"

"Why, no," returned the other, in a tone which

showed this omission to be a discovery; "not yet. I must, of course."

"Yes, she's really 'rather' beautiful. Also, she dances 'rather' better than any other girl in town. Go and perform your painful duty."

"Perhaps I'd better," said Richard thoughtfully, not perceiving the satire. "At any rate, I'll ask her for the next."

He found it unengaged. There came to Laura's face an April change as he approached, and she saw he meant to ask her to dance. And, as they swam out into the maelstrom, he noticed it, and remarked that it *was* rather warm, to which she replied by a cheerful nod. Presently there came into Richard's mind the thought that he was really an excellent dancer; but he did not recall that he had always formed the same pleasing estimate of himself when he danced with Laura, nor realize that other young men enjoyed similar self-help when dancing with her. And yet he repeated to her what Ray had said of her dancing, and when she laughed as in appreciation of a thing intended humorously, he laughed, too, but insisted that she did dance "very well indeed." She laughed again at that, and they danced on, not talking. He had no sense of "guiding" her; there was no feeling of effort whatever; she seemed to move spontaneously with his wish, not to his touch; indeed, he was not sensible of touching her at all.

"Why, Laura," he exclaimed suddenly, "you dance *beautifully!*"

She stumbled and almost fell; saved herself by clutching at his arm; he caught her; and the pair stopped where they were, in the middle of the floor. A flash of dazed incredulity from her dark eyes swept him; there was something in it of the child dodging an unexpected blow.

"Did I trip you?" he asked anxiously.

"No," she laughed, quickly, and her cheeks grew even redder. "I tripped myself. Wasn't that too bad — just when you were thinking that I danced well! Let's sit down. May we?"

They went to some chairs against a wall. There, as they sat, Cora swung by them, dancing again with her lieutenant, and looking up trancedly into the gallant eyes of the triumphant and intoxicated young man. Visibly, she was a woman with a suitor's embracing arm about her. Richard's eyes followed them.

"Ah, don't!" said Laura in a low voice.

He turned to her. "Don't what?"

"I didn't mean to speak out loud," she said tremulously. "But I meant: don't look so troubled. It doesn't mean anything at all — her coquetting with that bird of passage. He's going away in the morning."

"I don't think I was troubling about that."

"Well, whatever it was" — she paused, and laughed with a plaintive timidity — "why, just don't trouble about it!"

"Do I look very much troubled?" he asked seriously.

"Yes. And you don't look very gay when you're not!" She laughed with more assurance now. "I think you're always the wistfulest looking man I ever saw."

"Everybody laughs at me, I believe," he said, with continued seriousness. "Even Ray Vilas thinks I'm an utter fool. Am I, do *you* think?"

He turned as he spoke and glanced inquiringly into her eyes. What he saw surprised and dismayed him.

"For heaven's sake, don't cry!" he whispered hurriedly.

She bent her head, turning her face from him.

"I've been very hopeful lately," he said. "Cora

has been so kind to me since I did what she wanted me to, that I ——" He gave a deep sigh. "But if you're *that* sorry for me, my chances with her must be pretty desperate."

She did not alter her attitude, but with her down-bent face still away from him, said huskily: "It isn't you I'm sorry for. You mustn't ever give up; you must keep on trying and trying. If you give up, I don't know what will become of her!"

A moment later she rose suddenly to her feet. "Let's finish our dance," she said, giving him her hand. "I'm sure I won't stumble again."

CHAPTER SIXTEEN

THE two girls let themselves into the house noiselessly, and, turning out the hall-light, left for them by their mother, crept upstairs on tiptoe; and went through the upper hall directly to Laura's room — Cora's being nearer the sick-room. At their age it is proper that a gayety be used three times: in anticipation, and actually, and in after-rehearsal. The last was of course now in order: they went to Laura's room to "talk it over." There was no gas-fixture in this small chamber; but they found Laura's oil-lamp burning brightly upon her writing-table

"How queer!" said Laura with some surprise, as she closed the door. "Mother never leaves the lamp lit for me; she's always so afraid of lamps exploding."

"Perhaps Miss Peirce came in here to read, and forgot to turn it out," suggested Cora, seating herself on the edge of the bed and letting her silk wrap fall from her shoulders. "Oh, Laura, wasn't he gorgeous. . . ."

She referred to the gallant defender of our seas, it appeared, and while Laura undressed and got into a wrapper, Cora recounted in detail the history of the impetuous sailor's enthrallment; — a résumé predicted three hours earlier by a gleeful whisper hissed across the maritime shoulder as the sisters swung near each other during a waltz: "*Proposed!*"

"I've always heard they're horribly inconstant," she said, regretfully. "But, oh, Laura, wasn't he beautiful to look at! Do you think he's more beautiful than Val? No —don't tell me if you do. I don't want to hear it! Val was so provoking: he didn't seem to mind it at all. He's nothing but a big brute sometimes: he wouldn't even admit that he minded, when I asked him. I was idiot enough to ask; I couldn't help it; he was so tantalizing and exasperating — laughing at me. I never knew anybody like him; he's so sure of himself and he can be so cold. Sometimes I wonder if he really cares about anything, deep down in his heart — anything except himself. He seems so selfish: there are times when he almost makes me hate him; but just when I get to thinking I do, I find I don't — he's so deliciously strong, and there's such a *big* luxury in being understood: I always feel he *knows* me clear to the bone, somehow! But, oh," she sighed regretfully, "doesn't a uniform become a man? They ought to all wear 'em. It would look silly on such a little goat as that Wade Trumble, though: nothing could make *him* look like a whole man. Did you see him glaring at me? Beast! I was going to be so nice and kittenish and do all my prettiest tricks for him, to help Val with his oil company. Val thinks Wade would come in yet, if *I'd* only get him in the mood to have another talk with Val about it; but the spiteful little rat wouldn't come near me. I believe that was one of the reasons Val laughed at me and pretended not to mind my getting proposed to. He *must* have minded; he couldn't have helped minding it, really. That's his way; he's so *mean*—he won't show things. He knows *me*. I can't keep anything from him; he reads *me* like a signboard; and then about himself he keeps me guessing, and I can't tell when I've guessed right. Ray Vilas behaved disgustingly, of course; he was horrid and awful. I might have expected it. I suppose Richard was wailing *his* tiresome sorrows on your poor shoulder ——"

"No," said Laura. "He was very cheerful. He seemed glad you were having a good time."

"He didn't look particularly cheerful *at* me. I never saw so slow a man: I wonder when he's going to find out about that pendant. Val would have seen it the instant I put it on. And, oh, Laura! isn't George Wattling funny? He's just *soft!* He's good-looking though," she continued pensively, adding, "I promised to motor out to the Country Club with him to-morrow for tea."

"Oh, Cora," protested Laura, "no! Please don't!"

"I've promised; so I'll have to, now." Cora laughed. "It'll do Mary Kane good. Oh, I'm not going to bother much with *him* — he makes me tired. I never saw anything so complacent as that girl when she came in to-night, as if her little Georgie was the greatest capture the world had ever seen. . . ."

She chattered on. Laura, passive, listened with a thoughtful expression, somewhat preoccupied. The talker yawned at last.

"It must be after three," she said, listlessly, having gone over her evening so often that the colours were beginning to fade. She yawned again. "Laura," she remarked absently, "I don't see how you can sleep in this bed; it sags so."

"I've never noticed it," said her sister. "It's a very comfortable old bed."

Cora went to her to be unfastened, reverting to the lieutenant during the operation, and kissing the tire-woman warmly at its conclusion. "You're always so sweet to me, Laura," she said affectionately. "I don't know how you manage it. You're so good" — she laughed — "sometimes I wonder how you stand me. If I were you, I'm positive I couldn't stand me at all!" Another kiss and a hearty embrace, and she picked up her wrap and skurried silently through the hall to her own room.

It was very late, but Laura wrote for almost an hour in her book (which was undisturbed) before she felt drowsy. Then she extinguished the lamp, put the book away and got into bed.

It was almost as if she had attempted to lie upon the empty air: the mattress sagged under her weight as if it had been a hammock; and something tore with a ripping sound. There was a crash, and a choked yell from a muffled voice somewhere, as the bed gave way. For an instant, Laura fought wildly in an entanglement of what she insufficiently perceived to be springs, slats and bedclothes with something alive squirming underneath. She cleared herself and sprang free, screaming, but even in her fright she remembered her father and clapped her hand over her mouth that she might keep from screaming again. She dove at the door, opened it, and fled through the hall to Cora's room, still holding her hand over her mouth.

"Cora! Oh, Cora!" she panted, and flung herself upon her sister's bed.

Cora was up instantly; and had lit the gas in a trice.

"There's a burglar!" Laura contrived to gasp. "In my room! Under the bed!"

"What!"

"I fell on him! Something's the matter with the bed. It broke. I fell on him!"

Cora stared at her wide-eyed. "Why, it can't be. Think how long I was in there. Your bed broke, and you just thought there was some one there. You imagined it."

"No, no, no!" wailed Laura. "I *heard* him: he gave a kind of dreadful grunt."

"Are you sure?"

"*Sure?* He wriggled — oh! I could *feel* him!"

Cora seized a box of matches again. "I'm going to find out."

"Oh, no, no!" protested Laura, cowering."

"Yes, I am. If there's a burglar in the house I'm going to find him!"

"We mustn't wake papa."

"No, nor mamma either. You stay here if you want to —— "

"Let's call Hedrick," suggested the pallid Laura; "or put our heads out of the window and scream for —— "

Cora laughed; she was not in the least frightened. "That wouldn't wake papa, of course! If we had a telephone I'd send for the police; but we haven't. I'm going to see if there's any one there. A burglar's a man, I guess, and I can't imagine myself being afraid of any *man!*"

Laura clung to her, but Cora shook her off and went through the hall undaunted, Laura faltering behind her. Cora lighted matches with a perfectly steady hand; she hesitated on the threshold of Laura's room no more than a moment, then lit the lamp.

Laura stifled a shriek at sight of the bed. "Look, look!" she gasped.

"There's no one under it now, that's certain," said Cora, and boldly lifted a corner of it. "Why, it's been cut all to pieces from underneath! You're right; there was some one here. It's practically dismembered. Don't you remember my telling you how it sagged? And I was only sitting on the edge of it! The slats have all been moved out of place, and as for the mattress, it's just a mess of springs and that stuffing stuff. He must have thought the silver was hidden there."

"Oh, oh, oh!" moaned Laura. "He *wriggled* — ugh!"

Cora picked up the lamp. "Well, we've got to go over the house —— "

"No, no!"

"Hush! I'll go alone then."

"You *can't.*"

"I will, though!"

The two girls had changed places in this emergency. In her fright Laura was dependent, clinging: actual contact with the intruder had unnerved her. It took all her will to accompany her sister upon the tour of inspection, and throughout she cowered behind the dauntless Cora. It was the first time in their lives that their positions had been reversed. From the days of Cora's babyhood, Laura had formed the habit of petting and shielding the little sister, but now that the possibility became imminent of confronting an unknown and dangerous man, Laura was so shaken that, overcome by fear, she let Cora go

"We've got to go over the house!"

first. Cora had not boasted in vain of her bravery; in truth, she was not afraid of any man.

They found the fastenings of the doors secure and likewise those of all the windows, until they came to the kitchen. There, the cook had left a window up, which plausibly explained the marauder's mode of ingress. Then, at Cora's insistence, and to Laura's shivering horror, they searched both cellar and garret, and concluded that he had escaped by the same means. Except Laura's bed, nothing in the house had been disturbed; but this eccentricity on the part of a burglar, though it indeed struck the two girls as peculiar, was not so pointedly mysterious to them as it might have been had they possessed a somewhat greater familiarity with the habits of criminals whose crimes are professional.

They finally retired, Laura sleeping with her sister, and Cora had begun to talk of the lieutenant again, instead of the burglar, before Laura fell asleep.

In spite of the short hours for sleep, both girls appeared at the breakfast-table before the meal was over, and were naturally pleased with the staccato of excitement evoked by their news. Mrs. Madison and Miss Peirce were warm in admiration of their bravery, but in the same breath condemned it as foolhardy.

"I never knew such wonderful girls!" exclaimed the mother, almost tearfully. "You crazy little lions! To think of your not even waking Hedrick! And you didn't have even a poker and were in your bare feet — and went down in the *cellar* —— "

"It was all Cora," protested Laura. "I'm a hopeless, disgusting coward. I never knew what a coward I was before. Cora carried the lamp and went ahead like a drum-major. I just trailed along behind her, ready to shriek and run — or faint!"

"Could you tell anything about him when you fell on him?" inquired Miss Peirce. "What was his voice like when he shouted?"

"Choked. It was a horrible, jolted kind of cry. It hardly sounded human."

"Could you tell anything about whether he was a large man, or small, or —— "

"Only that he seemed very active. He seemed to be kicking. He *wriggled* — ugh!"

They evolved a plausible theory of the burglar's motives and line of reasoning. "You see," said Miss Peirce, much stirred, in summing up the adventure, "he either jimmies the window, or finds it open already, and Sarah's mistaken and she *did* leave it open! Then he searched the downstairs first, and didn't find anything. Then he came upstairs, and was afraid to come into any of the rooms where *we* were. He could tell which rooms had people in them by hearing us breathing through the keyholes. He finds two rooms empty, and probably he made a thorough search of Miss Cora's first. But he isn't after silver toilet articles and pretty little things like that. He wants really big booty or none, so he decides that an out-of-the-way, unimportant room like Miss Laura's is where the family would be most apt to hide valuables, jewellery and silver, and he knows that mattresses have often been selected as hiding-places; so he gets under the bed and goes to work. Then Miss Cora and Miss Laura come in so quietly — not wanting to wake anybody — that he doesn't hear them, and he gets caught there. That's the way it must have been."

"But why," Mrs. Madison inquired of this authority, "why do you suppose he lit the lamp?"

"To see by," answered the ready Miss Peirce. It was accepted as final.

Further discussion was temporarily interrupted

by the discovery that Hedrick had fallen asleep in his chair.

"Don't bother him, Cora," said his mother. "He's finished eating — let him sleep a few minutes, if he wants to, before he goes to school. He's not at all well. He played too hard, yesterday afternoon, and hurt his knee, he said. He came down limping this morning and looking very badly. He oughtn't to run and climb about the stable so much after school. See how utterly exhausted he looks! Not even this excitement can keep him awake."

"I think we must be careful not to let Mr. Madison suspect anything about the burglar," said Miss Peirce. "It would be bad for him."

Laura began: "But we ought to notify the policc —— "

"Police!" Hedrick woke so abruptly, and uttcred the word with such passionate and vehement protest, that everybody started. "I suppose you want to *kill* your father, Laura Madison!"

"How?"

"Do you suppose he wouldn't know something had happened with a squad of big, heavy policemen tromping all over the house? The first thing they'd do would be to search the whole place —— "

"Oh, no," said Mrs. Madison quickly. "It wouldn't do at all."

"I should think not! I'm glad," continued Hedrick, truthfully, "*that* idea's out of your head! I believe Laura imagined the whole thing anyway."

"Have you looked at her mattress," inquired Cora, "darling little boy?"

He gave her a concentrated look, and rose to leave. "Nothin' on earth but imagina——" He stopped with a grunt as he forgetfully put his weight on his left leg. He rubbed his knee, swallowed painfully, and, leaving the word unfinished, limped haughtily from the room.

He left the house, gloomily swinging his books from a spare length of strap, and walking with care to ease his strains and bruises as much as possible. He was very low in his mind, that boy. His fortunes had reached the ebb-tide, but he had no hope of a rise. He had no hope of anything. It was not even a consolation that, through his talent for surprise in waylayings, it had lately been thought necessary, by the Villard family, to have Egerton accompanied to and from school by a man-servant. Nor was Hedrick more deeply depressed by the certainty that both public and domestic scandal must soon arise from the inevitable revelation of his discontinuing his attendance at school without mentioning this important change of career at home. He had been truant a full fortnight, under brighter circumstances a matter for a lawless pride — now he had neither fear nor vainglory. There was no room in him for anything but dejection.

He walked two blocks in the direction of his school; turned a corner; walked half a block; turned north in the alley which ran parallel to Corliss Street, and a few moments later had cautiously climbed into an old, disused refuse box which stood against the rear wall of the empty stable at his own home. He pried up some loose boards at the bottom of the box, and entered a tunnel which had often and often served in happier days — when he had friends — for the escape of Union officers from Libby Prison and Andersonville. Emerging, wholly soiled, into a box-stall, he crossed the musty carriage house and ascended some rickety steps to a long vacant coachman's-room, next to the hayloft. He closed the door, bolted it, and sank moodily upon a broken, old horsehair sofa.

This apartment was his studio. In addition to the sofa, it contained an ex-bureau, three chair-like shapes, a once marble-topped table, now covered with a sheet of zinc, two empty bird cages, and a condemned whatnot. The walls were rather over-decorated in coloured chalks, the man-headed-snake motive predominating; they were also loopholed for firing into the hayloft. Upon the table lay a battered spy-glass, minus lenses, and, nearby, two boxes, one containing dried corn-silk, the other hayseed, convenient for the making of amateur cigarettes; the smoker's outfit being completed by a neat pile of rectangular clippings from newspapers. On the shelves of the whatnot were some fragments of a dead pie, the relics of a "Fifteen-Puzzle," a pink Easter-egg, four seashells, a tambourine with part of a girl's face still visible in aged colours, about two thirds of a hot-water bag, a tintype of Hedrick, and a number of books: several by Henty, "Twenty Thousand Leagues Under the Sea," "100 Practical Jokes, Easy to Perform," "The Jungle Book," "My Lady Rotha," a "Family Atlas," "Three Weeks," "Pilgrim's Progress," "A Boy's Life in Camp," and "The Mystery of the Count's Bedroom."

The gloomy eye of Hedrick wandered to "The Mystery of the Count's Bedroom," and remained fixed upon it moodily and contemptuously. His own mystery made that one seem tame and easy: Laura's bedroom laid it all over the Count's, in his conviction; and with a soul too weary of pain to shudder, he reviewed the bafflements and final catastrophe of the preceding night.

He had not essayed the attempt upon the mattress until assured that the house was wrapped in slumber. Then, with hope in his heart, he had stolen to Laura's room, lit the lamp, feeling safe from intrusion, and set to work. His implement at first was a long hatpin of Cora's. Lying on his back beneath the bed, and, moving the slats as it became necessary, he sounded every cubic inch of the mysterious mattress without encountering any obstruction which could reasonably be supposed to be the ledger. This was not more puzzling than it was infuriating, since by all processes of induction, deduction, and pure logic, the thing was necessarily there. It was nowhere else. Therefore it was there. It *had* to be there! With the great blade of his Boy Scout's knife he began to disembowel the mattress

For a time he had worked furiously and effectively, but the position was awkward, the search laborious, and he was obliged to rest frequently. Besides, he had waited to a later hour than he knew, for his mother to go to bed, and during one of his rests he incautiously permitted his eyes to close. When he woke, his sisters were in the room, and he thought it advisable to remain where he was, though he little realized how he had weakened his shelter. When Cora left the room, he heard Laura open the window, sigh, and presently a tiny clinking and a click set him a-tingle from head to foot: she was opening the padlocked book. The scratching sound of a pen followed. And yet she had not come near the bed. The mattress, then, was a living lie.

With infinite caution he had moved so that he could see her, arriving at a coign of vantage just as she closed the book. She locked it, wrapped it in an oilskin cover which lay beside it on the table, hung the key-chain round her neck, rose, yawned, and, to his violent chagrin, put out the light. He heard her moving but could not tell where, except that it was not in his part of the room. Then a faint shuffling warned him that she was approaching the bed, and he withdrew his head to avoid being stepped upon. The next moment the world seemed to cave in upon him.

Laura's flight had given him opportunity to

escape to his own room unobserved; there to examine, bathe and bind his wounds, and to rectify his first hasty impression that he had been fatally mangled.

Hedrick glared at "The Mystery of the Count's Bedroom."

By and by he got up, brought the book to the sofa and began to read it over.

CHAPTER SEVENTEEN

THE influence of a familiar and sequestered place is not only soothing; the bruised mind may often find it restorative. Thus Hedrick, in his studio, surrounded by his own loved bric-à-brac, began to feel once more the stir of impulse. Two hours' reading inspired him. What a French reporter (in the Count's bedroom) could do, an American youth in full possession of his powers — except for a strained knee and other injuries — could do. Yes, and would!

He evolved a new chain of reasoning. The ledger had been seen in Laura's room; it had been heard in her room; it appeared to be kept in her room. But it was in no single part of the room. All the parts make a whole. Therefore, the book was not in the room.

On the other hand, Laura had not left the room when she took the book from its hiding-place. This was confusing; therefore he determined to concentrate logic solely upon what she had done with the ledger when she finished writing in it. It was dangerous to assume that she had restored it to the place whence she obtained it, because he had already proved that place to be both in the room and out of the room. No; the question he must keep in mind was: What did she do with it?

Laura had not left the room. But the book had left the room.

Arrived at this inevitable deduction, he sprang to his feet in a state of repressed excitement and began to pace the floor — like a hound on the trail. Laura had not left the room, but the book had left the room: he must keep his mind upon this point. He uttered a loud exclamation and struck the zinc table-top a smart blow with his clenched fist.

Laura had thrown the book out of the window!

In the exaltation of this triumph, he forgot that it was not yet the hour for a scholar's reappearance, and went forth in haste to search the ground beneath the window — a disappointing quest, for nowhere in the yard was there anything but withered grass, and the rubbish of other frost-bitten vegetation. His mother, however, discovered something else, and, opening the kitchen window, she asked, with surprise:

"Why, Hedrick, what on earth are you doing here?"

"Me?" inquired Hedrick.

"What are you doing here?"

"Here?" Evidently she puzzled him.

She became emphatic. "I want to know what you are doing."

"Just standing here," he explained in a meek, grieved way.

"But why aren't you at school?"

This recalled what he had forgotten, and he realized the insecurity of his position. "Oh, yes," he said — "school. Did you ask me —— "

"Didn't you go to school?"

He began to speak rapidly. "Didn't I go to *school?* Well, where else could I go? Just because I'm here now doesn't mean I didn't *go*, does it? Because a person is in China right now wouldn't have to mean he'd never been in South America, would it?"

"Then what's the matter?"

"Well, I was going along, and you know I didn't feel very well and —— " He paused, with the advent of a happier idea, then continued briskly: "But that didn't stop me, because I thought I ought to go if I dropped, so I went ahead, but the teacher was sick and they couldn't get a substitute. She must have been pretty sick, she looked so pale —— "

"They dismissed the class?"

"And I don't have to go to-morrow either."

"I see," said his mother. "But if you feel ill, Hedrick, hadn't you better come in and lie down?"

"I think it's kind of passing off. The fresh air seems to be doing me good."

"Be careful of your sore knee, dear." She closed the window, and he was left to continue his operations in safety.

Laura had thrown the ledger out of the window; that was proved absolutely. Obviously, she had come down before daylight and retrieved it. Or, she had not. Proceeding on the assumption that she had not, he lifted his eyes and searched the air. Was it possible that the book, though thrown from the window, had never reached the ground? The branches of an old and stalwart maple, now almost divested of leaves, extended in rough symmetry above him, and one big limb, reaching out toward the house, came close to Laura's windows. Triumph shown again from the shrewd countenance of the sleuth: Laura must have slid the ledger along a wire into a hollow branch. However, no wire was to be seen — and the shrewd countenance of the sleuth fell. But perhaps she had constructed a device of silk threads, invisible from below, which carried the book into the tree. Action!

He climbed carefully but with many twinges, finally pausing in a parlous situation not far from the mysterious window which Laura had opened the night before. A comprehensive survey of the tree revealed only the very patent fact that none of the branches was of sufficient diameter to conceal the ledger. No silk threads came from the window. He looked and looked and looked at that window; then his eye fell a little, halted less than three feet below the window-ledge, and the search was ended.

The kitchen window which his mother had opened was directly beneath Laura's, and was a very long, narrow window, in the style of the house, and there was a protecting stone ledge above it. Upon this ledge lay the book, wrapped in its oil-skin covering and secured from falling by a piece of broken iron hooping, stuck in the mortar of the bricks. It could be seen from nowhere save an upper window of the house next door, or from the tree itself, and in either case only when the leaves had fallen.

Laura had felt very safe. No one had ever seen the book except that night, early in August, when, for a better circulation of air, she had left her door open as she wrote, and Hedrick had come upon her. He had not spoken of it again; she perceived that he had forgotten it; and she herself forgot that the memory of a boy is never to be depended on; its forgettings are too seldom permanent in the case of things that ought to stay forgotten.

To get the book one had only to lean from the window.

Hedrick seemed so ill during lunch that his mother spoke of asking Doctor Sloane to look at him, if he did not improve before evening. Hedrick said meekly that perhaps that would be best — if he did not improve. After a futile attempt to eat, he courteously excused himself from the table — a ceremony which made even Cora fear that his case might be serious — and, going feebly to the library, stretched himself upon the sofa. His mother put a rug over him; Hedrick, thanking her touchingly, closed his eyes; and she went away, leaving him to slumber.

After a time, Laura came into the room on an

errand, walking noiselessly, and, noticing that his eyes were open, apologized for waking him.

"Never mind," he returned, in the tone of an invalid. "I didn't sleep sound. I think there's something the matter inside my head: I have such terrible dreams. I guess maybe it's better for me to keep awake. I'm kind of afraid to go to sleep. Would you mind staying here with me a little while?"

"Certainly I'll stay," she said, and, observing that his cheeks were flushed, and his eyes unusually bright, she laid a cool hand on his forehead. "You haven't any fever, dear; that's good. You'll be all right to-morrow. Would you like me to read to you?"

"I believe," he answered, plaintively, "reading might kind of disturb my mind: my brain feels so sort of restless and queer. I'd rather play some kind of game."

"Cards?"

"No, not cards exactly. Something I can do lying down. Oh, I know! You remember the one where we drew pictures and the others had to guess what they were? Well, I've invented a game like that. You sit down at the desk over there and take some sheets of paper. I'll tell you the rest."

She obeyed. "What next?"

"Now, I'll describe some people and where they live and not tell who they are, and you see if you can guess their names and addresses."

"Addresses, too?"

"Yes, because I'm going to describe the way their houses look. Write each name on a separate sheet of paper, and the number of their house below it, if you know it, and if you don't know it, just the street. If it's a woman: put 'Miss' or 'Mrs.' before their name and if it's a man write 'Esquire' after it."

"Is all that necessary for the game?"

"It's the way I invented it and I think you might —— "

"Oh, all right," she acquiesced, good-naturedly. "It shall be according to your rules."

"Then afterward, you give me the sheets of paper with the names and addresses written on 'em, and we — we —— " He hesitated.

"Yes. What do we do then?"

"I'll tell you when we come to it." But when that stage of his invention was reached, and Laura had placed the inscribed sheets in his hand, his interest had waned, it appeared. Also, his condition had improved.

"Let's quit. I thought this game would be more exciting," he said, sitting up. "I guess," he added with too much modesty, "I'm not very good at inventing games. I b'lieve I'll go out to the barn; I think the fresh air —— "

"Do you feel well enough to go out?" she asked. "You do seem to be all right, though."

"Yes, I'm a lot better, I think." He limped to the door. "The fresh air will be the best thing for me."

She did not notice that he carelessly retained her contributions to the game, and he reached his studio with them in his hand. Hedrick had entered the 'teens and he was a reader: things in his head might have dismayed a Borgia.

No remotest glimpse entered that head of the enormity of what he did. To put an end to his punishing of Cora, and, to render him powerless against that habitual and natural enemy, Laura had revealed a horrible incident in his career — it had become a public scandal; he was the sport of fools; and it might be months before the thing was lived down. Now he had the means, as he believed, to even the score with both sisters at a stroke. To him it was turning a tremendous and properly scathing joke upon them. He did not hesitate.

That evening, as Richard Lindley sat at dinner with his mother, Joe Varden temporarily abandoned his attendance at the table to answer the front doorbell. Upon his return, he remarked:

"Messenger-boy mus' been in big hurry. Wouldn' wait till I git to door."

"What was it?" asked Richard.

"Boy with package. Least, I reckon it were a boy. Call' back from the front walk, say he couldn' wait. Say he lef' package in vestibule."

"What sort of a package?"

"Middle-size kind o' big package."

"Why don't you see what it is, Richard?" Mrs. Lindley asked of her son. "Bring it to the table, Joe."

When it was brought, Richard looked at the superscription with surprise. The wrapper was of heavy brown paper, and upon it a sheet of white notepaper had been pasted, with the address:

"Richard Lindley, Esq.,
1218 Corliss Street."

"It's from Laura Madison," he said, staring at this writing. "What in the world would Laura be sending me?"

"You might possibly learn by opening it," suggested his mother. "I've seen men puzzle over the outside of things quite as often as women. Laura Madison is a nice girl." She never volunteered similar praise of Laura Madison's sister. Mrs. Lindley had submitted to her son's plans concerning Cora, lately confided; but her submission lacked resignation.

"It's a book," said Richard, even more puzzled, as he took the ledger from its wrappings. "Two little torn places at the edge of the covers. Looks as if it had once had clasps —— "

"Perhaps it's the Madison family album," Mrs. Lindley suggested. "Pictures of Cora since infancy. I imagine she's had plenty taken."

"No." He opened the book and glanced at the pages covered in Laura's clear, readable hand. "No, it's about half full of writing. Laura must have turned literary." He read a line or two, frowning mildly. "My soul! I believe it's a novel! She must think I'm a critic — to want me to read it." Smiling at the idea, he closed the ledger. "I'll take it upstairs to my hang-out after dinner, and see if Laura's literary manner has my august approval. Who in the world would ever have thought she'd decide to set up for a writer?"

"I imagine she might have something to write worth reading," said his mother. "I've always thought she was an interesting-looking girl."

"Yes, she is. She dances well, too."

"Of course," continued Mrs. Lindley, thoughtfully, "she seldom *says* anything interesting, but that may be because she so seldom has a chance to say anything at all."

Richard refused to perceive this allusion. "Curious that Laura should have sent it to me," he said. "She's never seemed interested in my opinion about anything. I don't recall her ever speaking to me on any subject whatever — except one."

He returned his attention to his plate, but his mother did not appear to agree with him that the topic was exhausted.

"'Except one'?" she repeated, after waiting for some time.

"Yes," he replied, in his habitual preoccupied

and casual tone. "Or perhaps two. Not more than two, I should say — and in a way you'd call that only one, of course. Bread, Joe."

"What two, Richard?"

"Cora," he said, with gentle simplicity, "and me."

CHAPTER EIGHTEEN

MRS. LINDLEY had arranged for her son a small apartment on the second floor, and it was in his own library and smoking-room that Richard, comfortable in a leather-chair by a reading-lamp, after dinner, opened Laura's ledger.

The first page displayed no more than a date, now eighteen months past, and the line:

"Love came to me to-day."

The next page was dated the next day, and, beneath, he read:

"That was all I *could* write, yesterday. I think I was too excited to write. Something seemed to be singing in my breast. I couldn't think in sentences — not even in words. How queer it is that I had decided to keep a diary, and bound this book for it, and now the first thing I have written in it was *that!* It will not be a diary. It shall be *Your* book. I shall keep it sacred to You and write to You in it. How strange it will be if the day ever comes when I shall show it to You! If it should, you would not laugh at it, for of course the day couldn't come unless you understood. I cannot think it will ever come — that day! But maybe —— No, I mustn't let myself hope too much that it will, because if I got to hoping too much, and you didn't like me, it would hurt too much. People who expect nothing are never disappointed — I must keep that in mind. Yet *every* girl has a *right* to hope for her own man to come for her some time, hasn't she? It's not easy to discipline the *wanting* to hope — since *yesterday!*

"I think I must always have thought a great deal about you without knowing it. We really know so little what we think: our minds are going on all the time and we hardly notice them. It is like a queer sort of factory — the owncr only looks in once in a while and most of the time hasn't any idea what sort of goods his spindles are turning out.

"I saw You yesterday! It seems to me the strangest thing in the world. I've seen you by chance, probably two or three times a month nearly all my life, though you so seldom come here to call. And this time wasn't different from dozens of other times — you were just standing on the corner by the Richfield, waiting for a car. The only possible difference is that you had been out of town for several months — Cora said so this morning — and how ridiculous it seems now, I didn't even know it! I hadn't noticed it — not with the top part of my mind, but perhaps the deep part that does the real thinking had noticed it and had mourned your absence and was so glad to see you again that it made the top part suddenly see the wonderful truth!"

Lindley set down the ledger to relight his cigar. It struck him that Laura had been writing "very odd stuff," but interesting; and certainly it was not a story. Vaguely he recalled Marie Bashkirtseff: hadn't she done something like this? He resumed the reading:

"You turned and spoke to me in that lovely, cordial, absent-minded way of yours — though I'd never thought (with the top part) what a lovely way it was; and for a moment I only noticed how nice you looked in a light gray suit, because I'd only seen you in black for so long, while you'd been in mourning for your brother. . . ."

Richard, disturbed by an incredible idea, read these last words over and then dismissed the notion as nonsense.

". . . While you'd been in mourning for your brother — and it struck me that light gray was becoming to you. Then such a queer thing happened: I felt the great kindness of your eyes. I thought they were full of — the only word that seems to express it at all is *charity* — and they had a sweet, faraway look, too, and I've *always* thought that a look of wistful kindness was the loveliest look in the world—and you had it, and I saw it and then suddenly, as you held your hat in your hand, the sunshine on your hair seemed brighter than any sunshine I had ever seen — and I began to tremble all over. I didn't understand what was the matter with me or what had made me afraid with you — not of you — all at once, but I was so hopelessly rattled that instead of waiting for the car, as I'd just told you I meant to, I said I'd decided to walk, and got away — without any breath left to breathe with! I *couldn't* have gotten on the car with you — and I couldn't have spoken another word.

"And as I walked home, trembling all the way, I saw that strange, dazzling sunshine on your hair, and the wistful, kind look in your eyes — you seemed not to have taken the car but to have come with me — and I was uplifted and exalted oh, so strangely — oh, how the world was changing for me! And when I got near home, I began to walk faster, and on the front path I broke into a run and rushed in the house to the piano — and it was as if my fingers were thirsty for the keys! Then I saw that I was playing to you and knew that I loved you.

"I love you!

"How different everything is now from everything before. Music means what it never did: Life has leaped into blossom for me. Everywhere there is colour and radiance that I had never seen — the air is full of perfume. Dear, the sunshine that fell upon your head has spread over the world!

"I understand, as I never understood, that the world — so dazzling to me now — was made for love and is meaningless without it. The years until yesterday are gray — no, not gray, because that was the colour You were wearing — not gray, because that is a beautiful colour. The empty years until yesterday had no colour at all. Yes, the world has meaning only through loving, and without meaning there is no real life. We live only by loving, and now that this gift of life has come to me I love *all* the world. I feel that I must be so kind, kind, *kind* to *everybody!* Such an odd thing struck me as my greatest wish. When I was little, I remember grandmother telling me how, when she was a child in pioneer days, the women made the men's clothes — homespun — and how a handsome young Circuit Rider, who was a bachelor, seemed to her the most beautifully dressed man she had ever seen. The women of the different churches made his clothes, as they did their husbands' and brothers,' you see — only better! It came into my head that that would be the divinest happiness that I could know — to sew for you! If you and I lived in those old, old times — you *look* as if you belonged to them, you know, dear — and You were the young minister riding into the settlement on a big bay horse — and all the girls at the window, of course! — and I sewing away at the homespun for you! — I think all the angels of heaven would be choiring in my heart — and what thick, warm clothes I'd make you for winter! Perhaps in heaven they'll let some of the women sew for the men they love — I wonder!

"I hear Cora's voice from downstairs as I write — she's often so angry with Ray, poor girl. It does not seem to me that she and Ray really belong to each other, though they *say* so often that they do."

Richard having read thus far with a growing, vague uneasiness, looked up, frowning. He hoped Laura had no Marie Bashkirtseff idea of publishing this manuscript. It was too intimate, he thought, even if the names in it were to be disguised.

. . . "Though they *say* so often that they do. I think Ray is in love with *her*, but it can't be like *this*. What he feels must be something wholly different — there is violence and wildness in it. And they are bitter with each other so often — always 'getting even' for something. He does care — he is frantically "*in* love" with her, undoubtedly, but so insanely jealous. I suppose all jealousy is insane. But love is the only sanity. How can what is insane be part of it? I could not be jealous of You. I owe life to you — I have never lived till now."

The next writing was two days later:

. . . . "To-day as I passed your house with Cora, I kept looking at the big front door at which you go in and out so often — *your* door! I never knew that just a door could look so beautiful! And unconsciously I kept my eyes on it, as we walked on, turning my head and looking and looking back at it, till Cora suddenly burst out laughing, and said: 'Well, *Laura!*' And I came to myself — and found her looking at me. It was like getting back after a journey, and for a second I was a little dazed, and Cora kept on laughing at me, and I felt myself getting red. I made some silly excuse about thinking your house had been repainted — and she laughed louder than ever. I was afraid then that she understood — I wonder if she could have? I hope not, though I love her so much I don't know why I would rather she didn't know, unless it is just my *feeling* about it. It is a *guardian* feeling — that I must keep for myself, the music of these angels singing in my heart — singing of You. I hope she did not understand — and I so fear she did. Why should I be so *afraid?*" . . .

. . . . "Two days since I have talked to You in your book after Cora caught me staring at your door and laughed at me — and ten minutes ago I was sitting beside the *actual* You on the porch! I am trembling yet. It was the first time you'd come for months and months; and yet you had the air of thinking it rather a pleasant thing to do as you came up the steps! And a dizzy feeling came over me, because I wondered if it was seeing me on the street *that* day that put it into your head to come. It seemed too much happiness — and risking too much — to let myself *believe* it, but I couldn't help just wondering. I began to tremble as I saw you coming up our side of the street in the moonlight — and when you turned in here I was all panic — I nearly ran into the house. I don't know how I found voice to greet you. I didn't seem to have any breath left at all. I was so relieved when Cora took a chair between us and began to talk to you, because I'm sure I couldn't have. She and poor Ray had been having one of their quarrels and she was punishing him. Poor boy, he seemed so miserable — though he tried to talk to me — about politics, I think, though I'm not sure, because I couldn't listen much better than either of us could talk. I could only hear Your voice — such a rich, quiet voice, and it has a sound like the look you have — friendly and faraway and wistful. I have thought and thought about what it is that makes you look wistful. You have less to wish for than anybody else in the world because you have Yourself. So why are you wistful? I think it's just because you *are!*

"I heard Cora asking you why you hadn't come to see us for so long, and then she said: 'Is it because you dislike me? You look at me, sometimes, as if you dislike me!' And I wished she hadn't said it. I had a feeling you wouldn't like that 'personal' way of tálking that she enjoys — and that — oh, it didn't seem to be in keeping with the dignity of You! And I love Cora so much I wanted her to be finer — with You. I wanted her to understand you better than to play those little charming tricks at you. You are so good, so *high*, that if she could make a real friend of you I think it would be the best thing for her that could happen. She's never had a man-*friend.* Perhaps she *was* trying to make one of you and hasn't any other way to go about it. She can be so *really* sweet, I wanted you to see that side of her.

"Afterwhile, when Ray couldn't bear it any longer to talk to me, and in his desperation brazenly took Cora to the other end of the porch almost by force, and I was left, in a way, alone with you — what did you think of me? I was tongue-tied! Oh, oh, oh! You were quiet — but *I* was *dumb!* My heart wasn't dumb — it hammered! All the time I kept saying to myself such a jumble of things. And into the jumble would come such a rapture that You were there — it was like a pæan of happiness — a chanting of the glory of having You near me — I *was* mixed up! I could *play* all those confused things, but writing them doesn't tell it. Writing them would only be like this: 'He's here, he's *here!* Speak, you little fool! He's here, he's here! He's sitting beside you! *Speak,* idiot, or he'll never come back! He's here, he's beside you — you could put out your hand and touch him! Are you dead, that you can't speak? He's here, he's here, he's *here!*'

"Ah, some day I shall be able to talk to you — but not till I get more used to this inner song. It seems to *will* that nothing else shall come from my lips till *it* does!

"In spite of my silence — my outward woodenness — you said, as you went away, that you would come again! You said 'soon'! I could only nod — but Cora called from the other end of the porch and asked: '*How* soon?' Oh, I bless her for it, because you said, 'Day after to-morrow.' Day after to-morrow! Day after to-morrow! *Day after to-morrow!*

. . . . "Twenty-one hours since I wrote — no, *sang* — 'Day after to-morrow!' And now it is 'To-morrow!' Oh, the slow, golden day that this has been! I could not stay in the house — I walked — no, I *winged!* I was in the open country before I knew it — with You! For You are in everything. I never knew the sky was blue, before. Until now I just thought it was the sky. The whitest clouds I ever saw sailed over that blue, and I stood upon the prow of each in turn, then leaped in and swam to the next and sailed with *it!* Oh, the beautiful sky, and kind, green woods and blessed, long, white, dusty country road! Never in my life shall I forget that walk — this day in the open with my love — You! To-morrow! To-morrow! To-morrow! *To-morrow!*"

The next writing in Laura's book was dated more than two months later:

. . . . "I have decided to write again in this book. I have thought it all out carefully, and I have come to the conclusion that it can do no harm and may help me to be steady and sensible. It is the thought, not its expression, that is guilty, but I do not believe that my thoughts are guilty: I believe that they are good. I know that I wish only good. I have read that when people suffer very much the best thing is for them to cry. And so I'll let myself *write* out my feelings—and perhaps get rid of some of the silly self-pity I'm foolish enough to feel, instead of going about choked up with it. How queer it is that even when we keep our thoughts respectable we can't help having absurd *feelings* like self-pity, even though we know how rotten stupid they are! Yes, I'll let it all out here, and then, some day, when I've cured myself all whole again, I'll burn this poor, silly old book. And if I'm not cured before the wedding, I'll burn it then, anyhow.

"How funny little girls are! From the time they're little bits of things they talk about marriage—whom they are going to marry, what sort of person it will be. I think Cora and I began when she was about five and I not seven. And as girls grow up, I don't believe there was ever one who genuinely expected to be an old maid. The most unattractive young girls discuss and plan and expect marriage just as much as the prettier and gayer ones. The only way we can find out that men don't want to marry us is by their not asking us. We don't see ourselves very well, and I honestly believe we all think — way deep down — that we're pretty attractive. At least, every girl has the idea, sometimes, that if men only saw the whole truth they'd think her as nice as any other girl, and really nicer than most others. But I don't believe I have any hallucinations of that sort about myself left. I can't imagine — now — *any* man seeing anything in me that would make him care for me. I can't see anything about me to care for, myself. Sometimes I think maybe I could make a man get excited about me if I could take a startlingly personal tone with him from the beginning, making him wonder all sorts of you-and-I perhapses — but I couldn't do it very well probably — oh, I couldn't make myself do it if I could do it well! And I shouldn't think it would have much effect except upon very inexperienced men — yet it does! Now, I wonder if this is a streak of sourness coming out; I don't feel bitter—I'm just thinking honestly, I'm sure.

"Well, here I am facing it: all through my later childhood, and all through my girlhood, I believe what really occupied me most — with the thought of it underlying all things else, though often buried very deep — was the prospect of my marriage. I regarded it as a certainty: I would grow up, fall in love, get engaged, and be married — of course! So I grew up and fell in love with You — but it stops there, and I must learn how to be an Old Maid and not let anybody see that I mind it. I know this is the hardest part of it, the beginning: it will get easier by-and-by, of course. If I can just manage this part of it, it's bound not to hurt so much later on.

"Yes, I grew up and fell in love with You — for you will always be You. I'll never, never get over *that*, my dear! You'll never, never know it; but I shall love You always till I die, and if I'm still Me after that, I shall keep right on loving you then, of course. You see, I didn't fall in love with you just to have you for myself. I fell in love with You! And that can never bother you at all nor ever be a shame to me that I love unsought, because you won't know, and because it's just an ocean of good-will, and every beat of my heart sends a new great wave of it toward you and Cora. I shall find happiness, I believe, in service — I am sure there will be times when I can serve you both. I love you both and I can serve her for You and you for her. This isn't a hysterical mood, or a fit of 'exaltation': I have thought it all out and I know that I can live up to it. You are the best thing that can ever come into her life, and everything I can do shall be to keep you there. I must be very, very careful with her, for talk and advice do not influence her much. You love her — she has accepted you, and it is beautiful for you both. It must be kept beautiful. It has all become so clear to me: You are just what she has always needed, and if by any mischance she lost you I do not know what would become ——"

"Good God!" cried Richard. He sprang to his feet, and the heavy book fell with a muffled crash upon the floor, sprawling open upon its face, its leaves in disorder. He moved away from it, staring at it in incredulous dismay. But he knew.

CHAPTER NINETEEN

MEMORY, that drowsy custodian, had wakened slowly, during this hour, beginning the process with fitful gleams of semi-consciousness, then, irritated, searching its pockets for the keys and dazedly exploring blind passages; but now it flung wide open the gallery doors, and there, in clear light, were the rows of painted canvasses.

He remembered "that day" when he was waiting for a car, and Laura Madison had stopped for a moment, and then had gone on, saying she preferred to walk. He remembered that after he got into the car he wondered why he had not walked home with her; had thought himself "slow" for not thinking of it in time to do it. There had seemed something very "taking" about her, as she stopped and spoke to him, something enlivening and wholesome and sweet — it had struck him that Laura was a "very nice girl." He had never before noticed how really charming she could look; in fact he had never thought much about either of the Madison sisters, who had become "young ladies" during his mourning for his brother. And this pleasant image of Laura remained with him for several days, until he decided that it might be a delightful thing to spend an evening with her. He had called, and he remembered, now, Cora's saying to him that he looked at her sometimes as if he did not like her; he had been surprised and astonishingly pleased to detect a mysterious *feeling* in her about it.

He remembered that almost at once he had fallen in love with Cora: she captivated him, enraptured him, as she still did — as she always would, he felt, no matter how she treated him or what she did to him. He did not analyze the process of the captivation and enrapturement — for love is a mystery and cannot be analyzed. This is so well known that even Richard Lindley knew it, and did not try!

. . . Heartsick, he stared at the fallen book. He was a man, and here was the proffered love of a woman he did not want. There was a pathos in the ledger; it seemed to grovel, sprawling and dishevelled in the circle of lamp-light on the floor: it was as if Laura herself lay pleading at his feet, and he looked down upon her, compassionate but revolted. He realized with astonishment from what a height she had fallen, how greatly he had respected her, how warmly liked her. What she now destroyed had been more important than he had guessed.

Simple masculine indignation rose within him: she was to have been his sister. If she had been unable to stifle this misplaced love of hers, could she not at least have kept it to herself? Laura, the self-respecting! No; she offered it — offered it to her sister's betrothed. She had written that he should "never, never know it"; that when she was "cured" she would burn the ledger. She had not burned it! There were inconsistencies in plenty in the pitiful screed, but these were the wildest — and the cheapest. In talk, she had urged him to "keep trying," for Cora, and now the sick-minded creature sent him this record. She wanted him to know. Then what else was it but a plea? "I love you. Let Cora go. Take me."

He began to walk up and down, wondering what was to be done. After a time, he picked up the book gingerly, set it upon a shelf in a dark corner, and went for a walk outdoors. The night air seemed better than that of the room that held the ledger.

At the corner a boy, running, passed him. It was Hedrick Madison, but Hedrick did not recognize Richard, nor was his mind at that moment concerned with Richard's affairs; he was on an errand of haste to Doctor Sloane. Mr. Madison had wakened from a heavy slumber unable to speak, his condition obviously much worse.

Hedrick returned in the doctor's car, and then hung uneasily about the door of the sick-room until Laura came out and told him to go to bed. In the morning, his mother did not appear at the breakfast table, Cora was serious and quiet, and Laura said that he need not go to school that day, though she added that the doctor thought their father would get "better." She looked wan and hollow-eyed: she had not been to bed, but declared that she would rest after breakfast. Evidently she had not missed her ledger; and Hedrick watched her closely, a pleasurable excitement stirring in his breast.

She did not go to her room after the meal; the house was cold, possessing no furnace, and, with Hedrick's assistance, she carried out the ashes from the library grate, and built a fire there. She had just lighted it, and the kindling was beginning to crackle, glowing rosily over her tired face, when the bell rang.

"Will you see who it is, please, Hedrick?"

He went with alacrity, and, returning, announced in an odd voice. "It's Dick Lindley. He wants to see you."

"Me?" she murmured, wanly surprised. She was kneeling before the fireplace, wearing an old dress, which was dusted with ashes, and upon herh ands a pair of worn-out gloves of her father's. Lindley appeared in the hall behind Hedrick, carrying under his arm something wrapped in brown paper. His expression led her to think that he had heard of her father's relapse, and came on that account.

"Don't look at me, Richard," she said, smiling faintly as she rose, and stripping her hands of the clumsy gloves. "It's good of you to come, though. Doctor Sloane thinks he is going to be better again."

Richard inclined his head gravely, but did not speak.

"Well," said Hedrick with a slight emphasis, "I guess I'll go out in the yard a while." And with shining eyes he left the room.

In the hall, out of range from the library door, he executed a triumphant but noiseless caper, and doubled with mirth, clapping his hand over his mouth to stifle the effervescings of his joy. He had recognized the ledger in the same wrapping in which he had left it in Mrs. Lindley's vestibule. His moment had come: the climax of his enormous joke, the repayment in some small measure for the anguish he had so long endured. He crept silently back toward the door, flattened his back against the wall, and listened.

"Richard," he heard Laura say, a vague alarm in her voice, "what is it? What is the matter?"

Then Lindley: "I did not know what to do about it. I couldn't think of any sensible thing. I suppose what I am doing is the stupidest of all the things I thought of, but at least it's honest — so I've brought it back to you myself. Take it, please."

There was a crackling of the stiff wrapping paper, a little pause, then a strange sound from Laura. It was not vocal and no more than just audible: it was a prolonged scream in a whisper.

Hedrick ventured an eye at the crack, between the partly open door and its casing. Lindley stood with his back to him, but the boy had a clear view of Laura. She was leaning against the wall, facing Richard, the book clutched in both arms against her bosom, the wrapping paper on the floor at her feet.

"I thought of sending it back and pretending to think it had been left at my mother's house by mistake," said Richard sadly, "and of trying to make it seem that I hadn't read any of it. I thought of a dozen ways to pretend I believed you hadn't really meant me to read it ——"

Making a crucial effort, she managed to speak. "You — think I — did mean ——"

"Well," he answered, with a helpless shrug, "you sent it! But it's what's in it that really matters, isn't it? I could have pretended anything in a note, I suppose, if I had written instead of coming. But I found that what I most dreaded was meeting you again, and as we've got to meet, of course, it seemed to me the only thing to do was to blunder through a talk with you, somehow or another, and get that part of it over. I thought the longer I put off facing you, the worse it would be for both of us — and — and the more embarrassing. I'm no good at pretending, anyhow; and the thing has happened. What use is there in not being honest? Well?"

She did not try again to speak. Her state was lamentable: it was all in her eyes.

Richard hung his head wretchedly, turning partly

away from her. "There's only one way—to look at it," he said hesitatingly, and stammering. "That is—there's only one thing to do: to forget that it's happened. I'm — I — oh, well, I care for Cora altogether. She's got never to know about this. She hasn't any idea or — suspicion of it, has she?"

Laura managed to shake her head.

"She never must have," he said. "Will you promise me to burn that book now?"

She nodded slowly.

"I — I'm awfully sorry, Laura," he said brokenly. "I'm not idiot enough not to see that you're suffering horribly. I suppose I have done the most blundering thing possible." He stood a moment, irresolute, then turned to the door. "Good-bye."

Hedrick had just time to dive into the hideous little room of the multitudinous owls as Richard strode into the hall. Then, with the closing of the front door, the boy was back at his post.

Laura stood leaning against the wall, the book clutched in her arms, as Richard had left her. Slowly she began to sink, her eyes wide open, and, with her back against the wall, she slid down until she was sitting upon the floor. Her arms relaxed and hung limp at her sides, letting the book topple over in her lap, and she sat motionless.

One of her feet protruded from her skirt, and the leaping firelight illumined it ruddily. It was a graceful foot in an old shoe which had been re-soled and patched. It seemed very still, that patched shoe, as if it might stay still forever. Hedrick knew that Laura had not fainted, but he wished she would move her foot.

He went away. He went into the owl-room again, and stood there silently a long, long time. Then he stole back again toward the library door, but caught a glimpse of that old, motionless shoe through the doorway as he came near. Then he spied no more. He went out to the stable, and, secluding himself in his studio, sat moodily to meditate.

Something was the matter. Something had gone wrong. He had thrown a bomb which he had expected to go off with a stupendous bang, leaving him, as the smoke cleared, looking down in merry triumph, stinging his fallen enemies with his humour, withering them with satire, and inquiring of them how it felt, now *they* were getting it. But he was decidedly untriumphant: he wished Laura had moved her foot and that she hadn't that patch upon her shoe. He could not get his mind off that patch. He began to feel very queer: it seemed to be somehow because of the patch. If she had worn a pair of new shoes that morning. . . . . Yes, it was that patch.

Thirteen is a dangerous age: nothing is more subtle. The boy, inspired to play the man, is beset by his own relapses into childhood, and Hedrick was near a relapse.

By and by, he went into the house again, to the library. Laura was not there, but he found the fire almost smothered under heaping ashes. She had burned her book.

He went into the room where the piano was, and played "The Girl on the Saskatchewan" with one finger; then went out to the porch and walked up and down, whistling cheerily.

After that, he went upstairs and asked Miss Peirce how his father was "feeling," receiving a non-commital reply; looked in at Cora's room; saw that his mother was lying asleep on Cora's bed and Cora herself examining the contents of a dressing-table drawer; and withdrew. A moment later, he stood in the passage outside Laura's closed door listening. There was no sound.

He retired to his own chamber, found it unbearable, and, fascinated by Laura's, returned thither; and, after standing a long time in the passage, knocked softly on the door.

"Laura," he called, in a rough and careless voice, "it's kind of a pretty day outdoors. If you've had your nap, if I was you I'd go out for a walk." There was no response. "I'll go with you," he added, "if you want me to."

He listened again and heard nothing. Then he turned the knob softly. The door was unlocked; he opened it and went in.

Laura was sitting in a chair, with her back to a window, her hands in her lap. She was staring straight in front of her.

He came near her hesitatingly, and at first she did not seem to see him or even to know that she was not alone in the room. Then she looked at him wonderingly, and, as he stood beside her, lifted her right hand and set it gently upon his head.

"Hedrick," she said, "was it you that took my book to —— "

All at once he fell upon his knees, hid his face in her lap, and burst into loud and passionate sobbing.

CHAPTER TWENTY

VALENTINE CORLISS, having breakfasted in bed at a late hour that morning, dozed again, roused himself, and, making a toilet, addressed to the image in his shaving-mirror a disgusted monosyllable.

"Ass!"

However, he had not the look of a man who had played cards all night to a disastrous tune with an accompaniment in Scotch. His was a surface not easily indented: he was hard and healthy, clear-skinned and clear-eyed. When he had made himself point-device, he went into the "parlour" of his apartment, frowning at the litter of malodorous relics, stumps and stubs and bottles and half-drained glasses, scattered chips and cards, dregs of a night session. He had been making acquaintances.

He sat at the desk and wrote with a steady hand in Italian:

Most illustrious Moliterno:

We live but learn little. As to myself it appears

that I learn nothing — nothing! You will at once convey to me by *cable* five thousand lire. No; add the difference in exchange so as to make it one thousand dollars which I shall receive, taking that sum from the two-hundred and thirty thousand lire which I entrusted to your safekeeping by cable as the result of my enterprise in this place. I should have returned at once, content with that success, but as you know I am a very stupid fellow, never pleased with a moderate triumph, nor with a large one, when there is a possible prospect of greater. I am compelled to believe that the greater I had in mind in this case was an illusion: my gentle diplomacy avails nothing against a small miser — for we have misers even in these States, though you will not believe it. I abandon him to his riches! From the success of my venture I reserved four thousand dollars to keep by me and for my expenses, and it is humiliating to relate that all of this, except a small banknote or two, was taken from me last night by amateurs. I should keep away from cards — they hate me, and alone I can do nothing with them. Some young gentlemen of the place, whose acquaintance I had made at a ball, did me the honour of this lesson at the native game of poker, at which I — though also native — am not even so expert as yourself, and, as you will admit, Antonio, my friend, you are not a good player — when observed.

Unaided, I was a child in their hands. It was also a painful rule that one paid for the counters upon delivery. This made me ill, but I carried it off with an air of carelessness creditable to an adopted Neapolitan. Upon receipt of the money you are to cable me, I shall leave this town and sail immediately. Come to Paris, and meet me there at the place on the Rue Auber within ten days from your reading this letter. You will have, remaining, two hundred and twenty-five thousand francs, which it will be safer to bring in cash, and I will deal well with you, as is our custom with each other. You have done excellently throughout; your cables and letters for exhibition concerning those famous oil wells have been perfection; and I shall of course not deduct what was taken by these thieves of poker players from the sum of profits upon which we shall estimate your commission. I have several times had the feeling that the hour for departure had arrived; now I shall delay not a moment after receiving your cable, though I may occupy the interim with a last attempt to interest my small miser. Various circumstances cause me some uneasiness, though I do not believe I could be successfully assailed by the law in the matter of oil. You do own an estate in Basilicata, at least your brother does — these good people here would not be apt to discover the difference — and the rest is a matter of plausibility. The odious coincidence of encountering the old cow,

Pryor, fretted me somewhat (though he has not repeated his annoying call), and I have other small apprehensions — for example, that it may not improve my credit if my loss of last night becomes gossip, though the thieves professed strong habits of discretion. My little affair of gallantry grows embarrassing. Such affairs are so easy to inaugurate; extrication is more difficult. However, without it I should have failed to interest my investor — and there is always the charm. Your last letter is too curious in that matter. Licentious man, one does not write of these things while under the banner of the illustrious Uncle Sam — I am assuming the American attitude while here, or perhaps my early youth returns to me — a thing very different from your own boyhood, Don Antonio. Nevertheless, I promise you some laughter in the Rue Auber. Though you will not be able to understand the half of what I shall tell you — particularly the portraits I shall sketch of my defeated rivals — your spirit shall roll with laughter.

To the bank, then, the instant you read. Cable me one thousand dollars, and be at the Rue Auber not more than ten days later. To the bank! Thence to the telegraph office. Speed! V. C.

He was in better spirits as he read over this letter, and he chuckled as he addressed it. He pictured himself in the rear room of the bar in the Rue Auber, relating, across the little marble-topped table, this American adventure, to the delight of that blithe, ne'er-do-well outcast of an exalted poor family, that gambler, blackmailer and merry rogue, Don Antonio Moliterno, comrade and teacher of this ductile Valentine since the later days of adolescence. They had been school-fellows in Rome, and later roamed Europe together unleashed, discovering worlds of many kinds. Valentine's careless mother let her boy go as he liked, and was often negligent in the matter of remittances: he and his friend learned ways to raise the wind, becoming expert and making curious affiliations. At her death there was a small inheritance; she had not been provident. The little she left went rocketing, and there was the wind to be raised again: young Corliss had wits and had found that they could supply him — most of the time — with much more than the necessities of life. He had also found that he possessed a strong attraction for various women; already — at twenty-two — his experience was considerable, and, in his way, he became a specialist. He had a talent; he improved it and his opportunities. Altogether, he took to the work without malice and with a light heart. . . .

He sealed the envelope, rang for a boy, gave him the letter to post, and directed that the apartment should be set to rights. It was not that in which he had received Ray Vilas. Corliss had moved to rooms on another floor of the hotel, the day after that eccentric and somewhat ominous person had called to make an "investment." Ray's shadowy forebodings concerning that former apartment had encountered satire: Corliss was a "materialist" and, at the mildest estimate, an unusually practical man, but he would never sleep in a bed with its foot toward the door; southern Italy had seeped into him. He changed his rooms, a measure of which Don Antonio Moliterno would have wholly approved. Besides, these were as comfortable as the others, and so like them as even to confirm Ray's statement concerning "A Reading from Homer": evidently this work had been purchased by the edition.

A boy came to announce that his "roadster" waited for him at the hotel entrance, and Corliss put on a fur motoring coat and cap, and went downstairs. A door leading from the hotel bar into the lobby was open, and, as Corliss passed it, there issued a mocking shout:

"Tor'dor! Oh, look at the Tor'dor! Ain't he the handsome Spaniard!"

Ray Vilas stumbled out, tousled, haggard, waving his arms in absurd and meaningless gestures; an amused gallery of tipplers filling the doorway behind him.

"Goin' take Carmen buggy ride in the country, ain't he? Good ole Tor'dor!" he quavered loudly, clutching Corliss's shoulder. "How much you s'pose he pays f' that buzz-buggy by the day, jell'm'n? Naughty Tor'dor, stole thousand dollars from me — makin' presents — diamond cresses. Tor'dor, I hear you been playing cards. Tha'ssn't nice. Tor'dor, you're not a goo' boy at all — *you* know you oughtn't waste Dick Lindley's money like that!"

Corliss set his open hand upon the drunkard's breast and sent him gyrating and plunging backward. Some one caught the grotesque figure as it fell.

"Oh, my God," screamed Ray, "I haven't got a gun on me! He *knows* I haven't got my gun with me! *Why* haven't I got my gun with me?"

They hustled him away, and Corliss, enraged and startled, passed on. As he sped the car up

Corliss Street, he decided to anticipate his letter to Moliterno by a cable. He had stayed too long.

Cora looked charming in a new equipment for November motoring; yet it cannot be said that either of them enjoyed the drive. They lunched a dozen miles out from the city at an establishment somewhat in the nature of a roadside inn; and, although its cuisine was quite unknown to Cora's friend, Mrs. Villard (an eager amateur of the table), they were served with a meal of such unusual excellence that the waiter thought it a thousand pities patrons so distinguished should possess such poor appetites.

They returned at about three in the afternoon, and Cora descended from the car wearing no very amiable expression.

"Why won't you come in now?" she asked, looking at him angrily. "We've got to talk things out. We've settled nothing whatever. I want to know why you can't stop."

"I've got some matters to attend to, and —— "

"What matters?" She shot him a glance of fierce skepticism. "Are you packing to get out?"

"Cora!" he cried reproachfully, "how can you say things like that to *me!*"

She shook her head. "Oh, it wouldn't surprise me in the least! How do *I* know what you'll do? For all I know, you may be just that kind of a man. You *said* you ought to be going —— "

"Cora," he explained, gently, "I didn't say I meant to go. I said only that I thought I ought to, because Moliterno will be needing me in Basilicata. I ought to be there, since it appears that no more money is to be raised here. I ought to be superintending operations in the oil-field, so as to make the best use of the little I have raised."

"You?" she laughed. "Of course *I* didn't have anything to do with it!"

He sighed deeply. "You know perfectly well that I appreciate all you did. We don't seem to get on very well to-day —— "

"No!" She laughed again, bitterly. "So you think you'll be going, don't you?"

"To my rooms to write some necessary letters."

"Of course not to pack your trunk?"

"Cora," he returned, goaded; "sometimes you're just impossible. I'll come to-morrow forenoon."

"Then don't bring the car. I'm tired of motoring and tired of lunching in that rotten hole. We can talk just as well in the library. Papa's better, and that little fiend will be in school to-morrow. Come out about ten."

He started the machine. "Don't forget I love you," he called in a low voice.

She stood looking after him as the car dwindled down the street.

"Yes, you do!" she murmured.

She walked up the path to the house, her face thoughtful, as with a tiresome perplexity. In her own room, divesting herself of her wraps, she gave the mirror a long scrutiny. It offered the picture of a girl with a hard and dreary air; but Cora saw something else, and presently, though the dreariness remained, the hardness softened to a great compassion. She suffered: a warm wave of sorrow submerged her, and she threw herself upon the bed and wept long and silently for herself.

At last her eyes dried, and she lay staring at the ceiling. The doorbell rang, and Sarah, the cook, came to inform her that Mr. Richard Lindley was below.

"Tell him I'm out."

"Can't," returned Sarah. "Done told him you was home." And she departed firmly.

Thus abandoned, the prostrate lady put into a few words what she felt about Sarah, and, going to the door, whisperingly summoned in Laura, who was leaving the sick-room, across the hall.

"Richard is downstairs. Will you go and tell him I'm sick in bed — or dead? Anything to make him go." And, assuming Laura's acquiescence, Cora went on, without pause: "Is father worse? What's the matter with you, Laura?"

"Nothing. He's a little better, Miss Peirce thinks."

"You look ill."

"I'm all right."

"Then run along like a duck and get rid of that old bore for me."

"Cora — please see him?"

"Not me! I've got too much to think about to bother with him."

Laura walked to the window and stood with her back to her sister, apparently interested in the view of Corliss Street there presented. "Cora," she said, "why don't you marry him and have done with all this?"

Cora hooted.

"Why not? Why not marry him as soon as you can get ready? Why don't you go down now and tell him you will? Why not, Cora?"

"I'd as soon marry a pail of milk — yes, tepid milk, skimmed! I —— "

"Don't you realize how kind he'd be to you?"

"I don't know about that," said Cora moodily. "He might object to some things — but it doesn't matter, because I'm not going to try him. I don't mind a man's being a fool, but I can't stand the absent-minded breed of idiot. I've worn his diamond in the pendant right in his eyes for weeks; he's never once noticed it enough even to ask me about the pendant, but bores me to death wanting to know why I won't wear the ring! Anyhow, what's the use talking about him? He couldn't marry me right now, even if I wanted him to — not till he begins to get something on the investment he made with Val. Outside of that, he's got nothing except his rooms at his mother's; she hasn't much either; and if Richard should lose what he put in with Val, he couldn't marry for years, probably. That's what made him so obstinate about it. No; if I ever marry right off the reel it's got to be somebody with —— "

"Cora" — Laura still spoke from the window, not turning — "aren't you tired of it all, of this getting so upset about one man and then another and ——"

"*Tired!*" Cora uttered the word in a repressed fury of emphasis. "I'm sick of *everything!* I don't care for anything or anybody on this earth — except — except you and mamma. I thought I was going to love Val. I thought I *did* — but oh, my Lord, I don't! I don't think I *can* care any more. Or else there isn't any such thing as love. How can anybody tell whether there is or not? You get kind of crazy over a man and want to go the limit — or marry him perhaps — or sometimes you just want to make him crazy about you — and then you get over it — and what is there left but hell!" She choked with a sour laugh. "Ugh! For heaven's sake, Laura, don't make me talk. Everything's gone to the devil and I've got to think. The best thing you can do is to go down and get rid of Richard for me. I *can't* see him!"

"Very well," said Laura, and went to the door.

"You're a darling," whispered Cora, kissing her quickly. "Tell him I'm in a raging headache — make him think I wanted to see him, but you wouldn't let me, because I'm too ill." She laughed.

"Give me a little time, old dear: I may decide to take him yet!"

It was Mrs. Madison who informed the waiting Richard that Cora was unable to see him, because she was "lying down"; and the young man, after properly inquiring about Mr. Madison, went blankly forth.

Hedrick was stalking the front yard, mounted at a great height upon a pair of stilts. He joined the departing visitor upon the sidewalk and honoured him with his company, proceeding storkishly beside him.

"Been to see Cora?"

"Yes, Hedrick."

"What'd you want to see her about?" asked the frank youth seriously.

Richard was able to smile. "Nothing in particular, Hedrick."

"You didn't come to tell her about something?"

"Nothing whatever, my dear sir. I wished merely the honour of seeing her and chatting with her upon indifferent subjects. Why?"

"Did you see her?"

"No, I'm sorry to —— "

"She's home, all right," Hedrick took pleasure in informing him.

"Yes. She was lying down and I told your mother not to disturb her."

"Worn out with too much automobile riding, I expect," Hedrick sniffed. "She goes out about every day with this Corliss in his hired roadster."

They walked on in silence. Not far from Mrs. Lindley's, Hedrick abruptly became vocal in an artificial laugh. Richard was obviously intended to inquire into its cause, but, as he did not, Hedrick, after laughing hollowly for some time, volunteered the explanation:

"I played a pretty good trick on you last night."

"Odd I didn't know it."

"That's why it was good. You'd never guess it in the world."

"No, I believe I shouldn't. You see what makes it so hard, Hedrick, is that I can't even remember seeing you, last night."

"Nobody saw me. Somebody heard me though, all right."

"Who?"

"The nigger that works at your mother's—Joe."

"What about it? Were you teasing Joe?"

"No, it was you I was after."

"Well? Did you get me?"

Hedrick made another somewhat ghastly pretence of mirth. "Well, I guess I've had about all the fun out of it I'm going to. Might as well tell you. It was that book of Laura's you thought she sent you."

Richard stopped short; whereupon Hedrick turned clumsily, and began to stalk back in the direction from which they had come.

"That book — I thought she — sent me?" Lindley repeated, stammering.

"She never sent it," called the boy, continuing to walk away. "She kept it hid, and I found it. I faked her into writing your name on a sheet of paper, and made you think she'd sent the old thing to you. I just did it for a joke on you."

With too retching an effort to simulate another burst of merriment, he caught the stump of his right stilt in a pavement crack, wavered, cut in the air a figure like a geometrical proposition gone mad, and came whacking to earth in magnificent disaster.

Richard took him to Mrs. Lindley for repairs. She kept him until dark: Hedrick was bandaged, fed, lemonaded and blandished.

Never in his life had he known such a listener.

CHAPTER TWENTY-ONE

THAT was a long night for Cora Madison, and the morning found her yellow. She made a poor breakfast, and returned from the table to her own room,but after a time descended restlessly and wandered from one room to another, staring out of the windows. Laura had gone out; Mrs. Madison was with her husband, whom she seldom left; Hedrick had departed ostensibly for school; and the house was as still as a farm in winter — an intolerable condition of things for an effervescent young woman whose diet was excitement. Cora, drumming with her fingers upon a window in the owl-haunted cell, made noises with her throat, her breath and her lips not unsuggestive of a sputtering fuse. She was heavily charged.

"Now what in thunder do *you* want?" she inquired of an elderly man who turned in from the sidewalk and with serious steps approached the house.

Pryor, having rung, found himself confronted with the lady he had come to seek. Ensued the moment of strangers meeting: invisible antennæ extended and touched;—at the contact, Cora's drew in, and she looked upon him without graciousness.

"I just called," he said placatively, smiling as if some humour lurked in his intention, "to ask how your father is. I heard downtown he wasn't getting along quite so well."

"He's better this morning, thanks," said Cora, preparing to close the door.

"I thought I'd just stop and ask about him. I heard he'd had another bad spell — kind of a second stroke."

"That was night before last. The doctor thinks he's improved very much since then."

The door was closing; he coughed hastily, and detained it by speaking again. "I've called several times to inquire about him, but I believe it's the first time I've had the pleasure of speaking to you, Miss Madison. I'm Mr. Pryor." She appeared to find no comment necessary, and he continued: "Your father did a little business for me, several years ago, and when I was here on my vacation, this summer, I was mighty sorry to hear of his sickness. I've had a nice bit of luck lately and got a second furlough, so I came out to spend a couple of weeks and Thanksgiving with my married daughter."

Cora supposed that it must be very pleasant.

"Yes," he returned. "But I was mighty sorry to hear your father wasn't much better than when I left. The truth is, I wanted to have a talk with him, and I've been reproaching myself a good deal that I didn't go ahead with it last summer, when he was well, only I thought then it mightn't be necessary — might be disturbing things without much reason."

"I'm afraid you can't have a talk with him now," she said. "The doctor says —— "

"I know, I know," said Pryor, "of course. I wonder" — he hesitated, smiling faintly — "I wonder if I could have it with you instead."

"Me?"

"Oh, it isn't business," he laughed, observing her expression. "That is, not exactly." His manner became very serious. "It's about a friend of mine —at least, a man I know pretty well. Miss Madison, I saw you driving out through the park with him, yesterday noon, in an automobile. Valentine Corliss."

Cora stared at him. Honesty, friendliness, and grave concern were disclosed to her scrutiny. There was no mistaking him: he was a good man. Her mouth opened, and her eyelids flickered as from a too sudden invasion of light — the look of one perceiving the close approach of a vital crisis. But there was no surprise in her face.

"Come in," she said.

. . . . When Corliss arrived, at about eleven o'clock that morning, Sarah brought him to the library, where he found Cora waiting for him. He had the air of a man determined to be cheerful under adverse conditions: he came in briskly, and Cora closed the door behind him.

"Keep away from me," she said, pushing him back sharply, the next instant. "I've had enough of that for a while I believe."

He sank into a chair, affecting desolation. "Caresses blighted in the bud! Cora, one would think us really married."

She walked across the floor to a window, turned there, with her back to the light, and stood facing him, her arms folded.

"Good heavens!" he exclaimed, noting this attitude. "Is it the trial scene from a faded melodrama?" She looked steadily at him without replying. "What's it all about to-day?" he asked lightly. "I'll try to give you the proper cues if you'll indicate the general nature of the scene, Cora mine."

She continued to look at him in silence.

"It's very effective," he observed. "Brings out the figure, too. Do forgive me if you're serious, dear lady, but never in my life was I able to take the folded-arms business seriously. It was used on the stage of all countries so much that I believe most new-school actors have dropped it. They think it lacks genuineness."

Cora waited a moment longer, then spoke. "How much chance have I to get Richard Lindley's money back from you?"

He was astounded. "Oh, I say!"

"I had a caller, this morning," she said, slowly. "He talked about you — quite a lot! He's told me several things about you."

"Mr. Vilas?" he asked, with a sting in his quick smile.

"No," she answered coolly. "Much older."

At that he jumped up, stepped quickly close to her, and swept her with an intense and brilliant scrutiny.

"Pryor, by God!" he cried.

"He knows you pretty well," she said. "So do I — now!"

He swung away from her, back to his chair, dropped into it and began to laugh. "Old Pryor! Doddering old Pryor! Doddering old ass of a Pryor! So he did! Blood of an angel! what a stew, what a stew!" He rose again, mirthless. "Well, what did he say?"

She had begun to tremble, not with fear. "He said a good deal."

"Well, what was it? What did he tell you?"

"I think you'll find it plenty!"

"Come on!"

"*You!*" She pointed at him.

"Let's have it."

"He told me" — she burst out furiously — "he said you were a professional sharper!"

"Oh, no. Old Pryor doesn't talk like that."

She came toward him. "He told me you were notorious over half of Europe," she cried vehemently. "He said he'd arrested you himself, once, in Rotterdam, for smuggling jewels, and that you were guilty, but managed to squirm out of it. He said the police had put you out of Germany and you'd be arrested if you ever tried to go back. He said there were other places you didn't dare set foot in, and he said he could have you arrested in this country any time he wanted to, and that he was going to do it if he found you'd been doing anything wrong. Oh, yes, he told me a few things!"

He caught her by the shoulder. "See here, Cora, do you believe all this tommy-rot?"

She shook his hand off instantly. "Believe it? I know it! There isn't a straight line in your whole soul and mind: you're crooked all over. You've been crooked with *me* from the start. The moment that man began to speak, I knew every word of it was true. He came to me because he thought it was right: he hasn't anything against you on his own account; he said he *liked* you! I *knew* it was true, I tell you."

He tried to put his hand on her shoulder again, beginning to speak remonstratingly, but she cried out in a rage, broke away from him, and ran to the other end of the room.

"Keep away! Do you suppose I like you to touch me? He told me you always had been a wonder with women! Said you were famous for 'handling them the right way'—using them! Ah, that was pleasant information for *me*, wasn't it! Yes, I could have confirmed him on that point. He wanted to know if I thought you'd been doing anything of that sort here. What he meant was: Had you been using *me?*"

"What did you tell him?" The question rang sharply on the instant.

"Ha! That gets into you, does it?" she returned bitterly. "You can't overdo your fear of that man, I think, but *I* didn't tell him anything. I just listened and thanked him for the warning, and said I'd have nothing more to do with you. How *could* I tell him? Wasn't it I that made papa lend you his name, and got Richard to hand over his money? Where does that put *me?*" She choked; sobs broke her voice. "Every — every soul in town would point me out as a laughing-stock — the easiest fool out of the asylum! Do you suppose *I* want you arrested and the whole thing in the papers? What I want is Richard's money back, and I'm going to have it!"

"Can you be quiet for a moment and listen?" he asked gravely.

"If you'll tell me what chance I have to get it back."

"Cora," he said, "you don't want it back."

"Oh? Don't I?"

"No." He smiled faintly, and went on. "Now, all this nonsense of old Pryor's isn't worth denying. I have met him abroad; that much is true — and I suppose I have rather a gay reputation —— "

She uttered a jeering shout.

"Wait!" he said. "I told you I'd cut quite a swathe, when I first talked to you about myself. Let it go for the present and come down to this question of Lindley's investment —— "

"Yes. That's what I want you to come down to."

"As soon as Lindley paid in his check I gave him his stock certificates, and cabled the money to be used at once in the development of the oil-fields —— "

"What! That man told me you'd 'promoted' a South American rubber company once, among people of the American colony in Paris. The details he gave me sounded strangely familiar!"

"You'd as well be patient, Cora. Now, that money has probably been partially spent, by this time, on tools and labour and —— "

"What are you trying to —— "

"I'll show you. But first I'd like you to understand that nothing can be done to me. There's nothing 'on' me! I've acted in good faith, and if the venture in oil is unsuccessful, and the money lost, I can't be held legally responsible, nor can any one prove that I am. I could bring forty witnesses from Naples to swear they have helped to bore the wells. I'm safe as your stubborn friend, Mr. Trumble, himself. But now then, suppose that old Pryor is right — as of course he isn't — suppose it, merely for a moment, because it will aid me to convey something to your mind. If I were the kind of man he says I am, and, being such a man, had planted the money out of reach, for my own use, what on earth would induce me to give it back?"

"I knew it!" she groaned. "I knew you wouldn't!"

"You see," he said quietly, "it would be impossible. We must go on supposing for a moment: if I had put that money away, I might be contemplating a departure —— "

"You'd better!" she cried fiercely. "He's going to find out everything you've been doing. He said so. He's heard a rumour that you were trying to raise money here; he told me so, and said he'd soon —— "

"The better reason for not delaying, perhaps. Cora, see here!" He moved nearer her. "Wouldn't I need a lot of money if I expected to have a beautiful lady to care for, and —— "

"You idiot!" she screamed. "Do you think I'm going with you?"

He flushed heavily. "Well, aren't you?" He paused, to stare at her, as she wrung her hands and sobbed with hysterical laughter. "I thought," he went on, slowly, "that you would possibly even insist on that."

"Oh, Lord, Lord, Lord!" She stamped her foot, and with both hands threw the tears from her eyes in wide and furious gestures. "He told me you were married —— "

"Did you let him think you hadn't known that?" demanded Corliss.

"I tell you I didn't let him think *anything!* He said you would never be able to get a divorce: that your wife hates you too much to get one from you, and that she'll never —— "

"See here, Cora," he said harshly, "I told you I'd been married; I told you before I ever kissed you. You understood perfectly —— "

"I did not! You said you *had* been. You laughed

about it. You made me think it was something that had happened a long time ago. I thought of course you'd been divorced —— "

"But I told you —— "

"You told me after! And then you made me think you could easily get one — that it was only a matter of form and —— "

"Cora," he interrupted, "you're the most elaborate little self-deceiver I ever knew. I don't believe you've ever faced yourself for an honest moment in ——"

"Honest! *You* talk about 'honest'! You use that word and face *me?*"

He came closer, meeting her distraught eyes squarely. "You love to fool yourself, Cora, but the rôle of betrayed virtue doesn't suit you very well. You're young, but you're a pretty experienced woman for all that, and you haven't done anything you didn't want to. You've had both eyes open every minute, and we both know it. You are just as wise as —— "

"You're lying and *you* know it! What did *I* want to make Richard go into your scheme for? You made a fool of me."

"I'm not speaking of the money now," he returned

quickly. "You'd better keep your mind on the subject. Are you coming away with me?"

"What for?" she asked.

"What *for?*" he echoed incredulously. "I want to know if you're coming. I promise you I'll get a divorce as soon as it's possible ——"

"Val," she said, in a tone lower than she had used since he entered the room; "Val, do you want me to come?"

"Yes."

"Much?" She looked at him eagerly.

"Yes, I do." His answer sounded quite genuine.

"Will it hurt you if I don't?"

"Of course it will."

"Thank heaven for that," she said quietly.

"You honestly mean you won't?"

"It makes me sick with laughing just to imagine it! I've done some hard little thinking, lately, my friend — particularly last night, and still more particularly this morning since that man was here. I'd cut my throat before I'd go with you. If you had your divorce I wouldn't marry you — not if you were the last man on earth!"

"Cora," he cried, aghast, "what's the matter with you? You're too many for me sometimes.

I thought I understood a few kinds of women! Now listen: I've offered to take you, and you can't say —— "

"Offered!" It was she who came toward him now. She came swiftly, shaking with rage, and struck him upon the breast. "'Offered'! Do you think I want to go trailing around Europe with you while Dick Lindley's money lasts? What kind of a life are you 'offering' me? Do you suppose I'm going to have everybody saying Cora Madison ran away with a jail-bird? Do you think I'm going to dodge decent people in hotels and steamers, and leave a name in this town that — Oh, get out! I don't want any help from you! I can take care of myself, I tell you; and I don't have to marry *you!* I'd kill you if I could — you made a fool of me!" Her voice rose shrilly. "You made a fool of me!"

"Cora —— " he began, imploringly.

"You made a fool of me!" She struck him again.

"Strike me," he said. "I love you."

"Actor!"

"Cora, I want you. I want you more than I ever —— "

She screamed with hysterical laughter. "Liar,

liar, liar! The same old guff. Don't you even see it's too late for the old rotten tricks?"

"Cora, I want you to come."

"You poor, conceited fool," she cried, "do you think you're the only man I can marry?"

"Cora," he gasped, "you wouldn't do that!"

"Oh, get out! Get out *now!* I'm tired of you. I never want to hear you speak again."

"Cora," he begged. "For the last time —— "

"*No!* You made a fool of me!" She beat him upon the breast, striking again and again, with all her strength. "Get out, I tell you! I'm through with you!"

He tried to make her listen, to hold her wrists: he could do neither.

"Get out — get out!" she screamed. She pushed and dragged him toward the door, and threw it open. Her voice thickened; she choked and coughed, but kept on screaming: "Get out, I tell you! Get out, get out, damn you! Damn you, *damn* you! get out!"

Still continuing to strike him with all her strength, she forced him out of the door.

CHAPTER TWENTY-TWO

CORA lost no time. Corliss had not closed the front door behind him before she was running up the stairs. Mrs. Madison, emerging from her husband's room, did not see her daughter's face; for Cora passed her quickly, looking the other way.

"Was anything the matter?" asked the mother anxiously. "I thought I heard ——"

"Nothing in the world," Cora flung back over her shoulder. "Mr. Corliss said I couldn't imitate Sara Bernhardt, and I showed him I could." She began to hum; left a fragment of "rag-time" floating behind her as she entered her own room; and Mrs. Madison, relieved, returned to the invalid.

Cora changed her clothes quickly. She put on a pale gray skirt and coat for the street, high shoes and a black velvet hat, very simple. The costume was almost startlingly becoming to her: never in her life had she looked prettier. She opened her small jewel-case, slipped all her rings upon her fingers; then put the diamond crescent, the pendant, her watch, and three or four other things into the flat, envelope-shaped bag of soft leather she carried when shopping. After that she brought from her clothes-pantry a small travelling-bag and packed it hurriedly.

Laura, returning from errands downtown and glancing up at Cora's window, perceived an urgently beckoning, gray-gloved hand, and came at once to her sister's room.

The packed bag upon the bed first caught her eye; then Cora's attire, and the excited expression of Cora's face, which was high-flushed and moist, glowing with a great resolve.

"What's happened?" asked Laura quickly. "You look exactly like a going-away bride. What ——"

Cora spoke rapidly: "Laura, I want you to take this bag and keep it in your room till a messenger-boy comes for it. When the bell rings, go to the door yourself, and hand it to him. Don't give Hedrick a chance to go to the door. Just give it to the boy; and don't say anything to mamma about it. I'm going downtown and I may not be back."

Laura began to be frightened.

"What is it you want to do, Cora?" she asked, trembling.

Cora was swift and business-like. "See here, Laura, I've got to keep my head about me. You can do a great deal for me, if you won't be emotional just now, and help *me* not to be. I can't afford it, because I've got to do things, and I'm going to do them just as quickly as I can, and get it over. If I wait any longer I'll go insane. I *can't* wait! You've been a wonderful sister to me; I've always counted on you, and you've never once gone back on me. Right now, I need you to help me more than I ever have in my life. Will you ——"

"But I must know ——"

"No, you needn't! I'll tell you just this much: I've got myself in a devil of a mess ——"

Laura threw her arms round her: "Oh, my dear, dear little sister!" she cried.

But Cora drew away. "Now that's just what you mustn't do. I can't stand it! You've got to be *quiet*. I can't ——"

"Yes, yes," Laura said hurriedly. "I will. I'll do whatever you say."

"It's perfectly simple: all I want you to do is to take charge of my travelling-bag, and, when a messenger-boy comes, give it to him without letting anybody know anything about it."

"But I've got to know where you're going — I can't let you go and not ——"

"Yes, you can! Besides, you've promised to. I'm not going to do anything foolish ——"

"Then why not tell me?" Laura began. She went on, imploring Cora to confide in her, entreating her to see their mother — to do a dozen things altogether outside of Cora's plans.

"You're wasting your breath, Laura," said the younger sister, interrupting, "and wasting my time. You're in the dark: you think I'm going to run away with Val Corliss and you're wrong. I sent him out of the house for good, a while ago ——"

"Thank heaven for that!" cried Laura.

"I'm going to take care of myself," Cora went on rapidly. "I'm going to get out of the mess I'm in, and you've got to let me do it my own way. I'll send you a note from downtown. You see that the messenger ——"

She was at the door, but Laura caught her by the sleeve, protesting and beseeching.

Cora turned desperately. "See here. I'll come back in two hours and tell you all about it. If I promise that, will you promise to send me the bag by the ——"

"But if you're coming back you won't need ——"

Cora spoke very quietly. "I'll go to pieces in a moment. Really, I do think I'd better jump out of the window and have it over."

"I'll send the bag," Laura quavered, "if you'll promise to come back in two hours."

"I promise!"

Cora gave her a quick embrace, a quick kiss, and, dry-eyed, ran out of the room, down the stairs, and out of the house.

She walked briskly down Corliss Street. It was a clear day, bright noon, with an exhilarating tang in the air, and a sky so glorious that people outdoors were continually conscious of the blue overhead, and looked up at it often. An autumnal cheerfulness was abroad, and pedestrians showed it in their quickened steps, in their enlivened eyes, and frequent smiles, and in the colour of their faces. But none showed more colour or a gayer look than Cora. She encountered many whom she knew, for it was indeed a day to be stirring, and she nodded and smiled her way all down the long street, thinking of what these greeted people would say to-morrow.

"*I* saw her yesterday, walking down Corliss Street, about noon, in a gray suit and looking fairly radiant!" Some of those she met were enemies she had chastened; she prophesied their remarks with accu acy. Some were old suitors, men who had desired her; one or two had place upon her long list of boy-sweethearts: she gave the same gay, friendly nod to each of them, and foretold his morrow's thoughts of her, in turn. Her greeting of Mary Kane was graver, as was æsthetically appropriate, Mr. Wattling's engagement having been broken by that lady, immediately after his drive to the Country Club for tea. Cora received from the beautiful jilt a salutation even graver than her own, which did not confound her.

Halfway down the street was a drug-store. She went in, and obtained appreciative permission to use the telephone. She came out well satisfied, and went swiftly on her way. Ten minutes later, she opened the door of Wade Trumble's office.

He was alone; her telephone had caught him in the act of departing for lunch. But he had been glad to wait — glad to the verge of agitation.

"By George, Cora!" he exclaimed, as she came quickly in and closed the door, "but you *can* look stunning! Believe me, that's some get-up. But let me tell you right here and now, before you begin, it's no use your tackling me again on the oil proposition. If there was any chance of my going into it — which there wasn't, not one on earth — why, the very fact of your asking me would have stopped me. I'm no Dick Lindley, I beg to inform you: I don't spend my money helping a girl that I want, myself, to make a hit with another man. You treated me like a dog about that, right in the street, and you needn't try it again, because I won't stand for it. You can't play *me*, Cora!"

"Wade," she said, coming closer, and looking at him mysteriously, "didn't you tell me to come to you when I got through playing?"

"What?" He grew very red, took a step back from her, staring at her distrustfully, incredulously.

"I've got through playing", she said in a low voice. "And I've come to you."

He was staggered. "You've come ——" he said, huskily.

"Here I am, Wade."

He had flushed, but now the colour left his small face, and he grew very white. "I don't believe — you mean it."

"Listen," she said. "I was rotten to you about that oil nonsense. It *was* nonsense, nothing on earth but nonsense. I tell you frankly I was a fool. I didn't care the snap of my finger for Corliss, but—oh, what's the use of pretending? You were always such a great 'business man,' always so absorbed in business, and put it before everything else in the world. You cared for me, but you cared for business more than for me. Well, no woman likes *that*, Wade. I've come to tell you the whole thing: I can't stand it any longer. I suffered horribly because — because ——" She faltered. "Wade, that was no way to *win* a girl."

"Cora!" His incredulity was strong.

"I thought I hated you for it, Wade. Yes, I did think that; I'm telling you everything, you see — just blurting it out as it comes, Wade. Well, Corliss asked me to help him, and it struck me I'd show that I could understand a business deal, myself. Wade, this is pretty hard to say, I was such a little fool, but you ought to know it. You've got a right to know it, Wade: I thought if I put through a thing like that, it would make a tremendous hit with you, and that then I could say: 'So this is the kind of thing you put ahead of *me*, is it? Simple little things like this, that *I* can do, myself, by turning over my little finger!' So I got Richard to go in — that was easy; and then it struck me that the crowning triumph of the whole thing would be to get you to come in yourself. That *would* be showing you, I thought! But you wouldn't: you put me in my place — and I was angry — I never was so angry in my life, and I showed it." Tears came into her voice. "Oh, Wade," she said, softly, "it was the very wildness of my anger that showed what I really felt."

"About — about *me*?" His incredulity struggled with his hope. He stepped close to her.

"What an awful fool I've been," she sighed. "Why, I thought I could show you I was your *equal!* And look what it's got me into, Wade!"

"What has it got you into, Cora?"

"One thing worth while: I can see what I really am when I try to meet you on your own ground." She bent her head, humbly, then lifted it, and spoke rapidly. "All the rest is dreadful, Wade. I had a distrust of Corliss from the first; I didn't like him, but I took him up because I thought he offered the chance to show *you* what I could do. Well, it's got me into a most horrible mess. He's a swindler, a rank ——"

"By George!" Wade shouted. "Cora, you're talking out now like a real woman."

"Listen. I got horribly tired of him after a week or so, but I'd promised to help him and I didn't break with him; but yesterday I just couldn't stand him any longer and I told him so, and sent him away. Then, this morning, an old man came to the house, a man named Pryor, who knew him and knew his record, and he told me all about him." She narrated the interview.

"But you had sent Corliss away first?" Wade asked, sharply.

"Yesterday, I tell you." She set her hand on the little man's shoulder. "Wade, there's bound to be a scandal over all this. Even if Corliss gets away without being arrested and tried, the whole thing's bound to come *out*. I'll be the laughing-stock of the town — and I deserve to be: it's all through having been ridiculous idiot enough to try and impress you with my business brilliancy. Well, I can't stand it!"

"Cora, do you ——" He faltered.

She leaned toward him, her hand still on his shoulder, her exquisite voice lowered, and thrilling in its sweetness. "Wade, I'm through playing. I've come to you at last because you've utterly conquered me. If you'll take me away to-day, I'll *marry* you to-day!"

He gave a shout that rang again from the walls.

"Do you want me?" she whispered; then smiled upon his rapture indulgently.

Rapture it was. With the word "marry," his incredulity sped forever. But for a time he was incoherent: he leaped and hopped, spoke broken bits of words, danced fragmentarily, ate her with his eyes, partially embraced her, and finally kissed her timidly.

"Such a wedding we'll have!" he shouted, after that.

"No!" she said sharply. "We'll be married by a Justice of the Peace and not a soul there but us, and it will be now, or it never will be! If you don't ——"

He swore she should have her way.

"Then we'll be out of this town on the three o'clock train this afternoon," she said. She went on with her plans, while he, growing more accustomed to his privilege, caressed her as he would. "You shall have your way," she said, "in everything except the wedding-journey. That's got to be a long one — I won't come back here till people have forgotten all about this Corliss mix-up. I've never been abroad, and I want you to take me. We can stay a long, long time. I've brought nothing — we'll get whatever we want in New York before we sail."

He agreed to everything. He had never really hoped to win her; paradise had opened, dazing him with glory: he was astounded, mad with joy, and abjectly his lady's servant.

"Hadn't you better run along and get the license?" she laughed. "We'll have to be married on the way to the train."

"Cora!" he gasped. "You angel!"

"I'll wait here for you," she smiled. "There won't be too much time."

He obtained a moderate control of his voice and feet. "Enfield — that's my cashier — he'll be back from his lunch at one-thirty. Tell him about us, if I'm not here by then. Tell him he's got to manage somehow. Good-bye till I come back — Mrs. Trumble!"

At the door he turned. "Oh, have you — you ——" He paused uncertainly. "Have you sent Richard Lindley any word about ——"

"Wade!" She gave his inquiry an indulgent amusement. "If I'm not worrying about him, do you think you need to?"

"I meant about ——"

"You funny thing," she said. "I never had any idea of really marrying him; it wasn't anything but one of those silly half-engagements, and ——"

"I didn't mean that," he said, apologetically. "I meant about letting him know what this Pryor told you about Corliss, so that Richard might do something toward getting his money back. We ought to ——"

"Oh, yes," she said quickly. "Yes, that's all right."

"You saw Richard?"

"No. I sent him a note. He knows all about it by this time, if he has been home this morning. You'd better start, Wade. Send a messenger to our house for my bag. Tell him to bring it here and then take a note for me. You'd really better start — dear!"

"*Cora!*" he shouted, took her in his arms, and was gone. His departing gait down the corridor to the elevator seemed, from the sounds, to be a gallop.

Left alone, Cora wrote, sealed, and directed a note to Laura. In it she recounted what Pryor had told her of Corliss; begged Laura and her parents not to think her heartless in not preparing them for this abrupt marriage. She was in such a state of nervousness, she wrote, that explanations would have caused a breakdown. The marriage was a sensible one; she had long contemplated it as a possibility; and, after thinking it over thoroughly, she had decided it was the only thing to do. She sent her undying love.

She was sitting with this note in her hand when shuffling footsteps sounded in the corridor; either Wade's cashier or the messenger, she supposed. The door-knob turned, a husky voice asking, "Want a drink?" as the door opened.

Cora was not surprised — she knew Vilas's office was across the hall from that in which she waited — but she was frightened.

Ray stood blinking at her.

"What are you doing here?" he asked, at last.

CHAPTER TWENTY-THREE

IT IS probable that he got the truth out of her — perhaps all of it. That will remain a matter of doubt; Cora's evidence, if she gave it, not being wholly trustworthy in cases touching herself. But she felt no need of mentioning to any one that she had seen her former lover that day. He had gone before the return of Enfield, Mr. Trumble's assistant, who was a little later than usual, it happened; and the extreme nervousness and preoccupation exhibited by Cora in telling Enfield of his employer's new plans were attributed by the cashier to the natural agitation of a lady about to wed in a somewhat unusual (though sensible) manner.

It is the more probable that she told Ray the whole truth, because he already knew something of Corliss's record abroad. On the dusty desk in Ray's own office lay a letter, received that morning from the American Consul at Naples, which was luminous upon that subject, and upon the probabilities of financial returns for the investment of a thousand dollars in the alleged oil-fields of Basilicata.

In addition, Cora had always found it very difficult to deceive Vilas: he had an almost perfect understanding of a part of her nature; she could never far mislead him about herself. With her, he was intuitive and jumped to strange, inconsistent, true conclusions, as women do. He had the art of reading her face, her gestures; he had learned to listen to the tone of her voice more than to what she said. In his cups, too, he had fitful but almost demoniac inspirations for hidden truth.

And, remembering that Cora always "got even," it remains finally to wonder if she might not have told him everything at the instance of some shadowy impulse in that direction. There may have been a luxury in whatever confession she made; perhaps it was not entirely forced from her, and heaven knows how she may have coloured it. There was an elusive, quiet satisfaction somewhere in her subsequent expression; it lurked deep under the surface of the excitement with which she talked to Enfield of her imminent marital abduction of his small boss.

Her agitation, a relic of the unknown interview just past, simmered down soon, leaving her in a becoming glow of colour, with slender threads of moisture brilliantly outlining her eyelids. Mr. Enfield, a young, well-favoured and recent importation from another town, was deliciously impressed by the charm of the waiting lady. They had not met; and Enfield wondered how Trumble had compassed such an enormous success as this; and he wished that he had seen her before matters had gone so far. He thought he might have had a chance. She seemed pleasantly interested in him, even as it was — and her eyes were wonderful, with their swift, warm, direct little plunges into those of a chance comrade of the moment. She went to the window, in her restlessness, looking down upon the swarming street below, and the young man, standing beside her, felt her shoulder most pleasantly — though very lightly — in contact with his own, as they leaned forward, the better to see some curiosity of advertising that passed. She turned her face to his just then, and told him that he must come to see her: the wedding journey would be long, she said, but it would not be forever.

Trumble bounded in, shouting that everything was attended to, except instructions to Enfield, whom he pounded wildly upon the back. He began signing papers; a stenographer was called from another room of his offices; and there was half an hour of rapid-fire. Cora's bag came, and she gave the bearer the note for Laura; another bag was brought for Wade; and both bags were carried down to the automobile the bridegroom had left waiting in the street. Last, came a splendid cluster of orchids for the bride to wear, and then Wade, with his arm about her, swept her into the corridor, and the stirred Enfield was left to his own beating heart, and the fresh, radiant vision of this startling new acquaintance: the sweet mystery of the look she had thrown back at him over his employer's shoulder at the very last. "Do not forget *me!*" it had seemed to say. "We shall come back — some day."

The closed car bore the pair to the little grim marriage-shop quickly enough, though they were nearly run down by a furious police patrol automobile, at a corner near the Richfield Hotel. Their escape was by a very narrow margin of safety, and Cora closed her eyes. Then she was cross, because she had been frightened, and commanded Wade cavalierly to bid the driver be more careful.

Wade obeyed sympathetically. "Of course, though, it wasn't altogether his fault," he said, settling back, his arm round his lady's waist. "It's an outrage for the police to break their own rules that way. I guess they don't need to be in a hurry any more than *we* do!"

The Justice made short work of it.

As they stood so briefly before him, there swept across her vision the memory of what she had always prophesied as her wedding:—a crowded church, "The Light That Breathed O'er Eden" from an unseen singer; then the warm air trembling to the Lohengrin march; all heads turning; the procession down the aisle; herself appearing — climax of everything — a delicious and brilliant figure: graceful, rosy, shy, an imperial prize for the groom, who in these foreshadowings had always been very indistinct. The picture had always failed in outline there: the bridegroom's nearest approach to definition had never been clearer than a composite photograph. The truth is, Cora never in her life wished to be married.

But she was.

CHAPTER TWENTY-FOUR

VALENTINE CORLISS had nothing to do but to wait for the money his friend Antonio would send him by cable. His own cable, anticipating his letter, had been sent yesterday, when he came back to the hotel, after lunching in the country with Cora.

As he walked down Corliss Street, after his tumultuous interview with her, he was surprised to find himself physically tremulous: he had not supposed that an encounter, however violent, with an angry woman could so upset his nerves. It was no fear of Pryor which shook him. He knew that Pryor did not mean to cause his arrest — certainly not immediately. Of course, Pryor knew that Cora would tell him. The old fellow's move was a final notification. It meant: "Get out of town within twenty-four hours." And Corliss intended to obey. He would have left that evening, indeed, without the warning; his trunk was packed.

He would miss Cora. He had kept a cool head

throughout their affair until the last; but this morning she had fascinated him: and he found himself passionately admiring the fury of her. She had confused him as he had never been confused. He thought he had tamed her; thought he owned her; and the discovery of this mistake was what made him regret that she would not come away with him. Such a flight, until to-day, had been one of his apprehensions: but now the thought that it was not to be, brought something like pain. At least, he felt a vacancy; had a sense of something lacking. She would have been a bright comrade for the voyage; and he thought of gestures of hers, turns of the head, tricks of the lovely voice; and sighed.

Of course it was best for him that he could return to his old trails alone and free; he saw that. Cora would have been a complication and an embarrassment without predictable end, but she would have been a rare flame for a while. He wondered what she meant to do; of course she had a plan. Should he try again, give her another chance? No; there was one point upon which she had not mystified him: he knew she really hated him.

. . . The wind was against the smoke that day; and his spirits rose, as he walked in the brisk air with the rich sky above him. After all, this venture upon his native purlieus had been far from fruitless: he could not have expected to do much better. He had made his *coup*; he knew no other who could have done it. It was a handsome bit of work, in fact, and possible only to a talented native thoroughly sophisticated in certain foreign subtleties. He knew himself for a rare combination.

He had a glimmer of Richard Lindley beginning at the beginning again to build a modest fortune: it was the sort of thing the Richard Lindleys were made for. Corliss was not troubled. Richard had disliked him as a boy; did not like him now; but Corliss had not taken his money out of malice for that. The adventurer was not revengeful; he was merely impervious.

At the hotel, he learned that Moliterno's cable had not yet arrived; but he went to an agency of one of the steamship lines and reserved his passage, and to a railway ticket office and secured a compartment for himself on an evening train. Then he returned to his room in the hotel.

The mirror over the mantelpiece, in the front room of his suite, showed him a fine figure of a man: hale, deep-chested, handsome, straight and cheerful.

He nodded to it.

"Well, old top," he said, reviewing and summing up his whole campaign, "not so bad. Not so bad, all in all; not so bad, old top. Well played indeed!"

At a sound of footsteps approaching his door, he turned in casual expectancy, thinking it might be a boy to notify him that Moliterno's cable had arrived. But there was no knock, and the door was flung wide open.

It was Vilas, and he had his gun with him this time. He had two.

There was a shallow clothes-closet in the wall near the fireplace, and Corliss ran in there; but Vilas began to shoot through the door.

Mutilated, already a dead man, and knowing it, Corliss came out, and tried to run into the bedroom. It was no use.

Ray saved his last shot for himself. It did the work.

CHAPTER TWENTY-FIVE

THERE is a song of parting, an intentionally pathetic song, which contains the line, "All the to-morrows shall be as to-day," meaning equally gloomy. Young singers, loving this line, take care to pronounce the words with unusual distinctness: the listener may feel that the performer has the capacity for great and consistent suffering. It is not, of course, that youth loves unhappiness, but the appearance of it, its supposed picturesqueness. Youth runs from what is pathetic, but hangs fondly upon pathos. It is the idea of sorrow, not sorrow, which charms: and so the young singer dwells upon those lingering to-morrows, happy in the conception of a permanent wretchedness incurred in the interest of sentiment. For youth believes in permanence.

It is when we are young that we say, "I shall never," and "I shall always," not knowing that we are only time's atoms in a crucible of incredible change. An old man scarce dares say, "I have never," for he knows that if he searches he will find, probably, that he has. "All, all is change."

It was an evening during the winter holidays when Mrs. Lindley, coming to sit by the fire in her son's smoking-room, where Richard sat glooming, narrated her legend of the Devil of Lisieux. It must have been her legend: the people of Lisieux know nothing of it; but this Richard the Guileless took it for tradition, as she alleged it, and had no suspicion that she had spent the afternoon inventing it.

She did not begin the recital immediately upon taking her chair, across the hearth from her son; she led up to it. She was an ample, fresh-coloured, lively woman; and like her son only in being a kind soul: he got neither his mortal seriousness nor his dreaminess from her. She was more than content with Cora's abandonment of him, though, as chivalrousness was not demanded of her, she would have preferred that he should have been the jilt. She thought Richard well off in his release, even at the price of all his savings. But there was something to hope, even in that matter, Pryor wrote from Paris encouragingly: he believed that Moliterno might be frightened or forced into at least a partial restitution; though Richard would not count upon it, and had "begun at the beginning" again, as a small-salaried clerk in a bank, trudging patiently to work in the morning and home in the evening, a long-faced, tired young man, more absent than ever, lifeless, and with no interest in anything outside his own broodings. His mother, pleased with his misfortune in love, was of course troubled that it should cause him to suffer. She knew she could not heal him; but she also knew that everything is healed in time, and that sometimes it is possible for people to help time a little.

Her first remark to her son, this evening, was that to the best of her memory she had never used the word "hellion." And, upon his saying gently, no, he thought it probable that she never had, but seeking no farther and dropping his eyes to the burning wood, apparently under the impression that the subject was closed, she informed him brusquely that it was her intention to say it now.

"What is it you want to say, mother?"

"If I can bring myself to use the word 'hellion'," she returned, "I'm going to say that of all the heaven-born, whole-souled and consistent ones I ever knew Hedrick Madison is the King."

"In what new way?" he inquired.

"Egerton Villard. Egerton used to be the neatest, best-mannered, best-dressed boy in town; but he looks and behaves like a Digger Indian since he's taken to following Hedrick around. Mrs. Villard says it's the greatest sorrow of her life, but she's quite powerless: the boy is Hedrick's slave. The other day she sent a servant after him, and just bringing him home nearly ruined her limousine. He was solidly covered with molasses, over his clothes and all, from head to foot, and then he'd rolled in hay and chicken feathers to be a *gnu* for Hedrick to kodak in the African Wilds of the Madisons' stable. Egerton didn't know what a gnu was, but Hedrick told him that was the way to be one, he said. Then, when they'd got him scraped and boiled, and most of his hair pulled out, a policemen came to arrest him for stealing the jug of molasses at a corner grocery."

Richard nodded, and smiled faintly for comment. They sat in silence for a while.

"I saw Mrs. Madison yesterday," said his mother. "She seemed very cheerful; her husband is able to talk almost perfectly again, though he doesn't get downstairs. Laura reads to him a great deal."

He nodded again, his gaze not moving from the fire.

"Laura was with her mother," said Mrs. Lindley. "She looked very fetching in a black cloth suit and a fur hat — old ones her sister left, I suspect, but very becoming, for all that. Laura's 'going out' more than usual this winter. She's really the belle of the holiday dances, I hear. Of course she would be," she added, thoughtfully — "now."

"Why should she be 'now' more than before?"

"Oh, Laura's quite blossomed," Mrs. Lindley answered. "I think she's had some great anxieties relieved. Of course both she and her mother must have worried about Cora as much as they waited on her. It must be a great burden lifted to have her comfortably settled, or, at least, disposed of. I thought they both looked better. But I have a special theory about Laura: I suppose you'll laugh at me —— "

"Oh, no."

"I wish you would sometimes," she said wistfully, "so only you laughed. My idea is that Laura was in love with that poor little Trumble, too."

"What?" He looked up at that.

"Yes; girls fall in love with anybody. I fancy

she cared very deeply for him; but I think she's a strong, sane woman, now. She's about the steadiest, coolest person I know — and I know her better, lately, than I used to. I think she made up her mind that she'd not sit down and mope over her unhappiness, and that she'd get over what caused it; and she took the very best remedy: she began going about, going everywhere, and she went gayly, too! And I'm sure she's cured; I'm sure she doesn't care the snap of her fingers for Wade Trumble or any man alive. She's having a pretty good time, I imagine: she has everything in the world except money, and she's never cared at all about *that*. She's young, and she dresses well — these days — and she's one of the handsomest girls in town; she plays like a poet, and she dances well —— "

"Yes," said Richard; — reflectively, "she does dance well."

"And from what I hear from Mrs. Villard," continued his mother, "I guess she has enough young men in love with her to keep any girl busy."

He was interested enough to show some surprise. "In love with Laura?"

"Four, I hear." The best of women are sometimes the readiest with impromptu statistics.

"Well, well!" he said, mildly.

"You see, Laura has taken to smiling on the world, and the world smiles back at her. It's not a bad world about that, Richard."

"No," he sighed. "I suppose not."

"But there's more than that in this case, my dear son."

"Is there?"

The intelligent and gentle matron laughed as though at some unexpected turn of memory and said:

"Speaking of Hedrick, did you ever hear the story of the Devil of Lisieux, Richard?"

"I think not; at least, I don't remember it."

"Lisieux is a little town in Normandy," she said. "I was there a few days with your father, one summer, long ago. It's a country full of old stories, folklore, and traditions; and the people still believe in the Old Scratch pretty literally. This legend was of the time when he came to Lisieux. The people knew he was coming because a wise woman had said that he was on the way, and predicted that he would arrive at the time of the great fair. Everybody was in great distress, because they knew that whoever looked at him would become bewitched, but, of course, they had to go to the fair. The wise woman was able to give them a little comfort; she said some one was coming with the devil, and that the people must not notice the devil, but keep their eyes fastened on this other — then they would be free of the fiend's influence. But, when the devil arrived at the fair, nobody even looked to see who his companion was, for the devil was so picturesque, so vivid, all in flaming scarlet and orange, and he capered and danced and sang so that nobody could help looking at him — and, after looking once, they couldn't look away until they were thoroughly under his spell. So they were all bewitched, and began to scream and howl and roll on the ground, and turn on each other and brawl, and 'commit all manner of excesses.' Then the wise woman was able to exorcise the devil, and he sank into the ground; but his companion stayed, and the people came to their senses, and looked, and they saw that it was an angel. The angel had been there all the time that the fiend was, of course. So they have a saying now, that there may be angels with us, but we don't notice them when the devil's about."

She did not look at her son as she finished, and she had hurried through the latter part of her

"Poor Cinderella!"

"legend" with increasing timidity. The parallel was more severe, now that she put it to him, than she intended; it sounded savage; and she feared she had overshot her mark. Laura, of course, was the "other," the companion; she had been actually a companion for the vivid sister, everywhere with her at the fair, and never considered: now she emerged from her overshadowed obscurity, and people were able to see her as an individual — heretofore she had been merely the retinue of a flaming Cora. But the "legend" was not very gallant to Cora!

Mrs. Lindley knew that it hurt her son; she felt it without looking at him, and before he gave a sign. As it was, he did not speak, but, after a few moments, rose and went quietly out of the room: then she heard the front door open and close. She sat by his fire a long, long time and was sorry — and wondered.

When Richard came home from his cold night-prowl in the snowy streets, he found a sheet of note paper upon his pillow:

"Dearest Richard, I didn't mean that anybody you ever cared for was a d — l. I only meant that often the world finds out that there are lovely people it hasn't noticed."

. . . He reproached himself, then, for the reproach his leaving her had been; he had a susceptible and annoying conscience, this unfortunate Richard. He found it hard to get to sleep, that night; and was kept awake long after he had planned how he would make up to his mother for having received her "legend" so freezingly. What kept him awake, after that, was a dim, rhythmic sound coming from the house next door, where a holiday dance was in progress — music far away and slender: fiddle, 'cello, horn, bassoon, drums, all rollicking away almost the night-long, seeping through the walls to his restless pillow. Finally, when belated drowsiness came, the throbbing tunes mingled with his half-dreams, and he heard the light shuffling of multitudinous feet over the dancing-floor, and became certain that Laura's were among them. He saw her, gliding, swinging, laughing, and happy — and the picture did not please him: it seemed to him that she would have been much better employed sitting in black to write of a hopeless love. Coquetting with four suitors was not only inconsistent; it was unbecoming. It "suited Cora's style," but in Laura it was outrageous. When he woke, in the morning, he was dreaming of her: dressed as Parthenia, beautiful, and throwing roses to an acclaiming crowd through which she was borne on a shield upon the shoulders of four Antinouses. Richard thought it scandalous.

His indignation with her had not worn off when he descended to breakfast, but he made up to his mother for having troubled her. Then, to cap his gallantry, he observed that several inches of snow must have fallen during the night; it would be well packed upon the streets by noon; he would get a sleigh, after lunch, and take her driving. It was a holiday.

She thanked him, but half-declined. "I'm afraid it's too cold for me, but there are lots of nice girls in town, Richard, who won't mind weather."

"But I asked *you!*" It was finally left an open question for the afternoon to settle; and, upon her urging, he went out for a walk. She stood at the window to watch him, and, when she saw that he turned northward, she sank into a chair, instead of going to give Joe Varden his after-breakfast instructions, and fell into a deep reverie.

Outdoors, it was a biting cold morning, wind-swept and gray; and with air so frosty-pure no one might breathe it and stay bilious; neither in body nor bilious in spirit. It was a wind to sweep the yellow from jaundiced cheeks and make them rosy; a wind to clear dulled eyes; it was a wind to lift foolish hearts, to lift them so high they might touch heaven and go winging down the sky, the wildest of wild-geese.

. . . When the bell rang, Laura was kneeling before the library fire, which she had just kindled, and she had not risen when Sarah brought Richard to the doorway. She was shabby enough, poor Cinderella! looking up, so frightened, when her prince appeared.

She had not been to the dance.

She had not four suitors. She had none.

He came toward her. She rose and stepped back a little. Ashes had blown upon her, and, oh, the old, old thought of the woman born to be a mother! she was afraid his clothes might get dusty if he came too close.

But to Richard she looked very beautiful; and a strange thing happened: trembling, he saw that the firelight upon her face was brighter than any firelight he had ever seen.

THE END

RICHARD BIDDLE

A

MEMOIR

OF

SEBASTIAN CABOT;

The inscription on the portrait reads as follows:

"Effigies Seb. Caboti Angli, filii Johannis Caboti Veneti Militis Aurati, Primi Inventoris Terræ Novæ sub Henrico VII. Angliæ Rege."

PORTRAIT OF SEBASTIAN CABOT

From a copy of the original portrait purchased by Richard Biddle (author of this Memoir) from the heirs of Charles Joseph Harford of Bristol, England.

In the great fire at Pittsburgh in 1845, Mr. Biddle's Library and with it the "Harford picture" were completely destroyed. Fortunately two copies of the Cabot portrait had been already made. One in 1838 by John G. Chapman with Mr. Biddle's permission for the Massachusetts Historical Society, and another in 1841, with like permission, by Cephas G. Thompson for the New York Historical Society. It is from the latter copy that the illustration for this book has been made.

RICHARD BIDDLE

A

MEMOIR

OF

SEBASTIAN CABOT;

WITH

A REVIEW

THE HISTORY OF MARITIME DISCOVERY.

ILLUSTRATED BY DOCUMENTS FROM THE ROLLS

BOOKS FOR LIBRARIES PRESS
FREEPORT, NEW YORK

First Published 1831, Reissued 1915
Reprinted 1970

STANDARD BOOK NUMBER:
8369-5211-1

LIBRARY OF CONGRESS CATALOG CARD NUMBER:
73-107793

PRINTED IN THE UNITED STATES OF AMERICA

CONTENTS.

CHAP. XXII

CHAP. XXIII.

CHAP. XXIV.

CHAP. XXV.

CHAP. XXVI.

CHAP. XXVII.

CHAP. XXVIII.

BOOK II.

APPENDIX.

PREFACE.
(TO THE 1915 EDITION)

THIS volume is a reprint from the original American Edition, published by Lea and Blanchard of Philadelphia, in the year 1831. An English Edition appeared also in London the same year and was followed by a second edition issued there in 1832. The American Edition and the *first* English Edition are precisely alike in all respects. In the second London Edition a quotation from the New Interlude No. 5 is introduced at page 77, and this additional matter will be found in an appendix printed at the back of the book.

This issue of a modern Edition of the "Memoir of Sebastian Cabot" is undertaken by the surviving son of the author in testimony of his affectionate veneration for his father's memory.

Richard Biddle, at his death in 1847, was in his fifty-first year. A son of Charles Biddle (1745–1821), Vice-President of the Supreme Executive Council of Pennsylvania when Benjamin Franklin was its President, Mr. Biddle's early associations were connected with Philadelphia, and his legal studies pursued in his native city. In the same year of his admission to the Bar, however, he removed to Pittsburgh (Pa.), where he soon became distinguished in his profession.

In a Eulogy delivered in 1847, the year of Mr.

Biddle's death, before the members of the Pittsburgh Bar, and by one of its most distinguished members, a very vivid portrayal is given of the author's career at the Bar. The qualities of his indomitable energy are dwelt upon, and one sentence in the address, as foreshadowing his labors on this Memoir, seems apt enough to quote:—"his mind was of great power and his energy was invincible—no prospect of severe and interminable labor made him hesitate or falter."

After ten years of active professional life, he went abroad in 1828 and settled himself in London. Here he continued a diligent student, frequenting the Courts and Libraries. Just how he was led to undertake the farther voyage—for such it proved itself—into those unfathomed depths of legend and fact surrounding at that time the careers of the Cabots, it may not be possible to determine. In his own preface Mr. Biddle draws attention to some very loose and inaccurate statements appearing just then in a new Edition of the "Biographie Universelle." It is entirely possible that the erroneous and slighting remarks upon the voyages of the Cabots to which he adverts may have been the inducing cause for the exhaustive researches he undertook, lasting several years, and resulting in what has been recognized on high modern authority "as the best review of the history of maritime discovery relating to the period of which it treats that had appeared." (Deane (Charles), Voyages of the Cabots.)

The book on its appearance made a deep impression, and although published anonymously its authorship was no secret. From many reviews and notices of it that appeared at the time in English, French, Italian and American publications, we select and give excerpts from those published in the London Westminster Review, and in the North-American Review in this country.

In its issue of January, 1832, the Westminster Review remarks:

"This book is a phenomenon among the productions of the day, for various reasons—first, it is not a catch-penny, next it is written with the motive of discovering truth; again it is the result of hard labor, and acute investigation among the really original authorities; it is not written for money; it springs from studies, of such accuracy and minuteness as no ordinary pecuniary reward could pay. Again its title-page is much less comprehensive than the volume and altogether from these and other causes it forms a glorious exception from the poor and paltry spirit which actuates nine publications out of ten of those that load the counters of the modern book-seller. . . . The author of this volume is an American, he does honor to his country, and we cannot but take kindly the interest he has shown in vindicating for England the parentage of the land of his birth."

Quoting from the North-American Review of January, 1832:

"The author has well kept the honorable promise (contained in Preface) which he has thus virtually made. He never points out an error where he is not able to substitute the truth, and never sets up a theory or conjecture till he has a solid foundation of fact for it to rest upon . . . He seems perfectly acquainted with the contents of many rare and curious books of reference, the very titles of which are probably new to ninety-nine out of a hundred of his readers. . . . He has dragged into light manuscripts with the mould of centuries upon them, and forced them to give their tardy testimony in favor of the truth. . . . Nothing escapes his acuteness and penetration. . . . The book is indeed unrivalled in its way and is well worth the attentive study of a young lawyer as a model for a learned, acute and profound argument upon certain obscure and disputed points of history, which admits nothing that is irrelevant and rejects nothing that is important, and by which a cause that looks desperate at first is so triumphantly supported, that we wonder how the contrary impression could ever have prevailed." . . .

It is not claiming too much to say that Richard Biddle's "Memoir of Sebastian Cabot" was the pioneer in the work of investigation and verification that has resulted in the mass of literature issued since on the early voyages of the Cabots. His discovery among the Manuscripts in the Public Record Office, London, of the text of Henry VII's second letters patent, and his distinguishing thereby for the first time that there were *two* Cabot voyages, in 1497 and 1498, was an immense contribution to the subject. In fact Mr. G. P. Winship, in his exhaustive treatise on the literature of the Cabot Voyages, sums up his notes on Mr. Biddle's Memoir by saying that "The strictly historical investigation into the careers of the Cabots dates from the appearance of Mr. Biddle's volume."

In a preface to "John and Sebastian Cabot" by C. Raymond Beazley, Fellow of Merton College, Oxford, appearing in 1898, the author in noting the changes of opinion in Europe and America on certain points of history, leads off by saying, "Since the modern Cabot literature began with the appearance of R. Biddle's (American) Memoir in 1831." . . . Not a work on the Cabots but contains references to the Biddle Memoir (Harrisse has 36 references), and a note in Winship's Cabot Bibliography mentions that an account of Cabot by *Errizo*, appearing at Venice in 1855, "*is largely drawn from Biddle.*"

Mr. Biddle returned to Pittsburgh in 1832, after an absence of four years, and reëngaged in the practice of the law. In 1837 he was elected to Congress, and went to Washington the year following to attend its sessions. Mr. David Ritchie, when speaking of his election in the Eulogium referred to at the beginning of this notice, says: "No man was ever elected to that place with less intrigue or management or personal interference. He had earned such a position in this community (Pittsburgh) that the people desired his services and sent him to Congress without any solicitation on his part. . . . He had not been long in the house of representatives till his position was of the highest." He was reëlected in 1838, and served in the first session of '39 and '40, but in this year resigned "to the very great regret of his constituents, to whom his services gave almost universal satisfaction."

On the 17th of June, 1844, he was married to Ann Eliza Anderson, eldest daughter of John Anderson of Pittsburgh. This lady survived him many years, and passed the latter portion of her life in Philadelphia, although finally removing to her daughter's house in Pittsburgh, where she died May 6th, 1908.

Two children were born of this marriage: a son, Richard, now a resident of Tennessee, and a daughter, Grace, lately deceased, who married the Rev. J. Hall McIlvaine.

EDWARD BIDDLE.

December, 1915.

CORRECTION

In a Note at foot of page 79, a printed nought should clearly have been the figure 9—Thus for "10th August, 1407," read "10th August, 1497. To hym that found the New Isle, *10l.*"

RICHARD BIDDLE (1796–1847)
Author of a Memoir of Sebastian Cabot.

From the portrait by Thomas Sully, painted in 1821.

INTRODUCTION.

The following pages lay claim to the share of merit that may be due to a spirit of diligent research which took nothing at second hand where an original writer, or document, could be consulted, and would not be turned aside, by any authority, from the anxious pursuit, and resolute vindication, of the Truth. They are offered, therefore, with the confidence inspired by a consciousness of good faith. Yet the author is sufficiently aware that the public has nothing to do with the integrity of his purpose, or the patient industry with which it has been followed up, except so far as a valuable result may have been achieved.

What is now submitted made part, originally, of a much more extensive plan. But there was found, at every turn, so much to clear up, and the materials for rectification so multiplied, that it seemed impossible to treat the subject satisfactorily without giving to it, in connexion with any other, a cumbrous and disproportioned air. To hazard assertions, and to venture on the requisite plainness of criticism, without producing the evidence which justified a departure from received opinions could have effected no good purpose, and would have justly incurred the charge of presumption. Error was too deeply intrenched to permit a hope of dislodging it, unless through the regular, though tedious, forms of investment.

The author is very sensible of the dry and argumentative manner here imparted to topics which have usually been viewed, and treated, as susceptible of the highest embellishment. He can only hope that others may catch a feeling, such as gained on himself at every step, which, in the disentanglement of facts, rejects impatiently, rather than solicits, whatever does not conduce directly to the result. The mind seems to demand, with sternness, that this labour shall first be gone through, as the eye requires a solid foundation, and an assured elevation, before it can rest with complacency on the decorative acanthus.

Amidst a great deal of undeniably fine writing on the subject with which the present volume is connected, it would seem to have secured to itself less than any other of patient and anxious labour. The task of setting facts right has been regarded as an unworthy drudgery, while an ambitious effort is witnessed to throw them before the public eye in all the fantastic shapes, and deceptive colouring, of error. Gibbon remarks of Tillemont, that his inimitable Accuracy "*almost* assumes the character of Genius." Many writers of the present day seem to have constantly in view the tendency of the public mind to a classification of powers, and to dread lest any remarkable display of the quality in question, might be artfully seized on as characteristic, and thus prejudice their claims to the highest honours of authorship.

A new and urgent motive may be suggested for endeavouring to clear up, as speedily as possible, the confusion which has hence been suffered to gather round the best established facts, and left their recognition or denial at the mercy of chance or caprice. While a salutary jealousy of extensive Combinations, in the Political World, distinguishes the present age, there has been organised in that of Letters, almost unobserved in this country, a confederacy which has gradually drawn to itself, and skilfully consolidated, a power that may now be pronounced truly formidable. It has already begun to speak out plainly the language of dictation. The great literary achievement of modern France—the "*Biographie Universelle*"—is at length brought to a close, completing by the fifty-second volume its triumph over the alphabet. It is a work destined, unquestionably, to exercise an important influence over the Rights of the Dead of all Nations. When it stated that the list of contributors contains the names of more than three hundred writers of the highest literary eminence in France, from the year 1810, when the first volume appeared, to the present time, that every article is accompanied by the name of the author to whom it had been assigned in reference to his habitual studies, and that not a line appeared without having been previously submitted to several contributors in succession, it must be obvious that the character of such a work is matter of deep and universal interest.

A Supplement is announced, in which notice will be taken of any inaccuracy, after which doubt and controversy must cease.

"Les assertions ou les faits qu'on n'y pas rectifiés ou démentis devront par ce moyen etre regardés comme à peu-près incontestables et sans réplique."

Thus The Dead, of the most remote age, are summoned to appear before this tribunal, and a charge is to be taken for confessed, unless an Answer be put in before the period (which yet is left indefinite) when the Supplement shall go to press. We may smile at this sally of self-importance, but ought not to forget that the authority of these volumes, whether for good or evil, will unquestionably be extensive and commanding. Facts, and with them reputation, cannot, it is true, be irrevocably stereotyped; yet a perilous circulation may be given to the erroneous version, and a work which will influence, directly or indirectly, a majority of those whose opinions constitute fame, it were idle to treat with contempt, and unjust not to attempt to rectify, where its statements disparage a national benefactor.

It must be conceded that an omission of names cannot fairly be laid to the charge of the Biographie Universelle. The stream of time has been dragged with humane perseverance, and many who, it was supposed, had sunk to rise no more, are made to reappear at the surface. As to the more important question, how far, there are manifested, in general, extent and accuracy of knowledge, and skill in its display, it might be unjust to offer an opinion without going into much greater detail than is here practicable. But it is quite fair to assert that the many shameful marks of haste, heedlessness and gross ignorance which it falls within the present limited inquiry to expose—and more particularly in bibliography which is the subject of especial vaunt —may suffice to show how idle must be considered its claim to infallibility, even after the appearance of the Supplement. In the article devoted to the subject of the present Memoir, the generous conclusion is announced, after a tissue of errors, that although no evidence exists to establish the scene of his discoveries, yet they ought not to be deemed altogether fabulous, as some historians would represent ("comme fabuleuses ainsi que quelques historiens ont été tentes de le penser"). An effort is now made finally to secure his fame from the effects of either carelessness or malevolence.

BOOK I.

CHAP. I.

THE HIGHEST NORTHERN LATITUDE REACHED BY CABOT—AUTHORITIES COLLECTED BY HAKLUYT—ATTEMPT TO EXPLAIN THEIR SUPPOSED DISCREPANCE.

WITH a view to greater clearness, it is proposed to attempt, in the first instance, the settlement of certain points around which confusion has been suffered to gather, and which, demanding only a careful examination of authorities, may be advantageously considered apart from the narrative.

The first question—as one affecting materially the claim of Cabot to the character of an intrepid navigator—is as to the point to which he urged his way in the north, a fact with regard to which statements exist seemingly quite irreconcilable.

The volumes of Hakluyt, usually regarded as of the highest authority, are supposed to present, on this subject, a chaos which, so far from lending assistance to clear up difficulties, rather dims, and threatens every moment to extinguish, the feeble light supplied from other quarters. In the "Chronological History of Voyages into the Arctic Regions, &c. by John Barrow, F. R. S.," it is said (p. 32), "there is no *possible* way of reconciling the various accounts collected by Hakluyt, and which amount to no less a number than *six*, but by supposing John Cabot to have made one voyage at least previous to the date of the patent, and some time between that and the date of the return of Columbus." The hypothesis thus declared to be indispensable is directly at variance with the terms of the original patent, and with the language of every original writer; and an effort will, therefore, now be made to show, that the confusion complained of, does not exist in the materials for forming an opinion, but arises from the hasty and superficial manner in which they have been considered.

Taking up the accounts in the order in which they stand, they may be thus stated (Hakluyt, vol. iii. p. 6).

1. "An extract from the map of Sebastian Cabot, cut by Clement Adams, concerning his discovery of the West Indies, which is to be seen in his majesty's privy gallery, at Westminster, and in many other ancient merchants' houses." Nothing is said in this as to the latitude reached.

2. "A discourse of Sebastian Cabot," &c., wherein the narrator asserts, that he heard the pope's legate say, that *he* had heard Cabot state, that he sailed only to the 56° of latitude, and then turned about.

3. A passage in the preface to the third volume of Ramusio's Collection of Voyages. In this, the author says that in a written communication to him Sebastian Cabot stated that he reached the latitude of 67° and a half.

4. Part of the sixth chapter of the third decade of Peter Martyr d'Angleria, in which nothing is said of the latitude reached, but the fact is stated, that he proceeded so far north, that it was "in manner continually day-light."

5. The statement of Francis Lopez Gomara, who, according to Hakluyt, represents Cabot to have "sailed beyond the Cape of Labrador, until he found himself in 58° and better." Cabot is here also said to have found "the days very long, in a manner without any night, and for that short night that they had, it was very clear."

6. An extract from Robert Fabyan's Annals, and from a letter of Robert Thorn of Bristol, containing nothing as to the point under consideration.

Thus it is apparent that the discrepance exists on a comparison of the second, third and fifth items.

Postponing Gomara for the present, we pause on the two passages of Ramusio which are supposed to embody contradictory statements.

It is obvious that if the present were an inquiry in a court of justice affecting the reputation or property of a living person, the evidence which limits Cabot to 56° would be at once rejected as incompetent. The alleged communication from him is exposed, in its transmission, not only to all the chances of misconception on the part of the pope's legate, but admitting that personage to have truly understood, accurately remembered, and faithfully reported what he heard, we are again exposed to a similar series of errors on the part of our informant, who furnishes it to us at second hand. But the dead have not the benefits of the rules of evidence; and we must, therefore, look to the circumstances which affect its credibility. It appears thus in Hakluyt:—

"A discourse of Sebastian Cabot touching his discovery of part of the West India out of England in the time of king Henry the Seventh, used to Galeacius Butrigarius, the pope's legate in Spaine, and reported by the sayd legate in this sort:

"Doe you not understand, sayd he (speaking to certaine gentlemen of *Venice*), how to passe to *India* toward the North-west, as did of late a citizen of *Venice*, so valiant a man, and so well practised in all things pertaining to navigations, and the science of cosmographie, that at this present he hath not his like in *Spaine*, insomuch that for his vertues he is preferred above all other pilots that saile to the West Indies, who may not passe thither without his license, and is therefore called *Piloto Mayor*, that is, the grand pilot? And when we sayd that we knew him not, he proceeded, saying, that being certaine yeres in the city of *Sivil*, and desirous to have some knowledge of the navigations of the Spanyards, it was tolde him that there was in the city a valiant man, a Venetian borne, named *Sebastian Cabot*, who had the charge of those things, being an expert man in that science, and one that coulde make cardes for the sea with his owne hand, and that by this report, seeking his acquaintance, he found him a very gentle person, who entertained him friendly, and shewed him many things, and among other a large mappe of the world, with certaine particuler navigations, as well of the Portugals as of the Spanyards, and that he spake further unto him to this effect:

"When my father departed from *Venice*, many yeeres since, to dwell in *England*, to follow the trade of marchandises, hee tooke mee with him to the citie of *London*, while I was very yong yet having neverthelesse some knowledge of letters of humanitie, and of the sphere And when my father died in that time when newes were brought that *Don Christopher Colonus Genoese* had discovered the coasts of *India*, whereof was great talke in all the court of king Henry the Seventh, who then raigned, insomuch that all men with great admiration affirmed it to be a thing more divine than humane, to saile by the West into the East, where spices growe, by a way that was neuer knowen before, by this fame and report there increased in my heart a great flame of desire to attempt some notable thing. And understanding by reason of the sphere, that if I should saile by way of the North-west, I should by a shorter tract come into *India*, I thereupon caused the king to be advertised of my devise, who immediately commanded two caravels to bee furnished with all things appertaining to the voyage, which was as farre as I remember in the yeere 1496, in the beginning of sommer. I began therefore to saile toward the North-west, not thinking to finde any other lande than that of *Cathay*, and from thence to turn toward *India*; but after certaine dayes I found that the land ranne towards the north, which was to mee a great displeasure. Nevertheless, sayling along by the coast to see if I coulde finde any gulfe that turned, I found the land still continent to the 56 degree under our pole. And seeing that there the coast turned toward the East, despairing to finde the passage, I turned backe againe, and sailed downe by the coast of that land toward the equinoctiall (ever with intent to finde the said passage to *India*), and came to that part of this firme lande which is now called *Florida*, where my victuals failing, I departed from thence and returned into *England*, where I found great tumults among the people, and preparation for warres in Scotland; by reason whereof there was no more consideration had to this voyage.

"Whereupon I went into *Spaine* to the Catholique King, and Queene *Elizabeth*, which being advertised what I had done, entertained me, and at their charges furnished certaine ships, wherewith they caused me to saile to discover the coastes of Brasile, where I found an exceeding great and large river, named at this present *Rio de la Plata*, that is, the river of silver, into the which I sailed and followed it into the firme land, more then six score leagues, finding it every where very faire, and inhabited with infinite people, which with admiration came running dayly to our ships. Into this river runne so many other rivers, that it is in maner incredible.

"After this I made many other voyages, which I nowe pretermit, and waxing olde, I give myself to rest from such travels, because there are nowe many yong and lustie pilots and mariners of good experience, by whose forwardnesse I doe rejoyce in the fruit of my labours, and rest with the charge of this office, as you see."

In giving this conversation to his readers, Hakluyt professes to have derived it from the second volume of Ramusio, and subsequent compilers have assumed the accuracy of the reference. It seems, for the first time, to have occurred to the writers of the "Biographie Universelle," to look into the original, and they declare that no such passage is to be there found!

"Hakluyt dans sa collection nous a transmis la piece ou l'on trouve le plus de details sur la navigation et la vie de Sebastian Cabot. Il dit l'avoir tirée du second volume de la collection de Ramusio; mais *nous l'y avons cherchée en vain.* Cette piece est attribuée a Galearius Butrigarius légât du pape en Espagne qui dit tenir les particularités qu'elle contient d'un habitant de *Cadiz* lequel avait eu plusieurs conversations avec Sebastian." "Ramusio, connu par son exactitude n'a donné *aucun* extrait des navigations de Sebastian Cabot; *il se contente* de citer dans la preface de son 3e volume un passage d'une Lettre qu'il avoit reçue de lui.

A striking proof here occurs of the facility with which errors are fallen into in reporting even the written expressions of another when memory is relied on. The *Collaborateurs* of the Biographie Universelle are supposed to have just turned from the page of Hakluyt, and yet, in this brief statement, mark the changes! Butrigarius has no longer the conversation with Cabot, but gets his information at second hand, and this, too, from an inhabitant of Cadiz; thus utterly confounding both place and person, and making, also, the communication to have been the result of "many" conversations held with Cabot by this new member of the *dramatis personæ*, the "habitant de Cadiz." All this too, from those who bitterly denounce their predecessors for carelessness and inaccuracy!

But we have a yet more serious complaint to urge. When the charge is preferred against Hakluyt, of having made a fraudulent citation, we may be permitted to say, with some plainness, that after the lofty eulogium passed on Ramusio, by the associates of the Biographie Universelle, not only incidentally here, but in the article subsequently devoted to him, it is to the last degree discreditable, that a mere mistake of reference to the proper *Volume*, should have so completely baffled their knowledge of the work. Nor is the mention of Cabot confined, as they suppose, to the preface of the third volume: it occurs in five different places, as will be hereafter shown.

The passage immediately in question will be found not in the *second* but in the *first* volume of Ramusio. It is part of the interesting article entitled, "Discorso notabile sopra varii viaggi per liquali sono state condotte fino à tempi nostri le spetiarie," beginning at fol. 414. D. of the edition of 1554, and referred to in the index of all the editions under the titles

"Plata" and "Florida." Before proceeding to note the circumstances under which this conversation took place, it is proper to correct some of the errors of the translation found in Hakluyt.

And first, surprise must have been felt at the manner in which Cabot speaks as to the date of his own celebrated voyage. The "so farre as I remember" seems to indicate a strange indifference on the subject. The expression has passed into Purchas (vol. iii. p. 808), and all the subsequent authorities. In Harris's account (Voyages, vol. ii. p. 190), adopted by Pinkerton (vol. xii. p. 158), it is said, "The next voyage made for discovery was by Sebastian Cabot, the son of John; concerning which, all our writers have fallen into great mistakes, for want of comparing the several accounts we have of this voyage, and making proper allowances for the manner in which they were written, since I cannot find there was ever any distinct and clear account of this voyage published, though it was of so great consequence. On the contrary, *I believe* that Cabot himself kept no journal of it by him, since *in a letter he wrote* on this subject, he speaks *doubtfully* of the very year in which it was undertaken." The same unlucky phrase continues down to Barrow (p. 33), and to a work published during the present year (Lardner's Cyclopædia, History of Maritime Discovery, vol. ii. p. 137). North West Foxe (p. 16) had changed it to what seemed, to that critical personage, more correct, "as neere as I can remember."

Now there is not a syllable in the original to justify any such expression.

"Feci intender questo mio pensiero alla Maesta del Re il qual fu molto contento et mi armo due caravelle di tutto cio che era dibisogno *et fu del* 1496 *nel principio della state*."

It will not be understood, that we consider Cabot to have named the year 1496; but it is only important here to negative an expression which seems to argue such a looseness of feeling as to this memorable incident.

It may not be without interest to show the source of Hakluyt's error.

The first English writer on this subject is RICHARD EDEN, who published, in 1555, a black-letter volume, of which a good deal will be said hereafter, entitled, "Decades of the New World, &c." It consists of a translation of the three first Books of Peter Martyr d'Angleria, to which he has subjoined extracts from various other works of an early date on kindred subjects; and amongst the rest, this passage of Ramusio is given (fol. 251), as found in "The Italian Hystories of Navigations." Eden was, as appears from his book, a personal friend of Cabot; and when he came to the round assertion as to the date, 1496, which he knew to be incorrect, he qualified it by introducing (fol. 255) the words in question.

It is the less excusable for Hakluyt and the rest, to have blindly adopted such an interpolation, as there were other translations within reach, in which a correct and elegant version is given of the passage. The "Biographie Universelle" considers Hakluyt as first bringing it forward, but the whole is found in the celebrated Collection of De Bry, published ten years before. At the end of the second part of the *Grand Voyages*, is a cento of authorities on the subject of the discovery of America, in which the passage from Ramusio is correctly given. It is needless to say, that the "as farre as I remember" finds no place; "anno igitur 1496, in principio veris ex Anglia solvi."

Bare justice to Ramusio demands a reference to another passage in which the English translators have made him utter nonsense. The reader must have been struck with the absurd commencement of the passage in Hakluyt—"Do you not understand how to *pass to India* towards the North-West, as *did*, of late, a citizen of Venice, &c.;" after which, we are informed that this citizen of Venice abandoned the effort at 56° "despairing to find the passage!" Ramusio must not be charged with this blunder, for the original is, "Et fatto alquanti di pauso voltatosi verso di noi disse, Non sapete a questo proposito d'andare a trovar l'Indie per il vento di maestro quel che fece gia un vostro cittadino," ("and making somewhat of a pause, he turned to us and said—Do you not know, on this project of going to India by the N. W., what did formerly your fellow-citizen, &c.") not at all asserting the success of the enterprise, but only that it was suggested by the subject of the previous conversation. A correct translation is found in De Bry:—"An ignoratis inquit (erat autem sermo institutus de investiganda orientali India qua Thracias ventus flat) *quid egerit* civis quidam vester, &c."

A more material error remains to be pointed out. The speaker in Ramusio says, that finding himself some years *ago* in the City of Seville, and desiring, &c. ("che ritrovandosi gia alcuni anni nella Citta di Siviglia, et desirando, &c."); but on the page of Hakluyt this becomes, "being certain years in the City of Seville, and desiring, &c." The Latin version in De Bry is correct, "Quem ante aliquot annos invisi cum essem Hispali." The importance of the error is apparent. As truly translated the words confess the great lapse of time since the conversation, and of course the liability to error, while the erroneous version conveys only the idea of multiplied opportunities of communication, and a consequent assurance of accuracy. The same form of expression occurs in another part of the paragraph, and the meaning is so obvious, that it has not been possible to misunderstand it. When the Legate represents Cabot as stating that his father left Venice many years before the conversation, and went to settle in London to carry on the business of merchandise, the original runs thus, "partito suo padre da Venetia *gia* molti anno et andato a stare in Inghiltera a far mercantie." Again, in that passage, in the third volume, which is properly translated, "as many years past it was written unto me by Sebastian Cabot," the original is, "come mi fu scritto *gia* molti anno sono."

Having thus ascertained what is, in reality, the statement of Ramusio, we proceed to consider the circumstances under which the conversation took place. It occurs, as has been seen, in the course of a Treatise on the trade in Spices. After expatiating on the history of that trade, and the revolution caused by the discovery of the passage round the Cape of Good Hope, Ramusio says (Edit. of 1554, tom. iii. fol. 413 A.), that he cannot forbear to add a report of a conversation which he had heard at the house of his excellent friend Hieronimus Fracastor. He then proceeds to give the discourse, which is a very long one, on the subject of Cosmography, the conjectures of the ancients as to a Western World, and the discoveries which had taken place in the speaker's own time. It is only incidentally that Cabot's name is introduced, and with regard to the whole, Ramusio makes this candid prefatory remark, "Which conversation I do not pretend to be able to relate circumstantially as I heard it, for that would require a talent, and a memory beyond mine; nevertheless, I will strive briefly, and as it were by heads, to give what I am able to recollect"—("Il qual ragionamento non mi basta l'animo di poter scriver cosi particolarmente com' ie le udi, perche visaria dibisogno altro ingegno et altra memoria che non e la mia; pur mi sforzero sommariamente et come per Capi di recitar quel che io me potro ricordare.")

Now what is there to oppose to a report coming to us by a route so circuitous, and expressed at last in a manner thus hesitating? The positive and explicit information conveyed in Cabot's own letter. Nor does Ramusio confine himself to the statement contained in the Preface to his third volume, for in the same volume (fol. 417), is a discourse on the Northern Regions of the New World; in which, speaking of the Baccalaos, he says, that this region was intimately known to Sebastian Cabot, "Il quale a spese del Re Henrico VII., d' Inghiltera, scorse tutta la detta costa fino a gradi 67°. ("Who at the cost of Henry VII., king of England, proceeded along the whole of the said coast, as far as 67°.") It is plain, therefore, that the communication from Cabot had completely satisfied the mind of Ramusio, when we find him in this separate treatise assuming the fact asserted in the letter as conclusively settled.

This last consideration is strengthened by another circumstance. The passage in the third volume which refers to Cabot's letter, and which Hakluyt quotes as from the "Preface," is, in fact, part of a Discourse addressed to Hieronimus Fracastor, the very personage at whose house the conversation had taken place. Ramusio, in conveying the deliberate statement of Cabot, whose correspondent he had intermediately become, and whom he designates as "huomo di grande esperienza et raro nell' arte del navigare et nella scienza di cosmografia," does not think it necessary, even to advert to his own former representation. He is not found balancing, for a moment, between this written and direct information, and what he had before stated from a casual conversation with a third person, which had rested, for some time, insecurely, in his own confessedly bad memory, aside from the peril to which it had been subjected, before reaching him, of misconception on the part of Butrigarius, or of *his* forgetfulness during the years which elapsed between the interview with Cabot and the incidental allusion to what had passed on that occasion.

A comparison of the two passages shows further that no great importance was attached to the latitude reached; for in the latter, Ramusio is found to drop the half degree. It furnishes, too, an additional item of evidence, as to the scrupulous accuracy with which the language of the Letter is reported. In giving us that, he is exact even to the minutes; but when his eye is taken from the letter, and he is disengaged from the responsibility of a direct quotation, he slides into round numbers.

When we add, that in every fact capable of being brought to the test, the statement of the conversation is erroneous, and that the limited latitude is inconsistent with the continued day-light—a circumstance more likely to be remembered than a matter of figures—what can be more absurd, than, at the present day, to dwell on that which Ramusio himself, two hundred and seventy-five years ago, is plainly seen to abandon? Yet such has been the course pursued by every writer on the subject, and the only difference discoverable is in the shades of perversion.

To the account of the voyage to Hudson's Bay, by the Dobbs and California, drawn up by Henry Ellis, Esq., is prefixed a sketch of the previous attempts in pursuit of a North-West passage. After Ramusio's statement that Cabot reached the latitude of 67° and-a-half, the writer complacently adds, (p. 6)—

"There is an error in the latitude of ten degrees; but, however, it is plain from this account that the voyage was made for the discovery of a North-West passage, which was the reason I produced it. But *in a letter written by Sebastian Cabot himself to the Pope's Legate in Spain* (!) he gives a still clearer account of this matter, for therein he says, that it was from the consideration of the structure of the globe, the design was formed of sailing to the Indies by a North-West course. He *observes* further, that falling in with land unexpectedly (for he thought to have met with none till he had reached the coasts of Tartary), he sailed along the coast to the height of 56 degrees, and finding the land there run eastward, he quitted the attempt, and sailed southward."

Forster remarks (Northern Voyages, p. 267), "some say he went to 67° 30′ N. lat.; others reckon his most southerly track to have been to 58° N. lat. *He himself informs us*, that he reached only to 56° N. lat."

Mr Barrow (Chronological History of Voyages, &c. p. 33) says, "If there be any truth in the *report made to the pope's legate* in Spain, and printed in the collection of Ramusio," "it would appear by this *document*," &c. He then gives the conversation, not as "printed in the collection of Ramusio," for Mr Barrow could not have looked into that—but with all the absurd perversions of Hakluyt—and then, in official language, confers the title of "a Report," "a Document," on an unguarded error into which Ramusio had been betrayed, and which that honest personage hastened to correct!

The same absurd phraseology, with its train of errors, is copied into Dr Lardner's Cyclopædia (History of Maritime and Inland Discovery, vol. ii. p. 137). Foxe, who made a voyage into Hudson's Bay, in the reign of Charles I., says

(p. 13), " As concerning Sebastian Cabot, I cannot find that he was any further northward than 58°, and so returned along the land of America to the South, but for more *certainty!* hear *his own relation* to Galeatius Butrigarius, the pope's legate in Spain." After the "as neare as I can remember," &c. Foxe gravely adds, "Thus much *from himself.*"

In the "Historical Sketch of the Progress of Discovery, by William Stevenson, Esq.," which forms the eighteenth volume of Kerr's Collection of Voyages, published in 1824, it is said (p. 353), "The course he steered, and the limits of his voyage are, however, liable to uncertainty. *He himself informs us that he reached only* 56° *N. lat.*, and that the coast of America at that part tended to the east; but there is no coast of North America that answers to this description. According to *other* accounts he reached 67° and-a-half N. lat., but," &c. "It is most probable he did not reach further than Newfoundland."

It is impossible not to feel indignant at such statements from those who vie with each other in complaints of all preceding writers.

Though a matter of little moment, it may be noted that the conjecture is erroneous which connects the pope's legate, Galeatius Butrigarius, with the conversation at the house of Fracastor. Ramusio does not mention any name; withholding it, as he says, from motives of delicacy. The interview with Cabot at Seville, took place many years after his return, in 1531, from the La Plata; and the speaker, whoever he may have been, represents himself to have been led to make the call by a desire to "have some knowledge of the navigations of the Spaniards." Now, Galeatius Butrigarius, more than twenty years before this visit could have been made, is found on terms of intimacy with Peter Martyr (dec. 2. cap. 1), and not only well informed on the subject, but urging the historian to pursue his narrative, and the ensuing Decade is addressed, in consequence, to the Pope. It seems impossible that the legate so long afterwards—fifteen years, at least, subsequently to the publication of Peter Martyr's volume, describing the enterprise of Cabot—should have been actuated by this vague impulse of curiosity, and have been indebted for a knowledge of the discoverer of Baccalaos to the reports current at Seville during this his apparently first visit.

CHAP. II.

THE SUBJECT CONTINUED—GOMARA.

Of the passage in Gomara, Hakluyt presents the following version :—

"The testimonie of Francis Lopez de Gomara, a Spaniard, in the *fourth chapter* of the *second booke* of his generall history of the West Indies, concerning the first discoverie of a great part of the West Indies, to wit, from 58 to 38 degrees of latitude, by Sebastian Cabotà out of England.

"He which brought most certaine newes of the countrey and people of *Baccalaos*, (saith *Gomara*, was *Sebastian Cabote*, a Venetian, which rigged up two ships at the cost of king Henry the Seventh of England, having great desire to traffique for the spices as the Portugals did. He carried with him three hundred men, and tooke the way towards *Island* from beyond the Cape of Labrador, until he found himselfe in 58 degrees and better. He made relation, that in the moneth of July it was so cold, and the ice so great, that hee durst not passe any further: that the dayes were very long in a maner without any night, and for that short night that they had, it was very cleare. *Cabot* feeling the cold, turned towards the West, refreshing himselfe at Baccalaos; and afterwards he sailed along the coast unto 38 degrees, and from thence he shaped his course to returne into England."

There is to be noted here another of Hakluyt's loose and suspicious references. The Spanish work is not divided into "books," and the passage quoted occurs in the *first part*. This is said, after consulting the Saragossa edition of 1552—that of Medina del Campo, 1553—that of Antwerp, 1554—and the reprint of the work in Barcia's "Historiadores Primitivos" in 1749. A ready conjecture presents itself as to the source of Hakluyt's error. The work of Gomara was, at an early period, translated into French, by Fumee, in whose version, published in 1578, the matter is distributed into "Books," and the passage in question really becomes, according to his arrangement, the fourth chapter of the second Book. That Hakluyt was ignorant of the Spanish language, may be inferred from the circumstance, that when he has occasion (vol. iii. p. 499) to quote Oviedo, he gives us not the original but an *Italian* version of it by Ramusio. He was at Paris shortly after the appearance of Fumee's Translation, and remained there for some time, as is stated in the dedication of his first volume to Lord Charles Howard. We shall see, presently, how far he has been misled by relying on that translation. The following is Gomara's own language—

"Qui en mas noticia traxo desta tierra fue Sebastian Gaboto Veneciano. El qual armo dos navios en Inglaterra do tratava desde pequeno, a costa del Rey Enrique Septimo, que desseava contratar en la especiera como hazia el Rey d'Portugal. Otros disen que a su costa, y' que prometio al rey Enrique de ir por el norte al Catayo y traer de alla especias en menos tiempo que Portugueses por el Sur. Y va tambien por saber que tierra eran las Indias para poblar. Llevo trezientos hombres y camino la buelta de Islandia sobre cabo del Labrador, hasta se poner en cinquenta y ocho grados. Aunque el dize mucho mas contando como avia por el mes de Julio tanto frio y pedaços de yelo que no oso passar mas adelante, y que los dios eran grandissimos y quasi sin noche y las noches muy claras. Es cierte que a sesenta grados son los *dias* de diez y ocho *horas*, Diendo pues Gabota la frialdad y estraneza dela tierra, dio la buelta hazia poniente y rehaziendose en los Baccalaos corrio la costa hasta treynta y ochos grados y tornose de alli a Inglaterra."

"Sebastian Cabot was the first that brought any knowledge of this land. For being in England in the days of king Henry the Seventh, he furnished two ships at his own charges, or as some say, at the king's, whom he persuaded that a passage might be found to Cathay by the North Seas, and that spices might be brought from thence sooner by that way than by the viage the Portugales use by the sea of Sur. He went also to know what manner of landes those Indies were to inhabit. He had with him 300 men, and directed his course by the tract of island upon the Cape of Labrador, at fifty-eight degrees, affirming that in the month of July there was such cold and heaps of ice that he durst pass no further; also, that the days were very long, and in manner without night, and the nights very clear. Certain it is, that at the three score degrees, the longest day is of eighteen hours. But considering the cold and the strangeness of the unknown land, he turned his course from thence to the west, following the coast unto the thirty-eight degree, from whence he returned to England." (Eden's Translation, see Decades, fol. 318.)

The unwarrantable liberties taken by Hakluyt will appear at a glance. He drops, entirely, the passage of Gomara as to the length of the day in the latitude of 60°, though it stands in the middle of the paragraph. Again, Gomara states the contradictory assertions which he found, as to whether the expedition was fitted out at the cost of Henry VII. or of an individual. In Hakluyt's day this was deemed a matter of great importance; for in the passages in the third volume which relate to the North-West passage, and the colonization of America, considerable stress is laid, with a view to repel the pretensions of Spain, on the direct agency of the king of England. Hakluyt, therefore, boldly strikes out the words which show that Gomara had arrived at no conclusion on the point; and by this mutilation exhibits an unqualified averment that the whole was at the cost of Henry VII. No English reader would hesitate to cite the Spanish author, as candidly conceding that the enterprise was a national one, at the king's expense; and Mr Sharon Turner, in his "History of England during the Middle Ages," asserting anxiously the merits of Henry VII., declares (vol. iv. of second ed. p. 163, note 54), with a reference to Hakluyt, "*Gomara also mentions* that the ships *were rigged at Henry's costs*." Hakluyt wants here even the apology of having been misled by Fumee, as the French writer, and Richard Eden, fairly state the matter in the alternative.

As to the course pursued by Cabot, Hakluyt has strangely misunderstood the author. The words of Gomara are—"Llevo trezientos hombres y camino la buelta de Islandia y hasta se poner en cinquanta y ochos grados." The predecessors of Hakluyt in the work of translation were so numerous, as to leave him without apology for mistake. Richard Eden says, "He had with him three hundred men, and directed his course by the tract of Island (Iceland), upon the Cape of Labrador, at 58°." In the Italian translation of Augustin de Cravaliz, published at Rome in 1556, it is rendered "'Meno seco trecento huomini et navico alla volta d'Islanda sopra Capo del Lavoratore finchesi trovo in cinquanta otto gradi;' and in a reprint at Venice, in 1576, 'Meno seco trecento huomini et camino la volta de Islandia sopra del Capo del Lavoratore et fino a mettersi in cinquanta otto gradi.'"

That Cabot really took the route of Iceland is very probable. A steady and advantageous commerce had for many years been carried on between Bristol and Iceland, and is referred to in the quaint old poem, "The Policie of keeping the Sea," reprinted in Hakluyt, (vol. i. p. 201)—

"Of Island to write is little nede,
Save of Stockfish: yet, forsooth indeed,
Out of Bristowe, and costes many one,
Men have practised by needle, and by stone
Thitherwards," &c.

Seven years before, a treaty had been made with the king of Denmark, securing that privilege. (Selden's Mare Clausum, lib. 2. c. 32.) The theory in reference to which Cabot had projected the voyage would lead him as far North as possible, and it would be a natural precaution to break the dreary continuity at sea, which had exercised so depressing an influence on the sailors of Columbus, by touching at a point so far on his way and yet so familiarly known. Hudson, it may be remarked, took the same route.

We turn now to the translation of Fumee; "Il mena avec soy trois cens hommes et *print la route d' Island au dessus du Cap de Labeur*, jusques a ce qui il se trouva a 58 degrez et par dela. Il racomptoit," &c. Acquainted as we are with the original, it seems difficult to mistake even the French version. Hakluyt, however, had no such previous knowledge, and he confesses (Dedication to Sir Walter Raleigh, vol. iii. p. 301) that he was not a perfect master even of the French language. Obliged thus to grope after a meaning, his version is as follows, (vol. iii. p. 9)—"He carried with him 300 men, and *took the way towards Island from beyond the Cape of Labrador*, (!) until he found himself in 58° and better. He made relation," &c. The timid servility with which Hakluyt strove to follow Fumee is apparent even in the structure of the sentences, for it is improbable that two independent versions of Gomara would concur in such a distribution of the original matter.

It is difficult to understand how Hakluyt could consent to put forth such palpable nonsense. He is evidently quite aware that the word "Island" in the French could mean nothing but Iceland; and, indeed, it is the designation which he himself uniformly employs, particularly at p. 550, &c. of his first volume, where is given at great length—"The true state of Island," being a translation from a Latin work, entitled, "Brevis Commentarius de Islandia." Yet with this knowledge, and with all the means of a correct version, he represents Cabot as first reaching America and then proceeding *onward* to Iceland.

The version of Hakluyt is adopted by every subsequent English writer except LEDIARD, who, in his *Naval History,* seems to have paused over language seemingly so enigmatical. Not perceiving that a proper name was intended, he asked himself, in vexation, what "Island" could possibly be meant. Besides, the expression was ungrammatical, for it is not said "an Island," or "the Island," but simply, "towards Island." He therefore ventures on an amendment (p. 88)—"He took the way *towards the Islands,* (!) from beyond the Cape of Labrador, till he was *beyond* 58°." Having made grammar of the passage, he leaves the reader to make sense of it.

Wearisome as the examination may be, we have not yet reached the principal error of Hakluyt in reference to this short passage. It will be noted that the Spanish writer, after saying that Cabot reached the lat. of 58°, adds, "*aunque el dize mucho mas* contando como avia por el mes de Julio tante frio," &c. ("although he says much further, relating, how he had in the middle of July, such cold," &c.) Here, too, Hakluyt might have taken advantage of previous translations. In the Italian version of 1576, it is, "finchesi trovo in 58 gradi *benche egli dice di piu* et narrava come," &c.; and in that of 1556, "et fino a mettersi in 58 gradi *anchor che lui dice molto piu* il quale diceva." Hakluyt, however, relying on Fumee—"jusques a ce qu'il ce trouva a 58 degrez *et par dela,*" renders the passage "until he found himself in 58° *and better.*" Thus the Spanish writer, who had peremptorily fixed the limit of 58°, is made, without qualification, to carry Cabot to *an indefinite extent beyond it.**

The true version of the passage, not only renders it harmless, but an auxiliary in establishing the truth. That Gomara

* Campbell, in his Lives of the Admirals, changes Hakluyt's phrase into "somewhat more than fifty-eight degrees," for which he quotes Gomara.

should speak slightingly of Cabot was to be expected. His work was published in 1552, not long after our Navigator had quitted the service of Spain, and is dedicated to the Emperor Charles V., whose overtures for the return of Cabot, had been, as will be seen hereafter, rejected. Of the discoveries of Cabot, none, he says, were made for Spain (" ninguno fue por nuestros Reyes"), and we shall have repeated occasion to expose his disparaging comments on every incident of Cabot's life while in the service of that country. He is of little authority, it may be remarked, even with his own countrymen, and is most notorious for having, from a paltry jealousy of foreigners, revived and given currency to the idle tale that Columbus was guided in his great enterprise by the charts of a pilot who died in his house. We know, from Peter Martyr (Dec. 3. cap. 6), that, as early as 1515, the Spaniards were jealous of the reputation of Cabot, then in their service; and Gomara, writing immediately after the deep offence which had been given by the abandonment of the service of Spain, and the slight of the emperor's application, was disposed to yield an eager welcome to every falsehood. With regard to an account, then, from such a quarter, we would attach importance to it only from the presumed acquiescence of Cabot in the representation of a contemporary. Now, so far is this from the fact, the very passage, as at length redeemed from a perversion no less absurd than flagitious, furnishes, in itself, a triumphant proof, that the writer's assertion is in direct conflict with that of the Navigator. The importance of this argument is increased by the consideration that Gomara's work was published two years before Ramusio's third volume in the preface to which appears the extract from Cabot's letter. This shows that other means of information, and probably Cabot's map amongst the rest, were before Gomara. All that we care to know, under such circumstances, is the real statement of Cabot; and in answer to that inquiry we have the clear and precise language of his letter to Ramusio.

CHAP. III.

CABOT PENETRATED INTO HUDSON'S BAY.

On quitting the authorities which have so long been supposed to involve irreconcilable contradictions, the only remaining difficulty is that of selection from the numerous testimonials which offer, as to the real extent of the voyage. A few are referred to which speak in general terms of the latitude reached, before proceeding to such as describe particularly the course pursued.

In *De Bry* (Grand Voyages, iv. p. 69), is the following passage :—

"Sebastianus Gabottus, sumptibus Regis Angliæ, Henrici VII., per septentrionalem plagam ad Cataium penetrare voluit. Ille primus Cuspidem Baccalaos detexit (quam hodie Britones et Nortmanni, nautæ la coste des Molues hoc est Asselorum marinorum oram appellant) atque etiam ulterius *usque ad* 67 *gradum* versus polum articum."*

Belle-forest, in his Cosmographie Universelle, which appeared at Paris, in 1576 (tom. ii. p. 2175), makes the same statement.

In the treatise of Chauveton, "Du Nouveau Monde," published at Geneva, in 1579, he says (p. 141), "Sebastian Gabotto, entreprit aux despens de Henry VII., Rex d'Angleterre, de cercher quelque passage pour aller en Catay par la Tramontaine. Cestuy la descouvrit la pointe de Baccalaos, (que les mariniers de Bretaigne, et de Normandie appellent

---

* "Sebastian Cabot attempted, at the expense of Henry VII., King of England to find a way by the north to Cataia. He first discovered the point of Baccalaos, which the Breton and Norman sailors now call the Coast of Codfish; and, proceeding yet further, he reached *the latitude of sixty-seven degrees* towards the Arctic Pole."

La Coste des Molues) et plus haut *jusqu'a soixante sept degrez* du Pole."

There is a volume entitled, "A Prayse and Reporte of Martyne Frobisher's voyage to Meta Incognita, by Thomas Churchyard," published at London, in 1578 (in Library of British Museum, title *Churchyard*), wherein it is said, "I find that Gabotta was the first, in king Henry VII.'s days, that discovered this frozen land or seas *from sixty-seven towards the North*, and from thence towards the South, along the coast of America to 36 degrees and a half," &c.

Herrera, (dec. i. lib. 6. cap. 16) in rejecting the fraction, adopts the higher number, and states Cabot to have reached 68°.

We proceed now to establish the proposition which stands at the head of this chapter, but must first disclaim for it a character of novelty, since in Anderson's History of Commerce, (vol. i. p. 549), is found the following passage:—

"How weak then are the pretensions of France to the prior discovery of North America, by alleging that one John Verazzan, a Florentine, employed by their King, Francis I., was the first discoverer of those coasts, when that king did not come to the crown till about nineteen years after our Cabot's discovery of the whole coast of North America, from sixty-eight degrees north, down to the south end of Florida? So that, from beyond *Hudson's Bay* (*into which Bay, also, Cabot then sailed, and gave English names to several places therein*) southward to Florida, the whole compass of North America, on the Eastern coast thereof, does, by all the right that prior discovery can give, belong to the Crown of Great Britain: excepting, however, what our monarchs have, by subsequent treaties with other European powers, given up or ceded."

The same assertion appears in the work as subsequently enlarged into Macpherson's Annals of Commerce (vol. ii. p. 12).

The statement is sufficiently pointed; and it is not impossible, that Anderson, who wrote seventy years ago, and whose employments probably placed within his reach many curious documents connected with the early efforts to discover a North-West passage to India, may have seen one of Cabot's maps. As he is silent with regard to the source of his information, it is necessary to seek elsewhere for evidence on the subject.

A conspicuous place is, on many accounts, due to the testimony of Lord Bacon. Every student of English History is aware of the labour and research he expended on the History of Henry VII. He himself, in one of his letters, speaking of a subsequent tract, says, "I find Sir Robert Cotton, who poured forth what he had in my other work, somewhat dainty of his materials in this." We turn, then, with eagerness, to his statement as to Sebastian Cabot.

"He sailed, *as he affirmed at his return*, and made a card thereof, *very far westward*, with a quarter of the north *on the north side of Terra de Labrador*, until he came to the latitude of *sixty-seven degrees and a half*, finding the seas still open."

It would be idle to accompany this statement with any thing more than a request that a map of that region may be looked at in connexion with it.

The tract of Sir Humphrey Gilbert, on the North-West passage, was originally published in 1576. It is reprinted, with mutilations which will be mentioned hereafter, in Hakluyt. Referring, for the present, to the latter work, we find at page 16 of the third volume, the following passage:

"Furthermore, Sebastian Cabot, by his personal experience and travel, hath set forth and described this passage *in his Charts, which are yet to be seen in the Queen's Majesty's Privy Gallery at Whitehall*, who was sent to make this discovery by King Henry the VII., *and entered the same fret*, affirming that he sailed very far westward with a quarter of the north on the north side of Terra de Labrador, the 11th of June, until he came to *the septentrional latitude of sixty-seven degrees and a-half*, and finding the sea still open, said that he might and would have gone to Cataia, if the mutiny of the master and mariners had not been."

In the "Theatrum Orbis Terrarum" of the celebrated geographer Ortelius, will be found a map designated as "America sive Novi Orbis descriptio;" in which he depicts, with an accuracy that cannot be attributed to accident, the form of Hudson's Bay, and a channel leading from its northern extremity towards the pole. The publication preceded not only Hudson but Frobisher; and Ortelius tells us that *he had Cabot's map before him*. Prefixed to his work is a list, alphabetically arranged (according to the christian names), of the authors of whose labours he was possessed, and amongst them is expressly mentioned Sebastian Cabot. The map was of the World, "Universalem Tabulam quam impressam æneis formis vidimus.

The statement of the Portuguese writer *Galvano*, translated by Hakluyt, is curious, and though there is reason in many places to apprehend interpolation by Hakluyt, yet the epithet *Deseado* is plainly retained from the Portuguese; signifying the *desired* or *sought for*. It is unquestionable that this account, though not perfectly clear, represents Cabot's extreme northern labour to have been the examination of a bay and a river; and from the name conferred, we may suppose, that they were deemed to be immediately connected with the anxious object of pursuit. On the map of Ortelius, the channel running from the northern part of the bay has really the appearance of a river. After reaching the American coast, the expedition is said, by Galvano, to have gone "straight northwards till they came into 60° of latitude, where the day is eighteen hours long, and the night is very clear and bright. There they found the aire colde, and great islands of ice, but no ground in an hundred fathoms sounding; and so from thence, finding the land to turn eastwards, they trended along by it, discovering all the bay and river named Deseado, to see if it passed on the other side. *Then* they sailed *back againe,* till they came to 38° toward the equinoctial line, and from thence returned into England." (p. 33.)

A writer whose labours enjoyed in their day no little celebrity, and may be regarded, even now, as not unworthy of the rank they hold in the estimation of his countrymen, is the noble Venetian, *Livio Sanuto,* whose posthumous "Geografia," appeared at Venice, in 1588. The work, of which there is a copy in the library of the British Museum, owes its chief interest, at present, to certain incidental speculations on matters connected with Naval Science, of which the author was deeply enamoured. Repeated allusions occur to the map of "il chiarissimo Sebastiano Caboto." Having heard, moreover, from his friend Guido Gianeti de Fano, at one time ambassador at London, that Sebastian Cabot had publicly explained to the King of England the subject of the Variation of the Needle, Sanuto became extremely anxious, in reference to a long meditated project of his own, to ascertain where Cabot had fixed a point of *no variation*. The ambassador could not answer the eager inquiry, but wrote, at the instance of Sanuto, to a friend in England, Bartholomew Compagni, to obtain the information from Cabot. It was procured accordingly, and is given by Sanuto (Prima Parte, lib. i. fol. 2), with some curious corollaries of his own. The subject belongs to a different part of our inquiry, and is adverted to here only to show the author's anxious desire for accurate and comprehensive information, and the additional value thereby imparted to the passage (Prima Parte, lib. ii. fol. 17), in which he gives an account of Cabot's voyage corresponding minutely with that which Sir Humphrey Gilbert derived from the map hung up in Queen Elizabeth's Gallery.*

Some items of circumstantial evidence may be adverted to:

Zeigler, in his work on the Northern Regions, speaking of the voyage of Cabot, and the statement of his falling in with so much ice, remarks (Argent ed. of 1532. fol. 92. b.)—

"Id testatur quod non per mare vastum, sed propinquis littoribus in sinus formam comprehensum navigarit, quando ob eadem caussam sinus Gothanus concrescat quoniam strictus est, et fluviorum plurium et magnorum ostia salsam naturam in parva copia superant. Inter autem Norduegiam et Islandiam non concrescit ex diversa causa, quoniam vis dulcium aquarum illic superatur á vastitate naturæ salsæ." This testifieth that he had sailed not by the main sea, but in places near unto the land, comprehending and embracing the sea in form of a gulph; whereas for the same cause the Gulph of Gothland is frozen, because it is straight and narrow, in the which, also, the little quantity of salt water is overcome by the abundance of fresh water, of many and great rivers that fall into the gulph. But between Norway and Iceland the sea is not frozen, for the contrary cause, forasmuch as the power of fresh water is there overcome of the abundance of the salt water." (Eden's Decades, fol. 268.)

---

* "E quivi à punto tra questi dui extremi delle due Continenti giunto che fu il chiarissimo Sebastiano Caboto *in gradi sessenta sette e mezo* navigando allora per la quarta di Maestro verso Ponente ivi chiaro vide essere il mare aperto e spatiosissima senza veruno impedimento. Onde giudico fermamente potersi di la navigare al Cataio Orientale il che ancho haverche a mano a mano fatto se la malignatá del Padrone e de i marinari sollevati non lo havessero fatto ritornari à dietro."

Eden says, in a marginal note, "Cabot told me that this ice is of fresh water and not of the sea."

Great perplexity has been caused by the statement that the expedition under Cabot found the coast incline to the North-East. *He himself informs us* that he reached only to 56° N. lat., and that the coast in that part tended to the East. This seems hardly probable, for the coast of Labrador tends neither at 56° nor at 58° to the East." (Forster, p. 267.) So Navarette (tom. iii. p. 41) thinks that Ramusio's statement cannot be correct, because the latitude mentioned would carry the vessel to Greenland.

It is to be remembered, that the language of Cabot suggests that at the immediate point of arrest he was cheered by the prospect of success. We are led, then, to infer that the sanguine adventurer was, for some reason, inspired with fresh confidence in which his associates refused to participate; and that, terrified by the perils they had encountered, their dissatisfaction came to a head when they found a new career of peril suggested by what they deemed the delusive hopes of their youthful commander. Let us look into the subject with the aid which these suggestions afford. Bylot, who, after penetrating into Hudson's Bay, proceeded up its Northern channel on the west side, as far as 65° and-a-half, represented the coast as tending to the North-east. The Quarterly Review (vol. xvi. p. 168), in an article urging a new expedition in search of the North-West passage, refuses its belief to this statement. We turn, then, to Captain Parry's Narrative of his Second Voyage. It is apparent from an inspection of the map that the course pointed out by Cabot, for passing through the Strait, would conduct a navigator, without fail, to Winter Island. Now, from the very outset of Captain Parry's course from that point, we find him engaged in a struggle with the North-Eastern tendency of the coast. On the 13th of July he was off Barrow's River, which is in lat. 67° 18′ 45″; and having visited the falls of that river, his narrative is thus continued:—

"We found, on our return, that a fresh southerly breeze, which had been blowing for several hours, had driven the ice to some distance from the land; so that at four, P.M., as soon as the flood tide had slackened, we cast off and made all possible sail to the northward, steering for a headland, remarkable for having a patch of land towards the sea insular in sailing along shore. As we approached this headland, which I named after my friend Mr Edward Leycester Penrhyn, the prospect became more and more enlivening; for the sea was found to be navigable in a degree very seldom experienced in these regions, and the land trending two or three points to the westward of north, gave us reason to *hope* we should *now* be enabled to take a decided and final *turn* in *that anxiously desired direction.*"

Another remark is suggested by Captain Parry's Narrative. Every one who has had occasion to consider human testimony, or to task his own powers of recollection, must have observed how tenaciously circumstances remain which had affected the imagination, even after names and dates are entirely forgotten. The statement of Peter Martyr exhibits a trophy of this kind. He recalls what his friend Cabot had said of the influence of the sun on the shore along which he was toiling amidst mountains of ice; "vastas repererit glaciales moles pelago natantes et lucem fere perpetuam tellure tamen libera gelu liquefacto" (Decades, iii. lib. 6), a passage which Hakluyt (vol. iii. p. 8), borrowing Eden's version, renders, "he found monstrous heaps of ice swimming on the sea, and in manner continual day-light; yet saw he the land in that tract free from ice, which had been molten by the heat of the sun." Where do we look for this almost continual day-light, and this opportunity of noticing the appearance of the land? In that very channel, we would say, leading North from Hudson's Bay, where Captain Parry, later in the summer, whilst between 67° and 68°, and threatened every moment with destruction, thus records his own impressions (p. 261): "Very little snow was now lying upon the ground, and numerous streams of water rushing down the hills and sparkling in the beams of the morning sun, relieved in some measure the melancholy stillness which otherwise reigned on this desolate shore."

There has been held in reserve the piece of evidence which goes most into detail.

In the third volume of Hakluyt (p. 25), is found a Tract,

by Richard Willes, gentleman, on the North-West passage. It was originally published in an edition, that Willes put forth in 1577, of Richard Eden's Decades, and forms part of an article therein, which Hakluyt has strangely mangled, addressed to Lady Warwick, daughter of the Earl of Bedford. It was drawn up, as we shall have occasion to show, for the use of Sir Martin Frobisher. In this tract Willes combats the various arguments urged at that time against the practicability of the enterprise; and his statement of one of the objections advanced, furnishes an all important glimpse at the map of Cabot. In the following passage (3 Hakluyt, p. 25), the enemies of the enterprise are supposed to say:—

"Well, grant the West Indies not to continue continent unto the Pole. Grant there be a passage between these two lands; let the gulf lie nearer us than commonly in Cardes we find it, namely, *between* 61 *and* 64 *degrees north*, as Gemma Frisius, in his maps and globes, imagineth it, *and so left by our countryman, Sebastian Cabot, in his Table, which the Earl of Bedford hath at Cheynies;** let the way be void of all difficulties, yet, &c. &c."

And, again, Willes, speaking in his own person, says (3 Hakluyt, p. 26):—

"For that Caboto was not only a skilful seaman but a long traveller, and such a one as *entered personally that straight*, sent by King Henry VII. to make this aforesaid discovery as in his own *Discourse* of Navigation you may read in his Card, *drawn with his own hand*, that the *mouth* of the North Western *Straight* lieth *near the* 318 *meridian*, between 61 and 64 degrees in the elevation, *continuing the same breadth about ten degrees West*, where it *openeth southerly* more and more."

It is scarcely necessary to remind the reader that, until a comparatively recent period, longitude was measured, universally from Ferro, once supposed to be the most western part of the World; and that the computation of degrees from that point proceeded first over the old World, and thus made its journey of 360 degrees. Adding together, then, the 42 degrees which complete the circuit, and the distance between Ferro and Greenwich, we have within a few minutes, 60° west from Greenwich as the longitude named; and if we note

---

* On application in the proper quarter, it has been ascertained that this Document cannot, after diligent search, be found.

on a modern map, where that degree of longitude crosses Labrador, it will be seen how little allowance is necessary for the "*about* 318," which Willes, somewhat vaguely, states as the commencement of the strait. He probably judged by the eye of that fact, and of the distance at which the strait began to "open southerly."

A pause was, designedly, made in the midst of Willes's statement in order to separate what refers to Cabot's Map from his own speculations. The paragraph quoted concludes thus:—

"Where it openeth southerly more and more until it come under the tropic of Cancer, and so runneth into Mar del Sur, at the least 18 degrees more in breadth there, than it was where it first began; *otherwise, I could as well imagine this passage to be more unlikely than the voyage to Moscovia, and more impossible than it, for the far situation and continuance thereof in the frosty clime.*"

That Cabot represented the strait as continuing in the degree mentioned, or as presenting a southern route, is incredible, because we *know* that he was finally arrested at 67 degrees and-a-half whilst struggling onward. But the object of Willes was to meet the objection of those who contended that even supposing a passage could be found so far to the North yet the perils of the navigation must render it useless for the purposes of commerce. He represents them as saying (Hakluyt, vol. iii. p. 25):

"If any such passage be, it lieth subject unto ice and snow for the most part of the year. Before the sun hath warmed the air and dissolved the ice each one well knoweth that there can be no sailing. The ice once broken, through the continual abode the sun maketh a certain season in those parts, how shall it be possible for so weak a vessel, as a ship is, to hold out amid whole islands, as it were, of ice continually beating on each side, and at the mouth of that gulf issuing down furiously from the North, &c."

Willes, therefore, artfully concedes, as has been seen, the force of the objection, but attempts to elude it by adverting to the form of the Bay, and arguing that the break to the South held out the prospect of a safer route. In this effort he derived important assistance from the maps of Gemma

Frisius and Tramezine, both of which are yet extant, and really do make the strait expand to the South, and fall into the Pacific precisely in the manner he describes. He, therefore, couples the delineation of Cabot, from actual observation, with the conjectures of others, and draws certain inferences, "if the Cardes of Cabota and Gemmi Frisius, and that which Tramezine imprinted be true" (3 Hakluyt, p. 28). There is no difficulty, as has been said, in making the separation, when we advert to the fact that Cabot was actually at 67 degrees and-a-half, when the alarm of his associates compelled him to turn back.

The representation of Cabot may, in point of accuracy, be advantageously contrasted with that of more recent maps. Thus, on the one found in Purchas (vol. iii. p. 852), the 318th degree of longitude passes through nearly *the middle* of the "Fretum Hudson." In the "Voyages from Asia to America, for completing the discoveries of the North-West Coast of America," published at London, in 1764, with a translation of S. Muller's Tract, as to the Russian discoveries, there is a map by "Thomas Jefferys, Geographer to his Majesty," taken from that published by the Royal Academy of Sciences at St Petersburg. The old mode of computation is observed, and the 318th degree of longitude does not touch Labrador, but passes to the eastward of it.

Such is the evidence which exists to establish the fact assumed as the title of this chapter. There remains one obvious and striking consideration. Had Cabot been disposed to fabricate a tale to excite the wonder of his contemporaries, not only were the means of detection abundant, but he assuredly, would not have limited himself to 67 degrees and-a-half. To a people familiar with the navigation to Iceland, Norway, &c., there was nothing marvellous in his representation; nay, Zeigler, as we have seen, will not believe that great mountains of ice could have been encountered in that latitude. It is only by knowing the navigation of the Strait, and Bay, and northern channel, that we can appreciate the difficulties he had to overcome, and the dauntless intrepidity that found a new impulse in perils before which his terrified companions gave way.

CHAP. IV.

FIRST WORK OF HAKLUYT—MAPS AND DISCOURSES LEFT BY SEBASTIAN CABOT AT HIS DEATH READY FOR PUBLICATION.

An early work of Hakluyt, to which frequent reference will be made, contains a great deal of curious information, not to be found elsewhere, and is exceedingly important as a check on his subsequent volumes. It furnishes, moreover, honourable evidence of the zeal with which he sought to advance, on every occasion, the interests of navigation and discovery. The following is its title:—

"Divers voyages touching the discoverie of America and the Islands adjacent unto the same, made first of all by an Englishman, and afterwards by the Frenchmen and Britons: and certain notes of advertisements, for observations necessary for such as shall hereafter make the like attempt, with two mappes annexed hereunto, for the plainer understanding of the whole matter. Imprinted at London, for Thomas Woodcock, dwelling in Paule's Churchyard, at the signe of the Black Beare, 1582."

A reference will be found to it in the margin of p. 174. vol. iii. of Hakluyt's larger work. Dr Didbin, in his Library Companion (2d ed. p. 392), says, "I know of no other copy than that in the collection of my neighbour, Henry Jadis, Esq., who would brave all intervening perils between Indus and the Pole, to possess himself of any rarity connected with Hakluyt."* There is a copy in the Library of the British

* It may be inferred that we are not quite such enthusiasts as the gentleman referred to; those who are will find amongst the Harleian MSS. (No. 288, Art. 111) a very curious autograph letter from Hakluyt, dated Paris, July 1588, relative to an overture from France.

Museum, arranged, however, in the Catalogue, not to the title, Hakluyt, but "America." It is dedicated to "The Right Worshipful, and most vertuous Gentleman, Master Philip Sydney, Esq." Zouch, in his Life of Sir Philip Sydney (p. 317), thus refers to it: "Every reader conversant in the annals of our naval transactions, will cheerfully acknowledge the merit of Richard Hakluyt," &c. "His incomparable industry was remunerated with every possible encouragement, by Sir Francis Walsingham and Sir Philip Sydney. To the latter, as a most generous promoter of all ingenious and useful knowledge, he inscribed his first collection of voyages and discoveries, printed in 1582."

In a passage to the dedication he adverts to the English title to America:—

"I have here, right worshipful, in this hastie work, first put downe the *Title which we have* to that part of America, which is from Florida to 67 *degrees northward*, by the letters patent, granted to John Cabote and his three sons, Lewis, Sebastian, and Santius, with Sebastian's own certificate to Baptista Ramusio, of his discovery of America."

One Tract preserved in this volume, and which does not appear in the work as afterwards enlarged, is of great curiosity. It is a translation, published originally in 1563, of the detailed report made to Admiral Coligny by Ribault, who commanded the French expedition in 1562, to Florida, with a view to a settlement, and who actually planted in that year a French colony in what is now the state of South Carolina. Subsequently to the publication of this volume, Hakluyt was instrumental in causing to be published at Paris, in 1587, the volume of Basanier containing the Narrative of Laudonniere, who was second in command under Ribault. A comprehensive view is there given of all the voyages, and Hakluyt, therefore, in his larger work, omits the interesting report made by the chief of the expedition.

It is not a little remarkable, in reference to an incident so memorable, that the work of Ribault seems to be quite unknown in France. The "Biographie Universelle" (title Ribault) has a long article which manifests an entire ignorance of its subject, and is, indeed, written in a very careless manner. Thus, it is stated, that Ribault, after reaching Florida, proceeded northward along the coast, and landed at the mouth of a river where he placed a Pillar with the Arms of France, and that to the *next* river he gave the name of *May*. This is not only contrary to Ribault's account, but to that of Laudonniere (Basanier's Paris ed. of 1587, fol. 8. also, 3 Hakluyt, p. 308), and to the theory of the Biographie Universelle itself which identifies the May with the present St John. The mistake throws into confusion what in the original cannot be mistaken. It was on the river where he planted the Pillar that the name of May was conferred. Ribault, in this Tract, referring to the several navigators who had visited America, speaks of the "very famous" Sebastian Cabot, "an excellent pilot, sent thither by King Henry VII., in the year 1498." Hakluyt speaks of it as "translated by one Thomas Hackit," and remarks, "The Treatise of John Ribault is a thing that hath been already printed, but not nowe to be had unless I had caused it to be printed againe." The work, however, as originally published by Hackit, in London, in 1563, is in the Library of the British Museum (title in Catalogue, Ribault). It is more excusable in the French Biographer of Ribault, not to know of an important Memoir prepared by him, and which is found in the Lansdowne Manuscripts, on the policy of preserving peace with England, and of delivering up to her certain ports of France. It was, doubtless, prepared under the eye of Coligny, and transmitted by him to show the views of his party; and has an intimate connexion with the history of France at that period.

Passing, however, at present, from various items of this curious volume, to which occasion will be taken hereafter to refer, there is to be noticed a passage of the deepest interest in reference to the subject of this memoir. Great surprise has been expressed that Cabot should have left no account of his voyages, as this circumstance has even been urged against him as a matter of reproach. "Sebastian, *with all his know-*

ledge, and in the course of a long life, never committed to writing any narrative of the voyage to North America. The curious on the Continent, however, drew from him in conversation various particulars which gave a general idea," &c. (Historical account of North America, &c., by Hugh Murray, Esq., vol. i. p. 66.) Let us see how far the reproach on Cabot may be retorted on his country. In this work of 1582, after citing the patent granted by Henry VII. and the testimony of Ramusio, Hakluyt says:—

"This much concerning Sebastian Cabote's discoverie may suffice for a present taste, but shortly, God willing, shall come out in print ALL HIS OWN MAPPES and DISCOURSES *drawne and written by himselfe*, which are in the custodie of the worshipful Master William Worthington, one of her Majesty's Pensioners, who (because SO WORTHIE MONUMENTS should not be buried in perpetual oblivion) is very willing to suffer them to be overseene, and published in as good order as may be to the encouragement and benefite of our countrymen."

It may be sufficient here to say of William Worthington, that he is joined with Sebastian Cabot, in the pension given by Philip and Mary, on the 29 May 1557 (Rymer, vol. xv. p. 466). The probable fate of the Maps and Discourses will be considered on reaching the painful part of Cabot's personal history which belongs to this association.

CHAP. V.

COMPARATIVE AGENCY OF JOHN AND SEBASTIAN CABOT.

It has been seen, that by all the early writers, heretofore cited, who speak of the discoveries effected under the auspices of Henry VII., Sebastian Cabot is exclusively named. An inclination has, in consequence, sprung up at a more remote period to dwell on the circumstances which seem to indicate that injustice had been done to the father; and the alleged testimony of *Robert Fabyan*, the venerable annalist, is particularly relied on.

The feeling which prompts this effort to vindicate the pretensions of the father is entitled to respect; and certainly there can exist, at this late day, no other wish on the subject than to reach the truth. It is proposed, therefore, to look with this spirit into the various items of evidence which are supposed to establish the prevailing personal agency of John Cabot. They may be ranked thus:

1. The alleged statement of Robert Fabyan.

2. The language of more recent writers as to the character of the father.

3. The appearance of his name on the map cut by Clement Adams, and also in the patents.

As to the *first*, the authority usually referred to is found in Hakluyt (vol. 3. p. 9)—

"A note of Sebastian Cabot's first discoverie of part of the Indies taken out of the latter part of Robert Fabian's Chronicle, not hitherto printed, which is in the custodie of M. John Stow, a diligent preserver of antiquities."

"In the 13 yeere of K. Henry the 7 (by means of one *John Cabot, a Venetian*, which made himselfe very expert and cunning in knowledge of the circuit of the world, and islands of the same, as by a sea card and other demonstrations reasonable he shewed), the king caused to man and victuall a ship at Bristow to search for an island, which he said he knew well was rich, and replenished with great commodities: which shippe thus manned and victualled at the King's costs, divers marchants of London ventured in her small stocks, being in her, as chief patron, the said Venetian. And in the company of the said ship sailed, also, out of Bristow, three or foure small ships, fraught with sleight and grosse marchandizes, as course cloth, caps, laces, points, and other trifles, and so departed from Bristow in the beginning of May, of whom in this Maior's time returned no tidings."

There is added, by Hakluyt, a note of three savages brought from the newly-discovered region, "mentioned by the foresaid, Robert Fabian."

It may be remarked, in the first place, that the history of this "latter part of Robert Fabyan's Chronicle," well deserves the attention of antiquaries. Both Stow, in his Annals, subsequently published, and after him, Speed (p. 744), and Purchas (vol. iii. p. 808), speak of the exhibition, in 1502, of savages brought from the Newfoundland, and cite Fabyan, as authority for what is not to be found in his work as we now have it.* Assuming, however, as we may safely do, that Stow was possessed of a manuscript which he had reason to believe the work of a contemporary, the question remains as to its precise language. The passage in Hakluyt would evidently appear to be not an exact transcript from such a work. The expression, "of whom in this Mayor's time returned no tidings," is not in the manner of a Chronicler making a note of incidents as they occurred, but is very natural in a person looking over the materials in his possession for information on a particular point, and reporting to another the result of that examination. It is probable, therefore, that Hakluyt had asked Stow what light he could throw on the expeditions in the time of Henry VII., and that we have here the answer given to the inquiry. From what has already been seen, it may be conceived that Hakluyt would not hesitate to run his pen through whatever struck him as irreconcilable with the leading facts in his possession. The wealthy Prebendary would approach with no great reverence the labours of poor Stow, who having abandoned his business as a tailor, for the

* See Appendix (A).

unrequited labours of an antiquary, was reduced to such distress, that, through the royal munificence, a special license was granted to him to beg at the church doors. If, therefore, Hakluyt found the son's name introduced, he would not hesitate to make it give way to what he deemed the better evidence supplied by the record. Fortunately, however, we are not left to mere conjecture. In 1605 appeared Stow's own "Annals." The simplicity and good faith of this writer are so well known, as well as his intense reverence for whatever bore the stamp of antiquity, that we have no fear of his having committed what in his eyes would have been sacrilege, by changing one syllable of the original. Let it be remembered, then, that Hakluyt relies exclusively on what he obtained from Stow; and in reading the following passage from the Annals, we find what, doubtless, passed into Hakluyt's hands before it was subjected to his perilous correction. It occurs at p. 804 of the edition of 1605, and at p. 483 of that of 1631. "This year one *Sebastian* Gaboto, *a Genoa's sonne borne in Bristol,* professing himself to be expert in the knowledge of the circuit of the world and islands of the same, as by his charts and other reasonable demonstrations he shewed, caused the king to man and victual a ship," &c. The rest corresponds with the passage in Hakluyt, but there is not added, "of whom in this Mayor's time," &c.; thus confirming the conjecture as to the meaning of those words in the memorandum given to Hakluyt. Under the year 1502 we find the passage as to the exhibition of the savages, beginning, "This year were brought unto the king three men taken in the Newfoundland *by Sebastian Gaboto, before named, in anno* 1498." As authority for this last fact, he cites Robert Fabyan. Thus we have the best evidence that the contemporary writer, whoever he may have been, made not the slightest allusion to the father. Bacon, Speed, Thuanus, &c., all furnish the same statement.

The very phrase, "a Genoa's son," employed to designate Sebastian Cabot, may be considered as the not unnatural mistake of a contemporary, referring as it does to the country of Columbus, with whose fame all Europe was ringing from side to side.

It happens that we can trace the progress of Hakluyt's perversion. The communication from Stow first appears in the "Divers Voyages to America," &c. published in 1582. When given at that early period, as derived from "Mr John Stow, citizen," Hakluyt merely changes the words "a Genoa's son," into "a Venetian," without giving any name. He had not then heard of the patent of February 3, 1498, naming John Cabot exclusively, for the only document he quotes is the original patent of March 1496, in which both father and son are mentioned, and which describes the father as a Venetian. He struck out, therefore, only what he *then* knew to be incorrect. Subsequently, he received information of the second patent in favour of John Cabot, and in his enlarged work he not only furnishes a reference to that patent, but makes a further alteration of what he had received from Stow. Instead of "a Venetian," as in 1582, when he had the memorandum first before him, it becomes "*one John Cabot*, a Venetian," thus effecting, at the two stages of alteration, a complete change of what he had received, and yet for the statement as thus finally made, Fabian and Stow continue to be cited!

Hakluyt has, incautiously, suffered to lie about the evidence of his guilty deed, which should have been carefully buried. Thus there is retained the original title of the passage—"A note of *Sebastian Cabot's* first discovery of part of the Indies, taken out of the latter part of Robert Fabyan's Chronicle, not hitherto printed, which is in the custody of Mr John Stow, a diligent preserver of Antiquities." Now it is highly probable that all this, with the exception of the compliment, was the explanatory memorandum at the head of Stow's communication. It is incredible that Hakluyt himself should prefix it to a passage which does not contain the slightest allusion to Sebastian Cabot. Thus we see that in indicating to the printer the alterations in the new edition, the pen of Hakluyt, busied with amendment at the critical point, has spared, inadvertently, what betrays him by its incongruity with that which remains, and, like the titles of many acts of parliament, serves to show the successful struggle for amendment after the original draught.

As to the second paragraph, about the exhibition of the three savages, Hakluyt's conduct has been equally unjustifiable, but an exposure of it belongs to a different part of the subject.

Thus it is established by the testimony of the contemporary Annalist, that it was on a young man—the son of the rich merchant from Italy—that the public eye was turned in reference to the projected schemes of discovery.

The explanation that has been given furnishes at the same time an answer to the second ground adverted to in support of the father's pretensions—the encomiums bestowed on him by respectable writers. Singular as it may appear, they have all arisen out of the misconception as to Fabyan's meaning. Beyond this supposed allusion, there is not the slightent evidence that the father was a seaman, or had the least claim to nautical skill or the kindred sciences. We hear only of his going "to dwell in England to follow the trade of merchandise." Yet out of Hakluyt's perversion, mark how each successive writer has delighted to draw the materials for eulogy on this old gentleman.

"Thus it appears, from *the best authority that can be desired*, that of a contemporary writer, this discovery was made by Sir John Cabot, the father of Sebastian." (Campbell's Lives of The Admirals.) "Sir John Cabot was the original discoverer, of which honour he ought not to be despoiled, even by his son." (Ib.) The same language is found in M'Pherson's Annals of Commerce (vol. ii. p. 13. note), and in Chalmer's Political Annals of The Colonies (p. 8, 9), though it happens, singularly enough, that in correcting the supposed error, this last writer not only mistakes the name of the annalist (making him to be *John* Fabyan), but cites a work which does not contain the slightest allusion to these enterprises.

"He was, *it seems*, a man perfectly skilled in all the *sciences* requisite to *form* an accomplished seaman *or a general trader!*" (Campbell's Lives of the Admirals.)

"The father was a man of science, and had paid *particular* attention to the doctrine of the spheres. His studies, &c. He *seems* to have applied to Henry VII., who *accordingly* empowered him to sail," &c. (vol. xviii. Kerr's Voyages, p. 353. Essay by W. Stevenson, Esq.).

"John Caboto, a citizen of Venice, *a skilful Pilot and intrepid Navigator.*" (Barrow, p. 32.)

"Henry VII., disappointed in his hopes of forming an engagement with Columbus, gladly extended his protection to the Venetian, John Gavotta or Cabot, *whose* reputation as a skilful pilot was little inferior to that of the celebrated Genoese." (Dr Lardner's Cabinet Cyclopædia, Maritime and Inland Discovery, vol. ii. p. 136.)

We come now to the assertion, that on the map "hung up in the Queen's Privy Gallery," the discoveries indicated, are referred to the joint agency of the father and son. And here, the first consideration is, of course, as to the evidence that such a representation was made.

The map itself has disappeared, and we approach the statement of Hakluyt with a conviction that he would not hesitate, for a moment, to interpolate the name of *John* Cabot, if he thought that, thereby, was secured a better correspondence with the language of the original patent. No additional confidence is derived from *Purchas*, who copies all Hakluyt's perversions, and even repeats the citation of Fabyan, as found in Hakluyt's last work, though Stow's Annals had intermediately appeared, and the discrepance between Hakluyt's first and last work ought to have put him on his guard.

Sir Humphrey Gilbert makes not the slightest allusion to the father.

"Furthermore, *Sebastian Caboto*, by his personal experience and travel, hath set forth and described this passage in his charts, which are yet to be seen in the Queen Majesty's Privy Gallery at Whitehall, *who was sent* to make this discovery by king Henry VII."

It would certainly require less audacity to associate here the name of the father, as it is found in the patent, than to do that of which Hakluyt has already been convicted. Richard Willes, who, in the treatise already cited, and which is given in Hakluyt, addresses Lady Warwick "from the court," and speaks familiarly of Sebastian Cabot's map, makes no allusion to the father.

There is a treatise on "Western planting" copied into Hakluyt (vol. iii. p. 165), as "written by Sir George Peckham, Knt., the chief adventurer and furtherer of Sir Humphrey Gilbert's voyage;" in which, speaking of the English title to America, he says (p. 173), "In the time of the Queen's grandfather of worthy memory, king Henry VII., Letters Patent were, by his Majesty, granted to John Cabota, an Italian, to Lewis, Sebastian, and Sancius, his three sons, to discover remote, barbarous and heathen countries; which discovery was afterwards *executed* to the use of the Crown of England, in the said king's time, *by Sebastian and Sancius, his sons, who were born here in England.*" Thus, with a full knowledge of the introduction of the name of the father and the eldest brother into the Patent, Sir George seems to negative the idea that they took any part in the execution of the enterprise. Yet it must be admitted that this piece of evidence, strong as it seems, is weakened by noticing the statements coupled with it. He continues (p. 173), "In true testimony whereof, there is a fair haven in Newfoundland, knowen and called unto this day by the name of Sancius Haven, which proveth that they first discovered upon that coast, from the height of 63 unto the cape of Florida, as appeareth in the Decades." The reference here is to the Decades of Peter Martyr, which certainly do not bear out the conclusion. The writer probably determined the question of latitude by observing that Cabot, according to Willes, fixed the mouth of the Strait between 61° and 64°; and as to the Haven, the allusion is probably to *Placentia* Bay, or as it is written on the old maps of Newfoundland, *Plasancius*, a title which, as found in the mouths of seamen, might readily suggest to the ear the name of the youngest patentee.

There is one account that mentions John Cabot, but it was written subsequently to the publication, by Hakluyt, in 1582, of the patent containing the father's name, which would, of itself, suggest the association. It is the narrative, by Haies, of the Expedition of 1583 (see Hakluyt, vol. iii. p. 144), which we cite on the possibility that it may do no more than an act of justice, and because it serves to show how uniformly the claims of England in America have been rested on the discoveries in the time of Henry VII.

"The first discovery of these coasts (never heard of before), was well begun by John Cabot the father, and Sebastian his son, an Englishman born, &c. all which they brought and annexed unto the crown of England." "For not long after that Christopher Columbus had discovered the Islands and Continent of the West Indies for Spain, John and Sebastian Cabot made discovery also of the rest from Florida Northwards, to the behoof of England." "The French did but review that before discovered by the English Nation, usurping upon our right." "Then seeing the English nation only hath right unto these countries of America, from the Cape of Florida Northward, by the privilege of first discovery, unto which Cabot was authorised by regal authority, and set forth by the expense of our late famous King Henry VII., which right, also, seemeth strongly defended on our behalf by the bountiful hand of Almighty God, notwithstanding the enterprises of other nations, it may greatly encourage us upon so just ground as is our right," &c.

The fact that the father is named in the Patent does not furnish conclusive evidence that he embarked in either of the expeditions. The original grant conveys to him and his three sons, "and to the *heirs* of them and their *Deputies*," full power to proceed in search of regions before unknown, and the exclusive privilege of trading. Now it has never been supposed that *all* the sons engaged in the voyage, and yet the presumption is just as strong with regard to each of them as to the father, and even more so if we look to the appropriate season of life for perilous adventure. The truth seems to be this:—as it is probable that all the means of the family were embarked in this enterprise, it was no unnatural precaution that the patent should be coextensive in its provisions. It created them a trading corporation with certain privileges, and it might as well be contended, for a similar reason, that the Marquis of Winchester, the Earl of Arundel, and the other patentees of the Muscovy Company (1 Hakluyt, p. 268) actually sailed in the north-eastern voyages. The second patent is to the father alone. If we seek a reason for this departure from the original arrangement, it may be conjectured that some of the sons chose to give a different direction to a parental advance and their personal exertions, and that the head of the family thought fit to retain, subject to his own discretionary disposal, the proposed investment of his remaining capital. It is said* that one of the sons settled at Venice, and the other at Genoa. The recital of the discovery *by the Father* would, of course, be stated, under the circumstances, as the consideration of the second patent in his favour.

Another reason for the introduction of the father's name, concurrently at first with his son's, and afterwards exclusively, may perhaps be found in the very character of the King, whose own pecuniary interests were involved in the result. He might be anxious thus to secure the responsibility of the wealthy Venetian for the faithful execution of the terms of the patent, and finally think it better to have him solely named, rather than commit powers, on their face assignable, to young men who had no stake in the country, and who were not likely to make it even a fixed place of residence.

On the whole, there may at least be a doubt whether the father really accompanied the expedition. Unquestionably, the great argument derived from the pretended language of a contemporary annalist is not only withdrawn, but thrown into the opposite scale.

Supposing, however, John Cabot to have been on board,

---

* Campbell's Lives of the Admirals, vol. i. p. 310, on the authority of MS. remarks on Hakluyt.

we must, in inquiring what were his functions, carefully put aside the thousand absurdities which have had their origin in misconception as to the person intended by Fabyan; and remember, that we have not a tittle of evidence as to his character or past pursuits, except, as has been remarked, that he came to London "to follow the trade of merchandise." All that is said about his knowledge of the sphere—his perfect acquaintance with the sciences, &c., is merely an amplification of the remarks of Fabyan, as to Sebastian Cabot. If, then, he went at all, it was in all probability merely for the purpose of turning to account his mercantile skill and sagacity in the projected traffic which formed one of the objects of the expedition. There is nothing to control, in the slightest degree, the idea which presses on us from so many quarters, that the project had its origin with the son, and that its great object was to verify his simple, but bold proposition. that by pushing to the north a shorter route might be opened to the treasures of Cataya.

If the youth of Sebastian Cabot be objected to, as rendering his employment by Henry improbable, we must remember that the project was suggested to the English monarch at a period peculiarly auspicious to its reception. He had just missed the opportunity of employing Columbus, and with it the treasures of the New World. Instead of cold and cheerless distrust, there was a reaction in the public mind, with a sanguine flow of confidence towards novel speculations and daring enterprises. When, therefore, one-fifth of the clear gain was secured to the king, by the engagement of the wealthy Venetian, Henry yielded a ready ear to the bold theory and sanguine promises of the accomplished and enthusiastic young navigator.

CHAP. VI.

FIRST POINT SEEN BY CABOT—NOT NEWFOUNDLAND.

THE part of America first seen and named by Cabot, is generally considered to have been the present *Newfoundland*. This, however, will be far from clear if we look closely into the subject.

The evidence usually referred to as establishing the fact consists of an "extract taken out of the map of Sebastian Cabot, cut by Clement Adams," quoted by Hakluyt and Purchas.

This would seem to have been a broad sheet, on which an attempt was made to exhibit the substance of Cabot's statement as to the country he had discovered. From the stress laid by Hakluyt and Purchas upon the *Extract*, hung up in the privy gallery at Whitehall,* we may infer that they had never seen the original map. It would seem to have been executed after Cabot's death, and without any communication with him, for it offers conjectures as to his reasons for giving names to particular places which probably would not have been hazarded with the means so readily at hand, during his life, of attaining certainty on such points. The explanation was in Latin, and is thus given by Hakluyt, with a translation (vol. iii. p. 6)—

Anno Domini 1497, Joannes Cabotus Venetus, et Sebastianus illius filius eam terram fecerunt perviam, quam nullus prius adire ausus fuit, die 24 Junii, circiter horam quintam bene manè. Hanc autem appellavit Terram primum visam, credo quod ex mari in eam partem primum oculos injecerat. Namque ex adverso sita est insula, eam appellavit insulam Divi Joannis, hac opinor ratione,

* The disappearance of this curious document may probably be referred, either to the sales which took place after the death of Charles I., or to the fire in the reign of William III.

quod aperta fuit eo qui die est sacer Diuo Joanni Baptistæ: Hujus incolæ pelles animalium exuviasque ferarum pro indumentis habent, easque tanti faciunt, quanti nos vestes preciosissimas. Cum bellum gerunt, utuntur arcu, sagittas, hastis, spiculis, clavis ligneis et fundis. Tellus sterilis est, neque ullos fructus affert, ex quo fit, ut ursus albo colore, et cervis inusitatæ apud nos magnitudinis referta sit: piscibus abundat, iisque sane magnis, quales sunt lupi marini et quos salmones vulgus appellat; soleæ autem reperiuntur tam longæ, ut ulnæ mensuram excedant. Imprimis autem magna est copia corum piscium, quos vulgari sermone vocant Bacallaos. Gignuntur in ea insula accipitres ita nigri, ut corvorum similitudinem mirum in modum exprimant, perdices autem et aquilæ sunt nigri coloris."

The same in English.

"In the year of our Lord 1497, John Cabot, a Venetian, and his sonne Sebastian (with an English fleet set out from Bristoll), discovered that land which no man before that time had attempted, on the 24th of June, about five of the clocke early in the morning. This land he called *Prima vista*, that is to say, first seene; because, as I suppose, it was that part whereof they had the first sight from sea. That island which lieth out before the land he called the Island of *St John* upon this occasion, as I thinke, because it was discovered upon the day of *John the Baptist.* The inhabitants of this island use to weare beasts' skinnes, and have them in as great estimation as we have our finest garments. In their warres they use bowes, arrowes, pikes, darts, woodden clubs, and slings. The soil is barren in some places, and yeeldeth little fruit, but it is full of white bears, and stagges far greater than ours. It yeeldeth plenty of fish, and those very great as seales, and those which we commonly call *salmons;* there are soles, also, above a yard in length, but especially there is great abundance of that kind of fish which the savages call *baccalaos.* In the same island also there breed hauks, but they are so black that they are very like to ravens, as also their partridges and eagles, which are in like sort blacke."

As usual, it is necessary here, in the first place, to notice the passages in which Hakluyt has acted unfaithfully to the text. He was under an impression that Cabot first visited Newfoundland, and in this same volume that region is spoken of in very flattering terms, and its colonization earnestly recommended. At p. 153, we hear of Newfoundland—"There is nothing which our East and Northerly countries of Europe do yield, but the like also may be made in them as plentifully by time and industry, namely, rosin, flax, hemp, corn, and many more, all which the countries will afford, and *the soil is apt to yield.*" "The soil along the coast is not deep of earth, bringing forth abundantly peason, small, yet good feeding for cattle. Roses, passing sweet," &c. In the letter of Parmenius from Newfoundland (p. 162), the passage beginning

"But what shall I say, my good Hakluyt," &c., conveys a similar representation.

Mark now the liberties taken by Hakluyt. Cabot, in the *Extract*, is made to say, that the country called "Terra primum visa" was absolutely sterile—"tellus sterilis est." This Hakluyt renders "the soil is barren *in some places;*" and when Cabot says, "neque *ullos* fructus affert," the translator has it, "and yieldeth *little* fruit;" thus perverting, without hesitation, the original, which is yet audaciously placed beneath our eyes!

While on the subject of these efforts to obscure a document so little satisfactory in itself, reference may be made to another, of a date subsequent to the time of Hakluyt, but which has had an extensive influence on modern accounts. The country discovered is designated in the Latin, as "*Terra* primum visa," and distinguished from the "*Insula,*" or Island of St John, standing opposite to it. Hakluyt preserves the distinction, but in the well known book of Captain Luke Foxe, who professes to transfer to his pages the several testimonials on the subject of Cabot's discoveries so as to present them to his readers in a cheap form, the passage is thus put (p. 15)—

"In the year of grace 1497, John Cabot, a Venetian, and Sebastian his son, with an English fleet from Bristol, discovered *that Island*, which before that time no man," &c. With a view to economy of space, Foxe omits to copy Hakluyt's statement, that the "Extract" spoken of was hung up "in the Queen's Privy Gallery," and from this omission a hasty reader is led to infer that he speaks of a map in his own possession. Here was a fine trap for those who came after him; and the following passage from M'Pherson's Annals of Commerce (vol. ii. p. 13, note), may show how successful it proved. "Foxe quotes the following *inscription engraven near Newfoundland, in a map*, published by Sebastian, the son of John Cabot—'A.D. 1497, John Cabot, a Venetian, and Sebastian, his son, with an English fleet, set sail from Bristol, discovered *that Island*, which before that time no man had attempted.' " Thus we have—Foxe in possession of Cabot's map—on that map, "Newfoundland" marked—and, on the map, published by Sebastian Cabot, an *inscription* near Newfoundland, to the purport mentioned. It will be asked, with surprise, whether Foxe, culpable as he is, affords no greater countenance to M'Pherson. Positively not. So far from pretending to have any original documents, he says expressly, in his address to the reader, "It will be objected that many of these abstracts are taken out of other books, and that those are the voyages of other men. I answer, it is true that most of them are, for what are all those of Mr Hakluyt and Mr Purchas, but the collections and preservations of other mens' labours," &c. "I have abstracted those works of my predecessors, yet I have *interlaced* my own experience!" &c. Chalmers adopts, like M'Pherson, the perversion of Foxe.

We are bound, therefore, to look closely to the original language of this document, which is itself, unfortunately, a mere abstract; and in endeavouring to ascertain the country intended, we naturally pause on the very expressions which have been perverted, in order to accommodate them to the modern hypothesis. The unqualified language as to the sterility of the region, is certainly more applicable to Labrador than Newfoundland, and the distinction taken between the "Terra" and the "Insula," is calculated to strengthen the presumption that the former was intended.

As to the animals of this "*Terra primum visa*," we are told, it is "*full of white bears*, and deer larger than ours"—("*ursis albo colore* et cervis inusitatæ apud nos magnitudinis *referta*"). Now the haunts of the white bear are on the coast of Labrador, and they do not come so far South as Newfoundland in numbers to warrant such a description. The account, too, given by Peter Martyr, of the manner in which these bears catch the fish, which is their favourite food, strikingly recalls the lively description of similar scenes by Mr Cartwright, in his "Journal, during a residence of nearly sixteen years on the coast of Labrador." It is remarkable, that most English writers have been rather reluctant to copy Cabot's representation on this point, supposing it inapplicable to Newfoundland, where, though white bears may be occasionally seen, they are not "native here and to the manner born."

The introduction of an Island, "*St John*," into the "Extract," has contributed to mislead, the reader naturally referring it to the one of that name in the Gulf of St Lawrence. If we recollect, however, that the *Terra primum visa* was discovered on the 24th June, and the island on the same day (St John's day), it will seem improbable that Cabot, on the very day of discovery, could have penetrated so far. The description, also, is inapplicable, "quæ ex adverso sita est Insula"—"that island which lieth out before the land." We must remark, further, that the present St John was so named by Cartier, in 1534 (3 Hakluyt, p. 204), he having been employed from the 10th May, when he reached Newfoundland, to 24th June, in making a circuit of the Gulf which he entered through the strait of Belle Isle. But the most important, and conclusive piece of testimony, is furnished by Ortelius, who had the map of Cabot before him, and who places an island of St John in the latitude of 56° immediately on the coast of Labrador. This is, doubtless, the one so designated by Cabot.

Thus, without calling to our aid the terms of the second patent to Cabot, which recites the discovery of a *land and islands* on the first voyage, we reach the conclusion, that the main discovery—the "Terra," as distinguished from the "Insula"—could not have been the present island of Newfoundland.

There is little difficulty in tracing the history of this epithet. The whole of the northern region is designated, on the old maps, as *Terra Nova*, or New Land, and it has the appellation of "Newland," in the statute 33 Henry VIII. cap. ii.*

* Ruffhead's Statutes at large, vol. ii. p. 304.

Robert Throne of Bristol, in 1527, speaking (Hakluyt, vol. i. p. 214) of the North-West passage, says, "and if they will take this course after they be past the Pole towards the West, they should go in the back of *the Newfoundland* which of late was discovered by your Grace's subjects, until they come to the back side and South Seas of the Indies Occidental;" and again (p. 219), "if between *our Newfoundlands,* or Norway, or Island, the seas toward the North be navigable, we should go to these Islands a shorter way by more than 2000 leagues." On the same page, he mentions the circumstance of his father having been one of the "discoverers of Newfoundland;"—at p. 216, refers to "the land that we found, which is called here (in Spain) Terra de Labrador,"—and in another part of the same document speaks of "the Newfound island that we discovered."

The term, then, was employed, in the first instance, as a designation of all the English discoveries in the North. That it should afterwards settle down upon an inconsiderable portion, and come to be familiarly so applied, will not appear surprising if we recollect, that for almost a century the whole region was known only as a fishing station, and regarded as an appendage to the Grand Bank, and that the island was used, exclusively, in connexion with such pursuits. When long established, these designations are beyond the reach of considerations of taste or propriety. Thus, the term *West Indies,* once covering the whole of America, is now limited to groups of islands on its eastern side, even after a Continent and the Pacific Ocean are known to be interposed between them and that India in a supposed connexion with which the name had its origin. Parks and Squares may be laid out and named at will, but the familiar appellation of a thronged place of business will not yield even to an Act of Parliament; "expellas furca tamen usque recurret."

CHAP. VII.

CABOT DID NOT CONFER THE NAME "PRIMA VISTA."

THE question as to the name *Prima Vista* stands apart from that which has just been dismissed, and is in itself sufficiently curious.

It is to be remembered, that the description, in Latin, is not only the highest but the only authority on the subject, and that Hakluyt had no better materials for conjecture than we now possess. From this document we gather that John and Sebastian Cabot,

"Eam terram fecerunt perviam quam nullus prius adire ausus fuit die 24 Junii circiter horam quintam bene mane. Hanc autem appellavit *Terram primum visam* credo quod ex mari in eam partem primum oculos injecerat."

A passage thus translated by Hakluyt—

"They discovered that land which no man before that time had attempted, on the 24th June, about five of the clock, early in the morning. This land he called *Prima Vista, that is to say, first seen,* because *as I suppose* it was that part whereof they had the first sight from sea."

It is plain, that the original map could have furnished no clue to the motive for conferring the appellation, because the suggestion of the person who prepared the "Extract," is offered, confessedly, as a conjecture. We know only that there was something on the map which led him to consider the region as designated, "Terra primum visa." This bare statement will show how utterly gratuitous is Hakluyt's assumption, that the name given was Prima Vista; for it is obviously impossible to determine, whether it was in Latin, Italian, or English.

If the name *Prima Vista*, or Terra *primum Visa*, or *First Sight*, was conferred, why is nothing said of it in the various conversations of Sebastian Cabot? We hear continually of

Baccalaos, and find that name on all the old maps, but not a word of the other, which yet is represented as the designation applied to the more important item of discovery—to the "terra," as distinguished from the "insula."

The origin of the misconception is suspected to have been this: The Map of the New World which accompanies the copy of Hakluyt's work, in the King's Library, has the following inscription on the present Labrador, "This land was discovered by John et Sebastian Cabote, for Kinge Henry VII., 1497." Now, the "Extract" which we are considering, says, that John and Sebastian Cabot first discovered the land "which no man before that time had attempted" ("quam nullus prius adire ausus fuit"). These expressions are, of course, intended to convey an assertion found on the original map, of which it professes to give an abstract—an assertion equivalent, doubtless, to the language quoted from the map in Hakluyt. How would such an inscription run? Probably, thus: "*Terra primum visa* Joanne Caboto et Sebastiano illius filio die, 24 Junio, 1497, circiter horam quintam bene mane." To us who have just been called on to expose the absurd mistakes committed by men of the highest reputation for learning and sagacity, is it incredible, that the artist who prepared the broad sheet, should have hastily supposed the initial words to be intended as a designation of the country discovered—particularly, when in the Law, we have to seek at every turn a similar explanation of such titles, as *Scire-facias*, *Mandamus*, *Quo Warranto*, &c. &c.?

Such a designation might even have got into use without necessarily involving misconception. There is a tendency, in the absence of a convenient epithet, to seize, even absurdly, on the leading words of a description, particularly when couched in a foreign language. Thus the earliest collection of voyages to the New World is entitled, "Paesi novamente retrovati et Novo Mondo da Alberico Vespucio Florentino intitulato." It is usually quoted as the "Paesi novamente retrovati," and a bookseller, therefore, when asked for "Land lately discovered," exhibits a thin quarto volume, published at Vicenza in 1507. The same is the case with the "Novus Orbis," the "Fœdera," &c.

Another consideration may be mentioned. The island which "stands out from the land" was discovered on the 24th June, and named from that circumstance. One would suppose this to have been first encountered; and if so, the designation of "First Sight," would hardly be given to a point subsequently seen on the same day. Not only were the chances in its favour from its position, but we cannot presume that Cabot would have quitted immediately his main discovery, had that been first recognized, and stood out to sea to examine a small island, or that he would have dedicated to the Saint the inferior, and later, discovery of the day.

We repeat, all that is *known* on the subject is the appearance of the three Latin words in question on the original map. The rest is mere conjecture; first, of the artist, as to the meaning of the words, and then, of Hakluyt, yet wilder, that "Terra primum visa," must have been a translation of something in Italian. This solution explains why there is no reference to any such title in the conversations of Cabot, or in Ortelius who had the map of that navigator before him.

It is not improbable, that Hakluyt was assisted to his conclusion by the prominence given on the early maps of Newfoundland to a name conferred by the Portuguese. Though *he* has not put into words the reflection which silently passed through his mind, it becomes perceptible in others who have adopted his hypothesis. Thus, for example, we recognise its vague influence on Forster (p. 267), who supposes "that Sebastian Cabot had the first sight of Newfoundland *off Cape Bonavista.*"

The subject seems, indeed, on every side, the sport of rash and even puerile conceits. Dr Robertson tells us (Hist. of America, book ix.), "after sailing for some weeks due West, and nearly on the parallel of the port from which he took his departure, he discovered a large *Island,* which he called

Prima Vista, *and his sailors, Newfoundland!*—and *in a few days*, he descried a smaller Isle, to which he gave the name of St John." Thus is presented, gratuitously, to the imagination, a sort of *contest* about names, between the commander of the expedition and the plain-spoken Englishmen under his command.

CHAP. VIII.

RICHARD EDEN'S "DECADES OF THE NEW WORLD"—CABOT'S STATEMENT AS TO THE PLACE OF HIS BIRTH.

As reference has already been made, more than once, to the volume of Eden, and there will be occasion to draw further on its statements, a few remarks may not be out of place as to the claims which that rare and curious work presents to credit and respect. In selecting from the various tributes to its merits, that of *Hakluyt*, it is difficult to forbear a somewhat trite reflection on the fortuitous circumstances which influence the fate of books, as frequently as they are arbiters of fame and success in the pursuits of active life. Eden has, in our view, far stronger claims to consideration as an author, and to the grateful recollection of his countrymen, than the writer whose testimony it is proposed to adduce in his favour. He preceded the other half-a-century, and was, indeed, the first Englishman who undertook to present, in a collective form, the astonishing results of that spirit of maritime enterprise which had been everywhere awakened by the discovery of America. Nor was he a mere compiler. We are indebted to him for several original voyages of great curiosity and value. He is not exempt, as has been seen, from error, but in point of learning, accuracy, and integrity, is certainly superior to Hakluyt; yet it is undoubted, that while the name of the former, like that of Vespucci, has become indelibly associated with the new World, his predecessor is very little known. Hakluyt has contrived to transfer, adroitly, to his volumes, the labours of others, and to give to them an aspect artfully attractive to those for whom they were intended. The very title—" Navigations, Voyages, Traffiques and Discoveries of the *English Nation,*" is alluring, however inappropriate to the contents such an exclusive designation may be found; and as the size and typographical execution of the work conspire to render the enterprise a very creditable one, for the early era of its appearance, the national complacency has rallied round it as a trophy, with a sort of enthusiasm. "It redounds," says Oldys, "as much to the glory of the English nation as any book that ever was published in it;" and Dr Dibdin, in the passage of his Library Companion, beginning, "All hail to thee, Richard Hakluyt!" employs, in his way, a still higher strain of panegyric. For a decayed gentleman, then, like Eden, it may not be wise to slight a patronising glance of recognition from one who stands so prosperously in the world's favour.

To establish him, therefore, in the high confidence of most readers, it will be sufficient to find Hakluyt (vol. iii. p. 498) quoting a passage from "that learned and painefull writer, Richard Eden;" and again (vol. i. p. 242) adverting to the sanction which Eden gives to the account of Chancellor's voyage. In the second volume (part ii. p. 10) other passages are copied from Eden's work. The extract from Peter Martyr d'Angleria, relative to Sebastian Cabot, given in the third volume (p. 8), is taken, without acknowledgement, from Eden's Translation (fol. 118, 119). As to the "Discourse" relative to the same navigator, given in Hakluyt (vol. iii. p. 6), he takes from Eden (fol. 255), every thing but the erroneous reference to the *second* volume of Ramusio, which is a blunder of his own, into which also he has led his copyist Purchas. The voyages to Guinea, found in Eden (fol. 343), are original, and were drawn up, as he says, "that sum memorie thereof might remayne to our posteritie, if eyther iniquitie of tyme, consumynge all things, or ignorance creepynge in by barbarousnesse, and contempte of knowledge, should hereafter bury in oblivion so woorthy attemptes." Hakluyt, in making the transfer to his work (vol. ii. part ii. p. 9), retains the introductory expressions, without the slightest acknowledge-

[illegible], so that our gratitude is directed to *him*, for having preserved an account of these voyages, and for the patriotic [illegible] which prompted the undertaking. This is the more calculated to mislead, as, immediately after these voyages, credit is given to Eden (p. 10), for a description of Africa; and the reader, noting a temper apparently so fair and candid, at once pronounces original whatever is not expressly referred to others. There is a voyage in Hakluyt (vol. ii. part ii. p. 14), designated at the head of the page, as that of "M. John Lok," and the writer says, "my chief intent hath been to show the course of the same, according to the observation and ordinary custom of the Mariners; and as I received it at the hands of an expert Pilot, being one of the chief in this voyage." No one, unacquainted with Eden, would suppose, that this is copied, verbatim, from his volume (fol. 349). So, in reference to the unfortunate Portuguese, *Pinteado*, who sailed from Portsmouth, when we find in Hakluyt (vol. ii. part ii. p. 14), "all these aforesaid writings I saw under seal in the house of my friend, Nicholas Liete, with whom Pinteado left them," there is no intimation that he is merely repeating the language of Eden (fol. 349). Again, in Eden (fol. 357), is a curious account, which Chancellor gave him, of a waterspout, by which Cabot had been placed in imminent peril. This also is found in Hakluyt (vol. ii. part ii. p. 21), without acknowledgement, and wears there the appearance of a direct communication to himself.

Somewhat less than one-half of Eden's work is occupied with an English version of Peter Martyr. Then come translations from the most rare and curious accounts of voyages and travels, Oviedo, Gomara, Ramusio, Pigafeta, Americus Vesputius, Munster, Bastaldus, Ziglerus, Cardanus, Paulus Jovius, Sigismondus Liberus, Vannuccius Biringuczius. Amongst the articles most worthy of attention, may be mentioned those on metals and the working of mines in ancient and modern times (fol. 326 to 342), on the prices of precious stones and spices, and the trade in spices (fol. 233, 244), on Russia (fol. 249 to 263), and on the manners and customs of the Tartars (fol. 299, &c.).

The circumstances which first inspired the author with a resolution to prepare the work, are told with much simplicity. He was a spectator of the public entry into London of Philip and Mary. As the splendid pageant swept by, in all its pomp, pride, and circumstance, amidst the tumultuous acclamations of the populace, the array of functionaries civil and military, and the deafening bursts of martial music, he describes himself as almost lifted out of self-command by the excitement of the scene, and at the crisis when the royal pair actually passed near him as ready to break out into some wild sally of enthusiasm. Restrained, happily, from this piece of indiscretion, he resolved to set about some work which he might, in due season, exhibit as the offspring of his teeming loyalty, and humbly crave for it the royal blessing.*

Of the success of the work, on its appearance, we know nothing; but it seems to have struggled with many difficulties in its progress to the light, and of these not the least mortifying to Eden must have been the disheartening timidity of his publishers. It were injustice not to render a passing tribute of gratitude to the liberality of one of them, "Master Toy," without, however, attempting to lift the veil which a gentle and generous temper has thrown over the infirmity of his associates. Eden's pecuniary disinterestedness, his earnest hope that his labours might be useful to others, and

* "Cum in primo vestro ingressu in hanc celeberriman Londini urbem (illustrissimi Principes) cernerem quanto omnium applausu, populi concursu, ac civium frequentia, quanto insuper spectaculorum nitore, nobilium virorum splendore, equorum multitudine, tubarum clangore, cœterisque magnificis pompis ac triumphis, pro dignitate vestra accepti estis dum omnes quod sui est officii facere satagebant, ubi in tanta hominum turba vix unus reperitatur qui non aliquid agendo adventum vestrum gratulabatur, cœpi et ego quoque aliorum exemplo (proprius præsertim ad me accedentibus Celsitudinibus vestris) tanto animi ardore ad aliquid agendum accendi ne solus in tanta hominum corona otiosus viderer quod *vix me continebam quin in aliquam extemporariam orationem temere erupuissem*, nisi et præsentiæ vestræ majestas et mea me obscuritas a tam audaci facinore deteruissent. Verum cum postea penitius de hac re mecum cogitassem, &c."

his honest anxiety for merited reputation, serve to heighten our indignation at the manner in which he has been undeservedly supplanted and thrust from the public view.

"The partners at whose charge this booke is prynted, *although the coppy, whereof they have wrought a long space have cost them nought*, doo not, nevertheless, cease, dayly, to caule uppon me to make an end and proceede no further; affirmynge that the booke will bee of so great a pryce, and not every man's money; fearying rather theyr losse and hynderance than carefull to be beneficial to other, as is now in manner the trade of all men, which ordinarie respecte of private commoditie hath at thys time so lyttle moved me, I take God to witness that for my paynes and travayles taken herein, such as they bee, I may uppon just occasion thynke myself a looser manye wayes, except such men of good inclination as shall take pleasure and feele sum commoditie in the knowledge of these thinges shall thynke me woorthy theyr goode worde, wherewith I shall repute myselfe and my travayles so abundantly satisfyed, that I shall repute other men's gains a recompense for my losses" (fol. 303). Again, "and to have sayde thus much of these vyages it may suffice; for (as I have sayd before), wheras the partners at whose charges thys booke is prynted, wolde long since have me proceaded no further, I had not thought to have wrytten any thynge of these viages [to Guinea], but that the liberalitie of Master Toy encouraged me to attempt the same, whiche I speake not to the reproache of other in whom I thynke there lacked no good wyll, but that they thought the booke would be too chargeable" (fol. 360).

Compare the modest and ingenuous language of this excellent personage with that of the well-fed and boastful Hakluyt, who, in the dedication of his translation of Galvano to Sir Robert Cecil, says, "And for ought I can see, there had no great matter yet come to light if *Myselfe* had not undertaken that heavie burden, being never therein *entertained to any purpose*, until I *had recourse* unto yourself, of whose special favour and *bountiful* patronage I have been *often* much encouraged, &c. &c."

But the work is rendered yet more precious by information scattered through it, derived from the great seamen of that day with whom the author's turn of mind led him to associate. Sebastian Cabot he seems to have known familiarly, and one chapter (fol. 249) has, for part of its title, "lykewyse of the vyages of that woorthy owlde man Sebastian Cabote, *yet livynge in England, and at this present* the governor of the Company of the Marchantes of Cathay, in the citie of London."

In one of his marginal notes (fol. 268) he gives us Cabot's statement to him, that the icebergs were of fresh, and not of salt water; and again in the marginal note (fol. 255), we have what Cabot said as to the quantity of grain raised by him in the La Plata, corrected afterwards at fol. 317. Speaking of the voyage to the North-East projected by Cabot, in which Richard Chancellor, as pilot major, accompanied Sir Hugh Willoughby, and succeeded, after the death of his gallant but unfortunate commander, in opening the trade to Russia, Eden says (fol. 256), "And whereas I have before made mention howe Moscovia was in our time discovered by Richard Chancellor, in his viage toward Cathay, by the direction and information of the sayde master Sebastian, *who longe before had this secreate in his mynde,* I shall not neede here, &c." The account of Cabot's escape from the waterspout (fol. 357) has been already adverted to.

We may note here, that Forster, in his "Voyage and Discoveries in the North" (p. 269), gravely considers, and almost sanctions, a doubt of the French writer Bergeron whether the Sebastian Cabot so conspicuous in the reign of Edward VI. could have been the same who discovered the continent of America. It may serve to show the very slight preparation with which many works of reputation on these subjects have been got up, that in the course of the argument no reference is made to Eden, who conveys from the lips of the "good owlde man" himself, interesting particulars of his earlier voyages! So, also, in a more recent work,* the following expressions are found (p. 361), "We must now return to the period of the first attempt to find out a North-East passage to India. A society of merchants had been formed in London for this purpose. Sebastian Cabot, *either the son or the grandson of John Cabot*, and who held the situation of grand pilot of England, under Edward VI., was chosen governor of this society!"

---

* Historical Sketch of the Progress of Discovery, Navigation, and Commerce from the earliest records to the beginning of the nineteenth century. By William Stevenson, Esq., forming vol. xviii. of Kerr's Collection of Voyages, &c.

Another of Eden's personal friends seems to have been Richard Chancellor. At fol. 291, we find that celebrated mariner giving an account of the ingenuity of the Russians in the construction of their buildings; and at fol. 298, a further account of that people. He tells Eden (ib.) of an ambassador whom he saw there from the "province of Sibier," who gave him some curious information about the "Great Chan." He met also with the Ambassador of the Kinge of Persia, called the Great Sophie," who was not only civil, but very useful to him.

But it is time to turn to the more immediate object of this chapter—the birth-place of Cabot.

In order to comprehend the full value of the information supplied by Eden, it may be well to show, in the first place, how the matter has been treated by others.

"Sebastian Cabote is, by many of our writers, affirmed to be an Englishman, born at Bristol, but the Italians as positively claim him for their countryman, and say he was born at Venice, which, to speak impartially, I believe to be the truth, *for he says himself, that when his father was invited over to England, he brought him with him, though he was then very young*" (Harris's Collection of Voyages, vol. ii. p. 191). These expressions are copied, verbatim, by Pinkerton (Collection of Voyages and Travels, vol. xii. p. 160). In the history of Navigation, prefixed to Churchill's Collection of Voyages (vol. i. p. 39), said to have been drawn up by Locke, and found in his works (vol. x. Lond. ed. of 1823, p. 428), reference is made to "Sebastian Cabot, a Venetian, but residing in England." Purchas says of him (vol. iii. Pilgrims, p. 901), "He was an Englishman by breeding, *borne a Venetian*, but spending most part of his life in England, and English employments." Even when he states (vol. iii. p. 807), that on the "Effigies" of Sebastian Cabot hung up in the Royal Gallery, that personage is called an Englishman, he adds—"for his English breeding, condition, affection and advancement, termed an Englishman," and referring, on another occasion to the same document, says, "*He was born at Venice*, and serving Henry VII., Henry VIII., and Edward VI., was *accounted* English. *Galpano says*, he was born at Bristol." By Galpano, he means the Portuguese writer Galvano, or Galvam, in whose work, translated by Hakluyt, that statement is made (p. 66), as it is also by *Herrera* (Dec. i. lib. ix. cap. 13), whom Purchas himself quotes (vol. iv. p. 177 to that point.

In defiance of the contemporary "Effigies," and of these foreign authorities, most modern writers, Hume, Forster, Charlevoid, &c. have been led astray. The Quarterly Review (vol. xvi. p. 154, *note*) informs us that Henry VII. engaged "the *Cabots of Venice* in the *discovery of Newfoundland;*" and Mr Barrow, in his "Chronological History of Voyages, &c." (p. 36—7), speaks of the credit due to England, for having "so wisely and honourably enrolled this deserving foreigner in the list of her citizens."

Now it will scarcely be credited, that we have in Eden, a positive statement on the subject, from the lips of Sebastian Cabot himself. The following marginal note will be found at fol. 255—"SEBASTIAN CABOTE TOULD ME that he was borne in Brystowe, and that at iiii. yeare ould he was carried with his father to Venice, and so returned agayne into England with his father after certayne years, whereby he was *thought to have been* born in Venice." Thus, then, was the question conclusively settled 275 years ago! It is needless to repeat what has been already said, in another place, as to the slight credit due to the report of the conversation relied on by Harris, Pinkerton, and the rest, for there is, in fact, no discrepance to be reconciled. Cabot there states the circumstances which more immediately preceded the commission from Henry VII.; and the occasion did not lead to any detail of his own earlier history. Should Sir Edward Parry be recalled to embark on a new voyage of discovery, he might very naturally advert, hereafter, to the period of his return, and would scarcely deem it necessary to add that he had been in the country before. For the future, then, it is to be hoped that no perverse efforts will be made to obscure the claim of England to this Great Seaman. He owed to her his birth, and the language and associations of childhood. He returned thither while yet a boy ("*pene infans*" is the expression of Peter Martyr), and grew up there to manhood, when he was commissioned to go in quest of new regions, wherein he "set up the banner" of England. Under this banner, he was the first European who reached the shores of the American Continent. He ended, as he had begun, his career in the service of his native country, infusing into her Marine a spirit of lofty enterprise—a high moral tone—a system of mild, but inflexible discipline, of which the results were, not long after, so conspicuously displayed. Finally, he is seen to open new sources of commerce, of which the influence may be distinctly traced on her present greatness and prosperity. Surely it is as absurd as it is unnatural, to deny to such a man the claim which he seems to have anxiously preferred, and which has been placed on record under his direct sanction.

CHAP. IX.

THE PATENTS OF 5TH MARCH, 1496, AND 3RD FEBRUARY, 1498.

BEFORE proceeding to a close examination of the documents which establish the real history of these voyages, it may be well to advert to the reckless manner in which facts have been made to yield to any hypothesis which a short-sighted view has suggested as indispensable.

The following passage is found in Harris' Voyages (ed. of 1744—8, vol. ii. p. 190), and in Pinkerton's Collection (vol. xii. p. 158).

"But the year before that patent was granted, viz. in 1494, John Cabot, with his son Sebastian, had sailed from Bristol upon discovery, and had actually seen the *Continent of Newfoundland*, to which they gave the name of *Prima Vista*, or *first seen*. And on the 24th June, *in the same year*, he went ashore on an Island which, because it was discovered on that day, he called *St John's*; and of this Island he reported, very truly, that the soil was barren, that it yielded little, and that the people wear bearskin clothes, and were armed with bows, arrows, pikes, darts, wooden clubs, and slings; but that the coast abounded with fish, *and upon this report of his, the before-mentioned patent (of 5th March 1495) was granted.*"

Mr Barrow also says (p. 32),

"There is *no possible* way of *reconciling* the various accounts collected by Hakluyt, and which amount to no less a number than six, but by supposing John Cabot to have made one voyage, at least, previous to the date of the patent, and some time between that and the date of the return of Columbus, either in 1494 or 1495."

It must by this time be apparent, that the hypothesis thus started, is not only uncalled for, but would contradict every authentic account which has come down to us.

It is altogether irreconcilable with that very document which stands foremost of the "six," on the pages of Hakluyt —the extract from the map cut by Clement Adams, and hung up in the Privy Gallery—for it is there declared expressly, that at five o'clock in the morning, of the 24th June, 1497, was discovered that land, which no man before that time had attempted to approach ("quam *nullus* prius adire ausus fuit"). What possible motive can be imagined, on the part of Cabot, for disguising the fact of a discovery made so long before? The supposition is as absurd, as it is gratuitous. How, again, does it agree with the statement of Sebastian Cabot, that on the voyage made under the royal authority, he was surprised by the sight of land, "not thinking to find any other land than that of Cathay?" This is one of the "six" accounts which it is proposed to *reconcile* by assuming a discovery of the same region three years before!

The first patent bears date the 5th March, in the eleventh year of the reign of Henry VII. It is found in Rymer (Fœdera, vol. xii. p. 595), who correctly refers it to 5th March, 1496, the computation of this monarch's reign being from August, 1485. Hakluyt states it to be of 1495 (vol. iii. p. 5), looking, as we may infer, not to the Historical, but to the Legal or Civil year, which commenced, prior to 1752, on the 25th March.

The patent is in favour of John Cabot and his three sons, Lewis, Sebastian, and Sancius; and authorises them, their heirs, or *deputies*, to "sail to all parts, countries, and seas of the East, of the West, and of the North, under our banners and ensigns, with five ships of what burthen or quantity soever they be, and as many mariners or men as they will have with them in the said ships, upon their own proper costs and charges, to seek out, discover, and find whatsoever isles, countries, regions, or provinces of the heathen and infidels, whatsoever they be, and in what part of the world soever they be, which *before this time* have been *unknown to all Christians.*" It is plain, that a previous discovery, so far from being assigned as the ground for the patent, as Harris, Pinkerton, &c. assert, is negatived by its very terms. The patent would be inapplicable to any region previously visited by either of the Cabots, and confer no right. Assuming, what is obviously absurd, that the discovery could have been made without becoming at once universally known, yet the patentees must have been aware that they exposed themselves, at any moment when the fact should come out, to have the grant vacated on the ground of a deceptive concealment.

The patentees are authorised to set up the Royal banner, "in every village, town, castle, isle, or main land, by them newly found," and to subdue, occupy, and possess all such regions, and to exercise jurisdiction over them in the name of the King of England. One-fifth of the clear profit of the enterprise is reserved to the King, and it is stipulated that the vessels shall return to the port of Bristol. The privilege of exclusive resort and traffic is secured to the patentees.

The Second Patent is dated the third of February, in the thirteenth year of the reign of Henry VII., corresponding with third February 1498. The only evidence heretofore published on the subject, is contained in a brief memorandum found in Hakluyt (vol. iii. p. 6), who, we are persuaded, never saw the original. The person, also, who gave him the information of its existence, probably did not go beyond a list of the titles of instruments of that description kept for convenient reference. The memorandum of Hakluyt is as follows:—

"The King, upon the third day of February, in the thirteenth year of his reign, gave license to John Caboto to take six English ships in any haven or havens of the realm of England, being of the burden of two hundred tons or under, with all necessary furniture, and to take also into the said ships, all such masters, mariners and subjects of the King as willingly would go with him," &c.

Such being the whole of the information supplied, it is no wonder, that the most erroneous conjectures have been started.

Dr Robertson (History of America, book ix.) adopts the dates of Hakluyt. "This Commission (the first) was granted on March 5th, 1495, in less than two years after the return of Columbus from America. But Cabot (for that is the name he assumed in England, and by which he is best known) did not set out on his voyage for two years." Dr Robertson makes no express reference to the second commission, and having followed Hakluyt in referring that of the eleventh Henry VII. to 1495, he doubtless regarded the order of the thirteenth year of Henry VII. as merely a final permission for the departure of the expedition, made out in 1497 on the eve of its sailing.

In "The Naval History of England in all its Branches," by Lediard, it is said (p. 85) after giving the first patent—

"Hakluyt, from whom I have taken this commission, places in the margin, A.D. 1495. But, according to Rymer's Fœdera, it was dated March 5, 1496. To the ship granted by the king, of which, however, this commission makes no mention, some merchants of London added three more, laden with such slight commodities as were thought proper for commerce with barbarous people. By an extract from a record of the rolls, it appears, that though Cabot's commission was signed in March, 1495, or 1496, he did not go to sea on this expedition till the beginning of the year 1497. This record is in the following words." He then gives Hakluyt's notice of the patent of February 3, 1498.

The same notion that the second patent preceded discovery has found its way across the Atlantic, but with an observance of the historical computation as to dates. Thus, in the valuable Introduction to Marshall's Life of Washington, the first patent is correctly referred to March 5, 1496; and it is said, "The Expedition contemplated at the date of the commission appears not then to have been made, but in May (1498) Cabot, with his second son," &c.

Forster (p. 266) says, "In the 13th year of this king's reign, John Cabot obtained permission to sail with six ships of 200 tons burthen and under, on new discoveries. He did not sail, however, *till* the beginning of May, 1497 (!) and then, *by his own account*, had but two ships fitted out and stocked with provisions at the king's expense, &c."

In *Harris's* Voyages, &c. (Ed. of 1744—8, vol. ii. p. 190), and in Pinkerton (vol. xii. p. 158), after stating, not conjecturally, but as an unquestionable fact, that the first voyage was in 1494, it is added,

"The next voyage made for discovery was by Sebastian Cabot, the son of John, concerning which all our writers have fallen into great mistakes, for want of comparing the several accounts we have of this voyage, and making proper allowances for the manner in which they were written; since I cannot find there was ever any distinct and clear account of this voyage published, though it was of so great consequence. On the contrary, I believe that Cabot himself kept no journal of it by him; since, in a letter he wrote on this subject, he speaks doubtfully of the very year in which it was undertaken, though, from the circumstances he relates, that may be very certainly fixed. On the 3d of February, in the 13th year of the reign of King Henry VII. a new grant was made to John Cabot, by which he had leave given him to take ships out of any of the Ports of England, of the burthen of 200 tons, to sail upon discoveries; but before this could be effected, John Cabot died, and Sebastian, his son, applied himself to the king, proposing to discover a North-West Passage, as he himself tells us; and for this purpose, he had a ship manned and victualled at the king's expense, at Bristol, and three or four other ships were fitted out, at the expense of some merchants of that city, particularly Mr Thorne, and Mr Hugh Elliot. But whereas Sebastian Cabot himself says that he made this voyage in the summer of 1496, he must be mistaken; and he very well might, speaking from his memory only: and to prove this, I need only observe, that this date will not at all agree, even with his own account of the voyage; for he says expressly, it was undertaken after his father's death, who, as we have shown, was alive in the February following; so that it was the summer of the year 1497 in which he made this voyage, and what he afterwards relates of his return proves this likewise."

It is scarcely necessary to remark, that aside from all other considerations, the whole of their statement is in direct collision with the fact, that the discovery of the 24th June, 1497, is referred, on evidence which these writers do not undertake to question, to the joint agency of father and son. That, therefore, which should decisively control speculation, is blindly sacrificed to an effort to get over some minor difficulties which, in reality, have their origin only in the kindred misconceptions of preceding compilers.

All this obscurity will now disappear. After a tedious search there has been found, at the Rolls Chapel, the original patent of 3d February, 1498. The following is an exact copy:

"Memorandum quod tertio die Februarii anno regni Regis Henrici Septimi xiii.

ista Billa delibata fuit Domino Cancellario Angliæ apud Westmonasterium exe- [illegible]

"To the Kinge.

"Please it your Highnesse of your most noble and habundaunt grace to graunte to John Kabotto, Venecian, your gracious Lettres Patents in due fourme to be made accordyng to the tenor hereafter ensuyng, and he shall continually praye to God for the preservacion of your moste Noble and Roiall astate longe to endure.

"H. R.

"Rex.

"To all men to whom theis Presenteis shall come send Gretyng: Knowe ye that We of our Grace especiall, and for dyvers causis us movying, We Have geven and graunten, and by theis Presentis geve and graunte to our welbeloved John Kabotto, Venecian, sufficiente auctorite and power, that he, by him his Deputie or Deputies sufficient, may take at his pleasure VI Englisshe Shippes in any Porte or Portes or other place within this our Realme of England or obeisance, so that and if the said Shippes be of the bourdeyn of CC. tonnes or under, with their apparail requisite and necessarie for the safe conduct of the said Shippes, and them *convey and lede to the Londe and Isles of late founde by the seid John in oure name and by our commaundemente.* Paying for theym and every of theym as and if we should in or for our owen cause paye and noon otherwise. And that the said John, by hym his Deputie or Deputies sufficiente, maye take and receyve into the said Shippes, and every of theym all such maisters, maryners, Pages, and other subjects as of their owen free wille woll goo and passe with him in the same Shippes *to the seid Londe or Iles,* withoute anye impedymente, lett or perturbance of any of our officers or mnistres or subjects whatsoever they be by theym to the seyd John, his Deputie, or Deputies, and all other our seid subjects or any of theym passinge with the seyd John in the said Shippes to the seid Londe or Iles to be doon, or suffer to be doon or attempted. Geving in commaundement to all and every our officers, ministres and subjects seying or herying thies our Lettres Patents, without any ferther commaundement by Us to theym or any of theym to be geven to perfourme and socour the said John, his Deputie and all our said Subjects so passyng with hym according to the tenor of theis our Lettres Patentis. Any Statute, Acte, or Ordennance to the contrarye made or to be made in any wise notwithstanding."

Surely the importance of this document cannot be exaggerated. It establishes conclusively, and for ever, that the American continent was first discovered by an expedition commissioned to "set up the banner" of England. It were idle to offer an argument to connect this recital of 3d February, 1498, with the discovery of the 24th June, 1497, noted on the old map hung up at Whitehall. Will it not be deemed almost incredible that the very Document in the Records of England, which recites the great discovery, and plainly contemplates a scheme of colonization, should, up to this moment, have been treated by her own writers as the one which first gave the permission to go forth and explore?

Nay, this very instrument has been used as an argument against the pretensions of England; for it has been asked by foreigners who have made the computation, and seen through the mistake of Pinkerton and the rest, why the patent of 3d February, 1498, took no notice of discoveries pretended to have been made the year before. The question is now triumphantly answered.

The importance of negativing a notion that the English discoveries were subsequent to the patent of the 13th Henry VII., will strikingly appear, on reference to the claim of *Americus Vespucius*. The truth, as now established, places beyond all question—even crediting the doubtful assertions of Vespucius—the priority of Cabot's discovery over that of the lucky Florentine. The map in Queen Elizabeth's gallery made no false boast in declaring that on the 24th June 1497, the English expedition discovered that land "quam nullus prius adire ausus fuit."*

---

* The manner in which the precious Document referred to, and others of a similar kind, are kept, cannot be adverted to without an expression of regret. They are thrown loosely together, without reference even to the appropriate *year*, and are unnoticed in any Index or Calendar. It required a search of more than two weeks to find this patent of 3d February 1498, although the year and day of its date were furnished at the outset. Another document which appears in the present volume—the patent of Henry VII. to three Portuguese and others, dated 19 March, 1501, authorising them to follow up the discoveries of Cabot—has never before been published. This also was discovered, after a long search, not even folded up, but lying with one-half of the written part exposed, and, in consequence, so soiled and discoloured that it was with the greatest difficulty it could be decyphered, and some words finally eluded the most anxious scrutiny. And

this of two documents indispensable to the history of Maritime Discovery, and for the want of which, the account of these voyages has been completely unintelligible! An extraordinary compensation is claimed at the Rolls Chapel on account of the trouble attending a search amidst such a confused mass. For *finding* the documents, two guineas were demanded in addition to the cost of copies. The applicant is informed, that the charge must be paid, whether the document be discovered or not; so that the officer has no motive to continue perseveringly the irksome pursuit.

CHAP. X.

NAME OF CABOT'S SHIP—HOW FAR HE PROCEEDED ALONG THE COAST TO THE SOUTHWARD—SUBSEQUENT VOYAGE OF 1498.

THE name of the vessel which first touched the shores of the American continent is not without interest. The *Matthew*, of Bristol, had that proud distinction. A respectable writer* furnishes the following passage from an ancient Bristol manuscript in his possession:—

"In the year 1497, the 24th June, on St John's day, was Newfoundland found by Bristol men, in a ship called *The Matthew*."

The question how far Cabot, on quitting the north, proceeded along the coast of the Continent, has been the subject of contradictory statements. By some his progress is limited to a latitude corresponding with that of the straits of Gibraltar, while others insist on carrying him to the extreme point of the Atlantic sea coast. We can hardly be at a loss to decide, when it is recollected that while there is no direct authority for the latter opinion, and it is one which would readily be adopted, in mistake, from the vague use, originally, of the title *Florida*, the former has the direct sanction of Peter Martyr (Dec. iii. cap. vi.).

"Tetenditque tantum ad meridiem, littore sese incurvante, ut Herculei freti latitudinis *fere* gradus equarit; ad occidentemque profectus tantum est ut Cubam Insulam a læva longitudine graduum *pene* parem habuerit." "He was thereby brought so far into the South, by reason of the land bending so much to the south-

---

* "The History and Antiquities of the City of Bristol, compiled from original Records and authentic Manuscripts in public offices or private hands. By William Barrett. Bristol, 1789," p. 172. The same fact is stated in The History of Bristol by John Corry and the Rev. John Evans, vol. i. p. 213. (In King's Library, title in Catalogue *Corry*.)

ward, that it was there almost equal in latitude with the sea Fretum Herculeum having the North Pole elevate in a manner in the same degree. He sailed likewise in this tract so far towards the West, that he had the Island of Cuba on his left hand *in manner*, in the same degree of longitude." (Hakluyt, vol. iii. p. 9.)

Gomara, more definitely but perhaps only determining by conjecture the circumstantial statement of Peter Martyr, names, as has been seen, 38°. Hakluyt, in the dedication of his second volume to Sir Robert Cecil, boasts of the universal acknowledgement, even by foreigners, "that all that mighty tract of land, from 67 degrees northward, to the latitude *almost* of Florida, was first discovered out of England, by the commandment of King Henry VII.;" and again, in a marginal note of his third volume (p. 9), he states that Cabot discovered "the northern parts of that land, and from thence as far *almost* as Florida."

Peter Martyr informs us that a failure of provisions at this point compelled an abandonment of the further pursuit of the coast, and a return to England.

It has been preferred to settle the question before quitting the first voyage, because the progress to the southward *may* have taken place on that occasion, as a discovery of both "*Londe* and Isles" is recited in the second patent. Should a further development of the subject lead to an opinion that this incident, mentioned first by Peter Martyr, belongs to another voyage which that writer more probably had in view, there will be no difficulty in adjusting it hereafter to its proper place. *

* One piece of evidence has lately been brought to light from which it may be inferred that Cabot returned to England immediately after the discovery of the 24th June, 1497. In the account of the Privy Purse Expenses of Henry VII., is the following entry :—"10th August, 1407. To hym that found the New Isle, 10*l.*"

The document referred to, which forms one of the Additional MSS. in the British Museum, is in the hand-writing of Craven Orde, Esq., formerly one of the Secondaries of the office of the King's Remembrancer of the Court of Exchequer, and has recently been given to the public by Harris Nicolas, Esq., in his valuable *Excerpta Historica.* Mr N. remarks, "The originals, doubtless, form part of the muniments of the King's Remembrancer's Office, and though the great exertions which have been made to collate these extracts with them received every assistance from the King's Remembrancer and the other officers, they failed, because these

The interesting inquiry now arises as to subsequent voyages, made after the death of John Cabot which is supposed to have taken place shortly after the date of the second patent of 3rd February, 1498.

It cannot be supposed, for a moment, that Sebastian Cabot would lightly abandon what had been so hardly won. He was named in the original patent; and a right under the discovery vested in him, aside from his claim as the son of John Cabot. A large sum had been expended on the first voyage, and was now represented solely by the title to the newly discovered region. He must have been strangely insensible to his interests, as well as suddenly deficient in enterprise, to turn away, without further effort, from a pursuit which had thus far been crowned with the most flattering success.

The first item of evidence on the subject, is that supplied by Stow. Under the year 1498, and in the Mayoralty of William Purchas, there occurs, in the Annals, the following statement:—

"This yeere, one Sebastian Gaboto, a Genoas sonne, borne in Bristow, professing himselfe to be expert in knowledge of the circuit of the world and islands of the same, as by his charts and other reasonable demonstrations he shewed, caused the King to man, and victuall a ship at Bristow to search for an island, which he knew to be replenished with rich commodities: in the ship divers merchants of London adventured small stocks, and in the company of this ship, sailed also out of Bristow, three or foure small shippes fraught with sleight and grosse wares, as coarse cloth, caps, laces, points, and such other."

It has already been proved, in another place, that this was the statement made by Stow to Hakluyt, and that the substi-

---

MSS. are presumed to be in some of the numerous bags that are lying unarranged in Westminster Hall, an examination of which could only be effected at a sacrifice of time and expense, which no private individual can incur." Since the publication, it has been ascertained that a portion of what is supposed to be the original is in the possession of Sir Thomas Phillips, having been purchased by him at a sale of the effects of Mr Orde. Unfortunately, it does not go further back than the year 1502.

tution, by the latter, of the name of *John* Cabot took place afterwards, at two successive stages of alteration. The fact clearly appeared, by a reference to Hakluyt's earlier volume of 1582, and by the name of *Sebastian* Cabot, which yet lingers incautiously in the enlarged work at the head of Stow's communication, even after a change in the body of it. We have then before us, here, the honest result of Stow's researches.

There can be no mistake as to the period to which he would refer this incident; for the mayoralty of Purchas, is mentioned in the communication to Hakluyt (vol. iii. p. 9). When, too, under the year 1502, he speaks of the exhibition of savages, reference is made to what he had before stated as occurring in the time of that Mayor. Speed (747) so understands him and Purchas (Pilgrims, vol. iii. p. 808).

It appears, by the list of these functionaries found in the various Chroniclers, that the mayoralty of Purchas extended from 28 October, 1497 to 28 October, 1498. Unless then we suppose a mistake to have been committed, the voyage alluded to was subsequent to that of the original discovery.

A matter so simple as this has not escaped mis-statement. Thus, in M'Pherson's Annals of Commerce (vol. ii. p. 13, *note*), it is said, "We may depend on the contemporary testimony of Alderman Fabyan, who says that he sailed in the beginning of May in the mayoralty of John Tate, that is 1497, but returned in the subsequent mayoralty of William Purchas." Here is as much error as could be condensed into one sentence. Fabyan does *not* place the expedition in the mayoralty of Tate, but in that of Purchas, and we are told, that no tidings were heard of the expedition during that Mayor's time, viz. as late as October, 1498. It is, indeed, a singular fact that writers who on most topics are dull, common-place, and safe—who might be trusted, one would think, in poetry itself, without peril to their matter-of-fact character—instantly become imaginative on touching any part of Cabot's history.

In connexion with the statement of Stow, it may be mentioned that both Peter Martyr and the person, said to be Galeatius Butrigarius, who held the conversation with Cabot, at Seville, speak of a voyage from England subsequent to the father's death. Peter Martyr, in the passage usually cited on the subject, says nothing of dates, but writing afterwards in 1524, (Decade vii. cap. ii.) he refers to Cabot's voyage, as having taken place "twenty-six years since," that is, in 1498. To these statements, another is to be added, though it increases, perhaps, rather the number than the weight of authorities.

The first article in the third volume of Ramusio is a Summary of The Spanish Discoveries in the New World, drawn professedly from Peter Martyr, and entitled "Sommario della Historia dell' Indie Occidentali cavato dalli libri scritti dal Sig. Don Pietro Martire." It was first published anonymously, at Venice, in a separate form, in the year 1543,* and is quite unworthy of the place which it now occupies. The arrangement of Peter Martyr is entirely disregarded, and no reference is given to the original, by which any of the statements may be verified or disproved. Under the pretended sanction, too, of Peter Martyr, the writer has introduced many unfounded, and even absurd, assertions of his own. Thus the statement given in the original of the manner in which the bears catch fish, and which is confirmed by late accounts,† this writer has spun out‡ into a minute and ridiculous description. It is here stated that Cabot reached only 55°, an assertion which the Biographie Universelle (art. Cabot) copies and cites as from Peter Martyr, when there is nothing of the kind in the original. In repeating the expression of Peter Martyr, about the death of the father, this writer says—"after whose death, *finding himself very rich* and of great ambition,

---

* *Haym's* "Bibliotheca Italiana o sia notizia de Libro rari Italiani," p. 131.

† See Cartwright's Labrador.

‡ Ramusio, tom. iii. fol. 35, in Index "Bacalai," "*Sebastiano* Gabotto," and "orso."

he resolved," &c. ("da poi la morte del quale trovandosi ricchissimo et di grande animo deliberò," &c.) But, without laying any stress on such a statement, there is sufficient without it to supply an important auxiliary argument to that derived from the chroniclers.*

One circumstance is to be particularly noted. The second patent does not look to further discoveries, but merely authorises the patentee to revisit the Region already found, and to take thither such of the king's subjects as might be inclined to accompany him or his deputies.

According to Stow, the "Genoa's son" effected his object with the king, by a representation as to an Island "which he *knew* to be replenished with rich commodities," or as it is expressed in Hakluyt, "which he said he *knew well* was rich and replenished with great commodities." Thus the language of the patent and of the chronicles is in consonance as to the purpose of the voyage of 1498. It no longer had reference, exclusively, to the search for a North-West Passage. The place of destination was some known definite point, which was supposed to offer an advantageous opening for traffic.

The argument to be fairly drawn from this coincidence is placed in a very striking point of view, by referring to writers who approached the statement of the chronicles under the misconception that the reference was to the original expedition of 1497. Campbell, in The Lives of the Admirals

---

* It is obvious that the Will of John Cabot might throw much light on this subject. If, as is probable, he died at Bristol, it would be proved at Worcester. On application at the Bishop's Registry, the acting Registrar, Mr Clifton, writes thus: "The indices of Wills proved, and letters of administration granted do not extend farther back than the year 1600. Previous to this period, these documents are tied up in linen bags *without much form or order;* so that a search for the Will of John Cabot, or Gabot, or Kabot would be attended with *very considerable* trouble and expense, whilst the *chance* of discovering it would be uncertain." Aside from Historical purposes, it would be curious to see an instrument, dated some months before the time when Columbus (in August, 1498) first saw the Continent of America, which, probably, makes a disposition of the testator's interest in the tract of land lying between the present Hudson's Strait and Florida.

(article, *Sir John Cabot*), adopts Hakluyt's substitution of John Cabot's name, and thus speaks of the patent of 3rd February, 1498.

"In consequence of this license, the King at his own expense caused a ship to be equipped at Bristol : to this the merchants of that city, and of London, added three or four small vessels, freighted with proper commodities, which fleet sailed *in the spring of the year* 1497. Our old Chronicle writers, particularly Fabian, tell us of a very rich island which John Cabot promised to discover ; but *in this they seem to mistake the matter for want of thoroughly understanding the subject of which they were writing.* John Cabot was too a wise man to pretend to know, *before he saw it,* what country he should discover, whether island or continent ; *but what he proposed was to find a North-West passage to the Indies.*"

How does this patent of 3rd February 1498 scatter light around in every direction! After slumbering at the Rolls for upwards of three centuries, it reappears to vindicate, triumphantly, the fair fame of its venerable contemporaries thus flippantly assailed!

The same difficulty in reconciling the language of the ancient chronicles with the supposed allusion to the voyage of 1497, has led Harris* (ed. of 1744—8, vol. ii. p. 190) and Pinkerton (vol. xii. p. 158) to the positive assertion that John Cabot made a voyage as early as 1494, and that "upon this report of his," the first patent was granted. Mr Barrow also (p. 32) is, from the same cause, driven to the assertion that it is impossible to understand the various accounts "but by supposing John Cabot to have made one voyage at least previous to the date of the patent." It has been before shown, that such a supposition is not only inconsistent with every authentic statement, but at variance with the terms of the first patent itself. We now see that it is as unnecessary as it is unwarranted.

The plain distinction between the two voyages clears up

---

* It is but just to remark, that though the volume here referred to bears the name of Harris, and is so copied and cited by Pinkerton, yet the passages in question make no part of the original work. Daines Barrington, Esq. in his "Possibility of approaching the North Pole," &c. (ed. of 1818, p. 15), states, that the supplemental matter was furnished by Dr Campbell. No method is used to distinguish the original from what is interpolated ; and Pinkerton was, probably, thus misled.

an incidental difficulty. Many writers have been perplexed by finding that while some accounts speak of the enterprise as wholly at the expense of the Cabots, others represent the King to have had an interest in it. The reason is now obvious. The first vague exploratory voyage was at the expense of the individuals, to verify the speculations of Sebastian Cabot. The patent of 5th March, 1496, says expressly, that the enterprise is to be "at their own proper cost and charge." But when a specific discovery had been made, and the attention of the capitalists of London was drawn to the subject, the wary king himself yielded to the sanguine representations of the discoverers, and became a partner in the concern. This fact is very clearly established by the following entries in the Account of his Privy-Purse Expenses:—

"22d March, 1498. To Lanslot Thirkill, of London, upon a prest,* for his shippe going towards the New Ilande, 20*l.*"

"Delivered to Launcelot Thirkill, going towards the New Isle, in prest, 20*l.*"

"April 1, 1498. To Thomas Bradley, and Lancelot Thirkill, going to the New Isle, 30*l.*"

"To John Carter, going to the Newe Isle, in rewarde, 2*l.*"

At this point the subject attracted the attention of a Chronicler living in London. It is not unnatural that he should suppose the region discovered to be an island, and that the same expression should be used by the Keeper of the Privy Purse, and others, whose minds had not then embraced the idea of a new Continent. The Chronicler speaks of documents submitted to the inspection of the king, and of the nature of which he evidently knew only by vague report. The King himself, however, who had listened to the statements of "the Genoas son," and saw his map, who heard of the mighty rivers which were found issuing into the sea, knew from these "charts and other reasonable demonstrations," that here must be something more than an island, and we find, accordingly, in the patent of 3rd February, 1498, reference made to "the *Londe and Isles*," discovered.

* In the way of loan or advance.

To doubt, then, that a voyage took place in 1498, under Sebastian Cabot, violates every probability, is against strong collateral testimony, and rejects contemptuously the direct and positive averment of the ancient Chroniclers, at the very moment when we warm with indignation at the attempt of a shallow and presumptuous ignorance to depreciate them.

What was the result of the voyage? This is a question of more difficulty.

Peter Martyr and Gomara mention, as has been seen, that Sebastian Cabot had with him three hundred men. It is difficult to believe that such a number could have been taken in reference to a mere commercial enterprise, and absurd to connect them with the first exploratory voyage. The language, too, of the second patent seems to suggest that a settlement was intended, the royal permission to depart extending to "all such masters, mariners, pages *and other subjects, as of their own free will, will go and pass with him in the same ships, to the said Londe or Isles.*"

On a point so interesting as this, we may repeat here the language of Gomara. After mentioning that Sebastian Cabot was the first who brought intelligence of the Baccalaos, he proceeds:—

"El qual armo dos navios en Inglaterra do tratava desde pequeno a costa del Rey Enrique Septimo, quo desseava contratar en la especieria, como hazia el rey d' Portugal. Otros disen que a su costa. Y que prometio al rey Enrique de yr por el norte al Catayo y traer de alla especias en menos tiempo que Portuguese, por el sur. Y va tambien *par saber que tierra eran las Indias para poblar*. Llevo trezientos hombres y cammo la buelta de Isladia sobre cabo del Labrador. Y hasta se poner en cinquenta y ocho grados. Aunque el dize mucho mas contando como avia por el mes de Julio tato frio y pedaços de yelo que no oso passar mas adelante. Y que los dios eran grandissimos y quasi sin noche y las noches muy claras. Es cierte que a sesenta grados son los dies de diez y ocho horas. Diedo pues Gaboto la frialdad, y estraneza dela tierra, dio la vuelta hazia poniente *y rehaziendo se en los Baccalaos* corrio la costa hasta treienta y ochos grados y torno se de alli a Inglaterra." "Sebastian Cabot was the fyrst that browght any knowleage of this lande. For beinge in Englande in the dayes of Kyng Henry the Seventh, he furnysshed twoo shippes at his owne charges, or (as sum say) at the Kynges, whome he persuaded that a passage might be founde to Cathay by the North Seas, and that spices might be brought from thense soner by that way, then by the vyage the Portugales vse by the sea of Sur. *He went also to knowe what maner of landes those Indies were to inhabite. He had with hym three hundreth men,* and directed his course by the tracte of Islande vppon the cape of Labrador at lviii degrees: affirmynge that in the monethe of July there was such could and heapes of ise that he durst passe no further: also that the dayes were very longe and in maner without nyght, and the nyghtes very clear. Certayne it is, that the lx. degrees, the longest day is of xviii. houres. But consyderynge the coulde and the straungeness of the unknowen lande, he turned his course from thense to the West, folowynge the coast of the lande of Baccalos vnto the xxxviii. degrees, from whense he returned to Englande." (Eden's Decades, fol. 318.)

From these expressions it is plain that it was understood to have been part of the design to make the experiment of colonization.

Connected with this part of the subject is a curious passage in an old work by Thevet, the French Cosmographer. This writer is, deservedly, held in little estimation, his work being disfigured by the plainest marks of haste, as well as by the most absurd credulity. The only circumstance which could induce us to attach importance to his statement is, the allusion to conversations with Cartier, who, in 1534, visited the St Lawrence. Thevet not only refers to that navigator incidentally here, but in his subsequent larger work, entitled *Cosmographie Universelle*, speaks of Cartier repeatedly, as his intimate friend, and mentions (Paris Ed. of 1575, tom. ii. fol. 1014) having spent five months with him at St Malo. The work now particularly alluded to is entitled "Singularitez de la France Antarctique," published at Paris, in 1558, in which, speaking of the Baccalaos, there occurs (ch. 74, fol. 148) the following passage:—

"Elle fut decouverte premierement par Sebastian Babate Anglois lequel persuada au Roy d'Angleterre Henry Septiésme qu'il iroit aisement par la au pais de Catay vers le Nort et que par ce moyen trouveroit espiceries et autres choses aussi bien que le Roy de Portugal aux Indes, joint qu'il se proposoit aller au Peru et Amerique pour peupler le pais de nouveaus habitans et dresser la' une Nouvelle Angleterre, ce qu'il n' executa; vray est qu'il *mist bien trois cens hommes en terre,* du costé d'Irlande au Nort *on le froid fist mourir presque toute sa compagnie* encore que ce fust au moys de Juillet. Depuis Jaques Quartier (ainsi que luy mesme m' a recité) fist deux fois le voyage en ce pays la, c'est a scavoir l' an mil cinq cens trente cinq."

"It was first discovered by Sebastian Babate, an Englishman, who persuaded Henry VII. King of England, that he could go easily this way by the North to

Cathay, and that he would thus obtain spices and other articles from the Indies equally as well as the King of Portugal, added to which he proposed to go to Peru and America to people the country with new inhabitants, *and to establish there a New England* which he did not accomplish; *true it is he put three hundred men ashore* from the coast of Ireland towards the North *where the cold destroyed nearly the whole company*, though it was then the month of July. Afterwards Jaques Cartier (as he himself has told me) made two voyages to that country in 1534 and 1535."

The greater part of this is evidently a mere perversion of what appears in Gomara, changing the name of the commander to Babate, and Iceland to Ireland; and that which follows may be a random addition suggested by the reference in Gomara to one of the objects of Cabot's expedition, and to the reasons which compelled him to turn back.

On the other hand, while it seems somewhat harsh to impute to the author a reckless falsehood, it is possible that he may have derived his information from Cartier, who would be very likely to know of any such early attempt at settlement. Thevet seems, evidently, to turn from the book, whose influence is discernible on the general cast of the paragraph, in order to make a statement of his own, and instead of the general language of Gomara, to substitute specific assertions.

If, then, we can rely on what he says, it seems clear not only that Cabot proposed colonization, but that he actually put a body of men on shore with that view. It will be noted, on referring to the language of Gomara, in the original, that he represents Cabot when returning from his extreme northern point to have stopped at Baccalaos for refreshment ("y rehaziendo se en los Baccalaos"), and afterwards to have proceeded South to 38°. It may be, then, that before the renewed search for a Passage, which would seem to have continued an object of pursuit, he left a party to examine the country; who, on his return, dispirited by the dreariness of the region and perhaps by mortality, insisted on being taken off.

The statement of Thevet was held in reserve, that its loose and careless air might not seem to be imparted to that which has a fixed and authentic character. Up to a certain point

—the sailing of the expedition of 1498, under Sebastian Cabot, and its apparent objects—we have the clearest evidence. The next step we may hesitate, perhaps from excessive caution, to take, lest the support proffered by Thevet be illusive.

As we are indebted to Peter Martyr and Gomara for the length of the run along the coast to the Southward, it probably now took place, their reference evidently being, throughout, to the present voyage. It was on this occasion, doubtless, that three hundred men were taken out, so that the supposition is perhaps strengthened by noticing that Peter Martyr represents the expedition to have been arrested in the South by a failure of provisions.

One incident is deceptively connected by Hakluyt with this voyage. Stow speaks of an exhibition of savages in the year 1502; but Hakluyt, who derived this fact from him, has altered the date from the *seventeenth* to the *fourteenth* year of Henry VII. As he relies altogether on Stow's communication, it might be sufficient to point to that Annalist's own statement. The incident belongs to a voyage by different persons, on reaching which it will be shown, that in the original work of Hakluyt, of 1582, he correctly refers the exhibition to the seventeenth year, but afterwards changed the date, in order to accommodate it, in point of time, to the voyage of Cabot with which he erroneously connected it.

CHAP. XI.

VOYAGE TO MARACAIBO IN 1499.

As it is certain that Sebastian Cabot did not enter the service Spain until the 13th of September 1512, we are obliged to look anxiously round, in every direction, for information as to his employment during the intermediate period. It is impossible to believe that he could have passed in inactivity the period of life best adapted for enterprise and adventure, and to which he at the same time brought maturity of judgment and abundant experience. Yet the Records, so far as made public, furnish no evidence on the subject, for though commissions were granted, as we shall have occasion hereafter to show, by Henry VII., in 1501 and 1502, to Portuguese adventurers, with a view to discovery, yet the name of Cabot is sought for in vain.

Amidst this darkness of the horizon, there gleams up happily, in one quarter, a light which enables us to recognise objects with surprising clearness.

A valuable work has recently been published by the Rev. Mr Seyer, entitled, "Memoirs Historical and Topographical of Bristol and its Neighbourhood, from the earliest period down to the present time." At p. 208, of vol. ii., it is stated that some of the ancient Calendars of Bristol, under the year 1499, have the following entry:—

"This yeare, Sebastian Cabot borne in Bristoll, proffered his service to King Henry for discovering new countries; which had noe greate or favorable entertainment of the king, but he with no extraordinary preparation sett forth from Bristoll, and made greate discoveries."

We might be inclined, perhaps, to attach no great importance to this statement, and to view it as referring, with a mistake of date, to one of the Northern voyages, but that late disclosures absolutely compel us to seek some such clue to facts, which, without its aid, are altogether inexplicable.

In the recent work of Don Martin Navarette, who has spread out the treasures of the Spanish Archives, he remarks (tom. iii. p. 41), "Lo *cierto* es que Hojeda en su primer viage hallo a ciertas Ingleses por las immediaciones de Caquibacoa" —"what is *certain* is, that Hojeda in his first voyage, found certain Englishmen in the neighbourhood of Caquibacoa").

These expressions occur in that part of the work where the author adverts to the commissions which the English Records show to have been granted by Henry VII., and to his inability to refer to any other quarter the remarkable fact of the meeting. Such a connexion, however, is deceptive, because the earliest of these commissions bears date the 19th March 1501.

Hojeda sailed from Spain on the 20th of May 1499 (Navarette, tom. iii. p. 4), and was only one year absent.

The mere fact that Cabot is known not to have entered a foreign service until long after this period, would suffice to satisfy us that he was the only man who could have been the leader of such an enterprise from England, particularly as we find that when, two years afterwards, an expedition was projected, three Portuguese were called in and placed at its head. The Bristol manuscript seems to put the matter beyond doubt.

The expressions, also, there employed imply a slight of the subject on the part of the King, and probably embody a complaint uttered at the time. The voyage of 1498 had not, we may suspect, proved so productive as was anticipated, and the interest felt the year before now languished. Some complaint of this kind is discoverable in the conversation of Cabot at Seville, reported by Ramusio, though the neglect is certainly referred, in that report, to an erroneous period.

When we remember that Cabot, the year before, was stopped by the failure of provisions while proceeding Southward, he might naturally be expected to resume his progress along the coast on the first occasion, and he would thus be conducted to the spot where Hojeda found him. It is probable, therefore, that impatient of inactivity, and despairing of aid from the Crown, he threw himself into such a vessel as his private means enabled him to equip, and, as the Bristol manuscript expresses it, "with no extraordinary preparation set forth from Bristol and made great discoveries."

It may have been while he followed the bent of his genius in this desultory manner, that the spirit of enterprise awakened again in England, and his absence may account for the non-appearance of his name in the subsequent patents.

A less agreeable conjecture is suggested by the character of Henry VII. That shrewd and penurious monarch may have been influenced by the same feeling which induced Ferdinand of Spain to rid himself of Columbus, whose high estimate of what he had effected was found to mingle, inconveniently, with all his proposals for following up the Great Discovery. Henry may have preferred to listen to those with whom a bargain might be made solely in reference to prospective services. Avarice, a disease to which he was constitutionally subject and of which the symptoms became every year more apparent, had now reached his moral sense. Bacon, who wrote his History under the eye of James, a lineal descendant and professed admirer of that monarch, could not disguise the evidence of the infamous devices to which Henry resorted for the purpose of extorting money from his own subjects. Speaking of his escape from the difficulties which at one time beset him, and particularly from the long and vexatious feuds with Scotland, it is remarked—

"Wherefore nature, which many times is happily contained and refrained by some bands of fortune, began to take place in the King; carrying, as with a strong tide, his affections and thoughts unto the gathering and heaping up of treasure. And as kings do more easily find instruments for their will and humour, than for their service and honour, he had gotten for his purpose, or beyond his purpose, two instruments, Empson and Dudley, whom the people esteemed as his horse-leeches [illegible] bold men and careless of fame, and that took toll of their master's grist.

"Then did they also use to inthral and charge the subjects' lands with tenures in capite,' by finding false offices, and thereby to work upon them for wardships, liveries, primer seisins, and alienations, being the fruits of those tenures, refusing, upon divers pretexts and delays, to admit men to traverse those false offices according to the law. Nay, the King's wards, after they had accomplished their full age, could not be suffered to have livery of their lands, without paying excessive fines, far exceeding all reasonable rates. They did also vex men with informations of intrusion upon scarce colourable titles.

"When men were outlawed in personal actions, they would not permit them to purchase their charters of pardon, except they paid great and intolerable sums; *standing upon the strict point of law,* which upon outlawries giveth forfeiture of goods; nay, contrary to all law and colour, they maintained the king ought to have the half of men's lands and rents, during the space of two full years, for a pain in case of outlawry.

"And to show further the king's extreme diligence, I do remember to have seen long since a book of accompt of Empson's, that had the king's hand almost to every leaf, by way of signing, and was in some places postilled in the margin with the king's hand likewise, where was this remembrance :—

" 'Item, Received of such a one five marks, for a pardon to be procured; and if the pardon do not pass, the money to be repaid: except the party be some other ways satisfied.'

"And over against this 'memorandum' of the king's own hand,

" 'Otherwise satisfied.' "

"Which I do the rather mention, because it shews in the king a nearness, but yet with a kind of justness. So these little sands and grains of gold and silver, as it seemeth, helped not a little to make up the great heap and bank."

It is remarkable that the First Patent is to the father and the three sons, "and to the *heirs* of them, and each of them and their deputies;" and it is expressly provided that the regions discovered by them, "may not of any other of our subjects be frequented or visited, without the licence of the aforesaid John and his sons, and their deputies, under pain of forfeiture as well of the ships as of all and singular the goods of all them that shall presume to sail to those places so found." Under this grant, the "Londe and Isles" were discovered, and, of course, a right of exclusive resort to these regions, vested in the father and sons for an indefinite period. The patent of 3rd February, 1498, on the other hand, is very cautiously worded. The power given is to the father alone, described as a Venetian, and to his deputies without any words of inheritance. The whole merit of the discovery is, perhaps craftily, represented as embodied in the old man. The privilege given expired, in strictness, with John Cabot; and Sebastian, by having incautiously accepted and acted under such an instrument, might be held to recognise it as the consummation of all that had been previously done, and as a waiver of the terms of the first patent.

The Portuguese patentees of 19th March 1501, consent to receive the privilege of exclusive resort for only ten years; and it is provided that they shall not be interfered with, by virtue of any previous grant to a foreigner ("*extraneus*") under the great seal (" virtute aut colore alicujus concessionis nostræ sibi Magno Sigillo Nostro per antea factæ"). It is true the pen is drawn through this passage in the original Roll; but attention had evidently been drawn, in an adverse temper, to a claim that might be set up under the previous grant. It was, perhaps, thought better not to aim an ungracious, and superfluous blow at what had already expired. The clause is retained which secures the new patentees against molestation from any of the king's subjects, and this provision was considered as applying to the surviving sons who, in the original patent, are not, like the father, called Venetians, but were probably all born in England.

It is not, however, *certain* that Henry intended to supersede the claims of Cabot, so far as respected discoveries actually made. The general authority to the three Portuguese is as to lands " before unknown to all Christians;" and the reservation *may* mean more than a caution to respect the rights of foreign nations. The patent of 19th March 1501 gives a wider range for discovery than even the original one to the Cabots. It authorises discoveries to the *South;* ad omnes partes, regiones et fines maris Orientalis, Occidentalis, *Australis, Borealis* et Septentrionalis." The two marked words occur in this patent, and also in that of 9th December 1502, but are not found in that of 5th March, 1496.

However all this may be, the meagre evidence referred to

is all that remains to fill up fifteen years of Cabot's life subsequent to the first discovery.

One fact is too remarkable not to claim especial notice. Amerigo Vespucci accompanied Hojeda, and it is now agreed that this was the first occasion on which he crossed the Atlantic. Sebastian Cabot was found prosecuting his *Third* Voyage from England.* Yet, while the name of one overspreads the New World, no bay, cape, or headland recalls the memory of the other. While the falsehoods of one have been diffused with triumphant success, England has suffered to moulder in obscurity, in one of the lanes of the Metropolis, the very Record which establishes the discovery effected by her Great Seaman fourteen months before Columbus beheld the Continent, and two years before the lucky Florentine had been West of the Canaries.

---

* See Appendix (B.).

CHAP. XII.

CORRESPONDENCE BETWEEN FERDINAND OF SPAIN AND LORD WILLOUGHBY DE BROKE—CABOT ENTERS THE SERVICE OF SPAIN 13TH SEPTEMBER, 1512—REVISION OF MAPS AND CHARTS, IN 1515—APPOINTED A MEMBER OF THE COUNCIL OF THE INDIES—PROJECTED EXPEDITION TO THE NORTH UNDER HIS COMMAND, TO SAIL IN MARCH 1516—DEATH OF FERDINAND IN JANUARY, 1516—INTRIGUES—CABOT RETURNS TO ENGLAND.

THE disappearance of Cabot's Maps and Discourses, which were, so long after his death, in the custody of William Worthington, ready for publication, cannot but painfully recur to us in contemplating the long period during which we are absolutely without materials for even conjecturing the manner in which he was employed. These documents would, of course, have supplied abundant information; but in their absence we are compelled to pass abruptly to the new theatre on which he was called to perform a conspicuous part.

Singular as it may appear with regard to a fact so well settled, as the period at which he quitted his native country and entered the service of Spain, there exist on this point statements quite irreconcilable with each other, and yet equally unfounded. In the Conversation given by Ramusio, and with which the name of Butrigarius has been subsequently connected, Cabot is made to say that the troubles in England led him to seek employment in Spain where he was very graciously received by Ferdinand and Isabella. The queen died in 1504; and many English writers, relying on the Conversation, have assumed that Cabot entered a foreign service immediately after his return from the original discovery. Others say, that he first went abroad after the cxpedition from England in 1517. This assertion is found in the Biographia Britannica, Pinkerton, Rees, Aikin, Chalmers, Campbell's Lives of the Admirals, &c. The Biographie Universelle postpones his departure to 1526.

We are told by Peter Martyr (Decade iii. cap. vi.), that Cabot did not leave England until after the death of Henry VII., which occurred in 1509. The venerable Historian of the Indies is right, and we thus find completed the circle of errors in that deceptive Conversation. Herrera, the writer of the highest authority on these subjects—Historiographer of the King of Spain, and enjoying familiar access to every document, stated, more than two centuries ago, that Cabot received his appointment from the King of Spain on the 13th September 1512, and even furnished the particulars of the negotiation.

It may readily be conceived that the wily Ferdinand would be anxious to withdraw, if possible, from the service of a youthful monarch, full of enterprise and ambition, and with the accumulated treasures of his thrifty father, a Navigator who had opened to England the glorious career of discovery. He had little reason to hope that Henry would pay greater deference than his father to the Papal Bull. Vespucci, too, who had filled in Spain the office of Pilot-Major, was just dead, as appears by a provision for his widow (Navarette, tom. iii. p. 305), on the 28th March, 1512. The period was favourable to Ferdinand's purpose. Henry had, already, consented to mingle rashly in the dissensions of the Continent, which finally dissipated the hoards of his father and the resources of his kingdom; and in this very year, an army was despatched from England, in vessels provided by Spain, to co-operate with his crafty father-in-law. It is now that Herrera (Dec. i. lib. ix. cap. xiii.) speaks of the king's anxiety to discover the long sought strait, his views on Baccalaos, and his wish to gather round him all the ablest Cosmographers of the time. We are expressly told that these motives induced him.

"A traer a su servicio a Sebastian Gaboto, Ingles, por tenir noticia que era esperto hombre de Mar y para esto escrivio a Milort Ulibi Capitan General del Rey de Ingleterra que se le embiasse y esto fue a treze de Septembre deste anno Sebastian Gaboto vino a Castilla y el Rey le dio titulo da su Capitan, y buenas gages, y quedo en su servicio y le mando residir en Sevilla, para lo que se le ordenasse.*"

There is no difficulty in recognising, through the disguise of the Spanish orthography, the name of Lord Willoughby. That nobleman is found at the head of a Commission for levying troops, dated 29th March, 1511 (Rymer, vol. xiii. p. 297), and immediately followed by a letter from Ferdinand to Henry, dated Seville, 20th April, 1511, relative to the proposed co-operation. Lord Willoughby landed at Plaisance with the English army from the Spanish vessels on the 8th June, 1512 (Herbert's Life of Henry VIII., p. 20).

Surprise will doubtless be felt, that any misconception should exist as to a fact so clearly established. But Herrera is known in this country only through a wretched translation made about a century ago by a "Captain John Stevens," replete with errors, and in which many passages of the greatest interest are entirely omitted. Amongst the rest, not a syllable of what has just been quoted is found in it. Unfortunately, too, for the credit of those who cite Herrera, this translator has changed the order of Decades, Books, and Chapters, and yet given no notice that he had taken such a liberty. The reader, therefore, who attempts to verify the references of most English authors, will find them agreeing very well with the book of Stevens, but furnishing no clew to the passages of the original.

The Correspondence referred to by Herrera between Ferdinand and Lord Willoughby, would seem to have been

---

* "To draw into his service Sebastian Cabot, an Englishman, having heard of his ability as a seaman; and with this view he wrote to Lord Uliby, Captain-General of the King of England, to send him over, and it was on the 13th of September of this year (1512) that Cabot came to Spain. The King gave him the title of his Captain, and a liberal allowance, and retained him in his service, directing that he should reside at Seville to await orders."

extant about a century ago, if we may judge from the language used in the "Ensaio Cronologico Para La Historia General De Florida," published at Madrid in 1723. This work, though it appeared under the name of Cardenas, is understood to have been the production of Andre Goncalez Barcia, Auditor of the supreme council of War of the King of Spain. In the Introduction, the author, after conjecturing the motives which led Cabot to abandon England without reluctance, remarks—

"Y aunque conservo siempre la Fama de Cosmografo, no se hico caso de el, en Inglaterra, hasta que el Rei de Espana, por el mes de Septembre de 1512, entendiendo de Algunas Cosmografos que avia algun estrecho a la parte de la Tierra de los Baccalaos y otro a occidente, escrivio a Milord Ulibi, Capitan General de Inglaterra, le embiase a Gaboto, *lo qual egecuto luego, como cosa que le importaba poco.*"*

The readiness with which Lord Willoughby yielded to the request of the Spanish monarch, and his making light of the favour conferred, would seem to be facts that could only be gathered from the Correspondence itself. We may presume it to be not now in existence, or documents so curious would doubtless have been published by Navarette.

No specific duties were, in the first instance, assigned to Cabot; but his value was quickly discerned and appreciated. We find him, in 1515, mentioned (Herrera, Dec. ii. lib. i. cap. xii.) in connexion with an object, about which the King was very solicitous—a general revision of Maps and Charts; and in that year, Peter Martyr (Dec. iii. cap. vi.) speaks of him as holding the dignified and important station of a Member of the Council of the Indies. The same writer informs us

* "And though he maintained always his reputation as cosmographer, yet no account was made of him in England; and, at length, the King of Spain, in the middle of September 1512, understanding from cosmographers that there was a Strait in some part of the land of Baccalaos, communicating with another in the West, wrote to Lord Vlibi, Captain-General of England, to send Cabot to him. *which he did forthwith as a thing of little moment.*"

that an expedition had been projected to sail in March 1516, under the command of Cabot, in search of the North-West Passage.

"Familiarem habeo domi Cabotum ipsum et contubernalem interdum *Vocatus* namque ex Britannia a Rege nostro Catholico *post Henrici Majoris Britanniæ Regis mortem* concurialis noster est expectatque Indies ut navigia sibi parentur quibus arcanum hoc naturæ latens jam tandem detegatur. Martio mense anni futuri MDXVI. puto ad explorandum discessurum. Quæ succedent tua Sancitas per me intelliget modo vivere detur. Ex Castellanis non desunt qui Cabotum primum fuisse Baccalorum repertorem negant, tantumque ad Occidentem tetendisse *minime assentiuntur.**"

This passage, while it proves that his talents had been recognised and rewarded by the king, and that his personal character had endeared him to the historian, also shows that there already existed against the successful stranger, the same malignant jealousy to which Columbus fell a victim. Unfortunately for Cabot, Ferdinand died on the 23rd of January, 1516. This circumstance would seem to have put an end to the contemplated expedition, and it is probable that in the scenes which immediately followed, full scope was given to that feeling of dislike and pretended distrust, which had not dared to exhibit itself, in any marked manner, during the king's life. Charles V., occupied elsewhere, did not reach Spain for a considerable time. The original publication of the three first Decades of Peter Martyr has a Dedication to him, dated October 1516, in which the youthful sovereign is entreated to enter at once on a consideration of the wonders of that New World with which the work is occupied—" Come

* "Cabot is my very friend whom I use familiarly, and delight to have him sometimes keepe me companie in my own house. For being *called out of England* by the commandment of the Catholic King of Castile, *after the death of King Henry of England the Seventh of that name,* he was made one of our Council and assistance as touching the affairs of the New Indies, looking daily for ships to be furnished for him to discover this hid secret of nature. This voyage is appointed to be begun in March in the year next following, being the year of Christ 1516. What shall succeed, your Holiness shall be advertised by my letters if God grant me life. Some of the Spaniards deny that Cabot was the first finder of Baccalaos, and affirm that he went not so far westward." Eden's translation, Decades, fol. 119.

therefore most Noble Prince, elected of God, and enjoy that high Estate not yet fully understood," &c. During what may be called the interregnum, a scene of the most odious intrigue was exhibited.

"All the great qualities of Chievres, the Prime Minister, and favourite of the young King, were sullied with an ignoble and sordid avarice. The accession of his master to the Crown of Spain, opened a new and copious source for the gratification of this passion. During the time of Charles's residence in Flanders, the whole tribe of pretenders to office or to favour, resorted thither. They soon discovered that without the patronage of Chievres, it was vain to hope for preferment; nor did they want sagacity to find out the proper method of securing him. Vast sums of money were drawn out of Spain. Every thing was venal and disposed of to the highest bidder. After the example of Chievres, the inferior Flemish Ministers engaged in this traffic, which became as general and avowed as it was infamous.*"

A curious illustration of the truth of these representations is found amongst the papers lately published by Navarette. A letter occurs (tom. iii. p. 307), from Charles to Bishop Fonseca, dated Brussels 18th November 1516, which states a representation by Andres de St Martin, that on the death of Amerigo Vespucci, about five years before, the late king had intended to confer on the said St Martin the office of Pilot-Major, but that owing to accidental circumstances this intention was frustrated, and Juan Dias de Solis appointed. The latter being now dead, St Martin had preferred a claim to the appointment. Charles commands Fonseca to inquire into the facts, and also into the capacity and fitness of the applicant. We may conceive that, at such a period, the prospect was a cheerless one for Cabot, previously regarded, as has been seen, with obloquy. It is of evil omen, also, to find in authority the intriguer Fonseca, who has obtained an infamous notoriety as the enemy of Columbus against whom his most successful weapon was the Spanish jealousy of foreigners. Finding himself slighted, Cabot returned to England.

* Robertson's Charles V. Book I.

CHAP. XIII.

CABOT'S VOYAGE OF 1517 FROM ENGLAND IN SEARCH OF THE NORTH-WEST PASSAGE.

THE enterprising and intrepid spirit of our Navigator would seem to have found immediate employment, and he is again on the Ocean. He was aided, doubtless, by being able to point to his own name in Letters Patent, granted so long before by the father of the reigning monarch, whose provisions could not, in justice, be considered as extinct.

For a knowledge of this expedition, we are indebted, principally, to Richard Eden, that friend of Cabot, to whom a tribute of gratitude has been heretofore paid. He published in 1553 a work* bearing this title—

"A treatyse of the Newe India, with other new founde landes and Ilandes, as well Eastwarde as Westwarde, as they are known and found in these oure dayes after the description of Sebastian Munster, in his booke of Universal Cosmographie; wherein the diligent reader may see the good successe and rewarde of noble and honest enterprizes, by the which not only worldly ryches are obtayned, but also God is glorified, and the Christian fayth enlarged. Translated out of Latin into English, by Rycharde Eden. Præter spem sub spe. Imprinted at London, in Lombarde street, by Edward Sutton, 1553."

The volume is dedicated to the Duke of Northumberland. The checks are so many and powerful on a departure from truth, even aside from the character of the writer, as to relieve us from any apprehension of mis-statement. Cabot then resided in England, occupying a conspicuous station. The passage about to be quoted contains a reproach on a sea-officer, of the time of Henry VIII., and it is not likely that such expressions would be addressed to one who had been

* In the Library of the British Museum, title in catalogue, *Munster*.

Lord High Admiral in that reign, unless the facts were notorious and indisputable, particularly while many of them engaged in the expedition were living. The following is the language of the Dedication—

"Which manly courage (like unto that which hath been seen and proved in your Grace, as well in forene realmes as also in this our country) if it had not been wanting in other in these our dayes at such time as our sovereigne Lord of noble memory, King Henry the *Eighth*, about the same [eighth] yere of his raygne, *furnished and set forth certen shippes under the governaunce of Sebastian Cabot yet living*, and one Sir Thomas Perte, whose faynt heart was the cause that that viage toke none effect, if (I say) such manly courage whereof we have spoken had not at that tyme bene wanting, it myghte happelye have come to passe that that riche treasurye called *Perularia* (which is now in Spayne, in the citie of Civile and so named, for that in it is kepte the infinite ryches brought thither from the *newe-foundland of Peru* myght longe since have bene in the Tower of London, to the Kinges great honoure and welth of this his realme."

With this passage Hakluyt (vol. iii. p. 498) properly connects the language employed by Robert Thorne in 1527, in a letter addressed to Henry VIII. The object of Thorne (Hakluyt, vol. i. p. 212) was to urge a search for the passage in the North, and he suggests three routes—the North-Eastern, afterwards attempted by Willoughby—the North-Western—and, finally, a course directly over the Pole, giving a preference, so far as may be inferred from order in suggestion, to the first—

"Yet these dangers or darkness hath not letted the Spaniards and Portuguese and others, to discover many unknown realms to their great peril. Which considered (and that your Graces subjects may have the same light) it will seem your Graces subjects to be without activity or courage, in leaving to do this glorious and noble enterprise. For they being past this little way which they named so dangerous, (which may be two or three leagues before they come to the Pole, and as much more after they pass the Pole) it is clear, that from thenceforth the seas and lands are as temperate as in these parts, and that then it may be at the will and pleasure of the mariners, to choose whether they will sail by the coasts that be cold, temperate or hot. For they being past the Pole, it is plain they may decline to what part they list.

"If they will go toward the Orient, they shall enjoy the regions of all the Tartarians that extend toward the midday, and from thence they may go and proceed to the land of the Chinese, and from thence to the land of Cathaio Oriental, which is, of all the main land, most Oriental that can be reckoned from our habitation. And if, from thence, they do continue their navigation, following the coasts that return toward the Occident, they shall fall in with Malaca, and so with all the Indies which we call Oriental, and following the way, may return hither by the Cape of Buona Speransa; and thus they shall compass the whole world. And if they will take their course after they be past the Pole, toward the Occident, they shall go in the backside of the Newfoundland, and which *of late* was *discovered by your Grace's servants*, until they came to the backside and south seas of the Indies Occidental. And so continuing their voyage, they may *return through the strait of Magellan* to this country, and so they compass also the world by that way; and if they go this third way, and after they be past the Pole, go right toward the Pole antarctic, and then decline towards the lands and islands situated between the Tropics, and under the Equinoctial, without doubt they shall find there the richest lands and islands of the World of Gold, precious stones, balmes, spices, and other things that we here esteem most which come out of strange countries, and may return the same way.

"By this it appeareth, your Grace hath not only a great advantage of the riches, but also your subjects shall not travel halfe of the way that others do, which go round about as aforesaid."

He remarks again,

"To which places there is left one way to discover, which is into the North; for that of the four parts of the world, it seemeth three parts are discovered by other princes. For out of Spaine they have discovered all the Indies and seas Occidental, and out of Portugal all the Indies and seas Oriental: so that by this part of the Orient and Occident, they have compassed the world. For the one of them departing toward the Orient, and the other toward the Occident, met again in the course or way of the midst of the day, and so then was discovered a great part of the same seas and coasts by the Spaniards. So that now rest to be discovered *the said North parts*, the which it seemeth to me is only your charge and duty. *Because* the situation of this your realm is thereunto nearest and aptest of all others; and *also* for that *you have already taken it in hand*. And in mine opinion it will not seem well to *leave* so great and profitable an enterprise, seeing it may so easily and with so little cost, labor, and danger, be followed and obtained, though *heretofore* your Grace hath made *thereof* a proofe, and found not the commodity thereby as you trusted, at this time it shall be no impedient. For there may be now provided remedies for things, then lacked, and the inconveniences and lets removed, that then were cause that your Grace's desire took no full effect, which is, the *courses* to be changed, and followed the aforesaid new courses. And concerning the mariners, ships, and provisions, an order may be devised and taken meet and convenient, much better than hitherto. By reason whereof, and by God's grace, no doubt your purpose shall take effect. Surely the cost herein will be nothing, in comparison to the great profit. The labour is much less, yea nothing at all, where so great honour and glory is hoped for; and considering well the courses, truly the danger and way is shorter to us, than to Spain or Portugal, as by evident reasons appeareth."

It would seem impossible to doubt that the writer here puts distinctly to Henry, as the two grounds for looking to the North, the advantageous position of his own dominions in reference to a passage in that quarter, and the fact that his former experiment had taken that direction.

Hakluyt approached the subject under a misconception, the source of which will presently be pointed out, that Cabot had gone to the South on this occasion, and supposes that he finds a confirmation of it in that part of the passage quoted from Thorne, which speaks of a change of the courses. Not only, however, is this assumption against the evidence from other quarters, but Thorne's own words repel it. He had just suggested a passage by the North, and then eagerly anticipates and answers the objections which might be urged, and it naturally occurs to him as the most forcible of these, that the king had already made a proof in that quarter without success. Could he have apprehended such an objection to his project from a failure in the South? To suppose that he wished to combat the presumption against the existence of a strait arising from ill success *there,* will appear ridiculous, if we note that the passage in the South had been, in point of fact, discovered by Magellan, and is actually referred to by Thorne as affording a convenient route for the return voyage.

The words on which Hakluyt would lay this undue stress have ample operation when, aside from the various courses for attempting a North-West passage, here were two others suggested, and a seeming preference given to that by the North-East. Captain Parry took many different "courses" with a more limited object in view.

In the reference made by Thorne to the Newfoundland, "which *of late* was discovered *by your Grace's subjects,*" he evidently treats as an original discovery that further advance to the North, which we may presume to have been made on this occasion. The same person, in his letter to Dr Ley (1 Hakluyt, p. 219), speaking of the passage by the North, remarks, that he, probably, derived the "inclination or desire of this discovery" from his father, who, "with another merchant of Bristow, named Hugh Eliot, were the discoverers of *the Newfoundlands.*" Now, we have seen his previous application of the epithet, which is, in truth, most appropriate to the latest discovery. Couple this with another fact. The name of Thorne does not occur in any of the patents. Of the two to which we shall have occasion hereafter to advert, subsequent to those of the Cabots, one is dated 19th March, 1501, and is in favour of certain Portuguese, who are associated with three merchants of Bristol, Richard Ward, Thomas Ashehurst, and John Thomas. This is now, for the first time, published from the Rolls in the present volume. The last patent bears date 9th December, 1502, and is found in Rymer (vol. xiii. p. 37). The names of Ward and Thomas are dropped, and Hugh Eliot is associated with Ashehurst and the Portuguese. Thus the name with which Thorne connects that of his father does not appear until this late period. We have no doubt that when, after an interval of fifteen years, the reappearance of Cabot called attention to this patent, which had lain dormant, Thorne acquired from Ashehurst or his representatives the interest of that person. Robert Thorne, the son, speaks of the two associates, "my father, who, with another merchant of Bristow, named Hugh Eliot," a language well agreeing with the explanation suggested.

It appears from the epitaph of Robert Thorne (Stow's Survey of London, and Fuller's Worthies), that he was born in 1492, a circumstance that may assist in enabling us to suppose his father at a not very advanced age in 1516.

A striking instance of the inaccuracy of Purchas, occurs in his statement of the expression used by Thorne. He says (Pilgrims, vol. iv. p. 1812), "Robert Thorne, in a book to Doctor Leigh, writeth, that his father, with another merchant of Bristol, Hugh Eliot, were the *first* discoverers of the Newfoundlands." Had Thorne really said "*first*," he must have intended deception; but no such word is found either in the letter itself (Hakluyt, vol. i. p. 219), or in Hakluyt's subsequent reference to it (vol. iii. p. 10). The absence of the very epithet which Purchas deemed it necessary to interpolute, in order to suit his own notion of what was meant, [illegible] a strong argument to prove, what is sufficiently clear from the context, that Thorne alludes to the recent discovery made by the subjects of Henry VIII.

It may be repeated, then, that in his speculations on the North-West Passage, Thorne says, "And if they will take their course after they be past the Pole toward the West, they shall go on the back side of *the Newfoundland* which *of late* was discovered by *your Grace's subjects*, until they come to the back side and South seas of the Indies Occidental." Thus by advancing resolutely in the route before taken in the North by "his Grace's subjects," the Western side of the American Continent would be attained. Now it is remarkable, that in speaking of the effort made under the auspices of Hugh Eliot and his father, he says to Dr Ley (Hakluyt, vol. i. p. 219), "of which there is no doubt (as now plainly appeareth), if the mariners would then have been ruled and followed their pilot's mind the lands of the West Indies (*from whence all the gold cometh*) had been *ours*, for all is one coast as by the card appeareth and is aforesaid." Thus we find that the frustration of the object is imputed to those who refused to follow their pilot's wishes, and that the golden visions of Thorne are those belonging to a successful prosecution of the North-Western Discovery. Is it possible to hesitate about connecting this with the language of Eden as to the faint-heartedness of Sir Thomas Pert, and the general opinion, in 1553, that owing to that faint-heartedness the treasures of Peru were at Seville instead of the Tower of London?

The manner in which Hakluyt and subsequent writers have been betrayed into error with regard to this expedition remains to be considered.

CHAP. XIV.

HAKLUYT'S ERROR WITH REGARD TO THE VOYAGE OF 1517.

HAKLUYT was under an impression that there should be taken in connexion with this voyage a passage in the Spanish historian Oviedo, of which he found a translation in Ramusio. It is but just that he should be fully heard on this point—

"Moreover it seemeth that Gonsalvo de Oviedo, a famous *Spanish* writer, alludeth unto the sayde voyage in the beginning of the 13th chapter of the 19th booke of his generall and natural historie of the West *Indies*, agreeing very well with the time about which *Richard Eden* writeth that the foresaid voyage was begun. The author's wordes are these, as I finde them *translated into Italian* by that excellent and famous man *Baptista Ramusius*."*

After giving the Italian version, Hakluyt proceeds—

"This extract importeth thus much in English, to wit: 'That in the yeere 1517, an English rover, under the colour of travelling to discover, came with a great shippe unto the parts of Brasill, on the coaste of the firme lande, and from thence he crossed over unto this Iland of Hispaniola, and arrived neere unto the mouth of the haven of the citie of S. Domingo, and sent his shipboate full of men on shore, and demanded leave to enter into this haven, saying that he came with merchandise to traffique. But at that very instant the governour of the castle, Francis de Tapia, caused a tire of ordinance to be shot from the castle at the ship, for she bare in directly with the haven. When the Englishmen sawe this, they withdrew themselves out, and those that were in the shipboate, got themselves, with all speede, on ship-board. And in trueth the warden of the castle committed an oversight: for if the shippe had entred into the haven, the men thereof could not have come on lande without leave both of the citie and of the castle. Therefore the people of the ship seeing how they were received, sayled toward the Iland of S. John, and entering into the port of S. Germaine, the English men parled with those of the towne, requiring victuals and things needefull to furnish their ship, and complained of the inhabitants of the city of S. Domingo, saying that they came not to doe any harme, but to trade and traffique for their money and merchandise. In this place they had certaine victuals, and for recompense they gave and paid them with certain vessels of wrought tinne and other things. And

* Hakluyt, vol. iii. p. 499.

afterward they departed toward Europe, where it is thought they arrived not; for we never heard any more newes of them."*

Herrera has an account of the visit somewhat more at large (Dec. ii. lib. v. cap. iii.), and refers to the statement of Gines Navarro, the captain of a caravel of St Domingo, who happening to be at St John when the English vessel arrived at that Island, went off to her, supposing her to be of his own country. According to him, the ship was of two hundred and fifty tons burthen, and had on board sixty men. She was accompanied by a pinnace having two guns in her bows, with twenty-five men armed with crossbows and wearing corslets. The commander of the ship offered to show his instructions from the king of England ("la instruccion que llevaba de el Rei de Inglaterra"), and requested Navarro to proceed in company with his own vessel to show the way to St Domingo. The English were plentifully supplied with provisions, and had a great quantity of woollen and linen goods with other merchandise, for the purpose of traffic. They effected at St John's a barter of some tin, and proceeding afterwards to St Domingo, sent a boat ashore with a message that their object was trade, and remained off the island for two days. The commander of the fort sent to the authorities for instructions how to act, and not receiving a timely answer fired, on his own responsibility, at the strangers, on which they recalled their boat and went round to the Island of St John, and after remaining some time carrying on a barter with the inhabitants of the town of St Germain, disappeared.

The account which, according to Navarro, they gave of themselves, was this:—

"They said that they were Englishmen, and that the ship was from England, and that she and her consort had been equipped to go and seek the land of the Great Cham, that they had been separated in a tempest, and that the ship pursuing her course had been in a frozen sea, and found great islands of ice, and that taking a different course, they came into a warm sea, which boiled like water in a kettle, and lest it might open the seams of the vessel they proceeded to examine

* Ib.

the Baccalaos, where they found fifty sail of vessels, Spanish, French, and Portuguese, engaged in fishing; that going on shore to communicate with the natives, the pilot, a native of Piedmont, was killed; that they proceeded afterwards along the coast to the river Chicora, and crossed over thence to the island of St John. Asking them what they sought in these islands, they said that they wished to explore in order to make report to the King of England, and to procure a load of the Brasil wood."

Such was the report of Navarro. The officer commanding the fort was arrested, because by his precipitate conduct the opportunity was lost of ascertaining who were the intruders, and what their object. On the facts being reported to the emperor, he viewed them with great uneasiness, and "wished that in the Island of St Domingo they had proceeded in a different manner, and either by force or stratagem got possession of the vessel. He was struck with the inconveniences likely to result from English vessels frequenting those parts, and gave strict orders that on their again appearing, measures should be adopted for taking them and making an example of them."

These circumstances are adverted to, for the purpose of showing the attention which was excited by this visit, and the anxious examination, doubtless, undergone by Navarro who had communicated with the strangers. When Herrera was ordered by Philip II. to prepare his History, there were submitted to him documents of every description, even the most minute (Decade vi. lib. iii. cap. 19). His statement, then, which goes thus into detail, was, probably, derived from the Examination, and it establishes a representation, that the Englishmen spoke of the Baccalaos as a point at which they had touched on their *return* from a struggle with the perils of the navigation *further North*.

There is found in *Purchas* (Pilgrims, vol. iii. p. 855), a "Description of the West Indies," by Herrera, being the introduction to the history, with a remark, "This author hath written eight Decades of the Spanish Acts in the West Indies, which give great light to those parts, but would be too long for this work." The influence of the passage just quoted is curiously visible in Purchas. On reading it, he saw, at once, that the statement of [illegible] had reference to the visit spoken of by Oviedo, and it therefore passed into his mind that the expedition proceeded, in the first instance, to the North. When he had occasion, however, to advert to the circumstance afterwards, he evidently could not recollect whence he had derived the impression, or there would have been found a reference to Herrera in his ambitious margin, instead of the vague assertion: "Afterwards the same Sir Sebastian Cabot was sent, A.D. 1516, by king Henry the VIII., together with Sir Thomas Pert, Vice-Admiral of England, which *after coasting this Continent the second time, as I have read*, discovered the Coast of Brasil, and returned from thence to St Domingo and Porto Rico" (vol. iv. p. 1812).

A peculiar anxiety is felt with regard to this voyage, because it bears directly on our estimate of Cabot's character. He had taken up, with all the ardour which belongs to the conceptions of a man of his stamp, the opinion that a North-West passage was practicable, and we are grieved as well as surprised, to find him apparently faltering in the pursuit. We *know* from Peter Martyr, his undiminished confidence in 1515, and cannot understand why, immediately afterwards, he should be found in a confused, rambling voyage to the South, instead of following up his great purpose.

The examination thus far has assumed that the date given by Ramusio, in his translation of Oviedo, and adopted by Hakluyt, is correct. It now remains to show that there has been an entire misconception on this point, and that Hakluyt has paid the deserved penalty of his folly in quoting a Spanish book from an Italian translation.

The reference is correctly given to book xix. cap. xiii. of Oviedo; but on turning to the passage, he is found to represent the visit of the English ship as occurring not in 1517, but in 1527. There are in the library of the British Museum the edition of his work published at Seville in 1535, and the next edition, corrected by the author, published at

Salamanca, in 1547. In the king's library there is a copy of the latter edition. The date given in both editions is MDXXVII. It may be very idle to attempt to fortify the statement of a writer of the highest credit, and who resided in St Domingo at the very period in question; but the fact may be mentioned that his narrative had not only carried him up to this period but beyond it, for in a preceding chapter (the vii.) of the same book, he speaks of an incident which occurred in September, 1530.

As the reliance of Hakluyt is exclusively on the "famous Spanish writer Oviedo," it might be sufficient to shift to its proper side of the scale the weight which has been thus misplaced. The point, however, is one of interest, in reference to the subsequent voyage from England, in 1527, and we may draw to the rectification the testimony of Herrera.

That writer, it is true, affixes no date to the visit, and while considering, at an early period, the condition of the colonies, he adverts to this as one of the circumstances which had led to complaint and uneasiness. This sort of grouping is always dangerous in the hands of an ambitious and florid historian, anxious to be relieved from a chronological detail of isolated facts, and to treat them in combination, and in their supposed influence on results. He has, while considering an early incident, taken up this and others which, though posterior in point of time, yet preceded the measures of precaution, of which they, in succession, indicated the necessity. The question is placed beyond doubt by another occurrence almost contemporary. Oviedo, in the same chapter which refers to the visit of the English vessel, adds, that *about* a year afterwards ("desde a poco tiempo o en el siguiente anno"), a French corsair made its appearance at Cuba, guided by a villainous Spaniard, named Diego Ingenio ("guiado por un mal Espagnol llamado Diego Ingenio"). This incident is mentioned by Herrera, under the year 1529, and he states it to have taken place in the middle of October of that year (Herrera, Dec. iv. lib. vi. chap. xii.). His next chapter (xiii.) is occupied with the precautions taken for the security of the Indies, and they are expressly referred to the visit of the English and French Ships.* Thus is obtained a decided, though superfluous, confirmation of the accuracy of Oviedo.

So soon as we are assured of his real statement, the improbability that this visit could have been on the part of Cabot's expedition occurs with irresistible force.

Is it at all likely that one who had just quitted the service of Spain, and who knew the jealous system of exclusion adopted with regard to her American possessions, would be found engaged in a silly and confused attempt to carry on a commerce in that quarter? Again, is it not probable that Navarro would have recognized one whom we may presume to have been familiarly known to the seamen of that day? Would a man, moreover, who had been one of the captains of the King of Spain, and afterwards a member of the council of the Indies, have been anxious to open a communication with the authorities of St Domingo? Cabot would have known not only that the application was idle, but that it would subject him to the most odious reproaches, for endeavouring to turn against Spain the knowledge acquired by having so recently held a confidential post in her service.

This last consideration, indeed, suggests a pleasing reflection that his fame may be successfully relieved from the suspicion of having, even at a moment of pique, consented to engage in such an enterprise. The pure and lofty character to which all the incidents of his life lay claim, renders us unwilling to credit what could not but be deemed derogatory. His vindication has already, it is hoped, been made out; and when we come, in its proper place, to a voyage from England, in 1527, under totally different auspices, there will be seen

* "Con occasion de la nave Inglesa que havia llegada al Puerto de la Ciudad de Santo Domingo de la Isla Espanola, i de los Franceses de que se ha tratado en el capitulo precedente, el Obispo de Santo Domingo, Presidente del Audencia hiço una Junta de todos las Estados de la Isla, adonde se confirio lo que se debia hacer," &c.

the happy application of what Oviedo correctly refers to that year. By keeping separate the clews which Hakluyt has crossed and entangled, there will be attained, in each case, a point from which a survey may be made with the greatest clearness and assurance of accuracy.

CHAP. XV.

VOYAGE OF 1517 THE ONE REFERRED TO BY CABOT IN HIS LETTER TO RAMUSIO.

It being, then, certain that the expedition of 1517 had for its object the North-West Passage, was it on the 11th June 1517, that Cabot attained the point mentioned in his letter to Ramusio? The day of the month is given, not only in that letter but again by Sir Humphrey Gilbert (iii. Hakluyt, p. 16), from Cabot's map. Many circumstances of corroboration press on us. When Eden speaks, in magnificent phrase, of the opportunity lost to England of taking the lead of Spain, his language is naturally referable, as has been said, to the frustration of that great effort to find a way to Cataya which Cabot had already essayed, and which Peter Martyr, in 1515, expressly tells us he was on the eve of again undertaking. In the letter to Ramusio, Cabot declares that when arrested at 67° and-a-half by the timidity of his associates, he was sanguine of success, and that if not overruled he both could and would have gone to Cataya. Does not Eden, then, merely supply the name of the principal object of this reproach? Let us refer again to the language of Thorne, which applies, we know, to the expedition of 1517 (i. Hakluyt, p. 219), "Of the which there is no doubt, as now plainly appeareth, if the mariners would then have been ruled and followed their pilot's mind, the lands of the West-Indies, from whence all the gold cometh, had been ours." Can it be doubted that these several passages all point to the same incident?

In the work of Peter Martyr, written before this last voyage, no allusion is found to a mutiny in the North, but he mentions expressly that in the South the expedition was stop ped by a failure of provisions. While conveying such minute information he would hardly have failed to advert to a fact so remarkable in itself, and bearing moreover so directly on the question of the supposed practicability of the enterprise.

On the occasion alluded to, the lat. of 67° and-a-half had been attained on the 11th June. This could not have been in 1497, because land was first seen on the 24th of June of that year. With regard to the expedition of 1498, which Peter Martyr and Gomara are supposed more particularly to refer to, the month of July is named as that in which the great struggle with the ice occurred. Did not Cabot, then, instructed by experience, sail from England earlier in the year than on the former occasions? In order to be within the eighth year of Henry VIII. mentioned by Eden, he must have got off before the 22nd of April, if he sailed in 1517.

The advance on this occasion was so far beyond what had been made on former voyages, that Thorne does not hesitate to give to the region newly visited the designation of Newfoundland; and it was then probably that Cabot "sailed into Hudson's Bay and gave English names to sundry places therein."*

No date is mentioned by Ramusio for the voyage alluded to in Cabot's letter, though from his speaking of that Navigator as having made discoveries in the time of Henry VII., the reader might be led to refer it to that early period. One expression is remarkable. After stating Cabot's long-continued course West with a quarter of the North, and his reaching 67° and-a-half, Ramusio says that he would have gone further but for the "malignita del *padrone* et de marinari sollevati" (the refusal of the *master* and the mutinous mariners). We can hardly err in referring this allusion to Sir Thomas Pert, "whose faint heart," according to Eden, "was the cause that the voyage took none effect."

---

* Anderson's History of Commerce, vol. i. p. 549. M'Pherson's Annals of Commerce, vol. ii. p. 12.

It only remains to express a hope that as the errors with regard to this voyage had become so firmly fixed, and their rectification was so important to the fame of Cabot, the preceding tedious detail will be excused. Dr Robertson, who it appears by the list of authorities prefixed to his History of America knew of Oviedo only through the Italian translation, thus speaks of the memorable expedition:

"Some merchants of Bristol having fitted out two ships *for the southern regions of America,* committed the conduct of them to Sebastian Cabot, who had quitted the service of Spain. He visited the coasts of Brazil, and touched at the islands of Hispaniola and Porto Rico," &c. (Book ix.) And in a work of the present year (Lardner's Cyclopædia, Maritime and Inland Discovery, vol. ii. p. 138), it is said, "Sebastian Cabot sailed in 1516 with Sir *John* Pert to *Porto Rico,* and afterwards returned to Spain."

CHAP. XVI.

CABOT APPOINTED, IN 1518, PILOT-MAJOR OF SPAIN—SUMMONED TO ATTEND THE CONGRESS AT BADAJOS IN 1524—PROJECTED EXPEDITION UNDER HIS COMMAND TO THE MOLUCCAS.

THE result of the expedition of 1517, however it may have added in England to the fame of Cabot for ardent enterprise and dauntless intrepidity, was not such as to lead immediately to a renewed effort. There had been a failure; and a second expedition might be frustrated by similar causes. The merchants who were engaged in it had probably sustained a heavy loss, and the king was at that time full of anxious speculations about the affairs of the Continent. The horrible *Sweating-Sickness*, too, which, from July to December 1517, spread death and dismay not only through the court and the city, but over the whole kingdom, suspending even the ordinary operations of commerce, left no time to think of the prosecution of a distant and precarious enterprise. It is probable, therefore, that Cabot might have languished in inactivity but for the new and more auspicious aspect of affairs in Spain.

If the youthful successor of Ferdinand had looked into the volume dedicated to him by Peter Martyr, containing a faithful and copious account of that splendid empire in the west to which he had succeeded, he could not fail to be struck with the memorable enterprise of Cabot, and the estimate of his character by that honest chronicler. The records, too, would show the pains which had been taken to secure his services, and the posts of honour and confidence to which he had been rapidly advanced. It would doubtless be asked, what had been the issue of that expedition under his command, which it appeared was to sail in March 1516. Coupling its abandonment with what he found stated of the jealous denial of that Navigator's merits by the Spaniards, the sagacity of Charles could hardly fail to detect the secret causes of Cabot's disappearance.

Immediate measures in the way of atonement would seem to have been taken. In 1518 Cabot was named Pilot-Major of Spain.*

The appointment is noted in the general arrangement and scheme of reformation of that year, but we find it announced again in 1520, (Dec. ii. lib. ix. cap. vii.) with the instructions of the emperor that no pilot should proceed to the Indies without previous examination and approval by him.† Possibly, therefore, the final arrangement was not concluded until the visit of Charles V. to England in the latter year. It would seem that there was no intermediate Pilot Major between Juan de Solis and Cabot, for in a Royal order of 16th November 1523, relative to a charge in the time of De Solis, on the salary of the office (Navarette, tom. iii. p. 308), Cabot is spoken of as his successor.

The functions of this office, though of great importance and responsibility, supply, of course, but few incidents for record. We might expect to find the project of the North-West passage revived, but many considerations were opposed to it. The same reasons which suggested the passage in the North as so desirable to England, on account of her local position, would disincline Spain from the search; and we accordingly find, that the only feeble efforts in reference to it were those of Cortez and Gomez on the southern coast of North America. All eyes were directed to the South. Peter Martyr is even impatient that attention should be turned towards Florida where Ayllon had landed in 1523, and made a tedious report as to its productions. "What need have we of these things

* Herrera, Dec. ii. lib. iii. cap. vii. Ensaio Chronologico para la Florida, Introduccion.

† Diose titulo Piloto Major à Sebastian Gaboto con orden que ningun Pilot pasase à las Indias sin ser primero por el examinado i aprobado.

which are common with all the people of Europe? To the South! To the South! They that seek riches must not go to the cold and frozen North" (Dec. viii. cap. x.). The hopes of adventurers were directed to the Moluccas, through the passage which Magellan had been fortunate enough to find in 53°, through toils and perils so much less than those which had been encountered in vain in the North. The next mention we find of Cabot, is a reference to his opinion (Herrera, Dec. iii. lib. iv. cap. xx.), as to the existence of many islands worthy of being explored, in the same region with the Moluccas. Seeing that the spirit of enterprise had taken this direction, he seems to have looked to it as affording a chance of more active employment than his present office. An incident soon brought him conspicuously forward in connexion with this region.

Portugal had interposed an earnest representation that the Moluccas fell within the limits assigned to her under the Papal Bull, and she remonstrated, in the strongest terms, against any attempt on the part of Spain to carry on a commerce in that quarter.* The emperor decided, therefore, that a solemn conference should be held, at which the subject might be fully discussed and an opportunity afforded to Portugal of stating her pretensions. The son of Columbus, Ferdinand, was also present.†

In attendance on this remarkable assemblage, were the men most famed for their nautical knowledge and experience; not as members, but for the purpose of reference as occasion might arise. At the head of a list of these, we find the name of Cabot.‡ The conference was held at Badajos, in April 1524, and on the 31st May the decision was solemnly proclaimed, declaring that the Moluccas were situate, by at least 20°, within the Spanish limits. The Portuguese retired in disgust, and rumours immediately reached Spain, that the young king of Portugal was preparing a great fleet to maintain his pre-

* Peter Martyr, Dec. vi. cap. ix. † Peter Martyr, Dec. vi. cap. x.

‡ Gomara, cap. c.; Herrera, Dec. iii. lib. vi. cap. vi.; Eden, Decades, fol. 241.

tensions by force and to take and destroy any vessels which might be found presuming to urge a commerce in that quarter.*

Immediately after the decision, a company was formed at Seville to prosecute the trade which had received so high and solemn a sanction, and Cabot was solicited to take the command.† One of the parties to the association was Robert Thorne of Bristol, then resident in Spain, who with his partner was led into the adventure, "principally," as he says, "for that two English friends of mine, which are somewhat learned in cosmographie, should go in the same ships to bring me certain relation of the country, and to be expert in the navigation of those seas.‡ In September, 1524, Cabot received from the council of the Indies permission to engage in the enterprise, and he proceeded to give bond to the Company for the faithful execution of his trust.§ His original request was, that four ships properly armed and equipped should be provided at the expense of the Treasury, while the Company on its part should supply the requisite funds for the commercial objects.‖ The agreement with the emperor was executed at Madrid on 4th March, 1525,¶ and stipulated that a squadron of, at least, three vessels of not less than one hundred tons should be furnished, and one hundred and fifty men.** The title of Captain General was conferred on Cabot. The emperor was to receive from the Company four thousand ducats and a share of the profits.

It was proposed, instead of pushing directly across the Pa-

---

* Peter Martyr, Dec. vi. cap. x.

† Herrera, Dec. iii. lib. ix. cap. iii.

‡ Hakluyt, vol. i. p. 215. We may conjecture one of these to have been *Jorge Barlo* (George Barlow), who, with another, brought to Spain Cabot's Despatch from the La Plata (Herrera, Dec. iv. lib. iii. cap. i.).

§ Peter Martyr, Dec. vii. cap. vi.

‖ Ib.

¶ Herrera, Dec. iii. lib. ix. cap. iii.

** Peter Martyr, Dec. vii. cap. vi. Herrera, Dec. iii. lib. ix. cap. iii. Gomara says *two* hundred and fifty, but his assertion has no weight against the concurring testimony of the two Historians cited, one a member of the Council, and the other referring to official documents.

cific, after penetrating through the Strait, as Magellan had done, to proceed deliberately and explore on every side, particularly the western coast of the Continent.*

The arrangement at first was, that the expedition should sail in August, 1525;† but it was delayed by circumstances to which it may be proper now to advert as bearing on its ultimate fate.

---

* Peter Martyr, Dec. vii. cap. vi.

† Ib.

CHAP. XVII.

JEALOUSY OF THE CONTEMPLATED EXPEDITION ON THE PART OF PORTUGAL—MISSION OF DIEGO GARCIA, A PORTUGUESE.

In order to understand fully the circumstances which conspired to throw vexatious obstacles in the way of the expedition, and in the end to defeat its main object, we must go back to the voyage of Magellan that first opened to Spain a direct communication with those regions of which Portugal had before monopolised the lucrative commerce.

No sooner did the project of that intrepid navigator become known in Portugal than the utmost alarm was excited. Remonstrances were addressed to the government of Spain; threats and entreaties were alternately used to terrify or to soothe the navigator himself, and assassination was openly spoken of as not unmerited by so nefarious a purpose. Finding these efforts vain, a tone of bitter derision was adopted. The Portuguese said, that the king of Castile was incurring an idle expense, inasmuch as Magellan was an empty boaster, without the least solidity of character, who would never accomplish what he had undertaken."*

Had Magellan perished a month earlier than he did, these contemptuous sneers would have passed into history as descriptive of his real character. There is every reason to believe, that he fell a victim to the treachery infused into the expedition; and the pilot, Estevan Gomez, who openly urged retreat after a considerable progress had been made in the

* Decian los Portugueses que el Rei de Castilla perderia el gasto porque Hernando de Magallanes era hombre hablador, i de poca substancia, i que no saldria con lo que prometia." Herrera, Dec. ii. lib. iv. cap. x.

Strait, was, we know, a Portuguese.* The conduct of the Portuguese authorities to the surviving vessels was marked by cruelty and rapacity; and even the gentle spirit of Peter Martyr breathes indignation. Official notice was received that the ship Trinity had been captured and plundered by the Portuguese, and that this had been followed up by their going to the Moluccas, taking possession of them, and seizing property of every description.

"The Pilots and King's servants who are safely returned, say that both robberies and pillage exceed the value of two hundred thousand ducats, but Christophorus de Haro especially, the General director of this aromatical negociation, under the name of Factor, confirmeth the same. Our senate yieldeth great credit to this man. He gave me the names of all the five ships that accompanied the Victory, and of all the Mariners, and mean Officers whatsoever. And in our senate assembled he showed why he assigned that value of the booty or prey, because he particularly declared how much spices the Trinity brought.

"It may be doubted what Cæsar will do in such a case. I think he will dissemble the matter for a while, by reason of the renewed affinity, yet though they were twins of one birth, it were hard to suffer this injurious loss to pass unpunished."†

In reference to the voyage of Cabot, the alarm of the Porguese would seem to have been yet more serious; for they saw in it not a doubtful experiment, but a well concerted commercial enterprise. The emperor was besieged with importunities; the King of Portugal representing that it would be "the utter destruction of his poor kingdom," to have his monopoly of this trade invaded.‡ The honest historian is persuaded, that though a tie of consanguinity existed between the two monarchs by their common descent from Ferdinand and Isabella, and though the Emperor had given his sister Catherine, "a most delicate young lady of seventeen," in marriage to the King of Portugal, a step "so injurious to the kingdom of Castile, the chief sinews of his power," as the arrest of the expedition, would not be taken.§ So far as

* Herrera, Dec. ii. lib. ix. cap. xv. Purchas, vol. i. B. i. ch. ii.

† Peter Martyr, Dec. viii. cap. x.

‡ Peter Martyr, Dec. vii. cap. vii.

§ Peter Martyr, Dec. vii. cap. vii.

endearing domestic ties could influence such a matter, the apprehension here implied was to be yet further increased. A negotiation was going on for the Emperor's marriage to Isabella, the sister of the King of Portugal, and the ceremony took place in March, 1526. The dowry received was nine hundred thousand crowns, and rumours, in the course of the treaty, were current that one of the articles of the double alliance stipulated an abandonment of the Moluccas. Passing onward with the subject, it may be stated that early in 1529 the emperor relieved himself from all difficulty by mortgaging the Moluccas to the King of Portugal for three hundred and fifty thousand ducats, with the right of exclusive trade until redemption.* This step excited the utmost disgust in Spain, and it was openly said that he had better have mortgaged Estremadura itself. He would listen, however, to no representations on the subject. A proposition having been made to pay off the mortgage money, on condition that the applicants should have six years enjoyment of the trade, the Emperor, then in Flanders, not only rejected the offer, but sent a message of rebuke to the council for having entertained it. Aside from private feelings, he doubtless, as a politician, thought it unwise to put in peril an alliance so intimate and assured for any commercial purpose unconnected with the schemes of ambition by which he was engrossed.

Matters, however, had not reached this crisis before Cabot sailed; and the intense anxiety of Portugal could, therefore, look only to the indirect efforts at frustration, for which the intimate relations of the two countries might afford opportunities.

In all the accounts of Cabot's enterprise given by the Spanish historians, reference is found to an expedition under the command of a Portuguese,† named Diego Garcia. which left Spain shortly after Cabot; touched at the Canaries, as he had

* Herrera, Dec. iv. lib. v. cap. x.

† Herrera, Dec. iii. lib. x. cap. i.

done; found its way to the La Plăta; fixed itself in his neighbourhood; and, finally, by the misconduct of certain persons connected with it, brought on a general and overwhelming attack on Cabot, from the natives, who had previously, by a mixture of boldness and good management, been brought into alliance with him. Charlevoix (Histoire du Paraguay, tom. i. p. 28) supposes that Garcia was employed avowedly by Portugal; but according to Herrera (Dec. iii. lib. x. cap. i.), the expedition was fitted out by the Count D. Fernando de Andrada and others, for the La Plata, and consisted of a ship of one hundred tons, a pinnace, and one brigantine, with the frame of another to be put together as occasion might require. One great object was to search for Juan de Cartagena, and the French priest whom Magellan had put on shore. Garcia left Cape Finisterre on the 5th of August, 1526, and touching at the Canaries (where Cabot had been) took in supplies and sailed thence the 1st of September.

These plain matters of fact have been recently mis-stated. In Dr Lardner's Cyclopædia (History of Maritime and Inland discovery, vol. ii. p. 89), it is said, "Diego Garcia was sent with a single ship to the river of Solis; but as he *lingered on his way at the Canary Islands*, he was anticipated in his discoveries by Sebastian Cabot. That celebrated Navigator had sailed from Spain *a few months later* than Garcia," &c. Cabot sailed in April 1526. The fact is important, because had he left Spain under the circumstances stated, he could not have been ignorant of the claim of Garcia, under a grant, as is alleged, from the emperor, and his going to the same quarter would have been both fraudulent and absurd. His manifest ignorance on the subject corroborates the suspicion that, on finding the intrigues to arrest Cabot ineffectual, this expedition, under the command of the Portuguese, was hastily got up to watch his movements, and probably to act in concert with the disaffected, with an understanding as to certain points of rendezvous in case the mutineers should gain the mastery. It is important to note that in Peter Martyr, whose work embraces the early part of 1526,* no reference is made to any projected expedition to the quarter for which, as it is now said, Garcia was destined.

At Decade iv. lib. i. cap. i. Herrera resumes his abstract of Garcia's report. That personage is now off the coast of Brasil. He touched at the Bay of St Vincent, and there found a Portuguese of the degree of Bachelor, from whom he received refreshments, and whose son-in-law agreed to accompany him to the La Plata. In running down the coast he touched at the island of Patos (now St Catherine) in 27°, where Cabot had been before him, and, as Garcia asserts, had behaved in a very shameful manner, carrying off the sons of several chiefs who had treated him with great kindness. Proceeding up the La Plata, Garcia found the ships which Cabot, on ascending the river, had left under the charge of an officer. He resolved to follow in his brigantine; and here we are let into the character of this personage. While at St Vincent, he had hired, to his host the Bachelor, the ship of *a hundred tons*, to carry *eight hundred* slaves to Portugal; and "to colour," says Herrera, "his covetousness, he said, that he had protested to the Count Don Fernando de Andrada, that the vessel was useless, being much too large for the navigation and discovery of the La Plata."† Thus, with the blindness of an absurd prejudice, has the author consented to spread upon his pages all the malignant invective of this man against Cabot—to make it a part of the History of the Indies—and yet he winds up, at last, by telling us of Garcia's fraud, and of the falsehood by which it was sought to be disguised! The Portuguese, in order to break the force of indignation against himself, evidently laboured to turn the resentment of his employers on Cabot, by whom they supposed their views

* He speaks of the marriage of the Emperor with the sister of the King of Portugal, which took place in March, 1526.

† "Para dar color a esta codicia, dixo que havia protestado al Conde Don Fernando de Andràda que no le diese esta nave porque era mui grande e inutil para la navegacion i descubrimiento del Rio de la Plata." Herrera, Dec. iv lib. i. cap. i.

to have been thwarted. One reflection is obvious. If this man could be seduced from his duty by the Portuguese Bachelor, we may presume that the agents of Portugal had no great difficulty in negotiating with him and inducing him to give his voyage a turn to suit their purposes. Even supposing his employers, then, honest and sincere, we have no assurance that he did not act from sinister motives. We shall meet Garcia again in the La Plata.

There is another circumstance, somewhat posterior in point of time, but which serves to show the anxious expedients to which Portugal did not disdain to resort, even at the expense of its dignity. A Portuguese, named Acosta, returned with Cabot from Brazil, and immediately afterwards the king of Portugal was detected in an unworthy correspondence with him.* It is remarkable, also, that the complaints of the mutineers whom Cabot put ashore were brought to Spain by a Portuguese vessel.†

---

* Herrera, Dec. iv. lib. x. cap. vi.

† Ib. Dec. iv. lib. iii. cap. i.

CHAP. XVIII.

INTERFERENCE WITH THE ARRANGEMENTS FOR THE VOYAGE—MENDEZ APPOINTED SECOND IN COMMAND CONTRARY TO THE WISHES OF CABOT —DE ROJAS—THE SEALED ORDERS—PREJUDICES OF THE SPANISH HISTORIANS—EXPEDITION SAILS.

In a letter dated November, 1525, Peter Martyr * speaks of the expedition as at length about to sail. It was doomed, however, to yet further delays; and even in matters of detail the presence of an evil spirit is but too obvious.

Three ships were provided by the Emperor, to which a small caravel was added by an individual.† The principal authority over the arrangements would seem to have been exercised by certain agents or deputies (disputados) named by the freighters. They controlled Cabot, in every particular; and it is obvious, therefore, that the fate of the expedition lay in their integrity or corruptibility. The whole sum which the company had at stake is stated to have been only ten thousand ducats.

The leading subject of difference between Cabot and these persons, as appears by the meagre accounts left to us, was as to the person who should fill the office of Lieutenant-General. Cabot was anxious for the appointment of his friend De Rufis; but the choice of the agents fell on Martin Mendez who had been in one of Magellan's ships as Treasurer (contador), a situation bearing, it may be presumed, an analogy to the present office of Purser. They are said to have made the selection *on*

* Decade viii. cap. ix.

† Such is the account of Herrera, confirmed by Robert Thorne. Writers who make a different statement (Charlevoix, for example, in his *Histoire du Paraguay* tom. i. p. 25) have been misled by looking to the original requisition of Cabot instead of the limited force finally placed under his command.

account of their differences with Cabot.* These disputes rose to such a height that the Emperor was urged to appoint another commander. When it is stated that this same Martin Mendez was one of those expelled from the squadron, for mutiny, by Cabot who afterwards justified himself to the Emperor for having done so, we not only see the irksome position in which he was placed, but will, probably, deem the efforts to get rid of him the highest compliment to his energy and incorruptibility. A hollow compromise was at length effected by a provision, on paper, that Mendez should take part in nothing which was not expressly committed to him by Cabot, and never act except in the absence or disability of the chief.† Thus, with regard to an officer to whom the commander should be able to look, at every turn, for confidential counsel and cordial co-operation, the utmost that Cabot could procure was a stipulation that he should preserve a sullen indifference, and not be actively mischievous.

A number of young men of family, animated by the love of adventure, joined the Expedition, and amongst them three brothers of Balboa.

There are two personages destined to act, with Mendez, a conspicuous part, and who may therefore be here mentioned. The first was *Miguel de Rodas*, a sort of supernumerary, to whom no particular post was assigned, but who is stated to have been a man of great valour and nautical experience, and to have enjoyed the favour of the emperor.‡ The other was *Francisco de Rojas*, captain of one of the ships, the Trinidad. Though a slight difference is perceptible in the names, they would seem to have been brothers, for, at a subsequent period,§ in speaking of the leading conspirators, these two are describ-

---

* "Los disputados de los armadores *por diferencias que con el General avian tenido* quisieron que fuesse Martin Mendez y no Miguel de Rufis á quien pretendia llevar en este cargo Sebastian Gaboto." Herrera, Dec. iii. lib. ix. cap. iii.

† "Que no se occupasse sino en las cosas que el General le cometiese, y estando ausente o impedido, y no de otra manera porque le llevaba contra su voluntad." Herrera, Dec. iii. lib. ix. cap iii.

‡ Herrera, Dec. iii. lib. ix. cap. iii.

§ Herrera, Dec. iv. lib. i. cap i.

ed, with a yet further variation, as "los dos hermanos Roxas i Martin Mendez" ("the two brothers Roxas and Martin Mendez").

The most extraordinary part, however, of the arrangement, consisted of the *Sealed Orders*, of which a copy was given *to each vessel.** We are not informed at what time they were to be opened, but from the nature of their contents we may infer that it was to be done immediately on getting to sea, and from the sequel we may infer how idle would have been any injunction of forbearance. Provision was therein made for the death of Cabot, and *eleven* persons were named on whom, in succession, the command in chief was to devolve. Should this list be exhausted, a choice was to be made by general vote throughout the squadron, and in case of an equality of suffrages the candidates were to decide between themselves by casting lots! At the head of the list are found the three individuals just mentioned. It is remarkable that Gregario Caro, the captain of one of the ships and who is afterwards found in command of the fort in the La Plata when Cabot ascended further up the river, stands *last* on this list, after all the treasurers and accountants. This person is subsequently stated† to have been a nephew of the Bishop of Canaria, and seems to have acted throughout with integrity.

It would be difficult to imagine a scheme better calculated to nourish disaffection. Each individual of note found a provision by which he might be brought into the chief command, and was invited to calculate the chances of its reaching him through the successive disappearance of his predecessors on the list; and the crews, while under the pressure of severe discipline, not only saw a hope of bettering their condition by a change, but at each step approached nearer to the clause which placed the supreme power in their own gift. A contingency thus provided for they knew must have been deemed, at home, within the range of possible occurrences, and they

* Herrera, Dec. iii. lib. ix. cap. iii.

† Ib. Dec. iv. lib. i. cap. i.

would have little disposition to let the precaution be found a superfluous one.

While there exist so many causes for misunderstanding Cabot's conduct, and motives for misrepresenting it, the writer, unfortunately, whose statements have since been adopted almost without question, prepared his history under circumstances little inclining him to impartiality. The Decades of Peter Martyr terminate before the sailing of the expedition, and the venerable author complains, at the close, of the infirmities which then pressed on him in his seventieth year. The next work—that of Gomara—appeared in 1552, shortly after Cabot had abandoned the service of Spain, and returned to his native country. Charles V., in 1549, had made a formal, but ineffectual, demand on Edward VI. for his return.* That Gomara had his eye on him in this new and invidious position is evident, because in speaking of the conference at Badajos he incidentally mentions Cabot as one of the few survivors of those who had been present on that occasion (cap. C.). In a work, therefore, dedicated to the Emperor, we are not to look for a vindication of our navigator from the calumnies which might be current to his disadvantage; and we find, accordingly, every allusion to him deeply tinctured with prejudice. The mutineers, of whom a severe example was made, had enjoyed a high reputation at home, and were doubtless able to raise a clamorous party. Those who fitted out the expedition of Garcia, were led to regard Cabot invidiously, and when it is added that the mercantile loss of his own employers would unavoidably lead, on the part of some, to reproachful criticism, however unmerited, we see at once that his reputation lay at the mercy of a writer ready and eager to embody the suggestions of disappointment or malevolence.

But our patience is exhausted by the long detention of the expedition. It sailed at length in the beginning of April, 1526.†

* Strype's Memorials of the Reformation, vol. ii. p. 190.

† Gomara, cap. lxxxix. Herrera, Dec. iii. lib. ix. cap. iii. Robert Thorne (1 Hakluyt, p. 215) There has been a general misconception on this point in

English compilations, attributable, probably, to the wretched version of Herrera [illegible] which names April 1525 (Stevens' Translation, vol. iii. p. 380), in defiance of the work it professes to translate. The same mistake is found in Campbell's Lives of the Admirals, and the source of the author's error becomes manifest by his incautious citation of Herrera. The reference given is totally inapplicable to the original work, but corresponds exactly with the new and arbitrary distribution of Decades, books, and chapters by Stevens. In most recent works the date is mis-stated, amongst the rest by Mr Southey (History of Brasil, p. 52), and by the Quarterly Review (vol. iv. p. 459). The former writer, speaking of this voyage in 1526, infers from Cabot's being called Pilot-Major, that Americus Vespucius who had held that office was "probably" then dead (p. 52), a singular remark, as it is well known that Vespucius died fifteen years before. He was succeeded, as we have seen, by Juan Dias de Solis. Cabot's appointment as Pilot-Major in 1518, his attendance at Badajos, &c., are altogether unnoticed in the pretended translation of Stevens !

CHAP. XIX.

COMPLAINTS IN THE SQUADRON—PRETENDED CAUSES OF DISSATISFACTION —MUTINY—QUELLED BY THE ENERGY OF CABOT—HAPPY RESULTS— HIS CONDUCT JUSTIFIED TO THE EMPEROR—RIDICULOUS CHARGES SUGGESTED BY THE PORTUGUESE, DIEGO GARCIA.

We look for an explosion as the vessels quit the shore. It would seem, however, that the train was prepared to burn more slowly. The Squadron is seen to move on steadily and in silence, but beneath the fair and smiling canvass we know there is dark treachery.

In attempting to pierce the obscurity which veils the scenes that follow, and to place ourselves by the side of Cabot, we have unfortunately to rely on those whose very purpose is disparagement. Yet to that quarter we do not fear to turn, and have at least an assurance that we shall find whatever the most malignant industry could collect.

Something is said by Herrera as to a scarcity of provisions, owing, as far as he will speak out, to their injudicious distribution amongst the vessels. Now it is quite inconceivable that in an expedition prepared for the circumnavigation of the globe there should have been found this deficiency on the coast of Brasil, and the fact, moreover, would be disgraceful to the commanders of the other vessels, and to the agents at home. It is obvious that while nothing is more unlikely than such improvidence on the part of Cabot, it would be easy for disaffected officers to circulate amongst the men complaints of scarcity, and thus refer the odium of a limited allowance to the Commander-in-Chief.

We hear, also, that he did not take sufficient pains to soothe the angry feelings which had been excited at Seville.* Then

* The whole passage has that air of vagueness so characteristic of falsehood.

it seems that dissatisfaction arose not from any thing occurring during the voyage, but from continued brooding over antecedent griefs. Doubtless, Martin Mendez, of whose unfitness Cabot had made a representation, and against whose mischievous intermeddling he had been forced to obtain a stipulation, was in no very complacent mood, even if we put out of view the probability of his having been tampered with by the Portuguese. The complaint, too, that Cabot did not sufficiently exert himself to make others forget the late angry discussions, comes from the very persons who broke out into open mutiny, and whose statements, embittered by a recollection of the severe punishment inflicted on them, compose our evidence. It might be superfluous to add a word to this explanation, yet the remark cannot be forborne, that if there be one trait in the character of Cabot more clearly established than another, it is the remarkable gentleness of his deportment; and in every reference to him, by those who had enjoyed a personal intercourse, there breaks forth some endearing form of expression that marks affectionate attachment.

But pretexts will never be wanting where a mutinous temper exists. The squadron was running down the coast of Brasil when it seems to have been thought necessary to bring matters to a crisis. Murmurs became general and vehement. The Lieutenant-General Mendez, De Rojas, and De Rodas were louder than the rest in blaming the government of Cabot.* In a word, relying on the clamour they had raised, it is plain that these men now broke out into open insolence, presuming that disaffection would thus reach its height, and a new arrangement take place conformably to the indication of the Sealed Orders.

The situation of Cabot would to one of ordinary stamp have

"Porque le faltó la victualla por ser mal repartida y como por las diferencias de Sevilla, iban algunos animos mal satisfechos y el tuvo poco cuydado en sossegarlos nacieron murmuraciones y atrevimientos en el armada." Herrera, Dec. iii. lib. ix. cap. iii.

* "Teniente de General, Martin Mendez, al Capitan Francisco de Rojas y a Miguel de Rodas porque demàs que les tenia mala voluntad, con libertad reprehendian su govierno." Herrera, Dec. iii. lib. ix. cap. iii.)

been appalling. The three persons highest in authority, and to whom he ought to have been able to look for support at such a crisis, had artfully, and in concert, fomented discontent, and were now ready to place themselves at its head. He was in the midst of those who disliked and undervalued him as a foreigner. There were but two of his own countrymen on board. De Rojas, he might anticipate, had made sure of his own crew of the Trinidad, and De Rodas, a man of varied service and high reputation, was likely to rally round him the confidence and enthusiasm of the spirited young cavaliers, volunteers in the expedition. Cabot had performed no memorable service for Spain. There now comes over us, too, almost with dismay, what before had scarcely excited attention. The Spaniards, Peter Martyr said, denied that Cabot had achieved what he pretended, even in the service of England. Such an insinuation could not have escaped the eager malevolence of those now around him. Here then was exercised, harshly and haughtily, over Castilians, an authority yielded, incautiously, to the adroit falsehoods of the English adventurer!

But Cabot belonged to that rare class of men whose powers unfold at trying moments. There seems to belong to command on the Ocean a peculiar energy, the offspring of incessant peril and of that very insolation which throws the brave man on himself, and leads him to muse habitually over all the exigences that may, on a sudden, task to the uttermost his fortitude or his intrepidity. Cabot saw that his only safety lay in extreme boldness. He was no longer, as with Sir Thomas Pert, a mere guide in the career of discovery. A high responsibility was on him. He knew that by a daring exercise of that rightful authority, to which habit lends a moral influence, men may be awed into passive instruments, who, but the moment before, meditated fierce mutiny. His determination was instantly made, and well justified that reputation for dauntless resolution borne back to Spain and to England from this expedition. He seized De Rojas—took him out of his ship the Trinidad—and placing him with Mendez and de

Rodas in a boat, ordered the three to be put on shore. The [illegible] humiliation; and these men long afterwards are found dwelling with bitterness on the indignity, in their memorial to the Emperor.* The effect was instant. Discord vanished with this knot of conspirators. During the five years of service through which the expedition passed, full as they were of toil, privation, and peril, we hear not the slightest murmur; on the contrary, every thing indicates the most harmonious action and the most devoted fidelity.

Curiosity runs eagerly forward to learn the view taken by the Emperor of this high-handed measure. It can only be inferred from circumstances, for there is no account of any formal trial. That a thorough investigation took place cannot be doubted. Miguel de Rodas had been in the Victory, the ship of Magellan's squadron which effected the circumnavigation of the globe, had received from the Emperor a large pension for life, and a device for his Coat of Arms, commemorative of that achievement.† Martin Mendez had been in the same ship, and the device prepared for him is of a yet more flattering description.‡ It was doubtless found, without going into the question of Portuguese bribery, that their accidental association with so memorable an enterprise, had given to them a reputation quite beyond their merit, and that these very marks of distinction, and a certain feeling as veterans, had led to an insolent assumption which rendered it indispensable for Cabot to vindicate the ascendancy due to his station and to his genius. By a Portuguese vessel the three mutineers gave notice of their situation, and complained in the bitterest terms of the conduct of Cabot.§ The Emperor sent orders to have them conveyed to Spain in order that justice might be done. Hernando Calderon and Jorge Barlo despatched by Cabot, afterwards reached Toledo, and made re-

* "Con tanta afrenta suia." Herrera, Dec. iv. lib. iii. cap. i.

† Herrera, Dec. iii. lib. iv. cap. xiv.

‡ Ibid.

§ Herrera, Dec. iv. lib. iii. cap. i.

port of all that had taken place. The emperor yielded to the solicitations of Cabot for succour and permission to colonise the country (Herrera, Dec. iv. lib. iii. cap. i.), and the merchant adventurers declining to co operate in what had ceased to be a mercantile speculation, the Emperor undertook to bear the whole expense himself (Dec. iv. lib. viii. cap. xi.). As we never hear of any censure on Cabot, and know that he afterwards resumed his high and honourable office in Spain; and that when, long after, he went to England, the Emperor earnestly solicited his return, we cannot doubt that his vindication was complete.

A singular proof here occurs of the disingenuousness of the Spanish historians. It is manifest, that Cabot could not have escaped the sharpest rebuke, and punishment, without making out a clear justification of his conduct; yet, while not a syllable is given of his statement, which must, from the result, have triumphed, all the disparaging suggestions that malignity could invent, and the falsehood of which must have been established at the time, are eagerly detailed. There can only be wrung from Gomara a cold acknowledgement that the voyage was frustrated, "not so much, *as some say*, by his fault, as by that of his associates."*

It might be superfluous, under such circumstances, to examine these allegations, yet they are on their face so improbable, that we may safely advert to them, even in the absence of Cabot's Defence.

It is asserted, that at the island of Patos (the present St Catherine's), where he was treated with the utmost kindness by the inhabitants, and took in refreshments, he basely seized the sons of some of the principal chiefs and carried them forcibly away. This story is taken from the report of the Portuguese, Diego Garcia, who, although denounced for fraud on his own employers, is considered a good witness against Cabot. He represents himself to have subsequently visited

---

* "No tanto, *a lo que algunos dicen*, por su culpa como por la de su gente." Gomara, cap. lxxxix.

the island, and to have been very graciously received, notwithstanding the recent outrage. This last circumstance is not the least of the improbabilities involved in his tale, for putting that out of view, as well as the polluted source from which the charge proceeds, let us consider its claims to credit. The seizure is represented to have taken place not on the return, but on the outward voyage. What, then, was the object of so wanton a piece of cruelty? But further, the orders of the Council of the Indies were peremptory that no violence should be used. Peter Martyr (Dec. viii. cap. x.), speaking of the expedition of Gomez in 1524, adverts with indignation to his having brought away a number of natives, and expressly states it to be in violation of the standing orders of the Council. Now, Cabot had been, as early as 1515, a member of that Council, was familiar with the orders, and instrumental in framing them. He was in Spain when Gomez returned, and knew of the indignation excited by the abduction. Is it at all likely, then, that he would subject himself to a similar rebuke without any conceivable motive? It is remarkable, that in Cabot's own instructions to Sir Hugh Willoughby, long afterwards, we recognise the analogy to those of the Council of the Indies, for while he enjoins every effort, by gentleness, to get a thorough knowledge of the natives, he expressly forbids the use of "violence or force" (§. 23 of Instructions, Hakluyt, vol. i. p. 228).

We must advert again, more particularly, to the indignation which, in 1524, Peter Martyr expresses at the conduct of Gomez.

"Contrary to the laws made by us, that no violence should be offered to any nation, he freighted his ship with people of both sexes taken from certain innocent half-naked nations, who contented themselves with hovels instead of houses."*

It is with this historian that Cabot is found on terms of inti-

* "Contra Leges a nobis dictatas ne quis ulli gentium vim afferat, ab innoccutibus quibusdam seminudis populis magalibus pro domibus contentis," &c. (Dec. viii. cap. x.)

macy more than ten years before, and the good old man speaks of him as one of a congenial temper, or as Eden and Hakluyt have it, "Cabot is my very friend whom I use familiarly and delight to have him sometimes keep me company in my own house." At the moment of his penning the denunciation of Gomez, Cabot was his associate with the ripened friendship of the intermediate years. Yet Mr Southey (History of Brazil, p. 52) has not only consented to echo the calumny of a vile Portuguese convicted of fraud and falsehood, but adds this coarse and cruel invective—"Cabot touched at an island on the coast called Ilha dos Patos, or Duck Island, and there took in supplies; requiting the good will which the natives had manifested with *the usual villainy* of an old discoverer, by *forcibly* carrying away four of them." And the same writer (ib.) denounces, as "an act of cruelty," the energetic proceeding by which Cabot quelled the mutiny, and probably saved his own life.

Another item of criticism is derived from the report of the same Portuguese, Diego Garcia. He sailed from the Canaries on the first September, and before he reaches the Cape de Verd Islands a boast is uttered of his superior skill in the choice of a route. So earnest is the wish to make this impression, that we are again told he proceeded from the Cape de Verds "for Cape St Augustine [on the coast of Brazil], which he places in eight degrees ten minutes of Southern latitude, and this route, on account of the great currents from the rivers of Guinea, which drive the ships to the North-West, is perilous, and Sebastian Cabot did not know how to take advantage of it (as has been *already* said), because though he was *a great Cosmographer*, he was not *so great a Seaman*."*

---

* "Fue en demanda del Cabo de San Augustin, que este Piloto pone en ocho Grados, i un sesmo de Grado de la Vanda del Sur, de la otra parte de la Equinoctial. Y este Camino, por la grandes corrientes que salen de los Rios de Guinea, que baten los Navios a la Vanda del Norueste es peligroso ni le supo tomar Sebastian Gaboto (como se ha dicho) *porque aunque era gran Cosmografo, no era tan gran Marinero.*" Herrera, Dec. iii. lib. x. cap. i.

Now first as to the facts. Garcia's criticism seems to be that Cabot stood across the Atlantic before he got as far South as the Cape de Verd Islands. That this very point had been the subject of anxious deliberation we learn from Peter Martyr, (Dec. vii. cap. vi.) "Cabot will set off in the next month of August, 1525. He departs no earlier, because things necessary for an enterprise of such importance cannot be prepared, nor by the course of the heavens ought he to begin his voyage before that time; as he has to direct his course towards the Equinoctial when the sun," &c.*

It might be supposed, perhaps, that the vexatious delays had caused some change of the route originally projected; but so far is this from the fact, Herrera tells us expressly—

"After many difficulties Sebastian Cabot departed in the beginning of April of this year (1526), &c. He sailed to the Canaries and the Cape de Verd Islands, and thence to Cape St Augustine," &c.†

Thus he took the very route in which Garcia followed! Even supposing Herrera to be mistaken, and to have described the course originally resolved on at Seville, instead of that which Cabot actually pursued, the latter would only be found, in avoiding the Cape de Verds, opening a path which is more generally followed in modern times. Take it either way, the impudence and absurdity of the cavil are palpable. Yet note the manner in which an English writer of reputation has caught it up.‡

"Cabot's conduct in this voyage did not give satisfaction, and was thought unequal to the high reputation he had ac-

---

* "Est Cabotus, Augusto mense proximo anni MDXXV. discessurus, nec citius quidem quia nec prius queunt ad rem tantum necessaria parari nec per cœlorum cursus debet prius illud iter inchoari; oportet quippe tunc versus Equinoctium vela dirigere quando Sol," &c.

† "Despues de muchas dificultades partio Sebastian Gaboto à los primeros de Abril de este ano (1526), &c. Fue navegando a las Canarias y à las Islas de Cabo Verde, y despues al Cabo de San Agustin." Herrera, Dec. iii. lib. ix. cap. iii.

‡ "A Chronological History of the Discoveries in the South Sea or Pacific Ocean, &c. By James Burney, Captain in the Royal Navy," vol. i. p. 162.

quired. *The Spanish writers say of him* (!), that he was a better cosmographer than a mariner or commander."

Wearied as the reader may be, we must advert to another sneer of this Portuguese. In ascending the La Plata, Cabot proceeded with deliberation, examining carefully the country, and opening a communication with the different tribes on its banks. This was of course a work of time as well as of labour and peril. When Garcia arrived, he proceeded hastily up the river, and boasts that "in 26 days he advanced as far as Sebastian Cabot had done *in many months.*"* The folly of this idle vaunt has not deterred Herrera from making it a part of the History of the Indies; and it has found a ready place with English writers.

We might, indeed, be almost led to believe in a concerted plan, on the part of his countrymen, to defame this great navigator, were not the causes of misconception obvious. To some the perfidious translation of Stevens has proved a snare, and the few who proceeded further have been led, by an imperfect knowledge of the language, to catch at certain leading words and phrases, readily intelligible, and thus to present them apart from the context, which, in the original, renders the calumny harmless and even ridiculous.

---

* Herrera, Dec. iv. lib. i. cap. i.

CHAP. XX.

CABOT ENTERS THE LA PLATA—NECESSITY FOR CAUTION—HIS PREDECESSOR AS PILOT-MAJOR KILLED IN ATTEMPTING TO EXPLORE THAT RIVER—CARRIES THE ISLAND OF ST GABRIEL—HIS PROGRESS TO ST SALVADOR WHERE A FORT IS ERECTED—ITS POSITION—LOSS IN TAKING POSSESSION.

CABOT was left in the neighbourhood of the La Plata at the moment when, by a determined effort, he "shook to air" the mutiny that sought to fasten on him.

It is plain, that after expelling the three individuals who, in the event of his death, were named, in succession, to the command in chief, he would not have been justified in proceeding, with the squadron which the Emperor had confided to him, on the long and perilous voyage originally contemplated. He determined, therefore, to put into the La Plata and send advice of what had occurred. His predecessor in the office of Pilot-Major, Diego de Solis, had been slain in attempting to explore this river; Cabot now resolved to renew the experiment.

An additional reason for postponing, until further orders, the prosecution of the enterprise was the loss, by shipwreck, of one of the vessels. This fact is mentioned by Richard Eden (Decades, fol. 316), who has a chapter on the region of the La Plata in which he adverts to the expedition, in terms* that bespeak the reports conveyed to England, probably, by Robert Thorne, then at Seville, and his two friends who were engaged in it. He states the loss of the vessel, and

* "The Emperoure's Majestie and Kynge of Spayne Charles the fifte, sente forthe Sebastian Cabot (a man of great courage and skylfull in Cosmographie, and of no lesse experience as concernynge the starres and the sea) with commandment," &c.

that "the men that saved their lyves by swymmynge were receaved into the other shyppes."

It is the more necessary to understand the considerations by which Cabot was influenced, as in a recent work (Dr Lardner's Cyclopædia, History of Maritime and Inland Discovery, vol. ii. p. 89), the following strange assertion is found amidst a tissue of errors: "On touching at the mouth of the river in which Solis had lost his life, Cabot found two Spaniards who had deserted from that Commander, besides fifteen other stragglers from subsequent expeditions. All these men concurred in representing the country up the river as singularly rich in the precious metals, and *easily persuaded* Cabot to proceed in that direction!" Not the slightest allusion is made to the mutiny, or to the loss of one of the vessels. Thus, an Officer in command of the Emperor's squadron with specific orders, and under bond, moreover, to the merchants of Seville, is represented as abandoning his duty and becoming an *easy* dupe to the idle stories of some runaways!

At this point we have again to deplore the loss of Cabot's Maps. One of them described his course up the La Plata, and would seem to have been made public, for Eden (Decades, fol. 316) says, "From the mouth of the river, Cabot sayled up the same into the lande for the space of three hundreth and fiftie leagues, *as he wryteth in his own Carde.*" This statement is the more important, as the extent of his progress has been singularly misrepresented.

In the Conversation reported by Ramusio, and usually connected with the name of Butrigarius the Pope's legate, Cabot is made to say that he sailed up the La Plata more than *six hundred* leagues.* This is the passage, it may be remembered, which the Biographie Universelle could not find in Ramusio. Eden correctly translates it (Decades, fol. 255), but Hakluyt, who adopts his version with anxious servility up to this point, has "more than six *score* leagues!" (vol. iii. p. 7) thus furnishing a new proof of his utter faithlessness. The

* "Et andai all' insu per quello *piu de secento leghe.*" Ramusio, tom. i. fol. 415.

exaggeration of the original, as honestly given by Eden, prepares us for Ramusio's [illegible], [illegible] has already been made, that he could not pretend to trust his memory about the exact terms of the Conversation. Hakluyt, by an arbitrary and absurd reduction, not only obscures this presumptive evidence of general error, but leads us to infer—as such matters are usually over-rated—that, in point of fact, Cabot did not proceed so far. It will appear, presently, that there was no exaggeration in the statement of the "Card."

The career on which Cabot was now entering demanded circumspection as well as courage. De Solis with a party of fifty men had been fiercely assailed and cut off, the bodies of himself and his companions devoured by the ferocious natives, and the survivors of the expedition, who witnessed the scene from the ships, had left the river in dismay, and returned to Spain with the horrid news.* In accompanying Cabot we take Herrera as our principal guide (Dec. iii. lib. ix. cap. iii.). Running boldly up the river, which is to this day the dread of navigators, he reached a small island about half a league from the Northern shore, nearly opposite the present Buenos Ayres, and gave to it the name of Gabriel, which it yet bears. It is a short distance from Martin Garcia's island, so called after the Pilot of De Solis who was buried there (Eden's Decades, fol. 316). The natives had collected and made a very formidable show of resistance, but Cabot, according to Eden, "without respect of peril, thought best to expugne it by one meanes or other, wherein his boldness tooke good effecte as oftentymes chaunceth in great affayres" (Eden, fol. 316).

At this island Cabot left his ships, and proceeding seven leagues further in boats, reached a river to which he gave the name of St Salvador. As it offered a safe and commodious harbour, he returned and brought up the ships, but was

* Herrera, Dec. ii. lib. i. cap. vii. Peter Martyr, Dec. iii. cap. x. Gomara, cap. lxxxix. "Lo mataron; i comieron con todos las Espanoles que saco, i aun quebraron el batel. Los otros que de los Navios miraban, alcaron anclas i velas, sin osar tomar venganca de la muerte de su Capitan."

obliged to lighten them at the entrance of the river. Here he erected a Fort.

It is obvious, on looking at a map of this reign, and comparing it with the statement of Herrera, that the river spoken of might be either the Uruguay, which, on the right, takes a northern direction, or one of the various streams into which the Parana is broken by the islands at its mouth. Cabot would hardly follow the Uruguay, because it evidently struck into Brasil, and, at a much higher point of ascent, he is found avoiding, expressly for that reason, a great river on the right hand. In speaking of the position occupied by his ships he states it, according to Herrera, to be on the *Brasil*, meaning the northern side of the river, a mode of designation, which, supposing him, as we reasonably may, to have been aware of the general course of the great stream discovered by De Solis, would not distinguish any position up the Uruguay, both sides of which were equally within that region, according to the distribution with reference to which he spoke. But the position of St Salvador is conclusively settled by information from another quarter. In Hakluyt (vol. iii. p. 729), is "a Ruttier for The River Plate." The pilot who prepared it gives the various methods of striking the mouths of the Parana in proceeding from the island of Martin Garcia. A caution is interposed—"and if you fall into the mouth of the river which is called the Uruay you must leave it on the right hand." He adds that all the mouths of the Parana, which are five in number, have their eastern termination infested with shoals for an extent of more than two leagues. Describing one of the routes more particularly, he says, "From the isle of Martin Garcia unto *St Salvador*, is nine or ten leagues. This is an island which standeth two leagues within the *first* mouth, *where Sebastian Caboto took possession.*" The pilot, it will be seen, gives the name of St Salvador, not to the river, but to a port. Cabot himself does the same, for in describing the assault finally made on the upper fort by the natives, he speaks of a similar attack on the port of St Salvador, where the ships lay.* It seems certain, then, that the first position fortified by Cabot was in the most northern mouth of the Parana, on an island about two leagues from where it reaches the La Plata. On the map of Louis Stanislaus d'Arcy de la Rochette,† this most northern avenue is divided into two parts, the upper of which is designated as "Rio Paca," and the lower, that issues into the La Plata, as "Rio Naranjos." St Salvador was, of course, situated on the latter, or perhaps on the stream next in order to the south, which also communicates with the Rio Paca and thus forms with the Rio Naranjos a considerable delta. In a Memoir drawn up by Lopez Vaz, a Portuguese, and taken with the author by the fleet sent forth in 1586 by the Earl of Cumberland, the fort where Cabot left his ships is said to be then standing. Its distance from the sea is, however, misstated either by him or the translator (Hakluyt, vol. iii. p. 788).

It is desirable to fix this first point of occupation, not only as a matter curious in itself, but because Charlevoix (Histoire du Paraguay, tom. i. p. 27), with his usual wild inaccuracy, would throw the whole subject into confusion. He represents Cabot to have finally left the ships at the island of St Gabriel, and proceeded in boats up the Uruguay, by mistake, and he imagines two reasons why such a blunder was committed. He does not even allow the Uruguay to have been the

---

* "Lo mesmo hizieron de la poblacion que avian hecho en el puerto que llaman de S. Salvador adonde estaban los navios" (Herrera, Dec. iv. lib. viii. cap. xi.).

† "Colombia prima or South America, in which it has been attempted to delineate the extent of our knowledge of that continent, extracted chiefly from the original manuscript Maps of His Excellency, the late Chevalier Pinto; likewise from those of Joao Joaquim da Rocha, Joao da Costa Ferreira, El Padre Francisco Manuel Sobreviela, &c. And from the most authentic edited accounts of those countries. Digested and constructed by the late eminent and learned Geographer, Louis Stanislas D'Arcy de la Rochette. London, published by William Faden, Geographer to His Majesty and to His Royal Highness the Prince of Wales, June 4th, 1807." This Map is in the Topographical Department of the King's Library, British Museum.

St Salvador, but makes it one of the tributaries of that river a considerable distance up the stream.

In order to avoid the tedious interruption of the narrative, one other probable misconception was not adverted to at the moment. It has been assumed, with Herrera, that Cabot left his vessels at the island of St Gabriel, and proceeded thence in boats. More probably, however, the island of Martin Garcia was the one intended. Eden says expressly (fol. 316), that De Solis was killed in attempting to take possession of the island of Martin Garcia, and that it was the same afterwards carried by Cabot. We must bear in mind that Herrera is giving, somewhat loftily and reluctantly, the details of an expedition to which he attaches little importance, and he might not care for minute accuracy. He saw the name of Gabriel conferred by Cabot, and did not choose, perhaps, to occupy the page of his History with describing the further progress of six leagues before the ships were quitted. The account of Eden, who approached the subject in a different temper, is confirmed by other considerations. The island is spoken of by Herrera as one standing by itself. Now the St Gabriel is a group of small islets, correctly stated in the "Ruttier" to be five in number. But still more conclusively: Cabot's report, as given by Herrera, states that seven leagues from the island at which he left his ships, he came to the mouth of a river, which he called St Salvador, and to which he afterwards brought up his ships. Now the "Ruttier" speaks of the position at St Salvador, as nine leagues in all from the island of Martin Garcia, two of which being up the St Salvador, there is, of course, an exact correspondence. The St Gabriel group, on the contrary, is correctly stated in the "Ruttier" to lie six leagues lower down than the island of Martin Garcia. While the statement of Eden produces greater harmony in the accounts, the position of the fort is not contingent on success in this reconciliation, but seems conclusively settled by the language of the "Ruttier."

An incident is mentioned by Gomara,* but without the [illegible] occurring at this point, from which it would appear that the position was not gained without resistance. The natives killed and carried off two Spaniards but declared, in a spirit of fierce derision, that they would not eat them, as they were soldiers, of whose flesh they had already had a specimen in De Solis and his followers!

---

* Gomara, cap. lxxxix. "En el puerto de San Salvador que es otro Rio quarenta leguas arriba, que entra en el de la Plata, le mataron los Indios dos Espanoles i no los quisieron comer diciendo que eran Soldados que ia los havian probado en Solis i sus companeros."

CHAP. XXI.

CABOT PROCEEDS UP THE PARANA—ERECTS ANOTHER FORT CALLED SANTUS SPIRITUS, AND AFTERWARDS FORT CABOT—ITS POSITION—CONTINUES TO ASCEND—CURIOSITY OF THE NATIVES AS TO THE EXPEDITION —PASSES THE MOUTH OF THE PARANA—ENTERS THE PARAGUAY—SANGUINARY BATTLE THIRTY-FOUR LEAGUES UP THAT RIVER—THREE HUNDRED OF THE NATIVES KILLED, WITH A LOSS TO CABOT OF TWENTY-FIVE OF HIS PARTY—MAINTAINS HIS POSITION—GARCIA ENTERS THE RIVER—INTERVIEW WITH CABOT—MISTAKES OF CHARLEVOIX, &C.—CABOT RETURNS TO THE FORT "SANTUS SPIRITUS."

HAVING completed the Fort, and taken every precaution for the safety of the ships at St Salvador, Cabot resolved to ascend the Parana. Leaving, therefore, a party under the command of Antonio de Grajeda, he proceeded in the boats and a caravel cut down for the purpose. The point at which he next paused and built a second Fort, is not a matter of doubt. It was on the south bank of the Parana, near a river called by the natives Zarcaranna or Carcaranna. This name was subsequently changed by the Spaniards into Terceiro. On the map of De la Rochette, already referred to, and also on that of Juan de la Cruz Canoy Olmedilla,* it is designated at the early stages as Terceiro, but lower down, gathering strength, it re-assumes the aboriginal title. The Fort stood not immediately on the bank of this river but some miles further up the

* "Mapa Geografica de America Meridional dispuesto y gravado por de Juan de la Cruz Canoy Olmedilla, Geog^{fo.} Pens^{do.} de S. M. Individuo de la Rl. Academia de S^{n}. Fernando, y de la Sociedad Bascongada de los Amigos del Pais; teniendo presentes varios mapas y noticias originales con arreglo á observaciones astronomicas Año de 1775. Este Mapa de los Dominios Españoles y Portugueses en America Meredional, es una copia literal y exacta de un Mapa Español mui raro; compuesto y gravado en Madrid, año 1775, de orden del Rey España, por D^{n.} Juan de la Cruz Cano y Omedilla, Geo^{fo.} Pe^{do.} de S. M. C. Londres, Publicardo por Guillermo Faden, Geografo del Rey, y del Principe de Gales, Enero 1. de 1799."

Parana, as appears by the earliest maps, and by the small but admirable one of D'Anville, in vol. [illegible] of the "Lettres Edifiantes et curieuses."* On the great map of De la Rochette its position is marked with much precision. There is laid down the "Cart Road" from Buenos Ayres to Sante Fe, which passes through *El Rosario* and *S. Miguel;* then comes "el Rincon de Caboto, Fort destroyed;" then Calcachi, and, a little beyond this last, the river Monge. The same representation is made, substantially, by Juan de la Cruz Canay Olmedilla. The only remark of Cabot with regard to the natives of this quarter which Herrera repeats is, that they were intelligent ("gente de buena razon").

He left in this fort a garrison under the command of Gregorio Caro, who had commanded the Maria del Espinar, one of the ships of the squadron, and proceeded in person further up the river. His force must now have been inconsiderable, consisting, as it did, originally, of only one hundred and fifty men, increased perhaps by the gentlemen volunteers. Besides the loss of three principal officers, and inevitable mortality, he had weakened his numbers by leaving garrisons in two forts. Yet his plan was, undoubtedly, a prudent one of thus forming points on which he could fall back, in case of disaster, and break the force and rapidity of a rush towards the vessels. Herrera furnishes no account of his intermediate movements until he reaches the Parana. The incidents which occurred during that long and interesting route are therefore unknown, except from a slight glimpse given in the conversation reported in Ramusio. In ascending the river, Cabot is there represented as "fyndynge it every where verye fayre and inhabited with infinite people which with admyration came runnynge dayly to oure shyppes."†

---

* "Lettres Edifiantes et curieuses ecrites des Missions Etrangers par quelques Missionaires de la Campagnie de Jesus." The work is in the King's Library, British Museum (title in Catalogue *Epistolæ*).

† Richard Eden's Decades, fol, 255. The original in Ramusio, tom. i. fol. 415. "Trovandolo sempre bellissimo et habitato da infiniti popoli che per maraviglia correvano à vedermi."

On reaching the junction of the Parana and Paraguay, he saw that the direction of the former was to Brasil, and, therefore, leaving it on his right he ascended thirty-four leagues up the other.

The region on which he was now entering presented a new aspect. For the first time, the natives were found engaged in the cultivation of the soil, and, with the feeling that springs from exclusive property, they regarded the strangers with jealousy. The tribes in this quarter are marked, both on the old and the recent maps, as distinguished for ferocity and as the deadliest enemies of the Spaniards and Portuguese. A collision soon took place. Three of Cabot's men having, incautiously, strayed from the main body to gather the fruit of the palm tree, were seized by the natives. There followed a fierce and very sanguinary battle. Three hundred of the natives were killed, and Cabot lost twenty-five of his party.* He would seem to have maintained his position, for, among the incidents occurring below, to which it is time to turn, we find the commander of the lower fort apprised, by letter, of what had taken place.

The Portuguese Diego Garcia now re-appears in the narrative of Herrera. That personage, who had left Spain in August 1526, after touching at the Canaries and Cape de Verds proceeded to the coast of Brasil, and is found in January 1527† at the Abrolhos shoals. He visits the Bay of All Saints, the Island of Patos (now St Catherine), all places at which Cabot had touched, and finally the La Plata. We are now without dates, except that in ascending the river *Good Friday* is mentioned as the day of his departure from Santus Spiritus.‡ Of his previous history nothing is known, except from the anecdote told by Herrera of the fraud on his employers in hiring the principal vessel to the slave-dealer at Cape Vincent. We might charitably conclude that he was looking for Juan

* Herrera, Dec. iv. lib. i. cap. i.

† Ib., Dec. iv. lib. i. cap. i.

‡ Ib., Dec. iv. lib. i. cap. i.

de Cartagena and the French priest; but, unfortunately for [illegible] were put on shore by Magellan, at Port St Julien, in Patagonia, some fifteen degrees to the southward of the La Plata.

He found the ships of Cabot at St Salvador, as we left them, under the charge of Antonio de Grajeda, whose anxious vigilance was increased by a letter just received from Cabot, announcing the bloody affair above, and probably sent down with the wounded. Grajeda, seeing strangers approach, supposed that they were the mutineers whom Cabot had put on shore, the two brothers Roxas and Martin Mendez.* Under this impression, he manned his boats, and proceeded in force against them. At the moment of collision, Diego Garcia caused himself to be recognized, and the parties returned amicably together to St Salvador. Garcia here sent away his ship to fulfil the contract about the slaves, and brought his remaining small vessels to St Salvador, which was found, on examination, to offer the most secure harbour. Proceeding up the river with two brigantines and sixty men, he reached the Fort of *Santus Spiritus*, and required the commander, Gregorio Caro, to surrender it, as the right of discovery belonged not to Cabot, but to himself, under the orders of the Emperor. The answer of Caro was, that he held the Fort in the name of the Emperor and of Sebastian Cabot; but that he was willing to render it useful, in any way, to the new-comers. He begged, as a favour, of Garcia, that if, on ascending the river, he found that any of the Spaniards had been taken, he would use his efforts to ransom them, "because, although he knew that Cabot had defeated the Indians, yet it was impossible but that some must have been taken."† It is plain, from

* Here occurs the expression from which it is inferred, that the two mutineers whose names are so nearly alike were brothers, "vieron dos naos de Sebastian Gaboto cuio Teniente era Anton de Grajeda que salio con ciertos Canoas i un Batel armados pensando que eran *los dos Hermanos Roxas* i Martin Méndez, que iban contra el porque Sebastian Gaboto, por inquietos, los havia dexado en una isla desterrados entre los Indios." Herrera, Dec. iv. lib. i. cap. i.

† "Porque aunque sabia que Sebastian Gaboto havia desbaratado los Indios era imposible que no huviesen peligrado algunos." Herrera, Dec. iv lib. i. cap. i.

these expressions, that Cabot was known to have made good his stand. Caro personally pledged himself to the repayment of whatever Garcia might find it necessary to advance in the way of ransom; and he begged, if Cabot had fallen, that Garcia would not leave them in that country.*

On arriving at the junction of the Parana and Paraguay, Garcia, instead of proceeding to support Cabot, turned into the former river, about which he makes a report that Herrera declines to insert, as Nunez Cabeca de Vaca had subsequently examined it with greater care. At length, he reached the Port of *Santa Ana*, the name given by Cabot to his last position. Herrera, although not accurate as to distances, determines the place of meeting, by stating it to have been where the Indians had killed twenty-five Spaniards; and having his own authority for fixing that point thirty-four leagues up the Paraguay, we may suppose that Cabot, after chastising the natives, had come to a good understanding with them. He was employed, as we shall hereafter have reason to conclude, in diligently collecting information about the region from which had been brought the precious metals that he saw in this quarter.

Of the circumstances attending the interview at Santa Ana nothing is known; but Garcia, doubtless, repeated the remonstrance which he had addressed to the commander of the fort.

It was not in the character of Cabot, or consistent with his standing in Spain, to struggle for lawless, or even doubtful, power, and he descended the river in company with Garcia.

In the absence of any evidence as to these points, imagination has been drawn upon. Charlevoix, as has been already stated, supposes Garcia to have been sent into the La Plata by the *Captain-General of Brasil,* thus betraying an entire ignorance of the precise statement of Herrera, and of the fact that there was no such officer as he speaks of, until many

* "Que si hallase muerto a Sebastian Gaboto le rogaba que no los dexasse alli." Ib.

years after. To suit this main fiction, he fabricates a series of collateral incidents equally unfounded and ridiculous.*

* "Gabot vit arriver a son Camp un Capitaine Portugais nommé Diegue Garcias lequel avoit eté envoié par le Capitaine General de Bresil pour reconnoitre le pais et en prendre possession au nom de la Couronne de Portugal mais qui n'avoit pas assez de monde pour executer sa Commission malgré les Espagnols, qu'il ne s'etoit pas attendu de trouver en si grande nombre sur les bords du Paraguay. Gabot de son côté fit reflexion qu'il ne pourroit jamais *empecher les Portugais* de se rendre maitres du pays si ils y revenoient avec des forces superieures que la proximité du Bresel leur donnoit le moien d'y faire entrer en peu de tems; sur quoi il prit le parti de *faire quelques presens a Garcias pour l'engager a le suivre au Fort du S. Esprit.* Il y reussit!" &c. &c.

CHAP. XXII.

CABOT'S REPORT TO CHARLES V.—ITS PRESUMED CONTENTS—PROSPECT WHICH IT HELD OUT—PERU CONTEMPLATED IN HIS ORIGINAL PLAN OF 1524—SPECIMENS FOUND BY CABOT OF THE PRECIOUS METALS OBTAINED THENCE BY THE GUARANIS—EMPEROR RESOLVES ON A GREAT EXPEDITION—HIS PECUNIARY EMBARRASSMENTS—PIZARRO OFFERS TO MAKE THE CONQUEST OF PERU AT HIS OWN EXPENSE—REFLECTIONS—THE NAME RIO DE LA PLATA NOT CONFERRED BY CABOT—MISREPRESENTATION ON THIS AND OTHER POINTS.

On returning to the Fort of Santus Spiritus, Cabot made arrangements to convey to the Emperor intelligence of his discoveries. He prepared, also, a comprehensive statement of the incidents which had occurred since he left Seville, and of the circumstances which compelled him to abandon the expedition originally contemplated. This report is referred to by Herrera,* but while all the calumnies of Cabot's enemies are repeated, he furnishes, as has been before remarked, no part of the vindication which must have been conclusive. This document is probably yet in existence amongst the archives of Spain.

The bearers of the communication were Hernando Calderon, and an individual designated by Herrera in one place as Jorge Barlo, and in another as Jorge Barloque, conjectured to have been one of the two English gentlemen, friends of Thorne, who accompanied the expedition, and whose name, probably George Barlow, has undergone a slighter transformation than might have been anticipated.

Of the hopes and prospects which this communication held out we are ignorant; and only know that the Emperor re-

* Dec. iv. lib. iii. cap. i.

solved to fit out a great expedition, but that the execution of his intention was unfortunately too long delayed.

It may well be imagined that the expectations of Cabot had been raised to a high pitch, and that he eagerly solicited permission and means to follow up the enterprise. He had reached the waters which, rising in Potosi, fall into the Paraguay, and had, doubtless, ascertained the quarter to which the natives were indebted for those ornaments of the precious metals which he saw about their persons. Even from the fort on the Parana, the obstacles between him and Peru present no very formidable difficulty to the modern traveller. That he had his eye on that empire, the riches of which Pizarro was enabled, a few years afterwards, to reach by a different route, may be inferred from the care with which he is found collecting information, and the obvious facilities which they disclose. In an abstract given by Herrera of Cabot's final report to the emperor, there occur the following passages:—

"The principal tribe of Indians in that region are the *Guaranis*, a people warlike, treacherous, and arrogant, who give the appellation of slaves to all who speak a different language." "In the time of Guaynacapa, King of Peru, father of Atabilipa, these people made an irruption into his dominions, which extend more than five hundred leagues, and reached Peru, and after a most destructive progress, returned home in triumph," &c. "Cabot negotiated a peace with this tribe. By friendly intercourse he came to learn many secrets of the country, and *procured from them gold and silver which they had brought from Peru*," &c.*

It had been a part of Cabot's original plan, as stated by Peter Martyr, to visit the western coast of America; "Having passed the winding Strait of Magellan, he is to direct his course to the right hand in the rear of our supposed Continent." "He will scour along all the South side of our sup-

* "La relacion que hico al Rey fue que la mas principal generacion de Indios de aquella tierra son *los Guaranis*, gente guerrera, traydora y sobervia, y que llaman esclavos a todos los que no son de su lengua." Herrera, Dec. iv. lib. viii. cap. xi. "En tiempo de Guaynacapa, Rey de el Peru, Padre de Atabilipa, salieron grandes companias y caminando por todos las tierras de su nacion, que se estenden mas de quinientas leguas llegaron a tierra del Peru y despues de aver hecho grandes destruyciones se bolvieron vitoriosos a su naturaleca."—Ib. "Y haviendo hecho Sebastian Goboto la Paz con esta generacion, &c. con el amitad destos supo muchos secretos de la tierra y huvo de ellos oro y plata de la que traian del Peru."

posed Continent, and arrive at the Colonies of Panama and Nata erected on those shores, the bounds of the Golden Castile, and whosoever at that time shall be governor of that province called Golden Castile is to give us intelligence of his success."* Cabot now found himself within striking distance of these regions, and the intelligence received quickened his eagerness to reach them. The intervening obstacles were nothing to his restless activity and indomitable spirit, and the opposition to be encountered not worth a thought when he knew that a war-party of the savages, whom his own little band had so severely chastised, were able to overrun the Empire of Peru and carry off its treasures.

But however well disposed the Emperor might be to yield a ready belief to the representations of Cabot, the means were absolutely wanting to furnish the promised aid. The only key to this part of the history of Charles V., is a recollection of his struggles with pecuniary embarrassment. The soldiers of Bourbon had mutinied for want of pay, and were brought back to duty only by the great personal exertions and influence of their chief, and by the hope of plunder; and even after the sack of Rome, they refused to quit that city until the arrears due to them should be discharged, "a condition," says Dr Robertson,† "which they knew to be impossible." During the very year in which Cabot's messengers arrived, the Cortes had refused the grant of money solicited by the Emperor.‡ We have already had occasion to advert to the mortgage of the Moluccas to Portugal in 1529, as security for a loan, to the infinite chagrin of his Castilian subjects. Pizarro had the advantage of being able to employ personal importunity, and he asked no money. On 26th July 1528, the Emperor yielded to that adventurer a grant of the entire range of coast, which it had been part of Cabot's plan of 1524 to visit. At his own expense Pizarro engaged to raise a large force, "and to provide the ships, arms, and warlike stores requisite, towards subjecting to the Crown of Castile the

* Peter Martyr, Dec. vii. cap. vi.

† Life of Charles V., book v.

‡ Ib.

country of which the government was allotted to him."* He proceeded at once to the task, though it was not until February 1531 that he was enabled to set out from Panama on his successful, but infamous, career.

It were idle to indulge the imagination, in speculating on the probable result had the expedition to Peru been conducted by Cabot. With all the better qualities of Pizarro, it is certain that the very elevation of his moral character must have stood in the way of that rapid desolation, and fierce exaction, which have made the downfall of the Peruvian Empire a subject of vulgar admiration. In following Pizarro, the heart sickens at a tissue of cruelty, fraud, treachery, and cold-blooded murder, unrelieved even by the presence of great danger; for after the resistance at the island of Puna, which detained him for six months, no serious obstacles were encountered. Even the Guaranis, who had achieved an easy conquest over the unwarlike Peruvians, in the preceding reign, were guiltless of the atrocities which marked his progress. Of one thing we may be certain. Had the conquest fallen to the lot of Cabot, the blackest page of the History of Spanish America would have been spared. The murder of the Inca, to gratify the pique of an illiterate† ruffian, forms one of the most horrid images of History. It was no less impolitic than atrocious, and roused the indignation even of the des-

* Robertson's History of America, book vi.

† "Among all the European Arts, what he admired most was that of reading and writing; and he long deliberated with himself, whether he should regard it as a natural or acquired talent. In order to determine this, he desired one of the soldiers who guarded him, to write the name of God on the nail of his thumb. This he showed successively to several Spaniards, asking its meaning; and to his amazement, they all, without hesitation, returned the same answer. At length Pizarro entered; and on presenting it to him, he blushed, and with some confusion was obliged to acknowledge his ignorance. From that moment, Atahualpa considered him as a mean person, less instructed than his own soldiers; and he had not address enough to conceal the sentiments with which this discovery inspired him. To be the object of a barbarian's scorn not only mortified the pride of Pizarro, but excited such resentment in his breast, as added force to all the other considerations which prompted him to put the Inca to death." (Robertson's Hist. America.

peradoes who accompanied Pizarro. The career of Cabot who, at the Council Board of the Indies, had been a party to the order forbidding even the abduction of a Native, could not have been stained by crimes which make us turn with horror from the guilty splendour of the page that records them.

Reverting to the Despatch of Cabot to the Emperor, it remains to notice a charge against him of having conferred the name of *Rio de la Plata,* or River of Silver, with a view to colour his failure, and to encourage deceptive hopes. Now Gomara, who wrote half a century before Herrera, tells us expressly that this designation was given by the original discoverer, De Solis (cap. lxxxix.).

"Topo con un grandissimo Rio que los Naturales llaman Paranaguaca, que quiere decir Rio como Mar o Agua grande; vido en el muestra de Plata, *i nombrolo de ella.*" ("He fell in with an immense river which the natives called *Paranaguaca,* that is to say, a river like the sea or great water; he saw in it specimens of silver, and *named it from that circumstance.*")

Thus in a work dedicated to the Emperor, we find the origin of that name which Cabot is represented to have fraudulently conferred so long afterwards for the purpose of misleading him!

The same statement is made by Lopez Vaz (Hakluyt, vol. iii. p. 788), "The first Spaniard that entered this river and inhabited the same, was called Solis, who passed up a hundred leagues into it, *and called it by the name of Rio de La Plata, that is to say, The River of Silver.*"

Herrera gives a somewhat different account. In the chapter devoted to Garcia's expedition, he says after speaking of the precious metals obtained by Cabot,

"Tambien Diego Garcia huvo alguna cantidad de Plata de los Indios, desde donde se llamo este Rio de la Plata porque fue la primera que se traxo a Castilla de las Indios, i era de la que los Indios Guaranis traian en planchas i otras piecas grandes de las Provincias del Peru."*

* Herrera, Dec. iv. lib. i. cap. i. "*Diego Garcia* also obtained some portion of silver from the Indians, *whence* it was called Rio de La *Pláta,* or River of Silver, because this was the first of that metal brought to Spain from the Indies, and it was part of that which the Guaranis Indians obtained in plates and other large pieces from the Provinces of Peru."

Let us, then, for a moment, suppose Gomara and Lopez Vaz in error; and further, that the title was not a device of Garcia who was struggling to connect himself ostentatiously with this region—who boasts of his superior activity in exploring it—and with whose name, previously rendered infamous, Herrera more immediately associates the appellation. After all these concessions it would then appear that the epithet was one popularly applied (like *Brazil*, the *Spice* Islands, the *Sugar* Islands, &c.), from the article—the Silver of Potosi—which had been brought thence and attracted general attention and interest. There is not the least reason to suppose that it was conferred by Cabot, or that he concealed the quarter whence the treasure came—a fact which Herrera is found correctly stating from his Report. That document was doubtless full and explicit; giving a prominent place to the hopes which had been excited, but with a statement, also, of the great fertility of the country, its healthy climate, and general advantages for colonization, aside from the avenue it offered to those regions of the precious metals embraced in the plan of 1524.

But while of the Spanish writers, evil-disposed as they are to Cabot, no one has ventured to put forth any such charge of deception, his own countrymen have exhibited an eager anxiety to fasten on him the odious accusation. Two specimens may suffice :—

"Cabot, in the mean time, contrived to send home to the Emperor an account of his proceedings; and as he had found among the savages of the interior some ornaments of gold and silver, which he easily obtained in exchange for various trinkets, he *took advantage* of this slender circumstance *to represent the country as abounding in those metals;* and in conformity with his description, *he gave* the river the name of La Plata."*

"Juan Dias de Solis had discovered a prodigious river to which he gave his own name, and where he was killed and *eaten by an ambush* of savages. In 1525, [this error has already been exposed] Cabot, following the tract of Magalhaens, arrived at the same stream, and explored it as high as the Paraguay. A little gold and silver, which had been obtained from the natives, raised his opinion of the

* Dr Lardner's Cyclopædia, History of Maritime and Inland Discovery, vol. ii. p. 89.

V

importance of the country; the river was named Rio de la Plata, and many an adventurer was lured to his destruction by this deceptive title."*

It is scarcely necessary to add that the statement that Cabot was "*sent to the coast of Brasil, where* he made the important *discovery* of the Rio de la Plata,"† advances for him an unfounded claim. Some difference of opinion exists as to the time of the discovery by De Solis. Herrera, in the "Description de las Indias Occidentales" (cap. xxiv.), prefixed to his History, says, "Juan Diaz de Solis descubrio el Rio de la Plata ano de 1515 i Sebastian Gaboto Ingles iendo con armada por orden del Emperador," &c. ("Juan Diaz de Solis discovered the Rio de la Plata, and Sebastian Cabot, an Englishman, proceeding afterwards with a squadron by order of the Emperor," &c.). According to some accounts, the discovery of De Solis took place a few years before the date here mentioned; but no doubt exists as to the fact of an antecedent visit by him. It is not necessary to inquire here into the yet earlier claims of others.

* Quarterly Review, vol. iv. p. 459.

† Historical Account of Discoveries, &c. by Hugh Murray, Esq. (Vol. i. p. 65). The same idle assertion is made by Mr Barrow, in the Chronological History of Voyages, &c. p. 35.

CHAP. XXIII.

CABOT'S RESIDENCE IN THE LA PLATA—SUBJECTION OF REMOTE TRIBES —CLAIMS OF SPAIN RESTED ON THIS EXPEDITION—TREATY WITH THE GUARANIS—DETAILED REPORT TO THE EMPEROR AS TO THE PRODUCTIONS, ETC. OF THE COUNTRY—MISCONDUCT OF THE FOLLOWERS OF GARCIA—LEADS TO A GENERAL ATTACK FROM THE NATIVES—RETURN TO SPAIN.

Cabot's residence in the La Plata, though measured tediously by hope deferred, and finally blasted, was not passed inactively. The small force which remained, after one of the vessels had been despatched to Europe, might be supposed insufficient to enable him to maintain his position; yet it is certain that his operations were of a very bold and adventurous character. He seems to have pushed his researches as far as could be done without quitting the waters which enabled him to be promptly advised of the arrival of the expected reinforcement.

Of these operations we are left to gather the extent rather from circumstances than any direct information afforded by the Spanish historians. In a Memoir prepared by the Court of Spain, to resist the pretensions of Portugal in this quarter, it is made the leading argument, after an enumeration of a vast number of tribes, that Sebastian Cabot erected forts in the country, administered justice there in civil and criminal cases, and reduced all these nations under the obedience of the Emperor.*

It is impossible not to be struck by the reflection which

* Herrera, Dec IV lib viii. cap. XI "Que Sebastian Gaboto avia edificado en aquellas tierras fortalezas y exercitado justicia civil y criminal y traido a la obediencia Real todas las sobredichas generaciones."

this passage suggests, as to what may almost be termed the ubiquity of this adventurous and indefatigable seaman in the new world. While England has rested her claim at one extremity of it, and Spain at the other, on the personal agency of the same Native of Bristol, we have an assurance that he was found at the intermediate point, with a party of Englishmen, on the first visit of the individual whose name now overspreads the whole.

Some of the tribes referred to are named in the following passage of Herrera—

"The Guaranis occupy the islands. The principal nations are the *Charruas* and the *Quirondis.* On a river on the left-hand are the *Carcaras,* and yet further up the *Trimbus,* the *Curundas* and *Camis.* Yet higher are the *Quilbasas, Calchines* and *Chanas,* who are savages. After these come the *Mecoretas* and the *Mepenes,* who continue for an extent of 100 leagues. Beyond these are twenty-seven nations of different appellations, and languages and customs almost dissimilar, the names of which are omitted for fear of being tedious ("Que por no dar molestia se dexan de nombrar"*).

The incursion of the Guaranis into Peru, has been adverted to. On their return, some of the fierce invaders lingered on the way and permanently occupied the mountains, whence they annoyed the *Charcas,* their mode of warfare being to make night attacks, and after sweeping every thing before them to retire to their fastnesses quite secure from pursuit The Nation subjected to these vexatious attacks is found to occupy the same position on the modern maps.

As no supplies were received from Spain, subsistence must have been drawn from the labours of the party. Experiments were made on the fertility of the soil and the results carefully noted.† Cabot's final report to the Emperor described, with great minuteness, the various productions of that region, and spoke also of the wonderful increase of the hogs, horses, &c. brought out from Spain.‡ This Memoir would be, even at the present day, highly curious and interesting.

---

* Herrera, Dec. iv. lib. viii. cap. xi.

† Gomara, cap. lxxxix. Eden, fol. 255, and again, fol. 317.

‡ A brief abstract is found in Herrera, Dec. iv. lib. viii. cap. xi.

It is, doubtless, preserved in Spain, and there was probably a copy of it amongst the papers left with Worthington.

In the midst of his labours the same evil spirit which had pursued him to the La Plata was preparing a final blow. The Portuguese, Diego Garcia, would seem to have quitted the country immediately, with the specimens he had obtained of the precious metals, but he left behind a party of his followers. These men were guilty of some act which roused the wildest resentment of the Guaranis, with whom Cabot had made a treaty. It is expressly declared that the latter had no concern with the cause of exasperation,* but the vengeance of this fierce and sanguinary people made no distinction, and it was determined to sacrifice every white man in the country. Secret meetings were held, and a plan of action deliberately concerted.

A little before day-break the whole nation burst upon the feeble garrison of Santus Spiritus. It was carried, and the other position, at St Salvador, furiously assaulted. We have no particulars, but know that Cabot must have repelled the shock, for he was enabled to prepare for sea and to put on board the requisite supplies. This done, he quitted the ill-omened region.

Amongst the wild tales which have passed into traditions of the La Plata, one would represent Cabot to have fallen in the course of the sanguinary conflicts with the natives. This misconception is embodied in the "Argentina y Conquista Del Rio de la Plata," a poem on its early history, written by Don Martin de el Barco, and which finds a place in the Historiadores Primitivos (vol. iii.)—

"La muerte, pues, de aqueste ia sabida
El gran Carlos embia al buen Gaboto
Con una flata al gusto proveida
Como hombre que lo entiende i que es piloto;
Entro en el Paranna, i ia sabida
La mas fuerça del Rio ha sido-roto

---

* Herrera, Dec. iv. lib. viii. cap. xi. "Por algunas occasiones que dieron los soldados que fueron con Diego Garcia en que Sebastian Gaboto ne tuvo culpa."

Del Guarani, dejando fabricada
La Torre de Gaboto bien nombrada
Algunos de los suios se escaparon
De aquel Rio Timbuz do fue la guerra
A Sant Salvador Rio se bajaron
A do la demas gente estaba en tierra
A nuestra dulce Espana se tornaron, &c."*

---

* Another story, but too obviously false to screen the writer from the charge of fabrication, is found in Techo, and embellished by Charlevoix (Histoire du Paraguay, Tom. i. p. 29). It represents Cabot to have left behind a force of *one hundred and twenty men,* under the command of Nuno de Lara; and a series of romantic adventures is framed out of the attachment of a savage chieftain to *the wife* of Hurtado, one of the principal officers of the garrison!

CHAP. XXIV.

EMPLOYMENT OF CABOT AFTER HIS RETURN—RESUMES HIS FUNCTIONS AS PILOT-MAJOR—MAKES SEVERAL VOYAGES—HIS HIGH REPUTATION—VISIT OF A LEARNED ITALIAN—CABOT'S ALLUSION TO COLUMBUS.

Cabot must now, in 1531, have begun to feel the influence of advancing years, of which thirty-five had passed since the date of that patent from Henry VII. under which he made the great discovery in the north. The interval had been replete with toil, anxiety and peril. Yet though he resumed, as we shall see, the functions of Pilot-Major, an unbroken spirit of enterprise drew him afterwards, repeatedly, on the Ocean. We turn now to the only evidence which remains, scanty as it is, of the occupations of this part of his life.

Enough has been already said of the circumstances which prove that the defence submitted to the Emperor must have been completely successful. The Conversation in Ramusio, heretofore so often referred to, now offers its testimony as to the general opinion in Spain, of his conduct during the eventful period through which he has just been conducted.

The reputation brought from the La Plata could not have been equivocal, for in the scenes through which Cabot had passed, the most latent particle of fear or indecision must have started fatally into notice. The survivors of the expedition had seen Danger assume before him every terrifying form. In command of Spaniards he stood alone—an obnoxious stranger—in a fierce mutiny headed by brave and popular Spanish officers. He had been seen amidst sanguinary encounters, hand to hand, with hordes of ferocious savages, and extricating himself, on one occasion, only by a slaughter of more than three times the number of his own force. And finally, in the face of the blood-thirsty Guaranis, breaking furiously against his defences, he had calmly completed his arrangements and brought off all his people in safety. As the sail was spread, and they found themselves once more on the ocean, the overwrought anxieties of his companions would seem to have melted into gratitude to their brave and ever-faithful commander. In the last look at that scene, for years, of toil and peril, how many incidents thronged before them all associated memorably with Him who now stood on the deck guiding them back to their country! And the feelings of attachment and admiration with which they bade adieu to the La Plata, found an eager expression, as we shall see, in the earliest report, at home, of their eventful story.

In reverting to the Conversation in Ramusio, which discloses the popular fame that henceforward attached itself to Cabot, we must not be accused of inconsistency for deeming it worthy of credit. The errors established heretofore were those in matter of detail, with regard to which the memory might well be unfaithful. The speaker is now to tell of the circumstances that led to the interview, and of general remarks better calculated to make a vivid impression.

As this is the Conversation which the Biographie Universelle could not find in Ramusio, we may be the more minute in our quotations.

The learned speaker, after a long discussion on the subject of Cosmography, turns to the subject of the North-West Passage, and asks Fracastor and Ramusio if they had not heard of Sebastian Cabot, "so valiant a man and so well practised in all things pertaining to navigation and the science of cosmography, that at this present he hath not his like in Spain, insomuch that for his virtues he is preferred above all other pilots that sail to the West Indies, who may not pass thither without his license, and is therefore called Piloto-Mayor, that is, the Grand Pilot."*

* Eden's Decades, fol. 255. Hakluyt, vol. iii. p. 6. The original in Ramusio (tom. i. fol. 414 D. Ed. of 1554), "Cosi valente et pratico delle cose pertinenti

Receiving a reply in the negative, he proceeds to state, that finding himself at Seville, and being anxious to learn something of the maritime discoveries of the Spaniards, the public voice directed him to Sebastian Cabot as a very valiant man, ("un gran valent huomo") then living in that city, who had the charge of those things ("che havea l' carico di quelle"). A wish seized him to see Cabot ("subito volsi essere col detto"). He called, and we are now, for the first time, brought into a direct personal interview with this celebrated man.

"I found him a most gentle and courteous person, who treated me with great kindness and shewed me a great many things; amongst the rest a great Map of the world, on which the several voyages of the Portuguese and Spaniards were laid down."*

The conversation then turned on the voyage from England in the time of Henry VII. and the subsequent events in the La Plata. Speaking of his return from the latter expedition, Cabot says—

"After this I made many other voyages, which I now pretermit, and growing old I give myself to rest from such labours, because there are now many young and vigorous seamen of good experience, by whose forwardness I do rejoice in the fruit of my labours, and rest with the charge of this office as you see."†

It is delightful to notice the manner in which he refers to Columbus. No paltry effort is made to despoil that great man of any portion of his fame. He speaks of the effect which the news produced in England; "All men with great admiration affirmed it to be a thing more divine than human."‡ The

---

alla Navigatione et all Cosmographia che in Spagna al presente non v'e suo pari et la sua virtu l'ha fatto preporre a tutti li Pilotti che navigano all' Indie Occidentali, che senza sua licenza non possono far quel essèrcitio et per questo lo chiamano Pilotto Maggiore."

* "Lo trovai una gentilissima persona et cortese che mi fece gran carezze et mostrommi molte cose et fra l'altre un Mapamondo grande colle navigationi particolari, si di Portaghesi, come di Castigliani."

† "Feci poi molte altre navigationi le quali pretermetto et trovandomi alla fine vecchio volsi riposare essendosi allevati tanti pratichi et valenti marinari giovanni et hora me ne sto con questo carico che voi sapete, godendo il frutto delle mie fatiche."

‡ Eden's Decades, fol. 255. The original "dicendosi che era stata cosa piu tosto divina che humana, &c." Ramusio, tom. i. fol. 415.

influence on his own ardent temperament is well described, "by this fame and report there increased in my heart a great flame of desire to attempt some notable thing.*" While such expressions would rebuke an attempt to connect his name with the disparagement of Columbus, they heighten the gratification with which we recognise his claim to the place that a foreign poet of no contemptible merit—the companion of Sir Humphrey Gilbert in his voyage to the North, and writing from that region—has assigned to him:—

Hanc tibi jamdudum primi invenere Britanni
Tum cum magnanimus nostra in regione Cabotus
Proximus a magno ostendit sua vela Columbo.†

---

* "Mi nacque *un desiderio grande*, anzi un *ardor nel core* di voler far anchora io *qualche cosa segnalata, &c.*" Ib.

† Budeius—in Hakluyt, vol. iii. p. 143.

CHAP. XXV.

PERVERSION OF FACTS AND DATES BY HARRIS AND PINKERTON—CABOT'S RETURN TO ENGLAND—PROBABLE INDUCEMENTS—ERRONEOUS REASON ASSIGNED BY MR BARROW—CHARLES V. MAKES A DEMAND ON THE KING OF ENGLAND FOR HIS RETURN—REFUSED—PENSION TO CABOT—DUTIES CONFIDED TO HIM—MORE EXTENSIVE THAN THOSE BELONGING TO THE OFFICE OF PILOT-MAJOR—INSTANCES.

Of the manner in which the order and nature of Cabot's services have been misrepresented by English writers, some idea may be formed from the following passage of Harris transplanted into Pinkerton's Collection of Voyages (vol. xii. p. 160).

"Sebastian Cabot was employed by their Catholic Majesties, Ferdinand and Isabella, [Isabella having been dead twenty-two years, and Ferdinand ten years before he sailed] on a voyage for *the discovery of the coast of Brasil* (!) in which he had much *better success* than Americus Vespucius, who *missed the river of Plate*, whereas Cabot *found* it, and sailed up 360 *miles* [Hakluyt's six score leagues], *which* gave him such a character at the Court of their Catholic Majesties, that on his return [in 1531] he was declared piloto maggiore or grand pilot of Spain, and resided several years at Seville with that character, and had the examination and approbation of all the pilots intrusted by that government. Yet after some years, he thought fit to return into England, and was employed by King Henry VIII. in conjunction with Sir Thomas Pert, who was Vice-Admiral of England, and built a fine house near Blackwall, called Poplar, which name still remains, though the house is long ago decayed. This voyage of his was in 1516, [fifteen years before the return from the La Plata !] on board a ship of 250 tons with another of the like size." (Mistaken reference to the English Expedition of 1527.)

The motives which really induced Cabot to abandon a situation of high honour and emolument in Spain, as well as the exact period of his return to England, we have no means of determining. It is plain, from what will presently appear, that he had experienced no mortifying slight of his services, or attempt to withdraw the ample provision for his support. We are permitted, therefore, to believe that he was drawn to England by an attachment, strengthening with the decline of life, to his native soil and the scene of his early associations and attachments. The ties were not slight or likely to decay. Born in Bristol and returning from Venice whilst yet a boy, he had grown up in England to manhood, and it was not until sixteen years after the date of the first memorable patent that he entered the service of Spain, from which again he withdrew in 1516.

A reasonable presumption must, however, be distinguished from rash and absurd assertion. Mr Barrow supposes (Chronological History of Voyages, p. 36), that Cabot returned on the invitation of Robert Thorne of Bristol. Unfortunately for this hypothesis it appears* that Thorne died in 1532, sixteen years before the period at which Cabot quitted Spain.

The same writer remarks (p. 36), "His return to England was in the year 1548, when Henry VIII. was on the throne." Surely Mr Barrow cannot seriously think that, at this late day, his bare word will be taken against all the historians and chroniclers who declared that Henry VIII. died in January 1547†.

At his return Cabot settled in Bristol,‡ without the least anticipation, in all probability, of the new and brilliant career on which he was shortly to enter, fifty-three years after the date of his first commission from Henry VII.

Whatever may have been the motives of the Emperor for consenting to the departure of the Pilot-Major, he would seem to have become very soon alarmed at the inconvenience that might result from his new position. The youth who then filled the throne of England had already given such evidence of capacity as to excite the attention of Europe; and anticipations were universally expressed of the memorable part he was destined to perform. Naval affairs had seized his attention as a sort of passion. Even when a child "he knew all

---

* Fuller's Worthies, Somersetshire; and Stow's Survey of London.

† This blunder is gravely copied into Dr Lardner's Cyclopædia, History of Maritime and Inland Discovery, vol. ii. p. 138, together with Mr Barrow's assertion, that the pension of £166. 13*s.* 4*d.* was equal to *five hundred* Marks!

‡ Strype's Historical Memorials, vol. ii. p. 190.

the harbours and ports both of his own dominions and of France and Scotland, and how much water they had, and what was the way of coming into them."* The Emperor saw how perilous it was that a youthful monarch, with these predispositions, should have within reach the greatest seaman of the age, with all the accumulated treasures of a protracted life of activity and observation. A formal and urgent demand, therefore, was made by the Spanish ambassador, that "Sebastian Cabote, Grand Pilot of the Emperor's Indies, then in England," might be sent over to Spain "as a very necessary man for the Emperor, whose servant he was, and had a Pension of him."† Strype, after quoting from the documents before him, dryly adds, "Notwithstanding, I suspect that Cabot still abode in England, at Bristol, (for there he lived) having two or three years after set on foot a famous voyage hence, as we shall mention in due place." It is a pleasing reflection, adverted to before and which may here be repeated, that Cabot was never found attempting to employ, to the annoyance of Spain, the minute local knowledge of her possessions, of which his confidential station in that country must have made him master.

The Public Records now supply us with dates. On the 6th January, in the second year of Edward VI., a pension was granted to him of two hundred and fifty marks (166*l.* 13*s.* 4*d.*). Hakluyt (vol. iii. p. 10) seems irresolute as to the year, according the ordinary computation; for, at the close of the grant, in the original Latin, he declares it to be 1549, and at the end of his own translation, 1548. The former is undoubtedly correct, and so stated by Rymer (vol. xv. p. 181). The pension is recited to be "In consideratione boni et acceptabilis servitii nobis per dilectum servientem nostrum Sebastianum Cabotum impensi atque impendendi" (in consideration of the good and acceptable service done and to be done unto us by our beloved servant Sebastian Cabot).

The precise nature of the duties imposed on him does not

---

* Burnet's History of the Reformation, vol. ii. p. 225.

† Strype's Historical Memorials, vol. ii. p. 190.

appear. It is usually stated, and amongst others by Hakluyt, that the office of Grand Pilot of England was now created, and Cabot appointed to fill it; but this is very questionable.* Certain it is that his functions were far more varied and extensive than those implied in such a title. He would seem to have exercised a general supervision over the maritime concerns of the country, under the eye of the King and the Council, and to have been called upon whenever there was occasion for nautical skill and experience. One curious instance occurs of the manner in which the wishes of individuals were made to yield to his opinion of what was required by the exigences of the public service. We find (Hakluyt, vol. ii. part ii. p. 8) one James Alday offering as an explanation of his not having gone as master on a proposed voyage to the Levant, that he was stayed

"By the prince's letters which my master Sebastian Gabota had obtained for that purpose to my great grief."

He is called upon (Hakluyt, vol. iii. p. 719) to be present at the examination of a French pilot who had long frequented the coast of Brasil, and there is reason to believe that the minute instructions for the navigation of the La Plata (ib. p. 728) are from himself.

---

* See Appendix (C.).

CHAP. XXVI.

PUBLIC EXPLANATION BY CABOT TO EDWARD VI. OF THE PHENOMENA OF THE VARIATION OF THE NEEDLE—STATEMENT OF LIVIO SANUTO—POINT OF "NO VARIATION" FIXED BY CABOT—ADOPTED AFTERWARDS BY MERCATOR FOR HIS FIRST MERIDIAN—REFERENCE TO CABOT'S MAP—EARLY TESTIMONIALS—ALLUSION TO THE ENGLISH DISCOVERIES IN THE EDITION OF PTOLEMY PUBLISHED AT ROME IN 1508—FOURNIER—ATTENTION TO NOTE THE VARIATION BY THE SEAMEN OF CABOT'S SCHOOL—HIS THEORY, IF A NARROW ONE, WOULD HAVE BEEN THUS EXPOSED.

ALLUSION was made, on a former occasion, to the fact stated by the noble Venetian, Livio Sanuto, that Cabot had explained to the King of England the whole subject of the variation of the needle. There is reason to suppose, from what we know of Sanuto's life, that the incident to which he alludes must have occurred at the period now reached. His statement* is that many years before the period at which he wrote, his friend Guido Gianeti de Fano informed him that Sebastian Cabot was the first discoverer of this secret of nature which he explained to the King of England, near whom the said Gianeti at that time resided, and was held, as Sanuto understood from others, in the highest esteem. Cabot also showed the *extent* of the variation, and that it was *different* in *different* places.†

Sanuto being engaged in the construction of an instrument in reference to the longitude, it became with him a matter of eager interest to ascertain a point of no variation.

* The *Geographia* is in the Library of the British Museum, title in Catalogue "Sanuto." It was published at Venice, 1588, after the author's death.

† "Fu di tal secreto il riconoscitore, qual egli paleso poi al serenissimo Re d' Inghilterra, presso al quale (come poi da altri intesi) esso Gianetti all' hora honoratissimo si ritrovaa; et egli dimostro insieme, *quanta fusse questa distanza, e che non appareva in ciascun luogo la medesima.*" Lib. rim fol. 2.

"Conversing on this subject with Gianeti, he undertook to obtain for me, through a gentleman named Bartholomew Compagni, then in England, this information which he himself had not gathered."*

The person thus addressed sent word of what he had learned from Cabot, and Sanuto remarks that he had, subsequently, further assurance cf the accuracy of the report thus made to him. He saw a chart of navigation, executed by hand with the greatest care, and carefully compared with one by Cabot himself, in which the position of this meridian was seen to be one hundred and ten miles to the west of the island of Flores, one of the Azores.†

It is scarcely necessary to add that the First Meridian on the maps of Mercator, running through the most western point of the Azores, was adopted with reference to the supposed coincidence in that quarter of the true and magnetic poles.

In the course of the same memoir, Sanuto refers repeatedly to the Map, and adverts to the observations as to the variation of the compass made by Cabot at the Equator. The disappearance of this Document becomes at every turn a matter equally of astonishment and regret. Aside from the mass of papers left with Worthington, we have not only seen that the published map was hung up in the Gallery at Whitehall, but have actually traced a copy to Ortelius, to the Earl of Bedford, and now to Sanuto.

The assertion is found in almost all the old writers that Cabot was the first who noticed the variation. He was, at least, the first who gave to it an earnest attention, marked its degrees in various parts of the world, and attempted to frame a theory on the subject. His earliest transatlantic voyage carried him

---

* "Ragionatone io di questo col detto Gianneti, fece egli, che da un gentil' huomo nominato Bartolomeo Compagni, che in Inghilterre si tratteneva, s'intese cio, ch' egli dal detto Caboto ne seppe."

† "Et a quello ancora, che io dapoi vidi con gli occhi miei in una carta da navigare diligentissima fatta a mano, e tutta ritratta à punto da una propria del detto Caboto; nella quàle si riconosce il luogo del detto Meridiano esser per miglia cento e dieci lontano verso Occidente dalla Isola detta Fiori di quelle pur delli Azori."

to the very quarter where it is exhibited in a manner so sudden and striking, that modern navigators seem to concur in placing there one of the magnetic poles. The La Plata, too, is another theatre of its most startling appearance; and Cabot's long residence in that region must have secured his deliberate attention to the subject with the advantage of thirty years of intermediate observation and reflection.

There is a curious piece of evidence to show how early the Northern region discovered by Cabot was associated with the alarm which this phenomenon must, in the first instance, have excited

On the great Map of the World which accompanies the edition of Ptolemy published at Rome in 1508, is the following inscription, commencing far beyond *Terra Nova* and the *Insula Bacalaurus*—"Hic, compassus navium non tenet, nec naves quæ ferrum tenent revertere valent."*

It is impossible to doubt that the reference is to the well-known effect produced there on the compass. Beneventus, who prepared the supplemental matter for this edition of Ptolemy, professes to have a knowledge of the discoveries made by Columbus, by the Portuguese, and by the English ("Columbi et Lusitanorum atque Britannorum quos Anglos nunc dicimus").

Fournier, in his old, but yet highly-esteemed, Treatise on Hydrography, (Liv. xi. cap. x.) says, it was understood that Sebastian Cabot had noted with great exactness the variation in the places he had discovered on the Northern Coasts of America.†

As to Cabot's theory on the subject of the Variation, we are unable, in the absence of his Maps and Discourses, to offer even a conjecture. His exposition to the king would evidently seem to have been something more than a mere statement of isolated facts, and from the general recollection of

* "Here the ship's-compass loses its property, and no vessel with iron on board is able to get away."

† "Que Cabot remarqua *fort exactement* les declinaisons que l'aymant faisoit en divers endroits des costes Septentrionales de l'Amerique qu'il decouvrit."

the Venetian ambassador that he represented it as different in different places, it may be inferred that he did not treat it as absolutely regulated by mere distance from a particular meridian. There is another satisfactory reason for believing that he could not have placed it on any narrow ground. The Seamen brought up in his school, and sailing under his instructions, were particularly attentive to note the variation. Thus Stephen Burrough reports to us, (Hakluyt, vol. i. p. 290, &c.) within a short space, the degrees of it at three different points; and, where this was habitually done, an error of the great nautical Oracle—if we suppose one to have cheated his long experience and profound observation—would have been speedily detected and exposed.

CHAP. XXVII.

MISTAKE OF PURCHAS, PINKERTON, DR HENRY IN HIS HISTORY OF GREAT BRITAIN, CAMPBELL IN THE LIVES OF THE ADMIRALS, AND OTHER WRITERS, AS TO THE "KNIGHTING" OF JOHN OR SEBASTIAN CABOT.

THE present may be a fit occasion to notice an absurd misconception on the part of many authors of reputation, some of whom represent Sebastian Cabot to have received the honour of knighthood, while others confer it on the father.

Purchas (vol. iv. p. 1812), in his "English just Title to Virginia," refers to a Portrait of Sebastian Cabot which he had seen hung up in the King's Palace at Whitehall with this inscription; "Effigies Seb. Caboti Angli, filii Joannis Caboti militis aurati, &c." Here was a fair opening for controversy. Does the description "militis aurati" apply to the father or to the son? The same difficulty occurs, with a curious coincidence in the epithets, as that which Quinctilian (Inst. Orat. lib. vii. cap. 9) mentions, with regard to the Will of a Roman, who directed that there should be put up "statuam auream hastam tenentem," and the puzzle was whether the statue or the spear was of gold. After the unpardonable blunders which it has been necessary to expose, we may look with some complacency on the pursuit of this perplexing matter.

Purchas assumes that the words apply to the son, and accordingly we have "Sir Sebastian Cabot" running through his volumes. In a copy of verses addressed to "his friend Captain John Smith," and prefixed to the account of Virginia by the latter, Purchas exclaims—

> "Hail, Sir Sebastian! England's Northern Pole,
> Virginia's finder!"

and in a marginal note it is added, "America, named of Americus Vesputius which discovered less than Colon or Sir Sebastian Cabot, and the Continent later. Colon first found the Isles 1492, the Continent 1498, above a year after Cabot had done it. He was set forth by Henry VII., and after *by Henry VIII. knighted*, and made Grand Pilot of England by Edward VI." Captain Smith himself repeats all this—"Sebastian Cabot discovered much more than these all, for he sailed to about 40° South of the line, and to 67° towards the North, for which King Henry VIII. knighted him and made him Grand Pilot of England." In the general Index to Pinkerton's Collection of Voyages and Travels, the eye is caught, under the title *Cabot,* with the alluring reference "anecdotes of," and on turning to the place (vol. xiii. p. 4), the same statements are found. Now the difficulties are insurmountable as to Sebastian Cabot. In the last renewal of his pension in the reign of Mary (Rymer, vol. xv. p. 427 and 466), he is styled "Armiger," which shows that he had not, even up to that period, been knighted. In the Cotton MSS. (Claudius, C. iii.) is a paper, giving "the names and arms of such as have been advanced to the order of knighthood in the reigns of Henry VII., Henry VIII., Edward VI., Mary and Elizabeth," in which no notice is taken of him.

The point being thus clear with regard to the son, other writers have assumed as a matter of course, that the distinction must have been conferred on John Cabot. Accordingly, Campbell (Lives of the Admirals, art. *Sir John Cabot*) says of the father, "he then returned with a good cargo and three savages on board to England, where *it seems* he was knighted for this exploit, *since,* on the map of his discoveries drawn by his son Sebastian, and cut by Clement Adams, which hung in the Privy Gallery at Whitehall, there was this inscription under the author's picture—Effigies Seb. Caboti Angli filii Io. Caboti Venetiani Militis aurati." Thus Campbell derives his fact from Purchas, but draws a different inference from that writer. According to him, too, the knighting must have been, not by Henry VIII. as Purchas and Captain Smith have it, for there is reason to believe that the senior Cabot died before the commencement of that reign, but by Henry VII., particularly as it took place on Cabot's return, and the monarch last named lived thirteen years after the "exploit." Campbell, therefore, has a "Memoir of Sir John Cabot," and speaks again, with enthusiasm, of that "celebrated Venetian, Sir John Cabot."

This version has been the more generally adopted, and amongst the rest by Dr Henry (History of Great Britain, vol. vi. p. 618), who informs us, on the authority of Campbell, that "John Cabot was graciously received and knighted on his return." The same statement is made in the Biographia Britannica, &c.

To the utter confusion of all these grave authorities, a moment's consideration will show, that the words relied on do in themselves prove that knighthood had not been conferred. It is scarcely necessary to follow up this suggestion, by stating that in reference to one who had received that honour, they would have been not "*Militis* aurati," but "*Equitis* aurati." Though the term *miles* is sometimes applied, in old documents, even to Peers, yet, as a popular designation, the language of the inscription negatives the idea of knighthood. In the very works immediately connected with the subject of the present volume, the appropriate phrase perpetually occurs. Thus "*Eques* auratus" is used to designate Sir Humphrey Gilbert (Hakluyt, vol. iii. p. 137), Sir Hugh Willoughby (ib. p. 142), Sir Martin Frobisher (ib. p. 142), Sir Francis Drake (ib. p. 143). In the dedication of Lok's translation of Peter Martyr, it is in like manner used, and we see it, at this moment, on the "effigies" of Sir Walter Raleigh prefixed to the first edition of his History of the World. It will probably be deemed very superfluous to refer to Selden's Titles of Honour (p. 830), for a confirmation of what has been stated.

The weight of censure must fall on Purchas, who was originally guilty of the blunder. The others assumed the fact of the knighting, and only exercised their ingenuity in deciding whether the honour was conferred on the Father or the Son.

CHAP. XXVIII.

STAGNATION OF TRADE IN ENGLAND—CABOT CONSULTED BY THE MERCHANTS—URGES THE ENTERPRISE WHICH RESULTED IN THE TRADE TO RUSSIA—PRELIMINARY DIFFICULTIES—STRUGGLE WITH THE STILYARD—THAT MONOPOLY BROKEN DOWN—EARNESTNESS OF EDWARD VI. ON THE SUBJECT—HIS MUNIFICENT DONATION TO CABOT AFTER THE RESULT WAS DECLARED.

It is only from detached notes, such as those already referred to, and which meet the eye as it were by accident, that we can now form an idea of the diffusive nature of Cabot's services. One Great Enterprise, however, stands by itself, and was destined to exercise an important influence on the commerce and naval greatness of England.

An opportunity was afforded to Cabot of putting in execution a plan "which he long before had had in his mind,"* by its happening, incidentally, to fall in with the purposes of the London merchants. The period was one of great commercial stagnation in England.

"Our merchants perceived the commodities and wares of England to be in small request about us and near unto us, and that those merchandises which strangers, in the time and memory of our ancestors, did earnestly seek and desire, were now neglected and the price thereof abated, although they be carried to their own parts."†

In this season of despondency Cabot was consulted, and the suggestions which he made were adopted:

"Sebastian Caboto, a man in those days very renowned, happening to be in London, they began first of all to deal and consult diligently with him, and after much search and conference together, it was at last concluded, that three ships should be prepared and furnished out for the search and discovery of the northern

* Eden's Decades, fol. 256.

† Hakluyt, vol. i. p. 243.

part of the world, to open a way and passage to our men, for travel to new and unknown kingdoms "*

Such is the authentic history of the impulse given to English commerce at this interesting crisis. The influence of Cabot is not only attested by the passage quoted, but in the Letters Patent of Incorporation it is declared† that, in consideration of his having "been the chiefest setterforth of this journey or voyage, therefore we make, ordain, and constitute him, the said Sebastian, to be the first and present governor of the same fellowship and community by these presents, to have and enjoy the said office of governor to him, the said Sebastian Cabota, during his natural life, without amoving or dismissing from the same room."

But a difficulty was encountered in the alleged exclusive privileges of a very powerful body, whose odious monopoly had long exercised its baneful influence on English commerce and manufactures:

"The time was now at length come, that the eyes of the English nation were to be opened, for their discovering the immense damage which was sustained, by suffering the German merchants of the house or college in London, called the Steelyard, so long to enjoy advantages in the duty or custom of exporting English cloths, far beyond what the native English enjoyed; which superior advantages possessed by those foreigners began, about this time, to be more evidently seen and felt, as the foreign commerce of England became more diffused. The Cities of Antwerp and Hamburgh possessed, at this time, the principal commerce of the northern and middle parts of Europe; and their factors, at the Steelyard, usually set what price they pleased on both their imports and exports; and having the command of all the markets in England, with joint and united stocks, they broke all other merchants. Upon these considerations, the English company of merchant adventurers made pressing remonstrances to King Edward the Sixth's Privy Council. These Hanseatics were, moreover, accused (and particularly the Dantzickers) of defrauding the customs, by colouring, or taking under their own names, as they paid little or no custom, great quantities of the merchandise of other foreigners not entitled to their immunities. They were also accused of having frequently exceeded the bounds of even the great privileges granted to them by our Kings; yet, by the force of great presents, they had purchased new grants."‡

"Having, for the last forty-five years, had the sole command of our commerce, (says the author) they had reduced the price of English wool to one shilling and six-pence per stone. The Steelyard merchants were also excused from aliens duties,

* Voyage of Richard Chancellor, Hakluyt, vol. i. p. 243.

† Hakluyt, vol. i. p. 268.

‡ Anderson's History of Commerce, vol. ii. p. 80 M'Pherson's Annals of Commerce, vol. ii. p. 109

and yet all their exports and imports were made in foreign bottoms; which was a very considerable loss to the nation."*

"This is the substance of the whole business during King Edward the Sixth's reign, of reversing the privileges of the Steelyard merchants, taken from our histories, but more particularly from I. Wheeler's Treatise of Commerce, published in quarto, in the year 1601; and, as he was then Secretary to the Merchant Adventurers' Company, it may be supposed to be, in general, a true account, and is surely an useful part of commercial history. Wheeler adds, that by reversing these privileges, our own merchants shipped off in this year forty thousand cloths for Flanders. Rapin, in his History of England, observes, that the Regent of Flanders, as well as the City of Hamburgh, earnestly solicited to have the Steelyard merchants re-instated; but to no purpose."†

The extraordinary interest felt by Edward himself on this subject is manifest from his Journal, in which the incidents are noted.‡

"18th January, 1551. This day the Stiliard put in their answer to a certain complaint, that the merchant adventurers laid against them."

"25th January, 1551. The answer of the Stiliard was delivered to certain of my learned Counsel to look on and oversee."

"18th February, 1551. The merchant adventurers put in their replication to the Stiliards answer."

"23rd February, 1551. A decree was made by the Board, that upon knowledge and information of their charters, they had found; First, that they were no sufficient Corporation. 2. That their number, names, and nation, was unknown. 3. That when they had forfeited their liberties, King Edward IV. did restore them on this condition, that they should colour no strangers' goods, which they had done. Also, that whereas in the beginning they shipped not past 8 clothes, after 100, after 1000, after that 6000: now in their name was shipped 44000 clothes in one year, and but 1100 of all other strangers. For these considerations sentence was given, that they had forfeited their liberties, and were in like case with other strangers."

The difficulties which had to be struggled with, may be inferred from the pertinacity with which the defeated party followed up the matter, even after a decision had been pronounced. Thus, the following entries are found in the Journal of the young King:

"28th February, 1551. There came Ambassadors from Hamburg and Lubeck, to speak on the behalf of the Stiliard merchants."

"2d March 1551. The answer for the Ambassadors of the Stiliard was com-

---

* Ibid.

† Ibid.

‡ Published in Burnet's History of the Reformation, vol. ii. from the Cotton MSS.

mitted to the Lord Chancellor, the two Secretaries, Sir Robert Bowes, Sir John Baker, Judge Montague, Griffith Solicitor, Gosnold, Goodrich, and Brooks."

"3d May, 1551. The [illegible] men received their answer; which was, to confirm the former judgment of my Council."

The important agency of Cabot, in a result so auspicious not merely to the interests of commerce but to the public revenue, may be judged of from a donation bestowed on him, a few days after the decision.*

"To Sebastian Caboto, the great seaman, 200 pounds, by way of the king's majesty's reward, dated in March, 1551."

* Strype's Historical Memorials, vol. ii. p. 495.

CHAP. XXIX.

PREPARATIONS FOR THE EXPEDITION—PRECAUTIONS AS TO TIMBER—SHEATHING OF THE VESSELS NOW FIRST RESORTED TO IN ENGLAND—EXAMINATION OF TWO TARTARS—CHIEF COMMAND GIVEN TO SIR HUGH WILLOUGHBY—RICHARD CHANCELLOR—STEPHEN BURROUGH—WILLIAM BURROUGH—ARTHUR PET—THIS EXPEDITION CONFOUNDED WITH ANOTHER BY STRYPE AND CAMPBELL.

A TRIUMPH having been obtained over the obstacles which had heretofore impeded the career of English commerce, preparations were diligently made for the Expedition.

The measures adopted for the safety of the ships indicate the presence of great skill and providence; "strong and well-seasoned planks for the building" were provided, and the historian of the expedition is struck with one novel precaution. To guard against the worms "which many times pearceth and eateth through the strongest oak," it was resolved to "cover a piece of the keel of the shippe with thinne sheets of leade."* This is the first instance in England, of the practice of sheathing, but it had long before been adopted in Spain, and had thus engaged the attention of Cabot. It may, indeed, have been originally suggested by him, as the first use of it is referred to 1514, two years before which time we find him passing into the service of Ferdinand, and advancing rapidly to posts of distinction as his value became apparent.

Information was eagerly sought in every quarter as to the countries which the Expedition might visit. There were "two Tartarians" employed about the young king's stables. These persons were hunted up and an interpreter provided, "by whom they were demanded touching their country and the manners of their nation." But the poor creatures had

---

* Hakluyt, vol. i. p. 243.

no story to tell, and betrayed plainly their addiction to strong drink. There was waggery in the City even at that early day. "They were able to answer nothing to the purpose, being indeed more acquainted (as one there merily and openly said) to toss pots, than to learn the states and dispositions of people."*

The command of the expedition was an object of high ambition. Amongst those who pressed "very earnestly" for the post was Sir Hugh Willoughby, "a most valiant gentleman and well borne." He came recommended by a high reputation for "skill in the services of war," and it seems to have been thought no slight recommendation that he was of tall and commanding stature. The choice finally fell on him.

In command of one of the ships, and with the title of Pilot-Major, was Richard Chancellor. He had been bred up in the household of Henry Sydney, father of Sir Philip Sydney. His character and merits, coupled with his brilliant success on this occasion, and subsequent untimely fate, seem to have made a deep impression on his contemporaries. He not only proved a skilful and intrepid seaman, but his remarks on the customs, religion, laws and manners of the countries visited, show him to have possessed a cultivated intellect, as well as great shrewdness and powers of observation. He would seem to have attracted the attention and enjoyed the friendship of Cabot; for Eden (Decades, fol. 357), in adverting to one of the phenomena of the ocean, mentions that the fact he relates was communicated to him by Chancellor, who derived it from Cabot. His was the only ship that succeeded in doubling the North Cape, and making her way to Russia.

"For the government of other ships although divers men seemed willing, and made offers of themselves thereunto, yet by a common consent one Richard Chanceler, a man of great estimation for many good parts of wit in him, was elected, in whom alone great hope for the performance of this business rested. This man was brought up by one Master Henry Sidney, a noble young gentleman and very much beloved of King Edward."

The master of Chancellor's ship was Stephen Burrough,

---

* Hakluyt, vol. i. p. 445.

afterwards Chief Pilot of England, and of high rank in the navy. There was, also, on board his ship, apparently as a common seaman, William Burrows,* afterwards Comptroller of the Navy and author of a work on navigation, and who in after years conducted a squadron to the same quarter.† thur Pet, also, whose name is associated with a subsequent voyage, was in the same ship.‡

Some obscurity has been occasioned by confounding this memorable enterprise with another, entirely distinct and to a different quarter. Thus there is found in Strype§ the following passage:—

"In this month of May did the King grant letters of commendation, or safe conduct, for the three ships that were enterprising that noble adventure of seeking for a passage into the Eastern parts of the world, through the unknown and dangerous seas of the North. Of this expedition Sebastian Gabato, an excellent mariner of Bristow, but of Italian parentage, was a great mover, to whom the King, as a gratuity, had given 200 pounds. For this voyage, in February last, the King lent two ships, the *Primrose* and the *Moon*, a pinnace, to Barns, Lord Maior of London, Garrett, one of the Sheriffs, York and Windham, adventurers, binding themselves to deliver to the King two ships of the like burden, and good condition, in Midsummer, anno 1554. Sir Hugh Willoughby, a brave knight, was the chief Captain in this enterprise: to whom the King granted a passport to go beyond the seas, with four servants, forty pounds in money, his chain, &c."

Campbell (Lives of the Admirals, vol. i. p. 319) says,

"The accounts we have of this matter differ widely; but as I observe there is a variation in the dates of a whole year, so I am apt to believe, that there must have been *two* distinct undertakings; one under the immediate protection of the court which did not take effect; and the other by a joint stock of the merchants, which did. Of the first, because it is little taken notice of, I will speak particularly here; for the other will come in properly in my account of Sir Hugh Willoughby. When, therefore, this matter was first proposed, the King lent two ships, the Primrose and the Moon, to Barnes, Lord Mayor of London, Mr Garret, one of the Sheriffs, and Mr York, and Mr Wyndham, two of the adventurers, giving bond to the King to deliver two ships of like burden, and in as good condition, at Midsommer, 1554."

Thus has the Maritime History of England been written! The vessels in question made part of the Expedition *to Guinea*,

---

* Hakluyt, vol. i. p. 233

† Ibid. vol. i. p. 401.

‡ Ibid. vol. i. p. 233.

§ Historical Memorials, vol. ii. p. 402.

of which an account was given, at length, by Richard Eden (Decades, fol. 318).

" In the yeare of oure Lorde MLIII. the XII day of August, sayled from Porchemouth two goodly shyppes the *Primrose* and the Lion, with a Pynnesse cauled the *Moon*, being all well furnysshed," &c.

It seems that the enterprise was frustrated by the misconduct of "Captayne Wyndham." The persons spoken of as having given bond to the King, were members of the company of merchant adventurers.* The expedition to Guinea, thus obscured by Strype, Campbell, and succeeding writers, is that of which Eden, against the remonstrances of his Publishers, inserted an account, consenting to swell his volume, "that sum memorie thereof might remayne to our posteritie, if eyther iniquitie of tyme, consumynge all things, or ignorance creepyng in by barbarousness and contempte of knowledge should hereafter bury in oblivion so worthy attempts!" (fol. 343.)

* Hakluyt, vol. i. p. 269.

CHAP XXX.

INSTRUCTIONS FOR SIR HUGH WILLOUGHBY.

THE instructions prepared by Cabot for the government of this Expedition, have been justly regarded as a model, and as reflecting the highest credit on his sagacity, good sense, and comprehensive knowledge. They relate not only to the conduct to be observed in reference to the great object in view, but descend to minute suggestions, drawn from his long experience, for the interior arrangements and discipline. They are called "Ordinances, Instructions, and Advertisements of, and for the direction of the intended voyage for Cathay, compiled, made, and delivered by the right worshipful M. Sebastian Cabota, Esq. Governour of the Mysterie and Companie of the Merchants Adventurers for the discoverie of Regions, Dominions, Islands, and places unknowen, the 9th day of May, in the yere of our Lord God 1553, and in the 7th yere of the reigne of our most dread sovereigne Lord, Edward VI., by the grace of God, King of England, France, and Ireland, defender of the faith and of the Church of England and Ireland, in earth supreme head."*

They were made up in the form of a Book which was ordered to be publicly read once every week, "to the intent that every man may the better remember his oath, conscience, duty and charge." These instructions are too voluminous to be here introduced, but a few extracts, while they indicate the cast of Cabot's mind, must fill us with renewed regret that all the records of such a man's own labours should have been unfortunately lost to us:

* Hakluyt, vol. i. p. 226.

"7. Item, that the merchants, and other skilful persons in writing shall daily write, describe, and put in memorie the navigation of each day and night, with the points, and observations of the lands, tides, elements, altitude of the sunne, course of the moon and starres, and the same so noted by the order of the Master and Pilot of every ship to be put in writing, the Captaine-Generall assembling the masters together once every weeke (if winde and weather shall serve) to conferre all the observations, and notes of the said ships, to the intent it may appeare wherein the notes do agree, and wherein they dissent, and upon good debatement, deliberation, and conclusion determined, to put the same into a common leger, to remain of record for the company: the like order to be kept in proportioning of the Cardes, Astrolabes, and other instruments prepared for the voyage, at the charge of the Companie."*

"27. Item, the names of the people of every Island, are to be taken in writing, with the commodities and incommodities of the same, their natures, qualities, and dispositions, the site of the same, and what things they are most desirous of, and what commodities they will most willingly depart with, and what metals they have in hils, mountains, streames, or rivers, in, or under the earth."†

Attention to moral and religious duties is strictly enjoined.

"12. Item, that no blaspheming of God, or detestable swearing be used in any ship, nor communication of ribaldrie, filthy tales, or ungodly talke to be suffered in the company of any ship, neither dicing, tabling, nor other divelish games to be frequented, whereby ensueth not onely povertie to the players, but also strife, variance, brauling, fighting, and oftentimes murther, to the utter destruction of the parties, and provoking of God's most just wrath, and sworde of vengeance. These, and all such like pestilences, and contagions of vices, and sinnes to be eschewed, and the offenders once monished, and not reforming, to be punished at the discretion of the captaine and masters, as appertaineth."‡

"13. Item, that morning and evening prayer, with other common services appointed by the King's Majestie, and lawes of this realme, to be read and saide in every ship daily by the minister in the admirall, and the marchant or some other person learned in other ships, and the Bible or paraphrases to be read devoutly and Christianly to God's honour, and for his grace to be obtained, and had by humble and heartie praier of the navigants accordingly."§

There is much good sense in the following hints:—

"22. Item, not to disclose to any nation the state of our religion, but to passe it over in silence, without any declaration of it, seeming to bear with such laws and rights as the place hath where you shall arrive."‖

"23. Item, for as much as our people and shippe may appear unto them strange and wonderous, and theirs also to ours; it is to be considered, how they may be used, learning much of their natures and dispositions, by some one such person, as you may first either allure, or take to be brought aboord your ships, and there to

* Hakluyt, vol. i. p. 226.
† Ibid. p. 228.
‡ Ibid. vol. i. p. 227.
§ Ibid.
‖ Ibid. vol. i. p. 228.

learn as you may, *without violence or force*, and no woman to be tempted, or intreated to incontinence, or dishonestie."*

"26. Item, every nation and region is to be considered advisedly, and not to provoke them by any disdaine, laughing, contempt, or such like, but to use them with prudent circumspection, *with all gentlenes, and curtesie*, and not to tarry long in one place, untill you shall have attained the most worthy place that may be found in such sort as you may returne with victuals sufficient, prosperously."†

The difficulties experienced, from timidity and incredulity, are apparent from a passage of the 32d item, in which he speaks of the obstacles which had "ministered matter of suspicion in some heads, that this voyage could not succeed for the extremitie of the North Pole, lacke of passage, and such like, which have caused wavering minds, and doubtful heads, not only to *withdraw themselves from the adventure of this voyage*, but also *dissuaded others from the same*, the certainte whereof, when you shall have tried by experience, &c."‡

* Hakluyt, vol. i. p. 228.
† Ib.
‡ Ibid. vol. i. p. 229.

CHAP. XXXI.

THE EXPEDITION DROPS DOWN TO GREENWICH—SALUTES—ANIMATING SCENE—PROCEED TO SEA—VESSELS SEPARATED—FATE OF SIR HUGH WILLOUGHBY—CHANCELLOR REACHES WARDHOUSE—EARNESTLY DISSUADED FROM PROCEEDING FURTHER—HIS GALLANT RESOLUTION—CONFIDENCE OF THE CREW IN HIM—REACHES ARCHANGEL—EXCELLENT EFFECT OF OBSERVING CABOT'S INSTRUCTIONS AS TO DEPORTMENT TOWARDS THE NATIVES—SUCCESS OF CHANCELLOR.

On the 20th May, the squadron, consisting of three ships, dropped down to Greenwich:—

"The greater Shippes are towed downe with boates, and oares, and the Mariners being all apparelled in Watchet or skie-coloured cloth, rowed amaine, and made way with diligence. And being come neere to Greenewich (where the Court then lay), presently upon the newes thereof, the Courtiers came running out, and the common people flockt together, standing very thicke upon the shoare: the privie Counsel, they lookt out at the windowes of the Court, and the rest ranne up to the toppes of the towers: the shippes hereupon discharge their Ordinance, and shoot off their pieces after the manner of warre, and of the sea, insomuch that the tops of the hilles sounded therewith; the valleys and the waters gave an Eccho, and the Mariners, they shouted in such sort, that the skie rang againe with the noyse thereof. One stood in the poope of the ship, and by his gesture bids farewell to his friends in the best manner hee could. Another walkes upon the hatches, another climbes the shrowds, another stands upon the maine yard, and another in the top of the shippe. To be short, it was a very triumph (after a sort) in all respects to the beholders. But (alas) the good King Edward (in respect of whom principally all this was prepared) hee only by reason of his sicknesse was absent from this shewe, and not long after the departure of these Ships, the lamentable and most sorrowful accident of his death followed."*

There was some delay at Harwich; "yet at the last with a good winde they hoysted up sayle, and committed themselves to the sea, giving their last adieu to their native countrey, which they knew not whether they should ever returne to see againe or not. Many of them looked oftentimes

* Hakluyt, vol. 1. p. 245

backe, and could not refraine from teares, considering into what hazards they were to fall, and what uncertainties of the sea they were to make triall of."* Chancellor himself was moved. "His natural and fatherly affection, also, somewhat troubled him, for he left behinde him two little sonnes, which were in the case of orphanes if he spedde not well."†

After touching at Rost Island, and at a group called the Cross of Islands, it was agreed that in the event of a separation the ships should rendezvous at the Castle of Wardhouse in Norway. On the very day of the council at which this arrangement was made a furious tempest arose that dispersed the vessels.

The story of the gallant Chief of the Expedition is brief but horrible. Failing to make the contemplated progress to the eastward, it was resolved to winter in Lapland, and arrangements for that purpose were commenced on the 18th September. The rigour of the climate proved fatal to all. The two ships were long afterwards discovered with no living thing on board. A Journal was found of the incidents of the voyage, and a Will of Gabriel Willoughby, attested by Sir Hugh, dated as late as January, 1554. Over the frightful scenes witnessed by him who was reserved as the last victim of the elements there is thrown, like a pall, impenetrable darkness. As he stiffened into death, by the side of his unburied messmates, he saw the savage region yielded back, without further struggle, to the "unknown and also wonderful" wild beasts whose fearful numbers about the ships are noted in the last entry of the Journal.‡

Chancellor was more fortunate. He reached Wardhouse in safety, and having remained there several days resolved to proceed, notwithstanding the disheartening representations made to him.

---

* Hakluyt, vol. i. p. 245.

† Ib.

‡ Hakluyt, vol. i. p. 239. The Will found on board witnessed by Sir Hugh Willoughby was in the possession of Purchas (Pilgrims, vol. iii. p. 463)

"Remaining stedfast and immutable in his first resolution, he determined either to bring that to passe which was intended or els to die the death.*

"[illegible] which were with Master Chanceler in his Shippe, although they had great cause of discomfort by the losse of their companie (whom the foresaid tempest had separated from them) and were not a little troubled with cogitations and perturbations of minde, in respect of their doubtful course: yet notwithstanding, they were of such consent and agreement of minde with Master Chanceler, that they were resolute, and prepared under his direction and government, to make proofe and triall of all adventures, without all feare or mistrust of future dangers. Which constancie of minde in all the companie did exceedingly increase their Captain's carefulnesse."†

In this resolute spirit he again put to sea. "Master Chanceler held on his course towards that unknown part of the world, and sailed so farre, that he came at last to the place where he found no night at all, but a continuall light and brightnesse of the sunne shining clearly upon the huge and mightie sea. And having the benefite of this perpetuall light for certaine dayes, at the length it pleased God to bring them into a certaine great bay, which was one hundreth miles or thereabout over. Whereinto they entered somewhat farre and cast anchor."

He had now reached the Bay of St Nicholas. Landing near Archangel, then only a castle, there becomes visible the influence of Cabot's injunction, as to gentleness of deportment towards the natives and its happy result.

"And looking every way about them it happened that they espied a farre off a certain fisher boate which Master Chancellor, accompanied with a fewe of his men, went towards to commune with the fishermen that were in it, and to knowe of them what countrey it was, and what people, and of what maner of living they were: but they being amazed with the strange greatnesse of his shippe (for in those parts before that time they had never seen the like) beganne presently to avoyde and to flee: but hee still following them at last overtooke them, and being come to them, they (being in greate feare, as men halfe dead) prostrated themselves before him, offering to kisse his feete: but hee (according to his great and singular courtesie) looked pleasantly upon them, comforting them by signes and gestures, refusing those dueties and reverences of theirs and taking them up in all loving sort from the ground. And it is strange to consider how much favour afterwards in that place, this humanitie of his did purchase to himself. For they being dismissed spread by and by a report abroad of the arrival of a strange nation of a singular gentleness and

* Hakluyt, vol. i. p. 246.
† Ib.

courtesie, whereupon the common people came together offering to these newe-come ghests victuals freely."*

We may not follow further the movements of this intrepid navigator, or repeat the circumstances of his overland journey to Moscow, and his very curious and interesting account of Russia. He was received in the most cordial manner, and effected the necessary arrangements for a safe and extensive commercial intercourse.

---

* Ib.

CHAP. XXXII.

CHARTER TO THE COMPANY OF MERCHANT ADVENTURERS—SEBASTIAN CABOT NAMED GOVERNOR FOR LIFE—GRANT OF PRIVILEGES BY THE EMPEROR OF RUSSIA TO CABOT AND OTHERS—AN AMBASSADOR FROM THE EMPEROR EMBARKS WITH RICHARD CHANCELLER—SHIPWRECK—CHANCELLOR PERISHES—RECEPTION AND ENTERTAINMENT OF THE AMBASSADOR IN LONDON.

THE success of Chancellor gave a new impulse, and the dignity of a Charter, to the Association of Merchant Adventurers.*

In the instrument of incorporation Sebastian Cabot is named, as has been stated, Governor for Life, as "the chiefest setter forth" of the Enterprise.

There is preserved† "A copie of the first privileges granted to the English merchants, by John Vasilivich, by the Grace of God, Emperor of Russia, Great Duke of Novogrode, Moscovia," &c. After the recital it grants "unto Sebastian Cabota, Governor, Sir George Barnes, Knight, &c. Consuls, Sir John Gresham, &c., assistants, and to the communaltie of the afore-named fellowship, and to their successors for ever, and to the successors of every of them, these articles, grants, immunities, franchises, liberties, and privileges, and every of them hereafter following, expressed and declared, videlicet." Then follow ten clauses or articles placing the contemplated commercial intercourse on the most liberal and secure footing.

Passing a little onward we find an Ambassador from the Emperor arriving in England. This incident is connected with the melancholy death of Richard Chancellor, in whose ship the Ambassador had embarked. That intrepid navigator

* Dr Robertson (History of America, book ix.) heedlessly represents the Charter to have preceded the voyage of Sir Hugh Willoughby

† Hakluyt, vol. i. p. 265

was doomed to perish when almost within reach of those beloved "two little sonnes," the thoughts of leaving whom "in the case of orphanes if he spedde not well," had saddened his departure. The ship was driven ashore at Pitsligo in the North of Scotland, and by the fury of the tempest was broken to pieces on the rocks. Chancellor

"using all carefulness for the safetie of the bodie of the said Ambassadour and his trayne, taking the boate of the said Ship trusting to attaine the shore and so to save and preserve the bodie and seven of the companie or attendants of the same Ambassadour, the same boat by rigorous waves of the seas, was by darke night overwhelmed and drowned, wherein perished not only the bodie of the said grand pilot with seven Russes, but also divers of the Mariners of the said ship: the noble personage of the said Ambassadour with a fewe others (by God's preservation and speciall favour) only with much difficultie saved."*

A long account is given of the Ambassador's reception and entertainment at London. The following is an extract:†

"On the 27th February, 1557, he approached to the Citie of London within twelve English miles, where he was received with fourscore merchants with chaines of Gold and goodly apparell, as well in order of men-servants in one uniforme liverie, as also in and upon good horses and geldings, who conducting him to a marchant's house, foure miles from London, received there a quantitie of Gold, velvet and silke, with all furniture thereunto requisite, wherewith he made him a riding garment, reposing himself that night. The next day being Saturday and the last day of Februarie, he was by *the Merchants Adventuring for Russia, to the number of one hundred and fortie persons*, and so many or more servants in one liverie, as abovesaid, conducted towards the citie of London, where by the way he had not onely the hunting of the Foxe and such like sports shewed him, but also by the Queenes Maiesties commandment was received and embraced by the right honorable Viscount Montague, sent by her grace for his entertainment: he being accompanied with divers lustie Knights, esquires, gentlemen and yeomen to the number of three hundred horses, led him to the North partes of London, where by foure notable Merchants richly apparelled was presented to him a right faire and large gelding richly trapped, together with a foot cloth of orient crimson velvet enriched with gold laces, all furnished in most glorious fashion, of the present and gifte of the saide Merchants: whereupon the Ambassador at instant desire mounted, riding on the way towards Smithfield barres, the first limits of the liberties of the Citie of London. The Lord Maior accompanied with all the Aldermen in their Skarlet did receive him, and so riding through the Citie of London in the middle, between the Lord Mayor and Viscount Montague, a great number of Merchants and notable personages riding before, and a large troupe of servants and apprentices following, was conducted through the Citie of London (with great admiration and plausibilitie of the people running plentifully on all sides, and replenishing all streets in such

---

* Hakluyt, vol. i. p. 286.

† Ibid. vol. i. p. 287.

sort as no man without difficultie might passe) into his lodging situate in Fant church streete, where were provided for him two chambers richly hanged and decked, over and above the gallant furniture of the whole house, together with an ample and rich cupboard of Plate of all sortes, to furnish and serve him at all meales, and other services during his abode in London, which was, as is underwritten, until the third day of May: during which time, daily, divers Aldermen and the gravest personages of the said companie did visit him, providing all kind of victuals for his table and his servants, with all sorts of officers to attend upon him in good sort and condition, as to such an Ambassadour of honour doeth and ought to appertaine."

He remained in London until the third May, when he

"departed from London to Gravesend, accompanied with divers Aldermen and Merchants, who in good gard set him aboord the Noble shippe the Primrose, Admiral to the Fleete, where leave was taken on both sides and parts, after many imbracements and divers farewels not without expressing of teares."

CHAP. XXXIII.

VIEW OF THE TRADE OPENED WITH RUSSIA FROM THE LETTERS OF THE COMPANY TO THE AGENTS—PRICES OF ENGLISH MANUFACTURES—ARTICLES OBTAINED IN RETURN—EXTENSIVE ESTABLISHMENT OF ENGLISHMEN AT MOSCOW WHEN THAT CITY WAS DESTROYED BY THE TARTARS.

IT is not a little curious to look back into the early history of the Trade with Russia. The Letters which passed between the Company and its Agents apprise us of the nature and prices of the commodities interchanged, and furnish, probably, the earliest specimens extant of the English mercantile style. In one Letter it is said:*

"You shall understand we have fraighted for the parts of Russia foure good shippes tobe laden t here by you and your order: That is to say, the Primrose of the burthen of 240 Tunnes, Master under God John Buckland: The John Evangelist of 170 Tunnes, Master under God Lawrence Roundal: The Anne of London of the burthen of 160 Tunnes, Master under God David Philly, and the Trinitie of London of the burthen of 140 Tunnes, Master under God John Robins, as by their Charter parties may appeare: which you may require to see for divers causes. You shall receive, God willing, out of the said good ships, God sending them in safety for the use of the Company, these kinds of wares following, all marked with the general marke of the company as followeth, 25 fardels containing 207 sorting clothes, one fine violet in graine, and one skarlet, and 40 cottons for wrappers, beginning with number 1. and ending with number 52. The sorting clothes may cost the first peny *5l. 9s.* the cloth one with the other. The fine violet *18l. 6s. 6d.* The Skarlet *17l. 13s. 6d.* the cottons at *9l. 10s.* the packe, accompanying 7 cottons for a packe more 500 pieces of Hampshire Kersies, that is 400. watchets, 43 blewes, 53 reds. 15 greenes. 5 ginger colours. and two yellowes which cost the first penny *4l. 6s.* the piece, and 3 packes containing 21 cottons at *9l. 10s.* the packe, and part of the clothes is measured by Arshines. More 9. barrels of Pewter of Thomas Hasels making, &c. Also the wares bee packed and laden as is aforesayde, as by an invoyce in every shippe more plainly may appeare. So that when it shall please God to send the saide good shipps to you in safetie, you are to receive our said goods, and to procure the sales to our most advantage either for ready money, time or barter having consideration that you doe make good debts, and give such time, if you give any, as you may employ and returne the same

* Hakluyt, vol. i. p. 297.

against the next voyage; and also foreseeing that you barter to a profit, and for [illegible] [illegible] as be here most vendible, as waxe, tallowe, traine oile, hempe and flaxe. Of furres we desire no great plentie, [illegible] they be dead wares. And as for Felts we will in no wise you send any. And whereas you have provided tarre, and as we suppose, some hemp ready bought, our advise is, that in no wise you send any of them hither unwrought because our fraight is 4*l.* a tunne or little less: which is so deare, as it would not beare the charges: and therefore we have sent you 7. ropemakers, as by the copies of their covenants here inclosed shall appeare. Whom we will you set to worke with all expedition in making of cables and ropes of all sorts, from the smallest rope to xii inches: And that such tarre and hempe as is already brought to the water side, they may there make it out, and after that you settle their work in Vologhda or Colmogro as you shall think good, where their stuffe may be neerest to them: at which place and places you do assigne them a principall overseer, as well to see the deliverie of the stuffe unwrought, as also to take charge of the stuffe wrought, and to forsee that neither the yarne be burnt in tarring, nor the hempe rotted in the watering; and also to furnish them so with labourers, workmen and stuffe, as hereafter when these workmen shall come away, we be not destitute of good workmen, and that these may dispatch as much as possible they may, doing it *substancially,* for we esteem it a principall commoditie, and that *The Counsel of England doth well allowe.* Let all diligence be used that at the returne of these shippes we may see samples of all ropes and cables if it be possible, and so after to continue in worke, that we may have good store against the next yeere. Therefore they have neede to have a place to work in, in the winter: and at any hand let them have hempe ynough to spinne their stuffe: for seeing you have great plentie of hempe there, and at a reasonable price, we trust we shall be able to bring as good stuffe from thence, and better cheape then out of Danske: if it be diligently used, and have a good overseer.

"Let the chiefest lading of these foure shippes be principally in waxe, flaxe, tallowe and trayne oyle. And if there be any more wares then these ships be able to take in, then leave that which is least in valeu and grossest in stowage until the next shipping: for wee do purpose to ground our selves chiefly upon those commodities, as waxe, cables and ropes, traine oyle, flaxe and some linen yarne. As for Masts, Tarre, Hempe, Feathers, or any such other like, they would not beare the charges to have any considering our deere fraight. We have sent you a skinner to be there at our charges for meate, drinke and lodging, to view and see such furres as you shall cheap or buye, not minding neverthelesse, that you shall charge yourselves with many, except those which be most vendible, as good marterns mimures, otherwise called Lettis, and Mynkes. Of these you may send us plentie, finding them good and at a reasonable price. As for sables and other rich furres, they bee not every mans money: therefore you may send the fewer, using partly the discretion of the Skinner in that behalfe.

"We heare that there is great plentie of Steele in Russia and Tartarie, whereof wee would you send us part for an example, and to write your mindes in it what store is to be had: for we heare say there is great plentie, and that the Tartars steele is better than that in Russia. And likewise we be informed that there is great plentie of Copper in the Emperours Dominions: we would be certified of it what plentie there is, and whether it be in plates or in round flat cakes, and send us some for an example. Also we would have you to certifie us what kind of woollen cloth the men of Rie and Ruel, and the Poles and Lettoes doe bring to

2 A

Russia, and send the scantlings of them with part of the lists, and a full advice of the lengths and breadths, colours and prices, and whether they be strained or not: and what number of them may be utterred in a yeere, to the intent that we make provision for them for the like sorts, and all other Flemish wares which they bring thither and be most vendible there. And to certifie us whether our set clothes be vendible there or not: and whether they be rowed and shorne: because ofttimes they go undrest. Moreover, we will you send us of every commodity in that Country part, but no great quantity other than such as is before declared. And likewise every kind of Lether, whereof we be informed there is great store bought yeerely by the Esterlings and Duches for hie Almaigne and Germanie.

"More, that you doe send us for proofe a quantitie of such Earth, hearbes, or what thing soever it be, that the Russes do die, and colour any kind of cloth linen or wollen, Lether or any other thing withall: and also part of that which the Tartars and Turkes doe bring thither, and how it must be used in dying and colouring. Moreover that you have a special foresight in the chusing of your Tallowe, and that it may be well purified and tried, or els it will in one yeere putrifie and consume.

"Also that you certifie us the trueth of the weights and measures, and howe they do answere with ours, and to send us 3 robles in money, that we may try the just value of them.

"Also we doe send you in these ships ten young men that be bound Prentises to the Companie whom we will you to appoint every of them as you shall there find most apt and meete, some to keepe accompts, some to buy and sell by your order and commission, and some to send abroad into the notable cities of the Countrey for understanding and knowledge."

The spirit of commercial enterprise was fully kindled, and an eager desire appears to become the Carriers of the world. What a change from the utter prostration which led, just before, to the appeal to Him whose genius had been thus successfully invoked to quicken and to guide!

"We would you bought as much waxe principally as you may get. For if there be in that country so great quantity, as we be informed there is, it will be the best commodity we may have: for having that wholly in our hands, we may *serve our own Country and others.* Therefore seeing the Emperour doth minde, that such commodities as bee in his dominions shall not passe to Rie and Revel and Poland as they have done, but be reserved for us: therefore *we must so lay for it, that it may not be upon their hands that have it to sell,* always having consideration in the price and time as our next dispatch may correspond.

"Also we doe understand that in the countrey of Permia or about the river of Pechora is great quantitie of Yewe, and likewise in the countrey of Ugory, which we be desirous to have knowledge of, because it is a special commoditie for our Realme. Therefore we have sent you a young man, whose name is Leonard Brian, that hath some knowledge in the wood, to shew you in what sort it must be cut and cloven. So our minde is if there be any store, and that it be found to be good, that there you doe provide a good quantitie against the next yeere for the comming of our shippes. And because wee bee not sure what timber they shall finde there to make Casks, we have laden in these ships 140 Tunnes emptie

Caske, that is 94 tunnes shaken Casks and 46 tunnes whole, and ten thousand hoopes, and 480 wrethes of twigs; they may be doing with that till they can provide other timber, which wee would be glad to heare of. They have an example with them of the bignesse of the Caske they shall make. Neverthelesse, all such Buttes and Hoggesheads as may be found to serve we will shal be filled with traine Oyle.

"It shalbe very needeful that you doe appoynt certaine to see the romaging of the ships, and to give the master or Botswaine, or him that will take upon him to romage, a good reward for his labour to see the goods well romaged. If it be iij d. or iiij. d. the tunne, it shall not be amisse. For if it be not substantially well looked into, it may be a great deale of money out of our wayes.

"Also, because we reckon that from the Mosco will bee alwayes better conveyance of letters to us by land: our minde is that from time to time as occasion shall serve, our Agents shall write to him that shall lie at Mosco of all things that shall passe, that he may give us large instructions, as wel what is solde and bought, as also what lading we shall take, and what quantitie and kinde of goods wee shall send. For *we must procure to utter good quantitie of wares, especially the commodities of our Realme, although we afford a good penyworth, to the intent to make other that have traded thither, wearie, and so to bring ourselves and our commodities in estimation, and likewise to procure and have the chiefe commodities of that Country in our hands, as waxe and such others; that other Nations may be served by us and at our hands.* For wee doe understand that the greatest quantitie of waxe that commeth to Danske, Lubeck, and Hambourgh, commeth out of Russia. Therefore if wee should buy part, and they also buy, it would raise the price there, and would be little worth here. And all such letters of importance and secrecie as you doe send by land for any wares or otherwise, you must write them in *Cyphers* after the order of a booke sent you in the shippes: alwayes taking goode heede in placing of your letters and cyphers, that we may understand them by the same booke here, and to send them in such sort, that we may have them here by Christmas or Candlemas if it be possible. And because you cannot so certainly advertise us by letters of your doings, but some doubt may arise whereof we would most gladly be certified: our minde is therefore that with these ships you send us home one such yong man as is most expert in knowledge of that Countrey, and can best certifie vs in such questions as may be demanded, whome we will remit unto you againe in the next ships. We think Arthur Edwards will be fittest for that purpose nevertheless use your discretion in that matter.

"The prices of wares here at this present, are, bale flaxe twenty pound the packe and better, towe flaxe twenty-eight pounds the hundred, traine oyle at nine pounds the tunne, waxe at foure pound the hundred, tallow at sixteene shillings the hundred, cables and ropes very deare; as yet there are no shippes come out of Danske."

Though matters passed off so smoothly in public with the Ambassador, we are let here behind the curtain, and note some misgivings as to the character of himself and his countrymen:

"Also if the Emperour bee minded to deliver you any summe of money, or good waxe at as reasonable price as you may buye for readie money, wee will that you shall take it and lade it for our accomptes, and to come at our adventure, and hee to be payed at the returne of the shippes in velvets, sattens, or any other kinde of silke, or cloth of golde, cloth of tissue, or according as his commission shalbe that he shall send us in the shippes, and according to such paternes as hee shall send. *Wee doe not finde the Ambassadour nowe at the last so conformable to reason as wee had thought wee shoulde.. Hee is very mistrustfull, and thinketh everie man will beguile him.* Therefore you had neede to take heede howe you have to doe with him or with any such, and to make your bargains plaine, and to set them downe in writing. For *they be subtill people, and doe not alwaies speake the trueth, and thinke other men to bee like themselves.* Therefore we would have none of them to send any goods in our ships at any time, nor none to come for passengers, unlesse the Emperour doe make a bargaine with you, as is aforesaid, for his owne person.

"Have consideration how you doe take the roble. For although we doe rate it after sixteen shillings eight-pence of our money, yet it is not worth past 12 or 13 shillings sterling."*

The Agent at Vologda writes thus to the Agent at Colmogro:

"Worshipfull Sir, heartie commendations premised. These may bee to advertise you, that yesterday the thirtieth of this present came hither Robert Best, and brought with him two hundred Robles, that is one hundred for this place, and one hundred for you at Colmogro. As for hempe which is here at two robles and a halfe the bercovite, master Gray has written to buy no more at that price; for John Sedgewicke hath bought for sixe or seven hundred robles worth at Novogrode for one roble and a halfe the bercovite, and better cheape: and white Novogrode flaxe is there at three robles the bercovite. I trust he will doe much good by his going thither. As I doe understand Richard Johnson is gone to Novogrode with money to him, I doubt not but master Gray hath advertised you of all their doings, both at the Mosco and at Novogrod. And touching our doings heere, you shall perceive that wee have solde wares of this fourth voyage of one hundred and fortie robles, besides fiftie robles, of the second and third voyage since the giving up of my last account, and for wares of the countrey, you shall understand that I have bought, tried and untried, for 77 robles, foure hundred podes of tried tallowe, beside four hundred podes that I have given out money for, whereof God graunt good receipt when the time cometh, which is in Lent. And in browne flaxe and hempe I have bought seventeen bercovites, sixe podes and sixteene pound, which cost 28 robles, eleven altines two-pence. And as for other kindes of wares I have bought none as yet. And for Mastes to bee provided, you shall understand that I wrote a letter to Totma the 28 of this present for fiftie mastes, to wit, for 25 of fifteene fathoms, and 25 of fourteene fathoms, to be an arshine and a halfe at the small ende. And more, I have written for 30 great trees to be two archines and a half at the small end, and for the other that were provided the last yeere, I trust they shall be sent downe in the spring of the yeere. And as concerning the Ropemakers, you shall understand that their abiding place shall be with you at Colmogro, as I do thinke Master Gray hath advertised you. For, as Roger Boutinge, Master of the woorkes, doeth say, there is no place more meete for their purpose then with you; and there

---

* Hakluyt, vol. i. p. 297.

it will be made with lesser cost, considering that the pale is the one halfe of it: which is to set one pale more to that, and so for to cover it over, which as they say will be but little more. They thinke that it may be made sixteene foote broade, and one hundred and eighty fathoms long; and that in the middle way twentie foote from the pale towarde the water-side there may be a house made to tarre in, standing alone by itselfe for danger of fire. The Tarre house that they would have made, is to be fifteen fathoms long, and ten fathoms broade, and they would that house should be made first; for I thinke they will not tarre before they come there. And further they desire that you will provide for as much tarre as you may, for heere we have small store, but when the time commeth that it should be made, I will provide as much as I can here, that it may be sent downe when the nasade commeth. The stuffe that they have reddie spunne is about five thousand weight, and they say that they trust to have by that time they come downe yarn ynough to make 20 cables. As concerning a copie of the alphabet in ciphers Master Gray hath written hither that Robert Austen had one, which he willed that he shoulde deliver to you. Thus I surcease, beseeching God to preserve you in health, and send you your hearts desire."*

Another letter from the Company:

"This letter before written is the copie on one sent you by Thomas Alcock, trusting that he was with you long since. The 26 day of the last moneth wee received a letter from him dated in Stockholme in Sweden the 14 day of January, and we perceive by his letter that he had talked with a Dutchman that came lately from Mosco, who informed him that our friend Master Antony Jenkinson was returned to the Mosco in September last past, but how far he had beene, or what he had done, he could not tell. Also he wrote that one John Lucke, a joyner, was taken by the Lifelander, and put in prison. As yet we have not heard from the sayd John Lucke, nor know not whether he be released out of prison or not. We suppose that by him you wrote some letter which as yet is not come to our hands: so that we thinke he is yet in prison, or otherwise dispatched out of the way. The fifteenth day of December wee received a letter from Christopher Hodson dated in the Mosco the 29 of July, by the way of Danske; which is in effect a copie of such another received from him in our shippes. You shall understand that wee have laden in three good shippes of ours these kind of wares following: to wit, in the Shallowe of London, master under God Stephen Burrow, 34 fardels No. 136 broad short clothes, and four fardels No. 58 Hampshire Kersies: and 23 pipes of bastards and seckes, and 263 pieces of Raisins, and four hogsheds No. 154 pieces of round pewter, and ten hogsheds and poncheons of prunes, and one dryfatte with almonds. And in the Philip and Marie, Master under God Thomas Wade, 25 fardels No. 100 broad cloths, and three fardels No. 42 Hampshire Kersies, and thirtie pipes of seckes and bastards and 100 pieces of raisins. And in the Jesus of London, Master under God Arthur Pette, 10 fardels No. 40 broade shorte clothes, and twenty-seven pipes of bastards and seckes, as by the invoices herewith inclosed may appeare; also you shall receive such necessaries as you did write to bee sent for the rope-makers; trusting that you shall have better successe with them which you shall send us in these ships, then with the rest which

* Hakluyt, vol. i. p. 332.

you have sent us yet: for we as yet have sold none of them. And whereas we wrote unto you, in our former letter, that we would send you a hundred tunnes of salte, by reason it is so deare here we doe sende you but nine tunnes and a halfe, for it cost here ten-pence the bushel the first pennie : namely in the Swallow 6 tunnes and a halfe, in the Philip and Marie one tunne and a halfe, and in the Jesus one tunne and a halfe. The 4 hogsheads of round pewter goe in the Swallow, and in the Philip and Marie No. 154 pieces as is aforesaid. We send you three ships, trusting that you have provided according to our former writing good store of lading for them. If yee have more wares than will lade the ships, let it be traine oyle that you leave behinde ; the price is not here so good as it was : it is worth here 9 pound the tunne. We thinke it good you should let the smaller ship bring as much of the traine as she can carry. And that the masters of the ships do looke well to the romaging, for they might bring away a great deale more than they doe, if they would take paine in the romaging ; and bestowe the traine by it selfe, and the waxe and tallowe by it selfe : for the leakage of the trayne doth fowle the other wares much.

"We send you now but 100 Kersies : but against the next yeere, if occasion serve, wee will send you a greater quantitie, according as you shall advise us : one of the pipes of seckes that is in the Swallow, which hath two round compasses upon the bung is to be presented to the Emperour : for it is speciall good. The nete weight of the 10 puncheons of prunes is 4300. 2 thirds 1 Pound. It is written particularly upon the head of every Puncheon : and the nete weight of the fatte of Almonds is 500 li. two quarters. The raisins, prunes, and almonds you were best to dispatch away at a reasonable price, and particularly the raisins, for in keeping of them will be great loss in the waight, and the fruit will decay. We thinke it good that you provide against the next yeere for the comming of our shippes 20 or 30 bullocks killed and salted, for beefe is very deare here. Therefore you were best to save some of this salt that we doe send you in these ships for the purpose. The salt of that country is not so good. In this you may take the opinion of the Masters of the shippes. Foxe skins, white, blacke, and russet, will be vendible here. The last yere you sent none : but there were mariners that brought many. If any of the mariners doe bring any trifling furres or other commodities, we will they shall be registered in our pursers bookes, to the intent we may know what they be."*

In a subsequent communication it is said :

"The ware that we would have you provide against the comming of the shippes are Waxe, Tallowe, trayne Oyles, Flaxe, Cables and Ropes, and Furres such as we have written to you for in our last letters by the shippes : and from hencefoorth not to make any great provision of any riche Furres except principall Sables and Lettes : for now there is a Proclamation made that no furres shall be worne here, but such as the like is growing here within this our Realme. Also we perceive that there might be a great deal of tallowe more provided in a yeere than you send. Therefore our minde is, you should enlarge somewhat more in the price, and to send us if you can three thousand podes a yeere for we do most good in it. And likewise the Russes, if you would give them a reasonable price for their wares, woulde be the willinger to buy and sell with you, and not to carrie so much to Novogrode as they doe, but would rather bring it to Vologda to you, both Waxe, Tallowe, Flaxe, Hempe,

* Hakluyt, vol. i. p. 308.

and all kinde of other wares fitte for our countrey. Our minde is you should pro- [illegible] five hundred Loshhides, of them that be large and faire, and thickest in hande, and to be circumspect in the [illegible] them that be killed in season and well dried and whole. If they be good we may sell them here for sixteen shillings and better the piece, wee would have the whole skinnes, that is the necke and legges withall, for these that you sent now lacke their neckes and legges. Neverthelesse for this time you must send them as you may get them : If you coulde finde the meanes that the haire might be clipped off them, they woulde not take so much roome in the shippes as they doe. We perceive by your letters that the prices of waxe doe rise there with you, by reason that the Poles and Lifelanders doe trade into Russia by licence: which, if there should bee peace between them, woulde rise to a bigger price, and not be sufficient to serve them and us too, and likewise woulde bring downe there the prices of our commodities. Therefore we thinke it good you should make a supplication to the Emperour in the name of The Companie to returne the trade from Rye and Revel to us, especially for such wares as wee doe buy: promising that we will be bounde to take them at a reasonable price, as wee have bought them in times past : and likewise that we will bring to them such wares of ours, as are thought fit for the Countrey, and to sell them at such reasonable prices as wee have done."*

There would seem to have been very soon an extensive establishment at Moscow, and many Englishmen in the service of the Merchant Adventurers perished when that city was destroyed by the Tartars:

"Mosco is burnt every sticke by the Crimme the 24 day of May last, and an innumerable number of people : and in the English house was smothered Thomas Southam, Tofild, Waverley, Greene's wife and children, two children of Rafe, and more to the number of 25 persons were stifled in our beere seller: and yet in the same seller was Rafe, his wife, John Browne, and John Clarke preserved, which was wonderful. And there went into that seller Master Glover and Master Rowley also: but because the heate was so great, they came foorth again with much perill, so that a boy at their heeles was taken with the fire, yet they escaped blindfold into another seller, and there as God's will was they were preserved. The Emperour fled out of the field, and many of his people were carried away by the Crimme Tartar : to wit, all the yong people, the old they would not meddle with, but let them alone, and so with exceeding much spoile and infinite prisoners, they returned home againe. What with the Crimme on the one side, and with his cruelty on the other, he hath but few people left."†

* Hakluyt, vol. i. p. 306. † Ib. vol. i. p. 402.

CHAP. XXXIV.

THE CHARTER OF INCORPORATION—RECITES PREPARATIONS ACTUALLY MADE FOR VOYAGES TO THE NORTH, NORTH-EAST, AND NORTH-WEST—HOW FRUSTRATED—WHALE FISHERY—NEWFOUNDLAND FISHERY—THE AMBASSADOR OF THE SOPHY OF PERSIA AT MOSCOW—HIS EXPLANATION TO THE EMPEROR OF RUSSIA AS TO ENGLAND—FOLLOWED UP BY A MESSENGER TO PERSIA FROM ENGLAND WITH A LETTER TO THE SOPHY PROPOSING A COMMERCIAL INTERCOURSE.

It is only by looking closely to the terms of the Charter that we become aware of the extensive schemes of Commerce and Discovery which were contemplated, far beyond the scope of that of which the result has just been stated. The recital is as follows:

"Whereas we be credibly informed, that our right trustie, right faithfull, and welbeloved Counsailors, William Marques of Winchester Lord high Treasurer of this our Realme of England, Henrie Earle of Arundel Lord Steward of our housholde, John Earle of Bedford Lord keeper of our Privie Seale, William Earle of Pembroke, William Lorde Howard of Effingham Lorde High Admirall of our saide Realme of England, &c. *have* at their own adventure, costs, and charges, *provided*, *rigged*, and *tackled* certaine ships, pinnesses, and other meete vessels, and the same furnished with all things necessary have advanced and set forward, for to discover, descrie, and finde Isles, landes, territories, Dominions, and Seigniories unknowen, and by our subjects before this not commonly by sea frequented, which by the sufferance and grace of Almightie God, it shall chaunce them *sailing Northwards, Northeastwards, and Northwestwards*, or any partes thereof, in that race or course which other christian Monarches (being with us in league and amitie), have not heretofore by sea traffiqued, haunted, or frequented, to finde and attaine by their said adventure, as well for the glorie of God, as for the illustrating of our honour and dignitie royall, in the increase of the revenues of our crowne, and generall wealth of this and other our Realmes and Dominions, and of our subjects of the same, and to this intent our subjects above specified and named, have most humbly beseeched us, that our abundant grace, favour and clemencie may be gratiously extended unto them in this behalfe. Whereupon wee inclined to the petition of the foresaide our counsailors, subjects, and Marchants, and willing to animate, advance, further and nourish them in their said Godlie, honest, and good purpose, and, as we hope, profitable adventure, and that they may the more willingly and readily atchieve the same, of our speciall grace, certaine knowledge and 'meere motion, have graunted; and by these presents do graunt, for us, our heires [illegible], unto our said right trustie, and right faithfull, and right welbeloved Counsailors, and the other before named [illegible] of Marchants Adventurers of England, for the discovery of lands, territories, Isles, Dominions and Seigniories unknowen, and not before that late adventure or enterprise by Sea or Navigation, commonly frequented as aforesaid, shalbe from henceforth one bodie and perpetuall fellowship and communitie of themselves, both in deede and in name, and them by the names of Marchants Adventurers for the discoverie of lands, territories, Isles and Seigniories unknowen, and not by the Seas, and Navigations, before their said adventure or enterprise by Sea or navigation commonly frequented. We doe incorporate, name, and declare by these presents, and that the same fellowship or communalty from henceforth shalbe, and may have one Governor of the said Fellowship and Communitie of Marchants Adventurers."*

The prospects thus opened to England were doubtless overshadowed by the domestic turmoil which followed, and which separated the Noble Adventurers into virulent opposing factions. The war, too, with France, into which the country was plunged, to serve the purposes of Philip, called their attention and resources elsewhere, and it only remained to follow up the success which had dawned on the first mercantile speculations.

When we know that the extensive views of Cabot were thus controlled, and recall the sanguine expressions of his letter to Ramusio, how must our indignation kindle anew at such cruel and absurd mis-statements as those of Mr Ellis, who thus follows up the blunder on his part, already exposed, which converts the *Butrigarius* Conversation into *a Letter from Sebastian Cabot*.

"From this account we see plainly the true reason why all thoughts of a North-West passage were laid aside for near fourscore years. For the greatest part of this time Sebastian Cabot, Esq., in quality of governor of the Russia Company, was the great director and almost the sole manager of all our expeditions for discovery, as appears as well from the instructions drawn by him, for the direction of those who were employed to look for a North-East passage, as from several charters, commissions, and other public instruments, in which we find him mentioned with great honour, and treated as the father and founder of the English navigation. It does not indeed appear, that he ever declared in express terms, against making any further searches to the North-West; but *as it is evident from the Letter of his before-mentioned that he absolutely despaired of finding such a passage*, it may be fairly presumed, that during his life time, and considering the great influence he

* Hakluyt, vol. i. p. 267.

had in matters of this nature, no project for such a discovery would have met with any encouragement; and *therefore* we need not wonder, that even in that age, when hardly a year passed but some design or other, for promoting commerce and navigation was set on foot, this remained as silent and unthought of, as if it never had been proposed; or as if *a single* unsuccessful attempt upon a coast never before visited, had been sufficient to extinguish all hopes, and produce absolute despair of doing any good in a matter of such importance, the consequences of which were so well known to the enterprising navigators of those times."*

One of the results of the Northern Voyages was the opening the way to the Whale Fishery at Spitzbergen.†

An important Statute, 2d and 3d Edward VI. cap. 6, occurs to Newfoundland.‡ After reciting that within the few years last past, there had been exacted by certain officers of the admiralty divers great sums of the merchants and fishermen resorting to Newfoundland and other places, "to the great discouragement and hinderance of the same merchants and fishermen, and to no little damage of the whole commonwealth," it is forbidden, "to demand of any such merchants or fishermen any sum or sums of money, doles, or shares of fish, or any other reward, benefit, or advantage whatsoever it be, for any licence to pass this realm to the said voyages or any of them."

The claims of Cabot on the gratitude of his country for having opened to it this source of wealth and power have been freely recognised:—

"To come," says Sir William Monson, writing in 1610, "to the particulars of augmentation of our trade, of our plantations, and our discoveries, because every man shall have his due therein, I will begin with Newfoundland, lying upon the main continent of America, which the King of Spain challenges as first discoverer; but as we acknowledge the King of Spain the first light of the West and South-West parts of America, so we, and all the world must confess, that we were the first who took possession, for the crown of England, of the north part thereof, and not above two years difference betwixt the one and the other. And as the Spaniards have, from that day and year, held their possession in the West, so have we done the like in the North; and though there is no respect, in comparison of the wealth

---

* Voyage to Hudson's Bay, &c., to which is prefixed an Historical Account, &c. by Henry Ellis, Gent. p. 8.

† Anderson's History of Commerce, vol. ii. p. 83. M'Pherson's Annals of Commerce, vol. ii. p. 115.

‡ Ruffhead's Statutes at large, vol. ii. p. 412.

betwixt the countries, yet England may boast, that the discovery from the year aforesaid to this very day, hath afforded the subject annually, one hundred and twenty thousand pounds, and increased the number of many a good ship, and mariners, as our western parts can witness, by their fishing in Newfoundland.

"If this worthy man," says Campbell, "had performed nothing more, his name ought surely to have been transmitted to future times with honour, since it clearly appears that Newfoundland hath been a source of riches and naval power to this nation, from the time it was discovered, as well as the first of our plantations; so that, with strict justice, it may be said of *Sebastian Cabot*, that he was *the author of our Maritime Strength*, and opened the way to those improvements which have *rendered us so great, so eminent, so flourishing a people*."*

"By his knowledge and experience, his zeal and penetration, he not only was the means of extending the Foreign Commerce of England, but of keeping alive that Spirit of Enterprise which, even in his life time, was crowned with success, and which ultimately led to the most happy results for the nation, &c."†

Another branch of Commerce which grew out of the North-Eastern Voyages, is connected with some very curious circumstances.

Richard Chancellor informed Eden (Decades, fol. 198), that at Moscow he met the ambassador of the "Kinge of Persia, called the great Sophie," and was indebted to him for substantial favours. "The ambassador was appareled all in scarlet, and spoke much to the Duke in behalf of our men, of whose kingdom and trade he was not ignorant." It may excite a smile, at the present day, to find an Ambassador of the Sophy of Persia vouching for the commercial respectability of England; and the Russia Company itself, yet in existence, is probably not aware of the extent to which it may have been indebted to his good offices. The complacent feeling thus indicated led shortly after to the mission of Anthony Jenkinson. The Company writing to the Agent in Russia, say,‡ "We have a further hope of some good trade to be found out by Master Anthonie Jenkinson by reason we do perceive, by your letters, that raw silk is as plentiful in Persia as flax is in Russia, besides other commodities that may come from thence." One of the earliest acts of Elizabeth, after her accession, was to address a letter "To the right mightie and right victorious

* Campbell's Lives of the Admirals, art. Sebastian Cabot.

† Barrow's Chronological History, &c. p. 36.

‡ Hakluyt, vol. i. p. 307

Prince, the great Sophie, Emperor of the Persians, Medes, Parthians, Hircans, Carmanians, Margians, of the people on this side and beyond the river of Tigris, and of all men and nations between the Caspian Sea and the Gulfe of Persia." She asks his good offices toward the Agent of the Company:

> "For that his enterprise is onely grounded upon an honest intent, to establish trade of merchandise with your subjects, and with other strangers trafficking in your Realms." "We do hope that the Almightie God will bring it to pass, that of these small beginnings greater moments of things shall hereafter spring both to our furniture and honors, and also to the great commodities and use of our peoples, so that it will be knowen that neither the Earth, the Seas, nor the Heavens have so much force to separate us, as the godly disposition of natural humanity and mutual benevolence have to joyne us strongly together."*

---

* Hakluyt, vol. i. p. 341.

CHAP. XXXV

THE SEARCH-THRIFT DESPATCHED TO THE NORTH IN 1556 UNDER STEPHEN BURROUGH—CABOT'S ENTERTAINMENT AT GRAVESEND—INFLUENCE OF THE DEATH OF EDWARD VI. ON HIS PERSONAL FORTUNES—REVIVING HOPES OF THE STILYARD MERCHANTS—THEIR INSOLENT REFERENCE TO THE QUEEN IN A MEMORIAL ADDRESSED TO PHILIP—THE LATTER REACHES LONDON, 20TH MAY, 1557—NEW ARRANGEMENT AS TO CABOT'S PENSION ON 29TH MAY 1567—WILLIAM WORTHINGTON IN POSSESSION OF HIS PAPERS—ACCOUNT OF THAT PERSON—MANNER IN WHICH THE MAPS AND DISCOURSES HAVE PROBABLY DISAPPEARED—CABOT'S ILLNESS—AEFECTING ACCOUNT OF HIS LAST MOMENTS BY RICHARD EDEN.

AMIDST the stir and bustle of these commercial enterprises concerted by Cabot, or due to the impulse he had communicated, there occurs a remarkable anecdote of himself. Stephen Burrough, afterwards Chief Pilot of England and one of the four Masters having charge of The Royal Navy at Chatham, &c.,* had been with Richard Chancellor, on the first voyage, and was again despatched to the North in 1556, in a pinnace called the Search-thrift. His copious journal of the incidents of the voyage is preserved,† and an entry at the outset strikingly exhibits the anxious supervision of Cabot, and the apparent unwillingness to quit, up to the latest moment, the object of so much solicitude. At the Entertainment, too, provided at Gravesend, his countenance to the joyous amusements of the company not only shows the unbroken spirits of this wonderful man, but the terms in which Burrough records these minute incidents prove how well Cabot understood the character of those around him, and knew that

* See his Commission from Queen Elizabeth, dated 3d January, 1563, amongst the Lansdowne MSS. No. 116, art. iii.

† Hakluyt, vol. i. p. 274.

he was leaving, to cheer them amidst their perils, a grateful impression of kind and familiar sympathy at home.

"The 27 April being Munday, the *Right Worshipful Sebastian Caboto* came aboord our Pinnesse at Gravesende, accompanied with divers Gentlemen, and Gentlewomen, who after that they had viewed our Pinnesse and tasted of such cheere as we could make them aboord, they went on shore, giving to our mariners right liberall rewards: and *the good olde Gentleman* Master Cabota gave to the poore most liberall almes, wishing them to pray for the good fortune, and prosperous successe of the Serchthrift, our Pinnesse. And then at the signe of the Christopher, he and his friends banketted, and made me, and them that were in the company great cheere: and *for very joy that he had to see the towardness of our intended discovery*, he entered into the dance himselfe, amongst the rest of the young and lusty company: which being ended, hee and his friends departed most gently, commending us to the Governance of Almighty God."

A gloom now overspreads the history of Cabot, and we approach the closing scenes of his life with a painful conviction that they exhibit a signal instance of ingratitude and bad faith.

The untimely death of Edward VI. while it operated as a severe check on the advancing commercial prosperity of England, was no less inauspicious to the personal fortunes of him who had given the first great impulse. The generosity of the youthful monarch,—his ingenious and enterprising spirit,—and his fondness for the studies and inquiries connected with sea affairs—are in melancholy contrast with the close and sullen bigotry of Mary. It would form no recommendation to her that Cabot had been a personal favourite with a brother whom she regarded as a heretic and as her own persecutor. With her husband he was still less likely to find favour. Jealous of the growing commerce and maritime enterprise of England, Philip saw in Sebastian Cabot the man who had left his father's service, had refused peremptorily to return, and who was now imparting to others the benefit of his vast experience and accumulated stores of knowledge.

Edward died on the 6 July, 1553. On the 27 November, 1555, the pension to Cabot was renewed (Rymer, Fœdera, vol. xv. p. 427), but there is no clause having a retrospective character, to cover the intervening period, such as would be necessary if, as the fact of renewal implies, the pension made payable for life by the king and his successors was deemed to expire on the death of the reigning monarch.

The most alarming indication of the complete change in the aspect of affairs is the fact that the Stilyard merchants, by the influence of Charles V., through the marriage of his son with Mary, were enabled to obtain relief from the Act of the late King. "This," says Rapin, "was the first fruit of the Queen's alliance with the Emperor."

Their insolent confidence is strikingly apparent in one Document, which shews, at the same time, their knowledge of Philip's brutal disregard of the feelings of his wife.

"At an assembly of the *Hanses* at Lubeck, an Edict was published against all Englishmen, forbidding all trade or commerce with them, and staying the carrying out of Corne, which was provided for the service and necessitie of the Realme: yet for all these indignities, the said Queene was contented that Commissaries on both parts should meet in England, and agree upon, and set downe a certaine and immutable manner of Trade to be held, and observed on both sides: but the Hanses were so farre from accepting of this gracious offer, that they wholly refused it, as by a *Petition* of theirs *exhibited to King Philip,* the third of June 1557 appeareth, wherein they declare the cause of that their refusall to bee, for that they coulde not have in this Realme anie other iudges of their cause, but such as were suspected, *not sparing or excepting the Queene herselfe* of whose good will and favour they had received so often experience and triall.*"

A crisis approaches. Philip reached London on the 20th May, 1557, and the formal declaration of war against France took place immediately after.† The period was one of great pecuniary embarrassment with Mary, and she saw the dreaded necessity approaching for a demand on Parliament of money to enable her to promote the schemes of her husband.‡ We recall, at such a moment, with alarm, the almost incredible

* Treatise of Commerce by Wheeler, Ed. of 1601, p. 97.

† "Philip had come to London in order to support his partizans; and he told the Queen, that if he were not gratified in so reasonable a request, he never more would set foot in England. This declaration extremely heightened her zeal for promoting his interests, and overcoming the inflexibility of her Council." Hume, anno 1557.

‡ "Any considerable supplies could scarcely be expected from Parliament, considering the present disposition of the nation; and as the war would sensibly diminish that branch arising from the customs, the finances, it was foreseen, would fall short even of the ordinary charges of government; and must still more prove unequal to the expenses of war. But though the Queen *owed great arrears to all her servants,* besides the loans extorted from the subjects, these considerations had no influence with her." Ib.

baseness and ingratitude of this man, who, the year before, had withheld from his father, Charles V., the paltry pittance reserved on surrendering a mighty empire.*

On the 27th May, 1557, Cabot resigned his pension.† On the 29th, a new grant is made, but in a form essentially different.‡ It is no longer to him exclusively, but *jointly* with William Worthington; "eidem Sebastiano et dilecto servienti nostro Willielmo Worthington."

On the faee of this transaction Cabot is cheated of one-half of the sum which had been granted to him for life. This was done, no doubt, on the pretence that age prevented an efficient discharge of his duties, forgetting that the very nature of the grant for life had indulgent reference to such a contingency, and that Cabot by refusing to quit England had forfeited his pension from the Emperor.

That Worthington—probably a favourite of that dark hour—was thus provided for on pretence of aiding in the discharge of Cabot's functions seems placed beyond doubt by evidence found in Hakluyt. The dedication of the first volume of the greater work to the Lord High Admiral of England contains these remarkable expressions:

"King Edward VI., that Prince of Peerless hope, with the advice of his sage and prudent counsel, before he entered into the North-Eastern discovery, advanced *the worthy and excellent Sebastian Cabota* to be Grand Pilot of England, allowing him a most bountifull Pension of £166 by the year, during his life, as appeareth in his letters Patent, which are to be seen in the third part of my work. And if God had granted him longer life, I doubt not but as he dealt most royally in establishing that office of Pilot Major, *(which not long after to the great hindrance of the common-wealth, was miserably turned to other private uses)* so his Princely Majesty would have showed himself no niggard in erecting, &c. &c."

---

* Robertson's Charles V. anno 1556. "But though he might have soon learned to view with unconcern the levity of his subjects, or to have despised their neglect, he was more deeply afflicted with the ingratitude of his Son, who, forgetting already how much he owed to his father's bounty, obliged him to remain some weeks at Burgos, before he paid him the first moiety of that *small Pension*, which was all that he had reserved of so many kingdoms. As without this sum Charles could not dismiss his domestics with such rewards as their services merited, or his generosity had destined for them, he could not help expressing both surprise and dissatisfaction."

† Rymer, vol. xv. p. 427.

‡ Ib. p. 466.

The high functionary thus addressed was then in the service of Queen Elizabeth. The gross abuse, therefore, so indignantly denounced has no reference, we may be assured, to her, and we know that amongst the early acts of her reign was the appointment of Stephen Burrough to the office in question. The allusion, therefore, is to some dark tale of perversion between the death of Edward in 1553 and the accession of Elizabeth in 1558, and we can have little difficulty in coupling it with this mark of royal bounty at the expense of Cabot.

The allusion was, doubtless, well understood by the person addressed, for his father, then Lord High Admiral of England, is named, as we have seen, in the Charter of the Merchant Adventurers, (at the head of whom Cabot is placed) as one of the associates who had fitted out the vessels to prosecute discoveries in the North, North-West, and North-East.* Hakluyt alludes to this circumstance in his Dedication to the son.

We look round with some interest for information as to *William Worthington.* The only notice of him discovered is in a passage of Strype's Historical Memorials (vol. ii. p. 506), where amongst the Acts of Edward VI. the youthful monarch is found, with an easy liberality, forgiving him a large debt on his allegation that a servant had run away with the money.

"A Pardon granted to *William Worthington,* being indebted to the King for and concerning the office of Bailiff and Collector of the Rents and Revenues of all the Manors, Messuages, Lands, Tenements, and Hereditaments within the City of London, and county of Middlesex, which did belong to Colleges, Guilds, Fraternities, or Free Chappels, *in the sum of* 392 *pounds* 10 *shillings* 3 *pence*, as upon the foot of his account, made by the said William before Thomas Mildmay auditor of the said Revenues, manifestly it doth appear: In consideration of his service both in France and Scotland, and also his daily service and attendance, being one of the ordinary Gentlemen and Pensioners; and for that the Debt grew by *the unfaithfulness of his servant, who ran away with the same.* Granted in March, but the Patent signed in April."

---

* See the Charter in Hakluyt, vol. i. p. 268.

It will be remembered* that in Hakluyt's earliest work, published in 1582, he speaks of all Cabot's Maps and Discourses written with his own hand as then in the possession of William Worthington. The facts disclosed may, perhaps, assist to account for their disappearance. It is obvious that such documents would be secured, at any price, by the Spanish Court, at the period of Hakluyt's publication, when English enterprise was scattering dismay amongst the Spanish possessions of America. The work of Hakluyt (six years before the Armada) showed where they were to be found. The depositary of them was the very man who had been the object of Philip's bounty during his brief influence in England. Were they not bought up? There can be now only a conjecture on the subject, yet it seems to gather strength the more it is reflected on.

Suspicion may even go back farther, and suggest that a main object in associating this man with Cabot was to enable him to get possession of the papers that they might be destroyed or sent to Spain. The fact that Worthington had received them was probably too well known to be denied by him; and his remark to Hakluyt may have been a mere mode of evading that person's prying curiosity. The same alarm which dictated the demand on Edward VI. for the return of Cabot would lead Philip to seize, with eagerness, an opportunity of getting hold of these documents, so that the author's dreaded knowledge might expire with himself. Of one thing we may feel assured. Hakluyt, who is found attaching so much importance to an "Extract" from one of Cabot's Maps, was not turned aside from efforts to get a sight of this precious Collection, but by repeated and peremptory refusals, for which, if it really remained in Worthington's hands, there occurs no adequate motive. The language of the Dedication seems to betray something of the sharpness of a personal pique.

Sixty-one years had now elapsed since the date of the first

---

* See p. 40.

commission from Henry VII. to Sebastian Cabot, and the powers of nature must have been absolutely wearied out. We lose sight of him after the late mortifying incident; but the faithful and kind-hearted *Richard Eden* beckons us, with something of awe, to see him die. That excellent person attended him in his last moments,* and furnishes a touching proof of the strength of the Ruling Passion. Cabot spoke flightily, "on his death bed," about a divine revelation to him of a new and infallible method of Finding the Longitude which he was not permitted to disclose to any mortal. His pious friend grieves that "the good old man," as he is affectionately called, had not yet, "*even in the article of death*, shaken off all worldlie vaine glorie." When we remember the earnest religious feeling exhibited in the Instructions to Sir Hugh Willoughby, and which formed so decided a feature of Cabot's character, it is impossible to conceive a stronger proof of the influence of long cherished habits of thought, than that his decaying faculties, at this awful moment, were yet entangled with the problem which continues to this day to vex, and elude, the human intellect. The Dying Seaman was again, in imagination, on that beloved Ocean over whose billows his intrepid and adventurous youth had opened a pathway, and whose mysteries had occupied him longer than the allotted span of ordinary life. The date of his death is not known, nor, except presumptively, the place where it occurred. From the presence of Eden we may infer that he died in London. It is not known where his Remains were deposited. The claims of England in the new world have been uniformly, and justly, rested on his discoveries. Proposals of colonization were urged, on the clearness of the Title thus acquired and the shame of abandoning it. The

* See the Epistle Dedicatory to "A very necessarie and profitable book concerning Navigation compiled in Latin by Joannes Taisnerus, a publike Professor in Rome, Ferraria and and other Universities in Italie, of the Mathematicalles named a Treatise of Continual Motions. Translated into English by Richard Eden, Imprinted at London by Richard Jugge." There is a copy of the work in the King's Library, British Museum (title in Catalogue, *Eden*).

English language would probably be spoken in no part of America but for Sebastian Cabot. The Commerce of England and her Navy are admitted to have been deeply—incalculably—his debtors. Yet there is reason to fear that in his extreme age the allowance which had been solemnly granted to him for life was fraudulently broken in upon. His birthplace we have seen denied. His fame has been obscured by English writers, and every vile calumny against him eagerly adopted and circulated. All his own Maps and Discourses "drawn and written by himself" which it was hoped might come out in print, "because so worthy monuments should not be buried in perpetual oblivion," *have* been buried in perpetual oblivion. He gave a Continent to England: yet no one can point to the few feet of earth she has allowed him in return!

BOOK II.

CHAP. I.

VOYAGES SUBSEQUENT TO THE DISCOVERY BY CABOT—PATENT OF 19TH MARCH 1501, NOW FIRST PUBLISHED, IN FAVOUR OF THREE MERCHANTS OF BRISTOL AND THREE PORTUGUESE—NATIVES BROUGHT TO ENGLAND AND EXHIBITED AT COURT—ERRONEOUS REFERENCE OF THIS INCIDENT TO CABOT—HAKLUYT'S PERVERSION—SECOND PATENT 9TH DECEMBER 1502—DR ROBERTSON'S MISCONCEPTIONS—PROBABLE REASONS FOR THE ABANDONMENT OF THE ENTERPRISE.

It is now proposed to pass in review the efforts which have been made at different periods, and under various auspices, to follow up the project of Cabot, so far as may be necessary to exhibit the pervading influence of the original enterprise. This part of the subject has in it little of an attractive, or popular, character; yet the close and minute inquiry which it involves will, it is hoped, be sufficiently relieved by its high purpose of rendering an act of tardy justice to the fame of this great seaman. The same ignorance, or malevolence, which has so long obscured the evidence of what he himself achieved, has been even yet more successful in effecting its object by an absurd exaggeration of the merit of subsequent navigators.

Attention is naturally turned, in the first place, to the

country in which the scheme had its origin; and here we recognize distinctly the quickening impulse of its partial success, though rendered unavailing by accidental causes. The page of Lord Bacon which states the public exhibition by Cabot, on his return, of a "Card," showing his progress to 67° and-a-half, apprises us that "again in the sixteenth year of his reign, and likewise in the eighteenth, the King granted new commissions for the discovery and investing of unknown lands."

Singular as it may appear, the first of these interesting and curious documents has never yet been made public, and the reference to it in a subsequent paper printed by Rymer (vol. xiii. p. 42), has a mistake as to the date. After a tedious search at the Rolls Chapel, it has at length been discovered, and though, from unpardonable carelessness, a part of it has become illegible, yet no material portion is lost.

It was granted during the brief Chancellorship of the Bishop of Salisbury, and bears date 19th March, in the 16th year of Henry VII. (19th March 1501), and is in favour of *Richard Warde, Thomas Ashehurst*, and *John Thomas*, "Merchants of the Towne of Brystowe," and *John Fernandus, Francis Fernandus*, and *John Gunsolus*, "borne in the Isle of Surrys, under the obeisance of the Kyng of Portugale." The following are its leading provisions.

Authority is given to these persons, their heirs, factors and deputies, to sail to and explore, at *their own expense*, all Islands, Countries, regions, and provinces whatever, in the Eastern, Western, Southern, and Northern Seas heretofore unknown to Christians, and to set up the Royal Banner in such places as they may discover, and to subdue and take possession of the same in the name of the King of England. They are permitted to employ as many vessels as they may think proper, and of any burden.

The King's subjects, male and female, are permitted to go to and inhabit the regions which may be discovered, to take with them their vessels, servants, and property of every description, and to dwell there under the protection and government of the patentees, who are empowered to frame Laws and to enforce their execution. Theft, homicide, robbery, and violation of the female natives of the newly-discovered countries, are specially recited as offences to be provided against.

The exclusive privilege of trading to the newly-discovered countries is secured to the Patentees for ten years; and they may import thence gold, silver, precious stones, and all other products.

In special consideration of the great expense attending the enterprise, they are authorised to import for the term of four years in one vessel of any burden, all articles duty-free; but a *proviso* is eagerly added that this shall not affect the claim to duties on articles imported in *other* vessels.

All persons presuming to visit the newly-discovered regions without permission of the Patentees, even though subjects of a power in friendship and alliance with England, may be treated as enemies and expelled, or imprisoned and punished at the discretion of the Patentees.

They may appoint deputies for the government of all cities, towns, and other places, in the countries discovered.

The office of King's Admiral in those regions is conferred on them, and the survivors and survivor of them.

Lands are to be held by them, their heirs and assigns, by fealty only, without further or other claim or demand on the part of the King or his heirs.

The next clause forbids any interference with the Patentees by any foreigner under any grant before made, or which should afterwards be made, under the Great Seal.

The writing on the original parchment is then carefully erased from a considerable space which had been occupied, as we may conjecture, with the case of Cabot.

The three Portuguese are made denizens; yet even this act of grace is coupled with a qualification strikingly characteristic of the Monarch whose sign manual is affixed to the instrument. It is *provided* that they shall continue liable to pay duties *as aliens* on all merchandise exported or imported!*

The subsequent Patent bears date 9th December, in the eighteenth year of Henry VII. that is 9th December, 1502, and is found in Rymer (vol. xiii. p. 37). Of the original Patentees, the names of Richard Warde, John Thomas, and John Fernandus are dropped, and to those retained (Thomas Ashehurst, John Gunsolus and Francis Fernandus) is now added Hugh Elliott. The powers given to these four persons are essentially the same with those conferred on the former six; and in matters of detail a temper evidently less churlish is displayed. The exclusive right of trade to the new regions is extended to a period of forty years, and the exemption from duty on merchandise imported in one vessel, of whatever burden, to fifteen years; and before the instrument closes, the additional privilege is given of importation, duty free, for five years, in one other vessel of 120 tons. The last indulgence is seemingly wrung from the King, after a partial preparation of the instrument. The ungracious *proviso* which accompanied the original denization is also withdrawn, and they are to pay no higher duties than natural-born subjects.

It is specially provided that any discoveries made by the new patentees shall not be for the benefit of the former without an express agreement to that effect.

At this late period we cannot pretend to ascertain, with certainty, what was done under these Patents which evidently look to an extensive scheme of colonization.

That one voyage at least was made, may be inferred from various circumstances.

The provisions of the second Patent, of the 9th December 1502, have reference to the discovery of regions "not before discovered by the King's subjects under authority from the Great Seal" ("quæ antehac *ab aliis subditis nostris,* aut ab aliquibus hæredum et successorum suorum, potestatem, per

* As this document has not heretofore been made public, it is given at large in the Appendix (D.).

alias Literas Patentes sub Magno Sigillo Nostro in ea parte a [illegible] [illegible], reperta, inventa, investigata et recuperata non fuerunt"). No such expressions are found in the Patent of 19th March, 1501, the reference there being only to a former authority to a foreigner (extraneus), that is, the Venetian, John Cabot. We may therefore fairly infer, that the allusion is to some intermediate discovery by the Patentees of the 19th March, 1501, two of whom, Richard Warde and John Thomas, merchants of Bristol, are omitted in the second Patent.

The presumption is further strengthened by the following passage in Stow's Annals, under the year 1502—

"This year were brought unto the King three men taken in the Newfound Ilandes by Sebastian Gabato before named in anno 1498; these men were clothed in beast skins and did eate raw flesh, but spake such a language as no man could understand them, of the which three men two of them were seen in the King's Court at Westminster two years after clothed like Englishmen and could not be discerned from Englishmen."

Stow quotes as his authority Robert Fabyan, though, as has been remarked on a former occasion, no such passage is to be found in the printed work of that Annalist.

The coupling of Cabot's name here with the year 1498, may, perhaps, be supposed to refer merely to what had been said of him before, as the finder of the new region, and to be a mode of designating a country which had, as yet, received no familiar appellation. One obvious consideration arises on the face of the account to negative the idea that the savages exhibited in 1502, had been brought off by him in 1498. The author speaks, it will be seen, of the complete change in their aspect and apparel, after a lapse of two years. Now had they arrived with Cabot, they must have been in England four years prior to the exhibition. Where had they been kept in the intermediate period, and would they not, long before, have cast their skins and lost something of the savageness which afterwards disappeared so rapidly? To suppose that they had been recently "brought unto the King" by Cabot is against probability, when, while nothing is found with regard to him, the Records show a treaty with Henry VII. by others, executed a sufficient time before to fall in with this exhibition. These considerations would countervail even a positive statement, had one been made, by the old Annalist who, in a memorandum as to the strange sight he had witnessed at Westminster, would naturally refer it, without minute inquiry, to the discovery and the person he had before named. It is satisfactory to disengage Cabot from the cruel trick of bringing off the aborigines; this was plainly the first tribute to popular wonder from the New World. They had evidently just arrived, and were doubtless brought up to London to excite general curiosity and interest as to the new region preparatory to an effort which was successfully made in December, to obtain a relaxation of the terms of the original Patent. We may remark further, aside from the improbability of the three Portuguese remaining idle in England for nearly two years, that they would have come with an ill grace to ask for a new Patent had they made no experiment to ascertain how far the original one might be turned to account. Doubtless the modification was urged on the ground that the country was found, on examination, to offer none of the rich commodities specially referred to in the first patent,—neither gold, silver, nor precious stones,—and that it was impossible to expect, under the original terms, even a reimbursement of the expense incurred. We require some such explanation of the sudden extension from ten to *forty* years of the privilege of exclusive traffic.

Another instance of treachery on the part of Hakluyt is here to be noted, which may show how undeserving he is of confidence. The early part of the year 1502 falls within the *seventeenth* of Henry VII.* On turning to Hakluyt's original work, published in 1582, there will be found this same passage of Fabyan, as derived from "John Stowe Citizen a

* The following entries in the Account of the Privy Purse Expenses of Henry VII. are obviously to be connected with these Patents:—

"7 January 1502 To men of Bristol that found Th' Isle	£5
"30 September 1502 To the Merchants of Bristol that have bene in the Newe founde Launde	£20."

diligent searcher and preserver of Antiquities," and he there, while the [illegible] communication before him, actually states the *seventeenth* year of Henry VII. as the date of this exhibition of savages. But when he came to publish his larger, and more ambitious, work, he seems to have paused over the several scraps of information he had collected, and which appeared so little to harmonise. There is no evidence, it may be remarked, that he had any knowledge of the two Patents to the Bristol Merchants and the Portuguese. He thought it, then, unaccountable how Cabot should be found, at so late a period, exhibiting savages evidently just from the woods. He determined, therefore, to set the matter right, and the "seventeenth" year of his original work is actually converted into "fourteenth" so as to correspond with the date of Cabot's voyage. In the work of 1582, the passage is headed "Of three savage men which he brought home and presented unto the King in the XVII yeere of his raigne," but in 1600, (vol. iii. p. 9) "Of three savages which Cabot brought home and presented unto the King in the *fourteenth* yeare of his raigne mentioned by the foresaid Robert Fabian." Thus the names of Stowe and Fabyan, cited, in 1582, for the statement then made, are retained to sanction his own perversion eighteen years after!

Whatever may have been the result of these Commissions, a mere glance at their dates, and contents, will suffice to show how idle are the speculations by which respectable writers have sought to account for what they term the apathy of Henry VII. The following passage from Dr Robertson's History of America may serve as a specimen :—

"But by the time that Cabot returned to England, he found both the state of affairs and the King's inclination unfavourable to any scheme, the execution of which would have required tranquillity and leisure. Henry was involved in a War with Scotland, and his Kingdom was not yet fully composed after the commotion excited by a formidable insurrection of his own subjects in the West. An Ambassador from Ferdinand of Arragon was then in London: and as Henry set a high value upon the friendship of that Monarch, for whose character he professed much admiration, perhaps from its similarity to his own, and was endeavouring to strengthen their union by negotiating the marriage which afterwards took place between his eldest Son and the Princess Catharine, he was cautious of giving any offence to a Prince jealous to excess of all his rights.

"From the position of the Islands and Continent which Cabot had discovered, it was evident that they lay within the limits of the ample donative which the bounty of Alexander VI had conferred upon Ferdinand and Isabella. No person, in that age, questioned the validity of a paper grant; and Ferdinand was not of a temper to relinquish any claim to which he had a shadow of title. Submission to the authority of the Pope, and deference for an ally whom he courted, seem to have concurred with Henry's own situation, in determining him to abandon a scheme, in which he had engaged with some degree of ardour and expectation.

"No attempt towards discovery was made in England during the remainder of his reign; and Sebastian Cabot, finding no encouragement for his active talents there, entered into the service of Spain."

The four Commissions from Henry VII. bear date, respectively, 5th March 1496, 3rd February 1598, 19th March 1501, and 9th December 1502. Of these, the second was granted to John Cabot after the close of the war in Scotland, and the putting down of Perkin Warbeck's Insurrection in the West. The others follow at such intervals as show a continued patronage of the project, and there is not the slightest evidence of refusal, or even of hesitation, from the considerations suggested by Dr Robertson. At the very moment when, according to that writer, Henry was influenced by a dread of ecclesiastical censure, and a timid deference to foreign powers, he is found conferring under the Great Seal authority to make discoveries and to treat as enemies, and pursue to condign punishment, all who should presume to visit the countries discovered without permission, even though subjects of a monarch in alliance with England. As to the suggestion that the enterprise was finally abandoned on account of the contemplated marriage between Prince Arthur and Catherine, not only do we find the dates above-mentioned running over the period of negotiation, but it happens that the last patent (the one in Rymer) is dated seven months after the Prince's death. The indisposition of Henry to give way to arrogant pretensions is abundantly clear. The Patentees are to respect the prior discoveries of Portugal and other countries only where actual possession had been maintained, "in terris prius repertis *et* in quarum *possessione* ipsi Principes *jam existunt.*"

Dr Robertson had seen the title of the last Patent, as given by Rymer, but assuredly could not have read it, or he must have struck out the whole of the passage quoted. The reader will smile at the indolent credulity of the following sentence: "If any attempt had been made in consequence of this Patent, it would not have escaped the knowledge of a compiler so industrious and inquisitive as Hakluyt." We have just seen, that the writer on whose accuracy and research Dr Robertson relies so implicitly as to waive any examination for himself, has contrived, by a nefarious perversion, to obscure the very fact in question.

The real character of Henry VII. seems to have been that of a thrifty, calculating, *man of business*. Caring little about the niceties of the point of honour, he was inclined to submit to many slights, and some injustice, rather than go to War, which he shunned as the same prudent personage would, in private life, have deprecated a lawsuit, as a remedy involving, necessarily, much trouble and expense, and being, at last, of uncertain issue. He often obtained by negotiation what a more proud and impetuous spirit would have vindicated by the sword. But wherever the obvious interests of the country, or of his own coffers, were concerned, he was sturdy, persevering, fearless. The influence of his reign on the commercial history of England has never been adequately appreciated, because no one, since the time of Bacon, has taken up the subject in a temper to do him justice. There is nothing in his character to dazzle or excite, and Treaties of Commerce are a poor substitute for Battles to the light reader or brilliant historian.

In reference to the projects under consideration, it is plain that Henry did not, for one moment, suffer the Pope's Bull, or the remonstrances of Spain, to interfere with the eager and resolute pursuit of what seemed a profitable speculation. But when he found that the only quarter of the new world which remained unoccupied held out no prospect of speedy or rich returns, and that the prosecution of these enterprises, instead of proving a mine of wealth, only, perhaps, furnished an appeal to his princely generosity for pecuniary aid, his interest naturally languished.* The Foreigners who had resorted to

* That an intercourse was kept up for several years with the newly-discovered

his Court were obliged to seek, elsewhere, for Patrons either more ambitious of the mere glory of discovery or more long-sighted, in looking patiently to ultimate, though tardy, results. John Gunsolus, is doubtless the "Juan Gonzales, Portugais," whose name appears as a witness in the celebrated trial of the Fiscal with Diego Columbus (Navarette, Viages, tom. iii. p. 553). Of his own fair standing some proof is, perhaps, found in his being called on to testify to the estimation in which Alonzo Pinzon was held by the seamen of that period (Ib. p. 569). He mentions his having sailed with Diego de Lepe, and probably proceeded to England about the date (May, 1500) of the letter of the King and Queen of Spain to Dorvelos, which Navarette (tom. iii. p. 42) refers to a project on the part of Spain to follow up the discoveries of Cabot. Lepe himself, after his return, is found in the November of the same year at Palos, entangled in some vexatious law proceedings (Navarette, tom. iii. p. 80).

Repeated reference is found in Herrera to John and Francis Goncalez, but as there are several individuals thus designated it is impossible to know what incidents to refer to the English patentees.

---

region, is apparent from the following entries in the account of the Privy Purse Expenses of Henry VII.

"17 November, 1503. To one that brought hawkes from the Newfounded Island, 1*l.*

"8 April, 1504. To a preste [priest] that goeth to the new Islande, 2*l.*

"25 August, 1505. To Clays going to Richmount with wylde catts and popyngays of the Newfound Island, for his costs, 13*s.* 4*d.*

"To Portugales [Portuguese] that brought popyngais and catts of the mountaigne with other stuff to the King's grace, 5*l.*"

Can it have been that Sebastian Cabot, meanwhile, was attempting to colonize the new region? The mission of the Priest would seem to countenance the idea of a settlement; and we might thus account for the long disappearance of our Navigator, as well as for the language of Thevet (see p. 87 of the present volume).

CHAP. II.

FIRST VISIT OF COLUMBUS TO TERRA FIRMA ON HIS THIRD VOYAGE—APPRISED BEFORE LEAVING SPAIN OF CABOT S DISCOVERIES—PROJECTED EXPEDITION TO THE NORTH FROM SPAIN.

It cannot be supposed that the two great maritime contemporaries of Henry, would regard with indifference the enterprise of Cabot, since the "Card," which that navigator exhibited on his return, according to Lord Bacon, plainly showed how little respect was paid to the arrogant meridian line which had received the highest ecclesiastical sanction.

The Continent of America was first visited by Columbus in August 1498, in the course of what is called his Third Voyage, on which he sailed 30 May 1498. The bare mention of these dates will establish the impossibility that he could have been ignorant of the great discoveries of Cabot which, commencing at the point seen on the 24 June 1497, had extended over the "Londe and Isle," recited in the second patent. Not only had the first expedition returned, and the mariners been dispersed in every direction, but a new expedition, with the King at its head, is subsequently planned, and the royal authority, of 3rd February 1498, for its sailing precedes, by nearly four months, the departure of Columbus. To suppose him ignorant of events so momentous would involve an absurdity which becomes the more glaring in proportion as the circumstances are considered. The court of Henry VII. was filled with the agents of foreign powers,* through whom the news would not fail to be spread, at once, over Europe.

* "It grew also from the airs which the princes and states abroad received from their ambassadors and agents here; which were attending the court in great number," &c. "So that they did write over to their superiors in high terms concerning his wisdom and art of rule; nay, when they were returned, they did commonly maintain intelligence with him." Bacon's Henry VII.

With regard to Spain, as she would feel the deepest interest on the subject, so the circumstances are strongest to show a continued communication between the two countries. The authority in reference to the proposed marriage of Prince Arthur with Catharine, bears date 3rd January, 1496, and the negotiation runs through the whole of the period to 14th November, 1501, when the ceremony took place. It was by the intervention of the resident Spanish Ambassador, Don Pedro d'Ayola, that the truce between England and Scotland of 30 September, 1497, was brought about, and certain matters being left to the arbitrament of Ferdinand and Isabella, Henry's assent to the reference bears date 13 December, 1497.* That d'Ayola, in the active communications going on at such a period, omitted to speak of events so memorable in themselves, and which Spain must have regarded with such especial interest, is a proposition that it is superfluous to combat.

A project was soon formed to visit the region actually explored by Cabot. Navarette (Viages, tom. iii. p. 77) gives us a letter dated Seville, 6th May 1500, from the king and queen to a certain "Juan Dornelos o Dorvelos," touching a voyage of discovery, and supposes (ib. p. 42) that it had for its object to explore the seas, from the discovery of which Sebastian Cabot had returned ("que el plan dirigiese a renoncer los mares que acababa de descubrir Sebastian Caboto"). Nothing further appears with regard to it.

---

* Rymer, vol. xii. p. 672.

CHAP. III.

EXPEDITION FROM PORTUGAL—CORTEREAL—THE WORK ENTITLED "PAESI NOVAMENTE RITROVATI," &C.—LETTER OF THE VENETIAN AMBASSADOR AT LISBON ELEVEN DAYS AFTER THE RETURN OF CORTEREAL—REFERENCE TO THE PREVIOUS VOYAGE OF CABOT—TRINKETS FOUND AMONGST THE NATIVES—TRANSLATION OF THE "PAESI," &C. IN 1516.

THE voyage from Spain may not have taken place, but in another quarter a more decided result was produced; and we reach now an enterprise of some celebrity, undertaken directly from that country whose adventurers have been traced to England animated with the hope of turning to account the discoveries of Cabot.

After the recent shame to Portugal of the rejection of Columbus, her enterprising and sagacious monarch could not but take alarm at the departure of his subjects to seek the shelter, and to advance the glory, of a foreign flag. He had, moreover, the strongest motives of interest for wishing to anticipate the efforts of others to reach by a shorter route those regions of which he had heretofore monopolised the lucrative and envied commerce. Nor could the attempt be now deemed a very arduous one. The dispersion of a force of three hundred men, which, according to Peter Martyr, accompanied Cabot on the voyage spoken of by that historian, would leave not a single sea-port without many mariners eager to describe, and to exaggerate, the wonders of the region they had visited, and anxious, as well as competent, to act as guides in the prosecution of a new enterprise. We are quite prepared, therefore, to believe that the ready assent, and liberal countenance, of Emanuel might enable those who enjoyed them to get the start of such of his own subjects as had, perhaps, earlier conceived the project and repaired to England, but whose proposals had there to encounter all the delays produced by the cautious and penurious temper of the personage to whom they were addressed. It does not seem probable that Gunsolus and Fernandus would have resorted to England *after* an expedition for a similar purpose, and likely to cross their path, had been fitted out under the auspices of their own Sovereign. The voluminous treaty between them and Henry VII. may, perhaps, sufficiently explain the apparent tardiness of their subsequent movements. It wears, in every line, a character of anxious and elaborate preparation, and its terms are so harsh and narrow that they could not have been assented to without reluctance, and were found so impracticable that in the second patent, as we have seen, the necessity of a relaxation is conceded. The conduct of Emanuel presents an honourable contrast in every particular. He contributed largely from his own purse, and all the arrangements were marked by that spirit of liberality which constitutes on such occasions the truest economy.

The command of the Expedition was confided to Gaspar Cortereal, who had been brought up under the immediate eye of the king while Duke de Beja.* Of its result we happen, very fortunately, to possess an account from a disinterested quarter, remarkably clear and minute.

As early as the year 1507 there was published at Vicenza a Collection of Voyages and Travels under the title, "*Paesi novamente retrovati et Novo Mondo da Alberico Vesputio Florentino intitulato.*" The extreme scarcity of the work may be inferred from the circumstance that *Camus*, having all the libraries of Paris within his reach, deplores the absence of the original edition (Memoire sur la Collection des Grands et Petits Voyages, &c., p. 5), and *Navarette* (Colecion de los Viages, &c., tom. iii. p. 187) knew of it only through an acquaintance who had been in London. Haym (Bibliotheca Italiana o sia notizia de Libri rari Italiani) had not seen the Vicenza publication. In this precious volume is preserved

---

* Damiano Goes Chronico del Rey D. Manoel, cap. lxvi.

a letter from the Venetian ambassador in Portugal to his brothers, *written eleven days after the return of Cortereal.* The writer's opportunities for obtaining correct information were abundant. He saw the natives whom Cortereal had brought with him—heard from the adventurers themselves all the particulars of the voyage—and speaks of the hopes and speculations to which it gave rise at the Court to which he was accredited. When it is stated that of this Letter there was a most flagitious perversion in a Latin translation which appeared at Milan the next year, and which has poisoned all the subsequent accounts, the importance will be seen of noting carefully the language of the original. The letter appears, lib. vi. cap. cxxvi. and bears date 19th October 1501, seven months, it may here be remarked, subsequent to Henry VII.'s Patent to the three Portuguese. After a few remarks irrelative to the expedition, the writer thus continues—

"Adjr. VIII. del presente arivo qui una de le doe Caravelle quale questo serenissimo Re *lanno passato* mando a discoprire terra verso tramontana Capitaneo Gaspar Corterat: et referissi havere trouato terra ii M. miglia lonzi da qui tra maestro & ponente qual mai per avanti fo cognita ad alcun; per la costa de la qual scorseno forsi miglia DC in DCC. ne mai trovoreno fin: per el che credeno che sia terra ferma la qual continue in *una altra terra che lano passato, fo discoperta sotto la tramontana,* le qual caravelle *non posseno arivar fin la* per esser el mare agliazato & infinita copia de neue; Questo in stesso li fa credere la moltitudine de fiumare grossissime che anno trovate la che certo de una Insula none havia mai tante & cosi grosse: Dicono che questa terra e *molto populata* & le case de li habitanti sonno de alcuni legni longissimi coperte de foravia de pelle de passi. Hanno conducti qui VII. tra homini & femene & putti de quelli: & cum laltra Caravella che se aspecta d hora in hora ne vien altri cinquanta."

"On the 8th of the present month one of the two Caravels which his most Serene Majesty dispatched last year on a voyage of discovery to the North, under the command of Gaspar Corterat, arrived here, and reports the finding of a country distant hence West and North-West two thousand miles, heretofore quite unknown. They proceeded along the coast *between six and seven hundred miles* without reaching its termination, from which circumstance they conclude it to be of the mainland *connected with another region which last year was discovered in the North,* but which the Caravel *could not reach* on account of the ice and the vast quantity of snow; and they are confirmed in this belief by the multitude of great rivers they found, which certainly could not proceed from an island. They say that this country is *very populous,* and the dwellings of the inhabitants are constructed with timber of great length and covered with the skins of fishes. They have brought hither of the inhabitants, seven in all, men, women, and children, and in the other Caravel which is looked for every hour there are fifty more."

Describing the captives the Ambassador says—

"Questi sono de equal colore, figura, statura, et aspecto, similimi a cingani, vestiti de pelle de diversi animali, ma precipue de ludre; de instade voltano el pello i suso, et de in verno el contrario; et queste pelle non sonno cusite insieme In alcun modo, ne couze, ma cosi como sonno tolte da li animali se le meltono intorno lespalle et braze; et le parte pudibunde lgate cum alcune corde facte de nervi de pesse fortissime. Adeo che pareno homini salvatichi: sono molto vergognosi et mansueti; ma tanto ben facti de brazi & gambe & spalle che non se potria dire: Hanno signata la faza in modo de Indiani: chi da vi chi da viii. chi da manco segni. Parlano ma non sonno intesi dalcuno: Ampo credo chi sia sta facto parlare in ogni lenguazo possibile: Nela terra loro non hano ferro: ma fanno cortelli de alcune pietre: & similmente ponte de freze: Et quilli anchora hanno porta de la uno pezo de spada rotta dorata laqual certo par facta in Italia: uno putto de questi haveva ale orechie dui todini de arzento, che senza dubio pareno sta facti a Venetia: ilche mi fa creder che sia terra ferma, perche non e loco, che mai piu sia andato nave, che se haveria hauto notitia de loro. Hanno grandissima copia de salmoni, Arenge, *Stochafis*, & simil pessi: Hanno etiam gran copia de legnami, & fo sopra tutto de *Pini da fare arbori & antenne de nave*, per el che questo Serenissimo Re desegna havere grandissimo utile cum dicta terra si per li legni de nave, che ne haveva debesogno como per li homini ch seranno per excellentia da fatiga, & gli meglior schiavi se habia hauti sin hora."

"They are of like colour, figure, stature, and aspect, and bear the greatest resemblance to the Gypsies; are clothed with the skins of different animals, but principally the otter; in summer the hairy side is worn outwards, but in winter the reverse; and these skins are not in any way sewed together or fashioned to the body, but just as they come from the animal are wrapped about the shoulders and arms: over the part which modesty directs to be concealed is a covering made of the great sinews of fish. From this description they may appear mere savages, yet they are gentle and have a strong sense of shame and are better made in the arms, legs, and shoulders, than it is possible to describe. They puncture the face, like the Indians, exhibiting six, eight, or even more marks. The language they speak is not understood by any one, though every possible tongue has been tried with them. In this country there is no iron, but they make swords of a kind of stone, and point their arrows with the same material. There has been brought thence a piece of a broken sword which is gilt, and certainly came from Italy. A boy had in his ears two silver plates, which beyond question, from their appearance, were made at Venice, and this induces me to believe that the country is a Continent; for had it been an Island and visited by a vessel we should have heard of it. They have great plenty of salmon, herring, cod, and similar fish; and an abundance of timber, especially the *Pine, well adapted for masts and yards*, and hence His Serene Majesty contemplates deriving great advantage from the country, not only on account of the timber of which he has occasion, but of the inhabitants who are admirably calculated for labour, and are the best slaves I have ever seen."

When it is known from Lord Bacon (History of Henry VII.), and the earlier annalists, that the vessels which sailed with Cabot were "fraught with gross and slight wares fit for commerce with barbarous people," we can have no difficulty in deciding whither to refer the ear-rings and the fragments of the showy sword. Aside from the commercial relations of the father with his native city, such articles would naturally, at that period, have been drawn from Venice. It would be absurd to offer arguments to prove that the country further north, which Cortereal could not reach but of which he rightly conjectured he had found a continuation, was that discovered by Cabot.

An early French translation of the "Paesi, &c." appeared at Paris, without date, but usually referred by bibliographers to the year 1516. After the quaint old introductory "Sensuyt," its title is, "Le Nouveau Monde et navigations faictes par Emeric de Vespuce." It states the year 1500, instead of 1501, as the date of Pasquiligi's letter, and the 7th, instead of the 8th, October as the day on which Cortereal returned; but these errors are unimportant, as the editions in the original are unanimous, and even the fraudulent translation which remains to be noticed does not falsify the date of the letter. Dr Dibdin (Literary Companion, vol. i. p. 370, note) has fallen into a singular mistake with regard to this work, following Meusel, who was in his turn misled (Bibl. Hist. vol. iii. p. 265) by the prominence given on the title-page to the name "Emeric Vespuce." They suppose it to be a translation of another curious volume, of early date, occupied with the voyages of Americus Vespucius, and Dr Dibdin is, consequently, amazed at the "unaccountable" price given for it by Mr Heber. Its contents are precisely those of the "Paesi," the three first books being devoted to Cadamosto, &c., and the three last to various voyages and enterprises in the old and the new world. The name of Vespucius occurs only in the fifth book. The passages in *italics*, in which it follows correctly the original, are noted for the purpose of contrast hereafter with the Latin perversion. In comparing the following passages of Pasquiligi's letter (ch. cxxv. feuil. 78), with the original, it will be borne in mind that the league is of four miles.

"Le septiesme jour du dict moys d'Octobre arriva icy vne des deux caravelles de cestuy roy de Portugal; lesquelles l'an passe il avoit envoyez pour descouvrir la terre vers transmontane et en estoit capitaine Gaspard Cotrad. Et a rapporte avoir trouve, entre maistral et ponent, vne terre qui est loingtaine d'icy de cinq cens lieues. Laquelle auparavant iamais d'aucun n'avoit este congneue. Et par la coste d'icelle terre ilz allerent *environ CL lieues*, et iamais ne trouverent fin perquoy ils croyent que ce soit terre ferme laquelle est *voisine d'une aultre terre laquelle l'annee passee fut descouverte soulz la transmontane* lesquelles caravelles *ne peurent arriver jusques* la pourceque la mer estoit glacee et pleine de neige. Et la ont trouve vne multitude de tres gros fleuves; ilz disent que cest terre est *molt populee* et les maisons des habitans sont d'aucuns bois tres longs couvertes par dehors de peaulx de poisson. Ilz ont amene de ce pays la tant hommes que femmes et petis enfans huyt personnages: & dedans l'autre caravelle qui se attend d'heure en heure en vient aultre cinquante. Les gens icy sont de esgalle couleur, figure, stature, regard et semblable de egiptiens; vestus de peaulx de diverses bestes, mais principallement de louves. En l'este ilz tournent le poil par dehors et iver le contraire. Ft cestes peaulx en aulcune maniere ne sont point consues ensemble ni acoustrees, mais tout ainsi que elles sont ostees de la peau des bestes ilz les mettent tout alentour de leur espaulles et des bras. Les parties vergogneuses sont leiz avec auscunes cordes faictes des nerfz de poisson tres fortes. En facon qu'ilz semblent hommes saulvaiges. Ilz sont moult honteulx et doulx mais si bien faitz de bras et de jambes et d'espaulles qu'ils ne pourroyent estre mieulx. Leur visage est marquee en la maniere des Indiens; auscuns ont VI. marques auscuns VIII. et que plus moins. Ils parlent ma ilz ne sont entendus d'aulcuns et croy qu'il leur a este parle de tous langaiges qu'il est possible de parler. En leur pays il n'est point de fer, mais le cousteaulx sont d'aulcunes pierres, et semblablement leurs poinctes de leurs flesches; et ceulx des d'caravelles ont encores apporte d'icelle terre une piece d'espee rompue que estoit doree laquelle certainement semble avoir este faicte en Italie; un petit enfant de ces gens la avoit dedans les oreilles certaines pieces d'argent lesquelles sans doute sembloyent estre faiz a Venise laquelle chose me fait croire que ce soit terre ferme parceque ce n'est pas lieu que iamais plr y ayt este aulcunes navires car il eust este notice d'elles—Ilz ont tres grande habondance de saulmons harens, stoquefies et semblables poissons. Ilz ont aussi grande habondance de bois; & surtoutes de *Pins pour faire arbres et matz de navires* parquoy ce roy a delibere de avoir grant profit de la terre a cause des bois pour faire des navires car il en avait grant besoign et aussi des hommes lesquils seront par excellence de grant peine et les meilleurs esclaves qu'on saiche jusques a ceste heure."

The French translation, it will be seen, calls the Gypsies *Egyptians*, of which the English word is a corruption. They are styled Ægyptians in the Statute 22 Henry VIII. cap. x. but the designation of the Venetian Ambassador is that by which they were universally known in Italy. In the Dissertation of Grellman on this singular race, he remarks (chap. i.),

"The name of *Zigeuner* has extended itself farther than any other; these people are so called not only in all Germany,

Italy and Hungary (tzigany),* but frequently in Transilvania, Wallacia, and Moldavia (ciganis). Moreover the Turks and other Eastern Nations have no other than this name for them (tschingenes)."

The characteristics of the race are stated by Swinburne (Travels through Spain, p. 230)—

"Their men are tall, well-built, and swarthy, with a bad scowling eye, and a kind of favourite lock of hair left to grow down before their ears, which rather increases the gloominess of their features; their women are nimble, and supple-jointed; when young they are generally handsome, with very fine black eyes; when old they become the worst-favoured hags in nature."

It is remarkable that the early settlers in New-England were struck with the resemblance. Purchas (vol. iv. p. 1842) has "a Relation or Journal of a Plantation settled at Plimouth in New-England and proceedings thereof: Printed 1622, and here abbreviated." At p. 1849, we find in the month of March, the following entry:—

"Saturday in the morning we dismissed the savage and gave him a knife, and bracelet, and a ring; he promised within a night or two to come again and to bring with him some of the Massasoyts our neighbours with such beaver skins as they had, to truck with us. Saturday and Sunday reasonable fair days. On this day came again the Savage and brought with him five other tall proper men; they had every man a deer's skin on him, and the principal of them had a wild cat's skin or such like on one arm, &c. *They are of complexion like our English Gypsies, &c.*"

On the same page it is stated, that an Englishman named Hunt had practised the same infamous deception as Cortereal:

"These people are ill affected towards the English by reason of one Hunt, a master of a Ship who deceived the people and got them under color of trucking with them twenty out of this very place where we inhabit, and seven men from the Nausites and carried them away and sold them for slaves, like a wretched man (for twenty pounds a man) that care not what mischief he do them for his profit."

The passage in the Letter of the Venetian Ambassador answers, incidentally, an important purpose. A doubt has been suggested by Thomasius, Griselini, and the English geographer Salmon, whether Munster and Spelman do not err

---

* Is not here the original of *zany?*

in naming 1417, instead of 1517, as the era at which the gypsies made their appearance in Europe, and important references are connected with the rectification of the supposed mistake.

The Encyclopædia Britannica (Edinburgh Edition of 1812), under the title "Gypsies" remarks—

> "Munster, it is true, who is followed and relied upon by Spelman, fixes the time of their first appearance to the year 1417, but as he owns that the first whom he ever saw were in 1529, it is probably *an error of the press for* 1517, especially as other historians inform us that when Sultan Selim conquered Egypt in the year 1517 several of the Nations refused to submit to the Turkish yoke and revolted under *Zinganeus*, whence the Turks call them Zinganees."

The same suggestion is found in The London Cyclopædia. It must disappear, with its train of conjectures, before this Letter, written in 1501, which assumes the characteristics of the race to be so familiarly known as even to furnish a convenient illustration and save the necessity of a particular description. To those who hold the Hindostan origin of this people, and have been struck with the admirable Memoir of Captain Richardson in the Seventh volume of The Asiatic Researches, this item of evidence will be deeply interesting.

CHAP. IV.

THE REGION VISITED BY CORTEREAL—STATEMENTS OF THE THREE PORTUGUESE HISTORIANS, DAMIANO GOES, OSORIUS, AND GALVANO—OF GOMARA, HERRERA, AND FUMEE—EDITION OF PTOLEMY PUBLISHED AT BASLE 1540—THE NAME "LABRADOR," *i. e.* "LABORER."

The inquiry now arises as to the point at which Cortereal reached the American Continent, and followed the coast northwards for a space of between six and seven hundred miles.

Damiano Goes, a writer of the highest credit, the contemporary of Emanuel, and historiographer of Portugal, says (Chronica del Rey D. Manoel, cap. lxvi.), that it was—

"A region which on account of its great freshness, and the vast groves of trees all along the coast, he called Greenland" (terra que por ser muito fresca et de grandes arvoredos como o sam todas as que jazem per a quella banda lhe pos nome Terra Verde).

Another Portuguese writer, *Osorius* (De rebus Emanuelis, &c. lib. ii.) says, that Cortereal conferred the name on account of the singular amenity of the region ("ad terram tandem pervenit quam propter singularem amœnitatem *Viridem* appellavit").

There is a third writer of that country, Galvano, of whom a translation by Hakluyt appeared in 1601. He says (p. 35),

"In the year 1500, it is reported that Gasper Cortereal craved a general license of the King Emanuel, to discover *the New Foundland.* He went from the Island Terceira with two ships well appointed at his own cost, and he sailed into that climate which standeth under the North in 50 degrees of latitude, which is a land now called after his name, and he came home in safety unto the city of Lisbon."

It is abundantly clear that Cortereal began his career to the southward of the St Lawrence; and he may have reached the Gulf, and perhaps the southern extremity of Labrador.

Gomara, who, as we have seen, limits Cabot to 58 degrees,

says of Cortereal (ch. 37),—"Dexo su nombre a las ylas que estan a la boca del Golfo Quadrado y en mas de 50 grados," a passage translated by Richard Eden (Decades, fol. 318), "he named the Quadrado after his name, Cortesreales, lyinge in the L degrees and more."

Herrera, who conducts Cabot to 68, says of Cortereal (Dec. i. lib. vi. ch. 16), "No hico mas que dexar su nombre a las Islas que estan a la boca del Golfo Quadrado en mas de 50 grados." ("He did nothing more than give his name to the islands which are in the mouth of the Gulph Quadrado in upwards of 50 degrees.") *Fumee* (Histoire Generale des Indes, ch. xxxvii. fol. 48) makes the same statement.

In the edition of Ptolemy, published at Basle in 1540, the first of the Maps is entitled "Typus Orbis Universalis," on which is seen in the extreme North of the New World, "Terra Nova sive de Bacalhos," and below it, to the southward, is an island designated "Corterati," with a great stream in its rear, evidently intended for the St Lawrence and thus characterised "Per hoc fretum iter patet ad Molucas."

There can be no difficulty in understanding why the region whence it was supposed the fifty-seven unfortunate natives so well adapted for *Labour* had been stolen had received its present name. It was talked of as the *Slave Coast* of America, and the commercial designation which thus entered into the speculations of adventurers seems to have quickly supplanted the appellation conferred on it by Cortereal. A similar triumph of the vocabulary of the mart is found at the same period, and amongst the same people, in the case of *Brazil*. Barros (Decade i. lib. v. chap. 2) is indignant that the name of Santa-Cruz, given by Cabral should have yielded to one adopted "by the vulgar," from the wood which constituted, at first, its great export. So, in most of the old works, we find the Asiatic possessions of Portugal, designated as the *Spice* Islands, &c. It cannot be doubted that the objects of Cortereal's second voyage were Timber and Slaves. Twenty years before, there had been erected on the shores of Africa the Fort of D'Elmina, to follow up the suggestion of Alonzo Gonzales pointing out the southern Africans as articles of commerce. We readily comprehend, then, the exultation with which a new region was heard of, where the inhabitants seemed to be of a gentle temper, and of physical powers such as to excite the admiration of the Venetian Ambassador. That Cortereal on the subsequent visit fell a sacrifice to the just exasperation of the people whose friends and relatives—men, women, and children—he had perfidiously carried off, is very probable, and the shores of America were thus saved from witnessing all the horrors that have marked the accursed traffic in the other hemisphere.

The impressions made on the natives, of dread and detestation, seem not to have been speedily effaced. *Verrazani*, twenty-two years afterwards, passed along the coast from Florida to the latitude of 50 degrees, and it is curious to follow his narrative in connexion with our knowledge of Cortereal's base conduct, and its probable consequences to himself, and the brother who went to seek him. Verrazani speaks, in warm terms, of the kind and cordial reception he every where experienced in the first part of his route, and in the latitude of 41° 40′ he remained for a considerable time (see his Narrative in Ramusio, tom. iii. fol. 420). As he proceeds further North, we recognise the coincidence of his description of the country with that of Cortereal.

"Piena di foltissime selve; gli alberi dellequali erano abeti, cipressi et simili chi si generano in regioni fredde" ("full of thick woods, consisting of fir, cypress, and other similar trees of cold countries"). And so of the dress of the inhabitants, "Vestono di pelli d'orso et lupi cervieri et marini et d'altri animali" ("they clothe themselves with the skins of the bear, the lucerne, the seal, and other animals"). He is struck with the change of character, "Le genti tutte sons difformi dall' altre et quanto i passati erano d'apparenza gentili tanto questi erano di rozzezza et vitii pleni" ("the people differ entirely from the others, and in proportion as those before visited were apparently gentle, so were these full of rudeness and malevolence"). With vehement cries they forbade him to land ("continuamente gridando che alla terra non ci approssimassimo"), and a party which went on shore was assailed with the war-whoop and a flight of arrows ("et quando scendevamo al lito ci tiravano con li loro archi mettendo grandissimi gridi").

CHAP. V.

CIRCUMSTANCES WHICH HAVE LED TO ERRORS AS TO THE VOYAGE OF CORTEREAL—THE PORTUGUESE MAPS—ISLE OF DEMONS—THE FRAUD OF MADRIGANON IN THE "ITINERARIUM PORTUGALLENSIUM"—MR BARROW'S CHRONOLOGICAL HISTORY OF VOYAGES, &C.—DR LARDNER'S CYCLOPÆDIA—THE EDINBURGH CABINET LIBRARY.

HAVING determined the extent of Cortereal's progress to the North, it is time to advert to the circumstances which have conspired to pervert the history of his voyage.

There is yet extant a letter from Robert Thorne of Bristol, addressed from Seville, as early as the year 1527, to the English Ambassador, Doctor Ley (Hakluyt, vol. i. p. 214), in which he sends to the ambassador "a little Mappe or Carde of the World," with a great many curious remarks. It is here that he speaks of his father as one of those who had set forth the expedition of England, and of the happy consequences, "if the mariners would then have been ruled and followed their pilot's mind" (p. 219). Adverting to the controversy pending between Portugal and Spain, he declares that the islands in dispute belong to Spain, "as appeareth by the most part of all the Cardes by the Portingals, *save those which they have falsified of late purposely*" (p. 218). After speaking of the possessions of Spain in the new world, he says, "which maine land or coast goeth northwards, and finisheth in *the land that we found* which is *called here* Terra de Labrador" (p. 216).

Thus a quarter of a century before the time of Ramusio, and half a century before that of Ortelius, we find the map-makers of the country most renowned for nautical skill, and the sciences connected with it detected in falsification as national interest, or vanity, might prompt. It appears, further, that in the very quarter to which attention is now directed there had been, already, an invasion of the English pretensions so well concerted as to give currency to the spurious appellation, even among the rivals of the Portuguese, though it excited the indignation of Thorne who was old enough to remember all about the voyages of discovery set forth from his native city.

Another source of the absurdities which deform the early maps of this region, is found in that love of the marvellous and the terrible which, in all ages, has delighted to people remote and unknown countries with monsters and prodigies. The first discoveries of the Portuguese gave a new direction to vulgar wonder, and the exaggerations and falsehoods which ministered to it; and amongst other fictions it was pretended that there existed an island, the peculiar residence of Demons and fatal to all who approached it. No Map could venture to refuse this tribute to popular credulity, and, accordingly, in the celebrated edition of Ptolemy, published at Ulme in 1483, we find the "Insula Demonum" occupying a place in the *Sexta Tabula Asiæ*.

Just as these regions were becoming so well known, as rather to bring discredit on such tales, the New World was discovered, and abundant scope allowed to the fancy, particularly in the North, without much peril of detection. A difficulty seems to have been experienced at first in selecting a judicious site for the interesting emigrants. The island, saved from the wreck of their fortunes in the old world, is bandied about in all directions by Cosmographers with little regard to that good old saying which, without recommending unnecessary commerce with the Evil One, yet makes it a point of honesty to give him his due in unavoidable transactions. Ortelius, on whose map the "Insula Dæmonum" figures with St Brandon, Frisland, and all the other silly, or fraudulent fabrications of that day, places it not very far from Hudson's Strait. Ramusio, in his text, would give it a local habitation about half way between that Strait and Newfoundland, but in constructing the map which accompanies his third volume, he seems to have thought a great Gulf a much fitter place, and it, therefore, occupies a conspicuous station in the "Golfo Quadrado," or St Lawrence. It is about five times as large as Newfoundland, from which it is divided by a narrow strait. On it demons are seen, as well flying as on foot, with nothing to protect them from a climate so little suited to their former habits but a pair of wings and a ridiculously short tail; yet they are made, poor devils, to appear happy and even sportive.

It is time, however, to turn from this, comparatively harmless, foolery to the deliberate fraud, already adverted to, on the part of *Madriganon*, in his pretended translation of the "Paesi, &c." into Latin, in a book entitled "Itinerarium Portugallensium," published at Milan in 1508 (cap. cxxvi. fol. lxxx.).

"Ut igitur nova anni præsentis intelligatis scitote hic esse eam triremem quam superiore anno Rex Portugalliæ Serenissimus expediverat versus Aquilonem præfecto Gaspare Corterato qui nobis refert continentem invenisse distantem ad M. duo milia inter Chorum et Favonium hactenus toti *pene* orbi incompertam terram; cujus latus aiunt *ad milliaria prope DCCC* percurrisse, nec tamen finis compertus est quispiam; ideo credunt Continentem non Insulam esse, regioque videtur esse *conjuncta cuidam plagæ alias a Nostris peragratæ* quasi sub ipso Septentrione eousque celox tamen non pervenit ob congelatum æquor et ingruentes cælo nives. Argumento sunt tot flumina quæ ab illis montibus derivantur quod videlicet ibi magna vis nivium existat: arguunt propterea insulam non posse tot flumina emittere: Aiunt præterea *terram esse eximie cultam.* Domos subeunt ligneas quas cooperiunt pellibus ac coriis piscium: Huc adduxerunt viros septem sexus utriusque. In celoce vero altera quam præstolamur in horas advehuntur quinquaginta ejus regionis incolæ. Hi si proceritatem corporis, si colorem, si habitudinem, si habitum spectes cinganis non sunt absimiles. Pellibus piscium vestiunt et lutrarum et eorum imprimis qui instar vulpium pillosas habent pelles; eisque utuntur hieme pilo ad carnes verso ut nos; at æstate ritu contrario; neque eas consuunt aut concinant quovis modo, verum uti fert ipsa bellua eo modo utuntur, eis armos et brachia præcipue tegunt; inguina vero fune ligant multiplici, confecto ex piscium nervis. Videntur propterea silvestres homines, non sunt tamen inverecundi et corpora habent habilissima si brachia, si armos, si crura respexeris, ad simetriam sunt omnia. Faciem stigmate compungunt inuruntque notis multiiugis instar indorum, sex vel acto stigmatibus prout libuerit; hunc morem sola voluptas moderatur: Loquuntur quidem sed haud intelliguntur, licet adhibiti fuerint fere omnium linguarum interpretes: Eorum plaga caret prorsus ferro; gladios tamen habent sed ex acuminato lapide. Pari modo cuspidant sagittas *quæ nostris sunt acuminatiores:* Nostri inde attulerunt ensis confracti partem inauratam; quæ Italiæ ritu sabrifacta videbatur: Quidam puer illic duos orbes argenteos auribus appensos circumferebat qui haud dubie cœlati more nostro visebantur: *cælaturam Venetam imprimis præseferentes;* quibus rebus non difficulter adducimur Continentem esse potius quam Insulam, quia si eo naves aliquando applicuissent de ea comperti aliquid habuissemus. Piscibus scatet regio salmonibus videlicet et alecibus [*Stockfish* omitted, probably from scantiness of vocabulary] et id genus compluribus. Silvas habent omnifariam perinde ut omni lignorum genere abundet regio: *propterea naves fabricantur antennas et malos, transtra et reliqua quæ pertinent ad navigia:* ob id hic *Noster* Rex instituit inde multum emolumenti sumere: tum ob ligna frequentia pluribus rebus haud inepta, tum vel maxime ob hominum genus Laboribus *assuetum:* quibus ad varia eis uti quibit, *quandoquidem suapte natura hi viri nati sunt ad Labores* suntque meliora mancipia quam unquam viderim."

The principal perversions are noted in *italics*. Instead of "a region discovered last year," we have "a region *formerly* visited by *our countrymen*." The distance sailed along the coast becomes almost *eight* hundred miles. There is created amongst the natives a *preference* of Venetian manufactures. This region "very populous" according to the original, is converted into one "admirably cultivated," and instead of the Pine, &c. well suited for the spars of vessels, we have the natives actually engaged in ship building! The captives "adapted" to labour become "habituated" to it, and at length "born" to it; and in speaking of the king of Portugal, the ambassador is made to call him "our King." And this is a professed translation, by an ecclesiastic, dedicated to a high public functionary!

In order to comprehend fully the extensive influence which this fraud has exercised on the modern accounts of Cortereal's voyage, it will be necessary to advert briefly to a subsequent piece of imposture of which more will be said in another place

In the year 1558, there was published, at Venice, a little volume containing the adventures of two brothers, Nicholas and Antonio Zeno, in which an effort is made to show that they were acquainted with the New World long before the time of Columbus. It is not necessary to give more of the story at present, than that these persons, about the year 1380, were in an island somewhere in the Atlantic, designated as Frisland. They there conversed with a fisherman, who, twenty-six years before, had been carried by a tempest far to the westward, and been cast ashore, with a few companions, on a place called *Estotiland*, plainly designed, by the framer of the story, for the Northern Coast of America. After remaining a number of years in this country, the fisherman, with the aid of his transatlantic friends, *built a vessel* and recrossed the ocean to Frisland. The editor of the work gives the following digest of the information gathered as to the inhabitants of this newly-discovered region—"It is credible that in *time past* they have had *traffic with our men*, for he said that *he saw Latin books in the king's library.*" Again, "*They sow corn* and make beer and ale," &c. &c. An expedition was fitted out by the Prince of the Island, and sailed towards the west, but returned, as it would appear, without having reached Estotiland, so that the only visiter was the fisherman driven off his station and cast away there one hundred and forty-seven years, by computation, before the time of Cortereal's voyage.

It will be seen that the story, promulgated in 1558, is so framed as exactly to fall in with the perversion by the Itinerarium, half a century before, as to the probable intercourse with Venetians—the cultivation of the soil by the natives—and their building vessels fit to navigate the ocean. The only difference is, that the Itinerarium merely makes the supposed traffic precede generally the visit of Cortereal, but the author of the Zeni voyages carries it back beyond the disaster to the fisherman which must have occurred about the year 1354.

We are now prepared for the following passages from Mr Barrow, and another more recent writer. The parts enclosed in parenthesis appear as *Notes* in the works quoted.

"In the first collection of voyages which is known to have been published in Europe, and printed in Vicenza, by Francazano Montaboldo, (Mundo Nuovo e Paesi nuovamente retrovati, &c. Vicenza, 1507; a very rare book; translated into Latin, by Madrigano, under the title of 'Itinerarium Portugalensium e Lusitania in Indiam, &c.') there is inserted a letter from Pedro Pascoal, ambassador from the republic of Venice to the court of Lisbon, addressed to his brother in Italy, and dated 29th October, 1501, in which he details the voyage of Cortereal, as told by himself on his return.

"From this authority, it appears that having employed nearly a year in this voyage, he had discovered between West and North West, a Continent until then unknown to the rest of the world, that he had run along the coast *upwards* of *eight* hundred miles; that according to his conjecture this land lay *near a region formerly approached by the Venetians Nicholo and Antonio Zeno! almost at the North Pole!* and that he was unable to proceed farther on account of the great mountains of ice which encumbered the sea, and the continued snows which fell from the sky. He further relates that Cortereal brought fifty-seven of the natives in his vessel—he extols the country on account of the timber which it produces, the abundance of fish upon its coasts, and the inhabitants being robust and laborious." (Barrow, Chronological History, p. 40, 41.)

"From his own account it appears that having employed nearly a year in this voyage, he had discovered between West and North-West, a Continent till then unknown to the rest of the world; that he ran along the coast *upwards* of *eight* hundred miles; that according to his conjecture this land lay *near a region formerly approached by the Venetians* (*an allusion to the voyages of the Zeni*), *and almost at the North Pole*, and that he was unable to proceed further, &c." (Dr Lardner's Cyclopædia, Hist. of Maritime and Inland Discovery, vol. ii. p. 139.)

Our criticism on this epitome of errors is confined to the original wrong-doer. Not only does Mr Barrow fall an unresisting victim to the treachery of the monk, but, such is the influence of bad company, he himself is found taking, in his turn, rather dishonest liberties with his own guide. In the original, Cortereal is said to have passed along between six and seven hundred miles of the newly discovered coast without reaching its termination. Madrignanon stretches out the distance to *almost eight* hundred, while Mr Barrow insists on "*upwards*" of eight hundred. For all this, too, he vouches the wretched monk, whereas *his* audacity, as we have seen, did not *quite* enable him to reach the point over which the Secretary of the Admiralty, with the gathered impetus of so rapid a progress, takes a fearless leap.

In happy ignorance of the host of authorities which fix conclusively the limit of the voyage, this gentleman evinces an amiable anxiety to frame an apology for one of Cortereal's countrymen whose statement he found in Hakluyt's translation:

"Galvano places it, although with little accuracy, in 50°; *misprinted probably for 60° which would be correct!*" (Barrow, p. 39.)

We have forborne, as has been said, to press a censure of the writer in Dr Lardner's Cyclopædia, because he is merely a pitiable martyr to faith in his predecessor; but another work, published on the 1st of October last, does not merit the same forbearance, as it sets at equal defiance the genuine and the spurious authorities. The reference is to the "Narrative of Discovery and Adventure in the Polar Seas and Regions,

&c.; by Professor Leslie, Professor Jameson, and Hugh Murray, Esqre. F.R.S.E." forming vol. i. of the Edinburgh Cabinet Library. By this work it appears (p. 158) that Cortereal, "*immediately upon the discovery of the Western World*, resolved to follow *in the steps of Columbus*." We are informed further (ib.), "Respecting the details of this voyage, *there remain only detached shreds which Mr Barrow has collected with equal learning and diligence!*" The character of a work put forth under such auspices, may be gathered from the following passage (p. 159)—

"The natives are correctly described as of *small stature*—a simple and laborious race; and no less than fifty-seven being allured or carried on board were conveyed to Portugal. After a run along this coast estimated at 800 miles Cortereal came to a region *which appeared to some* (!) *as lying almost beneath the Pole*, and *similar* to that formerly reached by Nicolo and Antonio Zeno! Ramusio more explicitly states, &c. &c."

All the rest is in a similar strain. Only one part of the passage quoted calls for particular remark,—that as to the stature of the inhabitants. The writer is evidently anxious to give a sanction to his own absurd hypothesis that the natives whose wonderful symmetry and aptitude for labour extorted the admiration of the Venetian Ambassador—whose "goodly corporature" is specially mentioned by Richard Eden (Decades, 318)—were the Esquimaux of Labrador. Now, without relying on the circumstances already stated, we mention one fact. *Ramusio*, whose name is here invoked, devotes to the voyage of Cortereal about half a page, and expressly declares that the inhabitants were *large* and well proportioned, "gli habitanti sono huomini *grandi*, ben proportionati."

CHAP. VI.

DIFFUSIVE MISCHIEF OF THE ITINERARIUM PORTUGALLENSIUM—GRYNÆUS —MEUSEL—FLEURIEU—HUMBOLDT, &c.

THE perversion by Madrignanon has passed into the earliest and most esteemed Collections of Voyages and Travels, and thus exercised a mischievous influence on more recent works.

In the *Novus Orbis* of Grynæus published at Basle, in 1532, the Letter of Pasquiligi is given (p. 138) according to the version of the Itinerarium; and so in the edition of that work published in the same year at Paris (p. 121), and in the Basle Edition of 1555 (p. 99). Everywhere, indeed, we are presented with lamentable proofs of the blind confidence reposed in it, even as to other matters. Thus, the "Biographie Universelle" (art. Cadamosto) sharply rebukes Grynæus for having stated 1504, instead of 1454, as the year in which Cadamosto represents himself to have been at Venice previous to his voyage. The Itinerarium (cap. ii.) is the source of this error. The explanation does not, it is true, relieve Grynæus from censure. The mistake appears in the Basle Edition of the Novus Orbis of 1532 (page 5), in the Paris Edition of the same year (p. 3), and is not corrected in that of Basle in 1555 (p. 2).

So implicitly has Madrignanon been followed, that *Meusel* (Biblioth. Hist., original Leipsic Ed. vol. ii. part ii. p. 318) not only gives the year 1504, but finding a statement, on the same page, by Cadamosto as to his *age*, makes a calculation accordingly, and gravely informs us that the voyager must have been born in 1483—just, in fact, twenty-nine years after the expedition! Meusel finds out afterwards, in some way, that he was wrong, and throws the blame (vol. iii. p. 159, 160), like the "Biographie Universelle," on Grynæus.

Even in translating the title of that chapter of the "Paesi," ([illegible]) which contains the letter of Pasquiligi, the Itinerarium commits a blunder, that has been, in the same manner, perpetuated. In the original it runs thus: "Copia de una Lettera de Domino Pietro Pasqualigo Oratore della Illustrissima Signoria in Portugallo scripta (a soi fratelli) in Lisbona adj. xix. Octobrio, &c." The words indicating the address we have placed within a parenthesis, in order to mark, with more distinctness, the manner in which it is plain they must be read and understood. The place, as well as the time, mentioned are parts of the date of the letter, for Pasquiligi is obviously conveying intelligence from Lisbon, where Corte-real had arrived, to his brothers in Italy. Not attending to a matter so obvious, the Itinerarium (fol. lxxix.) represents the personages *addressed* as residing in Lisbon, "ad germanos suos *in Ulisbona commorantes!*" This absurdity also is copied into the *Novus Orbis* (Basle Ed. of 1532, p. 138; Paris Ed. same year, p. 121; and the Basle Ed. of 1555, p. 99).

Such, then, is the unhappy fate of a modern reader. By the writers who minister to his instruction it is deemed a wonderful effort to go back to the *Novus Orbis* of 1555. To consult the earlier editions of 1532 would be considered quite an affectation of research. Yet on reaching that distant point, it is plain we cannot read a single line without a distressing uncertainty whether it may not merely reflect the dishonesty, or ignorance, of an intermediate translator, instead of the meaning of the original work.

The question how far the author of the "Paesi" was indebted to previous publications, now finally lost, for part of his materials, particularly as to the first four books, is one of much curiosity, and with regard to which a great deal has been said by many learned critics who had plainly never examined any one of its pages; but the inquiry would here be irrelevant, as it is not pretended that the Letter of Pasquiligi and the others addressed to persons in Italy, given in Book Sixth, had ever before appeared in print. The remarks prepared on that point are, therefore, withheld, as they would unwarrantably swell a part of the subject which has already expanded beyond its due proportion.

The name *Labrador* or *Laborer*, connected with the perversion by the Itinerarium of "very populous" into "admirably cultivated," has led to a singular medley of errors in all the accounts of Cortereal's voyage. It would require a volume to exhibit them, but a reference to a few of the more recent writers will show how completely all the sources of information within their reach had been poisoned. Thus *M. Fleurieu*, in his Introduction to the *Voyage de Marchand* (tom. i. p. 5), says:—

"En 1500 ou 1501 Gaspar de Cortereal, Portugais, homme de naissance partit de Lisbone, arriva a Terre Neuve, en visita la cote orientale, se presenta á l'embouchure du fleuve Saint Laurent, decouvrit au-dessus du cinquantieme Parallile une Terre *qu'il nomma* de Labrador *parce qu'il* la *jugea propre au labourage et a la culture*, parvint, enfin, remontant vers le Nord á l'entreé d'un Detroit auquel il imposa le nom de Detroit d'Anian et qui plus de cent ans aprés fut appellé Detroit de *Hudson*,* &c."

It is to be regretted that Baron Humboldt (Essai Politique sur le Royaume de la Nouvelle Espagne, Lib. iii. ch. viii.) should have hastily given an incidental sanction to a passage replete with errors of every description.

Mr Barrow, with that wary caution which is generally the result of long official training, does not dwell on this perplexing point, but others have rushed in where he dared not tread:

"That part of it which being on this side of the 50th degree of N. latitude he thought was still *fit for tillage and cultivation* he named Terra de Labrador" (Forster, p. 450). "He arrived at Conception Bay in Newfoundland, explored the East Coast of that Island, and afterwards discovered the River St Lawrence. To the *next* country which he discovered *he gave* the name of Labrador, *because* from its latitude and appearance it seemed to him *better fitted for culture than his other discoveries in this part of America.*" (Kerr's Collection of Voyages, &c. vol. xviii. p. 354.) "He appears first to have reached Newfoundland, whence pushing to the North he came to that great range of Coast to which *from some very superficial observation* he gave the name of Labrador or the Laborers Coast" (Historical Account of Discoveries and Travels in North America, &c. by Hugh Murray, Esq. vol. i. p. 69).

Mr Barrow must have a further hearing (p. 41).

"To this evidence may also be added that of Ramusio, whose accuracy in such

---

* So the Biographie Universelle (art. Cortereal), "Ce detroit auquel il donna le nom d'Anian a recu depuis celui *d'Hudson*."

matters is well known. The following extract is taken from his discourse on Terra [illegible] and the Oriental Islands;—'In the part of the New World which runs to the North West, opposite to our habitable Continent [illegible] have sailed, the *first* of whom, as far as can be ascertained, was Gaspar Cortereal, a Portugueze, who arrived there in the year 1500 with two Caravels, thinking that he might discover some strait through which he might pass by a shorter voyage than round Africa, to the Spice Islands. *They* prosecuted their voyage in those seas until they arrived at a region of extreme cold; and in the latitude of 60° North they discovered a river filled with *Ice* [such is Mr Barrow's translation of Ramusio's word *neve*], to which they gave the name of Rio Nevado,—that is, *Snow* River. They had not courage however to proceed farther, all the coast which runs from Rio Nevado to Porto das Malvas (Mallow Port), which lies in 56° and which is a space of two hundred leagues, &c. &c.' "

The claims of Ramusio (who has merely put into words the representation of the Portuguese maps) to extraordinary accuracy, may be judged of by the assertion made at the outset of the foregoing Extract. He states Cortereal to be the first of whom he had heard as penetrating into this Northern region; yet *on the very same page* which thus conducts that navigator to 60° he represents Cabot to have advanced to 67°, and in the previous volume he had fixed the date of the latter enterprise as even earlier than the truth will warrant. Thus he is convicted of the plainest inconsistency, without drawing to our aid the fact just established, from the earliest and best authority, that Cortereal was defeated in an effort to reach that very Northern Region which had been discovered the year before.

The force of the other proofs establishing the discrepance between Ramusio's account and that of the Venetian Ambassador, is obscured by Mr Barrow's method of presenting the subject. He quotes, at first, as will be seen on referring to his volume, just enough to exhibit a progress, in seeming coincidence with Pasquiligi's Letter, and then turns to other matters. He does not revert to Ramusio until the reader's attention is diverted from the measurement of distances, which occurs as the first test, and even in the end he suppresses a part of Ramusio's statement on that subject. The limited distance is exhausted, as we see, between 60° and 56°, and here then would seem to be that region which Cortereal, on account of its amenity and smiling groves, denominated Greenland. But Mr Barrow's theory, and all the authorities, require that Cortereal should visit the River St Lawrence. Whatever scepticism may exist as to his having penetrated into Hudson's Bay, no doubt can

"occur in regard to the St Lawrence. Even without specific evidence, it might safely have been concluded; that as a passage to India was the grand object of research, so large an opening as is presented by the mouth of this river could not have escaped examination. Independent, however, of this general reasoning, the evidence furnished by Ramusio is decisive. In describing the principal places on that coast, he says, that beyond Capo de Gabo (Cattle Cape), which is in 54°, it runs two hundred leagues to the Westward, to a great river called St Lawrence, which some considered to be an arm of the sea, and which the Portuguese ascended to the distance of many leagues." (Barrow, p. 43.)

Thus we find the distance between 56° and 54° entirely thrown out of view, and yet there remains a computation of four hundred *leagues* of coast examined by Cortereal, viz., two hundred from Rio Nevado to 56°, and two hundred more from 54° to the St Lawrence. To meet this demand we have in the original only between six and seven hundred *miles*, increased by Madrignanon to *almost* eight hundred!

The river laden with snow (carico de Neve), and hence called *Rio Nevado*, is, doubtless, the St Lawrence, if indeed the name and the circumstances be not mere fiction. Mr Barrow, however, considers it to be Hudson's Strait, and finds a probability in "all the collateral circumstances of the Narrative," that the Portuguese on this occasion "actually *entered* Hudson's *Bay*" (p. 42). Now it will surely be considered rather singular that a person familiar with the miniature streams of Portugal, should thus misapply epithets, even if we suppose him to have erroneously regarded the Strait as terminating in itself, and as thus forming a great Bay or Gulf; yet Mr Barrow is persuaded that Cortereal called the Strait *Snow River*, after he had ascertained it to be neither River, Bay nor Gulf, but a mere medium of communication between different parts of the ocean!

On the map of Ortelius the Northern Coast of America is studded with Portuguese names. The Letter of Thorne furnishes a satisfactory clew to this nomenclature. The fidelity of the representation of Hudson's Bay is too striking to have been the result of chance. Having, then, negatived the possibility that Cortereal could have penetrated into it, we revert, with perfect confidence, to the belief that Cabot's Map, which the geographer expressly states to have been before him, must have been made use of. No difficulty remains if we suppose that Ortelius was anxious to employ all his materials, so as not to appear behind the knowledge of his time, and that having adopted the configuration of the English Navigator he affixed, conjecturally, the names found in profusion on the maps got up at Lisbon.

However this may have been, we quit the voyage of Cortereal with the certainty that he claimed for it neither originality of purpose nor success of execution, but admitted, on the contrary, that he had completely failed in an effort to reach the point attained by his predecessor.

CHAP. VII.

PROJECT OF CORTES IN 1524.

A CONSIDERABLE interval now occurs without any materials for the present review; and the second Expedition of Cabot from England, in 1517, has already been considered at large.

Proceeding to the year 1524 we reach the project of the celebrated Cortes, of which the history is, fortunately, much less involved than that of Cortereal. As it was attended, indeed, with no interesting results, even a passing notice would be superfluous were it not that the spirit of misrepresentation has here also been perversely active and successful.

We must be indebted again to Mr Barrow, whose work, indeed, is invaluable in reference to our present task, as it not only embodies, in a cheap and convenient form, all the mistakes of its predecessors, but generally supplies a good deal of curious original error:

"Cortez, the conqueror and viceroy of Mexico, had received intelligence of the attempt of Cortereal to discover a Northern passage from the Atlantic into the Pacific, and of his having entered a strait to which he gave his name. Alive to the importance of the information, he *lost not a moment* in fitting out three ships well manned, of which he is said to have taken the command in person, though nominally under the orders of Francisco Ulloa, to look out for the opening of this strait into the Pacific, and to oppose the progress of the Portuguese and other Europeans who might attempt the passage. Little is known concerning this expedition of Cortez, but that it soon returned *without meeting with Cortereal, &c.*"*

From all this the reader naturally infers, that while the eyes of Europe were turned, at that period, on Cortereal, no one had heard of the discoveries of Cabot, or at least that they were deemed of minor importance, After what has been said, in the preceding Chapter, of the subordinate and unsuccessful

* Barrow's Chronological History of Voyages, p. 54.

character of the Portuguese enterprise, it will no doubt be thought extraordinary that such an erroneous estimate should have been made at that early day. There is no difficulty in clearing the matter up from the very letter of Cortes himself, in which he apprises the Emperor of his views on the subject. The letter, dated 16th of October, 1524, will be found in Barcia's Historiadores Primitivos, tom. i. p. 151, and is faithfully rendered by Ramusio (vol. iii. fol. 294). After expressing great zeal for the service of the Emperor, he remarks that it seemed to him no other enterprise remained by which to manifest his devotion than to examine the region between the river Panuco (in Mexico) and Florida recently discovered by the Adelantado Ponce de Leon, and also the *Coast of the said Florida towards the North until it reaches the Baccalaos*, holding it for certain that along this coast is a strait conducting to the South Sea ("descubrir entre el Rio de Panuco i la *Florida,* que es lo que descubrio el Adelantado Juan Ponce de Leon, i de alli *la Costa de la dicha Florida por la parte del Norte hasta llegar a los Bacallaos;* porque se tiene cierto que en aquella costa ai estrecho que pasa a la Mar del Sur"). He states as a part of his plan that certain vessels in the Pacific should sail concurrently along the western coast of America, while the others, "as I have said, proceed up to the point of junction with the Baccalaos, so that on the one side or the other we cannot fail to ascertain this secret" ("como he dicho *hasta la juntar con los Bacallaos;* asi por una parte i por otra no se deja de saber el secreto").

The reader can now judge of Mr Barrow's correctness. The Viceroy "receives intelligence of the attempt of Cortereal;" of his having "entered a strait" which Mr Barrow pronounces Hudson's Strait, and "loses not a moment" in endeavouring to follow up that alarming success, when it appears that in point of fact the interval thus measured by a "moment" was at least twenty-three years, and the proposed survey of Cortes from Florida point expressly stops short at the Baccalaos. There is not the slightest reason for supposing that Cortes had ever heard of Cortereal's voyage which amounted, as we have seen, to an unsuccessful effort, at first, to tread in the steps of Cabot, and was afterwards turned into a mere kidnapping speculation. But it is material to remark that Cortes has no other designation for the region in the North than that which Peter Martyr, in his Decades, published eight years before, had stated to have been conferred on it by Cabot.

We will not fatigue and disgust the reader by quoting from other writers passages having the same tendency to obscure the just fame of the English Navigator.

CHAP. VIII.

VOYAGE OF STEPHEN GOMEZ IN THE SERVICE OF SPAIN.

THE expedition next in order, in point of time, is that of Stephen Gomez, fitted out by order of the Emperor Charles V. There is a very slight and unsatisfactory notice of it in *Purchas* who, instead of resorting to the original sources of information which are many and copious, contents himself with referring to a small tract by *Gaspar Ens*, published at Cologne in 1612. It would be ungenerous to treat this obscure writer with harshness, for he very modestly states that the accounts at large being in foreign languages or in bulky volumes ("peregrinis linguis aut magnis voluminibus"), his humble object was to prepare a brief digest of the principal heads ("quocirca operæ pretium putavi si *præcipua* variorum navigationum et descriptionum Occidentalis Indiæ *Capita* lectori communicarem"). Such is the authority on which Purchas gravely relies, and it is curious to note how completely Mr Barrow has, in consequence, been misled (p. 52).

"In point of time, however, there is *one solitary* voyage on record though the particulars of it are so little known as almost to induce a *suspicion whether* any such voyage was ever performed, which takes precedence of *any foreign voyage on the part of English Navigators* (!): it is that of a Spaniard, or rather, perhaps, judging from the name, of a Portuguese. To what part of the coast of *America or* (!) Newfoundland or Labrador he directed his course is *not at all known*. It is evident, however, that he returned without bringing back with him any hope of a passage into the Eastern Seas, having contented himself with seizing and bringing off some of the natives of the coast on which he had touched. It is said that one of his friends, accosting him on his return, inquired of him with eagerness what success he had met with and what he had brought back, to which Gomez replying shortly 'esclavos' (slaves), the friend concluded he had accomplished his purpose and brought back a cargo of (cloves). On this, says Purchas, he posted to the court to carry the first news of this spicy discovery, looking for a great reward, but the truth being known caused hereat great laughter. *Gaspar, in his History of the Indies, is the only authority for this voyage!*"

Some surprise may be felt that Mr Barrow should designate this writer in a familiar way, by his Christian name, evidently on a slight acquaintance, while his own countrymen are quoted not as "Richard" or "Samuel," but as "Hakluyt," and "Purchas." The difference of manner seems to proceed from no want of respect for the German, but from really supposing that in the reference found in Purchas to "Gasparus *Ens*. l. ii. c. xxv." the marked word probably alluded, in some quaint way, to the contents of the book, and made no part of the name. But aside from this singular misconception, the whole scope of the Secretary's remarks betrays a more comprehensive ignorance of the subject than could have been thought possible. Nothing can be more erroneous than to say, that "Gaspar" is the only writer who speaks of this voyage. There is, on the contrary, not a single author of reputation on the history of the New World who does not give an account of it, and of those who wrote *prior to* 1612 we may particularly mention *Peter Martyr* (Decade vi. ch. x., and again Decade viii. ch. x.) *Oviedo* (Somm. de la natural y general historia, &c. ch. x.), *Ramusio* (vol. iii. fol. 52, in Index title "Stefano"), *Gomara* (ch. xl.), *De Bry* (Gr. Voy. part iv. p. 69), *Fumee* (Hist. Gen. des Indes, fol. 49), *Herrera* (Dec. iii. lib. viii. ch. viii.), the Portuguese writer, *Galvano*, translated by Hakluyt (Ed. of 1601, p. 66), *Eden* (Decades, fol. 213), and *Sir William Monson* (Naval Tracts, Book iv.)

The first named of these writers, who was himself a member of the Council of the Indies, is more than usually minute with regard to this voyage. After describing the conference at Badajos in 1524, he says, "Decretum quoque est ut Stephanus quidam Gomez artis et ipse maritimæ peritus alia tendat via qua se inquit reperturum *inter Baccalaos et Floridas* jamdiu nostras terras iter ad Cataiam" (Dec. vi. ch. x.).*

* "It is decreed that one Stephanus Gomez (who also himself is a skilful navigator) shall go another way, whereby, *betweene the Baccalaos and Florida*, long since our countries, he saith he will finde out a waye to Cataia" (M. Lok's translation, London, 1612, fol. 246).

He then proceeds to describe the equipment, and the Instructions given by the Council. In the 8th Decade, ch. x. we have an account of the return of Gomez—of the country visited by him—and of his having, in violation of the standing orders on that subject, forcibly brought off some of the inhabitants ("contra leges a nobis dictatas ne quis ulli gentium vim afferat"). The jest arising out of the mistake of the word "esclavos" for "clavos" is not forgotten. All this is faithfully rendered in Lok's translation (fol. 317). In *Oviedo* (Sommario, ch. x. fo. xiv.), we have the report made to the Emperor on the return of Gomez:—

"Despues que V. M. esta en esta cibdad de Toledo llego a qui en el mes de Noviembre el Piloto Estevan Gomez el qual en el anno passado de Mil y quinientos y veynte y quatro par mandado de V. M. fue ala parte del Norte y hallo mucha tierra *continuada con la que se llama de los Baccalaos* discurriendo al occidente et pues *en XL. grados y XLI.* y assi algo mas y algo menos de donde traxo algunos Indios y los ay de llos al presente enesta cibdad los quales son de mayor estatura quel los de la tierra firma segun lo que dellos paresce comun y porque el dicho piloto dize que vido muchos de llos y que son assi todos: la colores assi como los de tierra firma, y son grandes frecheros y andan cubiertos de cueros de venados y otros animales y ay en aquella tierra excellentes martas, zebellinas y otros ricos enforros y d'stas pieles truxo algunas el dicho Poloto, &c."

This passage is copied from the edition of *Oviedo* in The Library of the British Museum, published at Toledo on the 15th February, 1526, eighty-six years before "*Gaspar's*" time. It will be found in *Ramusio* at the place indicated above, and is thus translated by Richard Eden in his "Decades" (fol. 213), published at London in 1555.

"Shortly after that Your Majestie came to the Citie of Toledo there arryved in the moneth of November Stephen Gomez the Pilot, who the yeare before, of 1524, by the commandement of Your Majestie sayled to the Northe partes and founde a greate parte of Lande *continuate from that which is called Baccalaos* discoursynge towarde the West to *the 40th and 41st degree* whense he brought certeyn Indians (for so caule wee all the nations of the new founde landes) of the which he brought sum with him from thense who are yet in Toledo at this present, and of greater stature than other of the firme lande as they are commonly. Theyr coloure is much lyke the other of the firme lande. They are great archers and go covered with the skinnes of dyvers beasts both wild and tame. In this lande are many excellent furres, as marterns, sables, and such other ryeh furres of the which the sayde Pylot brought some with him into Spayne, &c."

It is of a voyage set forth under such auspices, and the results of which are thus minutely detailed, that Mr Barrow declares "to what part of the Coast of America, *or* (!) Newfoundland, or Labrador he directed his course is not *at all* known." In vain has the Father of this portion of History given us the Decree of a Council at which he was personally present—and in vain has another Historian preserved the official report to the Emperor; Mr Barrow will have it, that "so little is known as almost to induce a *suspicion whether* any such voyage was *ever* performed." While the writers of every language in Europe are full of its details—while *Eden*, who wrote half a century before the time of Gaspar Ens, gives us, in plain English, the very degrees of latitude visited by Gomez—while an account of the voyage is supplied by Sir William Monson, with whose writings it may be considered the official *duty* of a Secretary of the Admiralty to be familiar—that gentleman insists that "the *only* authority for the voyage" is the paltry compend published in 1612! Such is the mode in which the British Public is ministered to on the History of Maritime Enterprise, and such the character of a book which Dr Dibdin pronounces, in his Library Companion, "a work *perfect* in its kind!"

Mr Barrow, it has been seen, throws out a suggestion that Gomez, from his name, was probably a native of Portugal, and finding it somewhere stated that he sailed with Magellan, appeals, in another passage of the book, to that fact with some complacency, as countenancing his shrewd conjecture. A writer on such subjects ought surely to have known that in the brief narrative which we have of Magellan's memorable, but tragic, expedition, Gomez occupies a prominent, though not very creditable place, and that both *Herrera* (Dec. ii. lib. ix. ch. xv.) and *Purchas* (vol. i. book ii. ch. ii. p. 34) expressly state him to have been a Portuguese. The "Biographie Universelle," on the other hand, not only pronounces Gomez a Spaniard, but asserts, in the mere wantonness of rounding off a sentence, that his misconduct towards Magellan is to be attributed to impatience at being placed under the command of a Portuguese (Art. *Gomes*)!

Keeping in view our leading purpose, it is proper to note,

emphatically, that in every account of this voyage distinct reference is made to the antecedent discoveries of Cabot—to the "Baccalaos" which had been rendered universally known by the work of Peter Martyr, published eight years before.

It must be evident that if the Historian just named confided in Cabot's veracity he could not have anticipated a successful result to the enterprise of Gomez, for he had described our navigator as ranging along the coast of America with the same object in view, as far south as the latitude of Gibraltar. True, he tells us at the same time, that the Spaniards were inclined to speak slightingly of Cabot (Dec. iii. c. 6), but his own language of respect, and even affection, shows that he himself cherished no disparaging suspicions, and we are, therefore, curious to know what part he took in the Council of the Indies when Gomez submitted his offer to find a passage in the very quarter which Cabot had carefully explored in vain. To the surprise of all those who have not looked closely into the subject, there will be found in the 8th Dec., c. 10, the following expressions:—

"Nunc ad Stephanum Gomez quem in calce porrecti libelli (incipientis 'Priusquam') cum una missum caravela dixi ad fretum aliud inter Floridam tellurem et *Baccalaos satis tritos* quærendum. Is nec freto neque a se promisso Cataio repertis regressus est intra mensem decimum a discessu. *Inanes hujus boni hominis fore cogitatus existimavi ego semper et præposui;* non defuere in ejus favorem suffragia."*

The good old man tells, with great glee, the jest about "esclavos," and chuckles at the momentary triumph of Cabot's enemies:—

"Ubi accessit in portum Clunium unde vela fecerat unus quidam audito navis ejus adventu et quod *esclavos* (id est servos) adveheret nil ultra vestigans citatissimo equorum cursu ad nos venit anhelo spiritu inquiens clavis et preciosis gemmis onus-

---

* "Now I come to Stephanus Gomez, who, as I have said in the ende of that Booke presented to your Holiness beginning ("Before that"), was sent with one Caravell to seeke another Straight between the land of Florida and the *Bacalaos sufficiently known and frequented.* He neither findinge the Straight nor Cataia which he promised, returned backe within tenn Monethes after his departure. *I always thought and presupposed this good man's imaginations were vayne and frivolous.* Yet wanted he no suffrages and voyces in his favour and defence" (Lok's translation, fo. 317).

tam affert navim Stephanus Gomez, opimam se habiturum strenam arbitratus est. Ad hanc hujus hominis ineptiam erecti qui rei faverent, universam obtunderunt cum ingenti applausu curiam per aphæresim dictione detruncata pro esclavis clavos esse advectos præconando (esclavos enim Hispanum idioma servos appellat et gariophyllos nuncupat clavos) postea vero quam a clavis in esclavos fabulam esse transformatam Curia cognovit cum fautorum jubilantium erubescentia risum excitavit."*

Of Gomara's account it might be superfluous to say any thing; but he was Cabot's contemporary, and the passage illustrates what has been said, in another place, as to his narrow feeling of jealousy towards that Navigator who had a few years before abandoned the service of Spain to rejoin that of his native country, and whom the King of England had refused, as we have seen, to send back on the requisition of Charles V. After stating the departure of Gomez in pursuit of the strait ("en demanda de un estrecho que se ofrecio de haller en tierra de *Baccalaos*"), his return without success, and the jest about the "esclavos," he says (c. xl.) that Gomez visited a region "que aun no estaba par otro vista; bien que dicen como Sebastian Gabato la tenia primero tanteada" ("which had never before been seen by any one, *though they say* that it was first discovered by Sebastian Cabot"). These are his churlish expressions at a moment when he has no other epithet by which to designate the country visited, but that conferred on it by the very man whose merits he strives, in this despicable temper, to depreciate!

In the "Narrative of Discovery and Adventure in the Polar Seas, &c. by Professor Leslie, Professor Jameson, and

* "And when he came into the haven of Clunia from whence he set sayle, a certayne man hearing of the arrivall of his Shippe and that hee had brought *Esclavos*, that is to say slaves, seekinge no further, came postinge unto us with pantinge and breathless spirit sayinge that Stephanus Gomez bringeth his Shippe laden with cloves and precious Stones: and thought thereby to have received some rich present or reward: They who favoured the matter, attentive to this mann's foolish and idle report, wearied the whole Court with exceedinge great applause, cutting the word by *aphæresis* proclaimynge that for *esclavos* hee hadd brought *clavos* (for the Spanish tongue calleth slaves *esclavos* and cloves *clavos*), but after the Court understoode that the tale was transformed from *clavos* to slaves they brake foorth into a great laughter to the shame and blushinge of the favourers who had shouted for joy" (Lok's translation, fol. 317).

Hugh Murray, Esq. F.R.S.E." published on the 1st October last, there is found (p. 161) the following passage:—

"Only one very early voyage (from Spain to the North) is mentioned, that namely, which was undertaken in 1524 by Gomez, with a view of discovering a shorter passage to the Moluccas. He is *said* to have brought home a few of the natives; but no record is preserved *either of the events which attended his enterprise or even of the coast on which he arrived.* There remains of it, as has been observed, only a jest, and one so indifferent as not to be worth repeating."

The writer might be excused, perhaps, for not knowing that Oviedo, in 1526, and Richard Eden, in 1555, name 40 and 41 degrees of latitude as points visited by Gomez, but what shall we say of his overlooking the following passage in a popular work, published in 1817?

"Une ancienne carte manuscrite dressee en 1529 par Diego Ribeiro, cosmographe Espagnol, a conservé le souvenir du voyage de Gomez: on y lit au dessous de l'emplacement occupé par les états de New York, de Connecticut et de Rhode-Island *Terre D'Etienne Gomez qu'il decouvrit en 1525 par l'ordre de S. M. Il y a beaucoup d'arbres, beaucoup de rodoballas, de saumons, et de soles; on n'y trouve pas d'or.*" (Biographie Universelle, tit. *Gomes.*)

The Diego Ribeiro here named had been, on 10th June, 1523, appointed Royal Cosmographer, with a large salary, and the duty committed to him of preparing charts, astrolabes, and other nautical instruments (Navarette, Introd. tom. i. p. cxxiv. note 2). The Map with a valuable memoir, published at Weimar in 1795, is in the Library of the British Museum.

CHAP. IX.

EXPEDITION FROM ENGLAND IN 1527.

ERRONEOUS STATEMENT THAT ONE OF THE VESSELS WAS NAMED "DOMINUS VOBISCUM"—THEIR NAMES THE "SAMPSON" AND "THE MARY OF GUILFORD"—LETTERS FROM THE EXPEDITION DATED AT NEWFOUNDLAND, ADDRESSED TO HENRY VIII. AND CARDINAL WOLSEY—THE ITALIAN NAVIGATOR, JUAN VERRAZANI, ACCOMPANIES THE EXPEDITION AND IS KILLED BY THE NATIVES—LOSS OF THE SAMPSON—THE MARY OF GUILFORD VISITS BRAZIL, PORTO RICO, &C.—ARRIVES IN ENGLAND, OCTOBER 1527—ROBERT THORNE OF BRISTOL—HIS LETTER COULD NOT HAVE LED TO THIS EXPEDITION.

THE Second Expedition under the auspices of Henry VIII. in 1527, to discover a North-West Passage, has not been more fortunate than the First, in 1517, in escaping perversion. The statement of Hakluyt (vol. iii. p. 129) is this:—

"Master Robert Thorne of Bristoll, a notable member and ornament of his Country, as wel for his learning as great charity to the poore, in a letter of his to King Henry the 8th and a large discourse to Doctor Leigh, his Ambassador to Charles the Emperor (which both are to be seene almost at the beginning of the first volume of this my Work) exhorted the aforesaid King, with very weighty and substantial reasons, to set forth a discovery even to the North Pole. And that it may be known that this his motion took present effect, I thought it good herewithall to put down the testimonies of two of our Chroniclers, M. Hall and M. Grafton, who both write in this sort. 'This same moneth' (say they) 'King Henry the 8th sent two faire Ships wel manned and victualled, having in them divers cunning men to seek strange regions, and so they set forth out of the Thames the 20th day of May in the 19th yeere of his raigne, which was the yeere our Lord 1527.'

"And whereas Master Hall, and Master Grafton say, that in those Ships there were divers cunning men, I have made great inquiry of such as, by their yeeres and delight in Navigation, might give me any light to know who those cunning men should be, which were the directors in the aforesaid Voyage. And it hath been tolde me by Sir Martine Frobisher, and M. Richard Allen, a Knight of the Sepulchre, that a Canon of Saint Paul in London, which was a great Mathematician, and a Man indued with wealth, did much advance the action, and went therein himselfe in person, but what his name was I cannot learne of any. And furthur they tolde that one of the ships was called the Dominus Vobiscum, which is a name likely to be given by a religious man of those dayes: and that sayling very farre North-westward, one of the Ships was cast away as it entered into a dangerous Gulph, about the great opening, betweene the North parts of Newfoundland, and the [illegible] by her Majestie, Meta Incognita. Whereupon the other ship shaping her course towards Cape [illegible], and the [illegible] oftentimes putting their men on land to search the state of those unknown regions, returned home about the beginning of October, of the yere aforesayd. And thus much (by reason of the great negligence of the writers of those times, who should have used more care in preserving of the memories of the worthy actes of our Nation) is all that hitherto I can learne or find out of this voyage."

This is copied into every History of Discovery since that period down to Mr Barrow, Dr Lardner, and the Edinburgh Cabinet Library, with the same expression of regret and indignation that no record should have been preserved of the persons and vessels employed in the enterprise.

Incredible as it may appear, after what has been said, there is found in Purchas (vol. iii. p. 809), the very Letter written by John Rut, the commander of one of the vessels engaged in this expedition, to Henry VIII. from Newfoundland, and an account of another Letter written from the same place by Albert de Prato, an Ecclesiastic, to Cardinal Wolsey. The Letter to the King thus appears in Purchas, with some obvious imperfections:—

"Pleasing your Honorable Grace to heare of your Servant John Rut, with all his company here, in good health, thanks be to God and your Graces ship, *The Mary of Guilford*, with all her [a blank in Purchas] thanks be to God; and if it please your honorable Grace, we ranne in our course to the Northward, till we came into 53 degrees, and there we found many great Ilands of Ice and deepe water, we found no sounding, and then we durst not goe no further to the Northward for feare of more Ice, and then we cast about to the Southward, and within foure dayes after we had one hundred and sixtie fathom, and then we came into 52 degrees and fell with the mayne Land, and within ten leagues of the mayne Land we met with a great Iland of Ice, and came hard by her, for it was standing in deepe water, and so went in with Cape de Bas, a good Harbor, and many small Ilands, and a great fresh River going up farre into the mayne Land, and the Mayne Land all wildernesse and mountaines and Woods, and no naturall ground, but all mosse, and no inhabitation nor no people in these parts: and in the woods we found footing of divers great beasts, but we saw none not in ten leagues. And please your Grace, *The Samson* and wee kept company all the way till within two dayes before we met with all the Ilands of Ice, that was the first day of July at night, and there rose a great and a marvailous great storme, and much foule weather; I trust in Almightie Jesu to heare good newes of her. And please your Grace, we were considering and a writing of all our order, how we would wash us and what course we would draw and when God do and foule weather that with the Cape de Sper shee should goe, and he that came first should tarry the space of sixe weeks one for another, and watered at Cape de Bas ten dayes, ordering of your Graces ship and fishing, and so departed towards the Southward to seeke our fellow: the third day of August we entered into a good Haven, called St John, and *there we found eleven saile of Normans, and one Brittaine, and two Portugall Barkes, and all a fishing*, and so we are readie to depart toward Cape de Bas, and that is twentie five leagues, as shortly we have fished, and so along the Coast till we may meete with our fellow, and so with all diligence that lyes in me toward parts *to that Ilands that we are commanded by the Grace of God as we were commanded at our departing*: and thus Jesu save and keepe your Honorable Grace, and all your honorable Rever. in the Haven of Saint John, the 3 day of August, written in haste, 1527.

"By your Servant John Rut to his uttermost of his power."

The Letter to Cardinal Wolsey from *Albert de Prato* was thus addressed:—

"Reverend. in Christo Patri Domino Cardinali et Domino Legato Angliæ." It began

"Reverendissime in Christo Pater Salutem. Reverendissime Pater, placeat Reverendissimæ paternitati vestræ scire, Deo favente postquam exivimus a Plemut quæ fuit X. Junii," &c.

Purchas says, "the substance is the same with the former, and therefore omitted." The date is "apud le Baya Saint Johan in Terris Novis die X. Augusti 1527, Revr. Patr. vest. humilis servus, Albertus de Prato."

We have here the name of the master of the vessel, and also that, it is to be presumed, of the Canon of St Paul's, and learn, further, that neither of the vessels was called the "Dominus Vobiscum," but that one was "*The Mary of Guilford*," and the other "*The Samson*." We may infer that the latter perished in the "marvellous great Storm," by which the two vessels were separated.

The direct Correspondence with the King and the Cardinal sufficiently assure us of the interest taken by these personages in the enterprise, and the commands of which Rut speaks "at our departing" as to the ultimate destination of the vessels were doubtless from the Monarch to whom the letter is addressed.

We have to state, in reference to this enterprise, a conviction that there went in it the celebrated Italian Navigator, Juan Verrazani, over whose fate a singular mystery has existed. The circumstances which seem to establish the fact are the following:—

In the year 1524, Verrazani, employed by Francis the First, coasted North America from the latitude of 34° to 50°. The account of his voyage, found in Ramusio, is dated at Dieppe, 8th July, 1524. From this period we have no distinct intelligence of him. It is said that he made a subsequent voyage, but whence or whither is unknown, for the French and Italian writers do not offer even a conjecture as to the circumstances under which it took place. That he made it in the service of France will appear improbable when we look at the history of that period.

On the 24th February 1525 the disastrous battle of Pavia was fought, and Francis was conducted a prisoner to Madrid. The deplorable condition of the country is thus described:—

> "Meanwhile France was filled with consternation. The King himself had early transmitted an account of the rout at Pavia in a letter to his Mother delivered by Pennalosa which contained only these words, 'Madam, all is lost except our Honour.' The officers who made their escape when they arrived from Italy brought such a melancholy detail of particulars as made all ranks of men sensibly feel the greatness and extent of the calamity. France *without its Sovereign, without money in her Treasury, without an Army, without Generals to command it, and encompassed on all sides by a victorious and active enemy, seemed to be on the very brink of destruction.*"*

On the 5th June, 1525, the mother of Francis appointed commissioners to seek relief from Henry VIII. (Rymer's Fœdera, vol. xiv. p. 37), and ultimately a loan was obtained of two millions of crowns (ib. p. 130). Every document of that period serves to show the utter prostration of France, and the anxiety to exhibit a sense of gratitude to England for having suddenly become from an enemy a preserver. Thus, there appears (Rymer, vol. xiv. p. 232) a document from the King of France, dated 25 September 1527, having reference to the inconvenience to which the commerce of England might be subject in Flanders in consequence of her new position, and appointing Commissioners to secure to English merchants equivalent privileges in his dominions. It closes thus:

---

* Robertson's Charles V. Book iv

"Cæteraque denique omnia et singula agere, promittere et concludere in hoc negotio suisque circumstantiis et dependentiis quibuscunque quæ nosmetipsi si præsentes agere et concludere possemus, *etiam si talia forent quæ mandatum requirerunt magis speciale*, promittentes bona fide et verbo nostro regio. Nos omnia et singula per dictos oratores et Procuratores nostros pacta promissa et conclusa impleturos et præstituros, nec ullo unquam tempore *quovis quæsito colore*, infracturos aut contraventuros sed perpetuó observaturos."

Under such circumstances it would be no matter of surprise to find the impatient Navigator turning to the same country to which his late employers had become supplicants, and tendering his services to a Monarch whose means were as abundant as his spirit was sanguine and enterprising. An expedition, then, is fitted out at this precise period under the auspices of the King and Cardinal Wolsey. If the slightest evidence could be discovered of communication with Verrazani, we would feel quite assured that the one party would be as anxious to secure his aid as the other to proffer it.

This link is supplied by Hakluyt. In that early work, of 1582, the "Divers Voyages," we find the following statement:—

"Master John Verarzanus, which had been thrice on that coast, *in an old excellent Map which he gave to Henry VIII.*, and is yet in the custodie of Master Locke, doth so lay it out as is to be seene in the Map annexed to the end of this boke being made according to Verarzanus' plot."

It is impossible to withstand a conviction that Henry while intent on this enterprise would eagerly enlist the services of such a navigator as Verrazani fortunately thrown out of employment, and so well acquainted with the American Coast, that Hakluyt, more than half a century afterwards, found his Map to exhibit the most accurate representation of it.

The rumours which remain as to the fate of this navigator must now be examined.

Ramusio (tom. iii. fol. 417) does not state in whose service the last voyage was made, though from its connexion with that of 1524 the reader might be hastily led to suppose that both were from the same country. It is needless to repeat what has been said as to the improbability that France, during a period of dismay and beggary, engaged in fitting out exploratory voyages. So soon after the peace of Cambray as she could recruit her exhausted resources, we find the well-known expedition of Cartier, in 1534. When such clear and anthentic information exists with regard to this last voyage, as well as of the previous one of 1524 under Verrazani, is it at all likely that not the slightest trace would be found of an intermediate expedition, had one been despatched? The circumstances attending the death of Verrazani, are thus given by Ramusio:—

"Et nell' ultimo viaggio che esso fece havendo voluto smontar in terra con alcuni compagni furono tutti morti da quei popoli et in presentia di coloro che erano rimasi nelle navi furono arrostiti et mangiati."*

Such was the horrible tale which Ramusio found current in Italy. It is plain, then, that the survivors who beheld the cruelties practised on the unfortunate captives must have got back in safety, and made report of the dreadful scene. Yet in the annals of no other country but England is the slightest allusion found to the departure, or return, of any such expedition.

There will now be perceived the importance of having settled on a former occasion,† that *Oviedo*, in his history of the West Indies, represents the visit of an English ship at Porto Rico, &c., to have occurred, not in 1517, but in 1527. It was then shown that Herrera, in subsequently stating the same transaction, had given in greater detail the testimony of Gines Navarro, the Captain of the Caravel, who had immediately gone off to the English ship. Let us now turn again to Navarro's statement:—

"They said that they were Englishmen, and that the ship was from England, and that she and her consort had been equipped to go and seek the land of the Great Cham, that they had been separated in a tempest, and that the ship pursuing her course had been in a frozen sea and found great islands of ice, and that taking

---

* "In the last voyage which he made, having gone on shore with some companions, they were all killed by the natives, and roasted and eaten in the sight of those who remained on board."

† See page 112.

a different course they came into a warm sea which boiled like water in a kettle, and lest it might open the seams of the vessel, they proceeded to examine the Baccalaos where they found fifty sail of vessels, Spanish, French, and Portuguese, engaged in fishing, that going on shore to communicate with the natives, *the Pilot, a native of Piedmont, was killed;* that they proceeded afterwards along the coast to the river Chicora, and crossed over thence to the Island of St John. Asking them what they sought in these islands, they said, that they wished to explore in order to make report to the King of England; and to procure a load of the Brazil wood."*

Comparing this with the letter of Rut, is it necessary to enforce the coincidence in the year—the sailing of the two ships from England—the separation by tempest—the struggle with the ice in the North—the return to Baccalaos—the vessels found there engaged in fishing?

Mark too the death of the Italian pilot, under circumstances which correspond so well with the sad tale reported to the friends of Verrazani and recorded by Ramusio!

It was probably the death of Verrazani, and despair of being rejoined by the Sampson, that induced Rut, the main object being frustrated, to seek the only market which remained for the merchandise with which the Mary of Guilford was freighted.

Navarro says, that the English spoke of having proceeded along the coast as far South as the River of *Chicora.* Now, in describing the movements of the expedition to Florida under Ayllon, in 1523, Peter Martyr (Dec. vii. ch. ii.) says, "'They affirm that these provinces lie under the same parallel of latitude with Andalusia in Spain! They thoroughly examined

* Dixeron que eran Ingleses, i que la nao era de Inglaterra, i que aquella i otra se avian armado, para ir á buscar la Tierra del gran Cán, i que un temporal las havia apartado: i que siguiendo esta nao su viage dieron en un mar elado, i que hallaban grandes Islas de ielo: i que tomando otra derrota, dieron en otra mar caliente, que hervia como el agua en una caldera; i porque no se les derritasse la brea, fueron á reconocer á los Bacallos, adonde hallaron cinquenta Naos Castellanas Francesas, i Portuguesas, pescando, i que alli quisieron salir en tierra, para tomar lengua de los Indios, i les *mataron al Piloto, que era Piamontes* i que desde alli avian costeado hasta el Rio de Chicora, i que desde este Rio atravesaron a la Isla de san Juan; i preguntando les le que buscaban en aquellas Islas, dixeron, que las querian ver, para dar relacion al Rei de Inglaterra i cargar de Brasil (Herrera, Dec. ii. lib. v. cap. iii.).

the principal countries, *Chicora* and Duhare." Peter Martyr supposes these regions to "join the Baccalaos discovered by Cabotus from England." Amongst the provinces connected with the two first described, he (ib.) expressly mentions *Arambe,* and when we find Frobisher stating to Hakluyt (3 Hakl. 129) a tradition that the surviving ship of the Expedition of 1527, after the disaster in the North, "shaped her course towards Cape Breton and the Coasts of *Arambec,*" we find a degree of harmony pervading these unconnected accounts that is truly surprising.

It would be too much, however, to expect a minute accuracy in every particular of Navarro's report as to what he heard on board the English ship. An error is probably committed by misplacing one of the incidents. The alarm about the opening of the seams of the vessel from extreme heat, which appears so absurd as referred to the North, becomes quite intelligible, when we recollect that the English are represented by Oviedo to have attempted to run down the coast of Brazil. The effect produced on the Mary of Guilford was, doubtless, the same as that experienced during the third voyage of Columbus, in 1498, when precisely the same apprehension are represented to have seized his crew.

The name of Robert Thorne is associated by Hakluyt and subsequent writers with this Expedition, but evidently without due consideration. Thorne, a native of Bristol, was a merchant-tailor of London,* who went to Spain and is said, without further particulars as to date, to have addressed the letter found in Hakluyt to Henry VIII. from Seville "*in* 1527." As the Expedition left the Thames on the 20th May, 1527, it is plainly absurd to suppose that a letter written during that year could have been forwarded—its suggestions considered and adopted—the course resolved on—the commanders selected—vessels suitable for such an enterprise prepared—and all the arrangements completed so as to admit of this early departure. Nor is there any evidence that the letter

* Stow's Survey of London ; Fuller's Worthies.

in question was ever forwarded. It was handed to Hakluyt, as he states in his work of 1582, by Cyprian Lucar, a son of Thorne's executor. No doubt Verrazani proceeded to England immediately on discovering that in the confused and exhausted state of France he had no chance of employment; and not more than sufficient time would thus be allowed for maturing all the necessary arrangements. Aside from the enterprising temper of Henry VIII., Verrazani was, perhaps, in some measure indebted for success in his application to the mood of Wolsey, whose resentment at the supposed treachery of Charles V. as to the election of a Pope had at this time passed into the politics of England. The Cardinal's zeal on behalf of the Expedition may have been quickened by knowing how much its success would startle and annoy the Emperor. We have already seen, in considering the voyage of 1517 with which this has been confounded, what alarm was created by intelligence of the visit of the Mary of Guilford to the Islands. The Emperor was struck with the inconveniences likely to result,* and gave strict orders to seize and make an example of any future intruders.

The abrupt termination of the enterprise prevents our being able to trace distinctly the influence on it of Cabot's previous voyages. Verrazani, in 1524, did not get further North than 50°, and so far as the Mary of Guilford advanced beyond that point we see only an effort to reach Hudson's Strait. It would be absurd to suppose that the King who is found possessed of Verrazani's more limited map had not before him the bolder one of Cabot. In addition to "the Card" which Lord Bacon speaks of as having been exhibited by Cabot, the history of the more recent voyage of 1517 must have been perfectly well known. Thorne speaks familiarly to Henry VIII. of the discoveries made on that occasion by "your Grace's subjects," and the very mariners employed ten years before would of course be sought for and engaged anew.†

* "Los inconvenientes que podria haver de la navigacion de esta Nacion a los Indias." Herrera, Dec. ii. lib. v. c. iii.

† See Appendix (E.).

A future part of the subject will be understood more readily by noting here, that Frobisher was aware of the course taken on this occasion and of the loss of one of the ships in "a dangerous gulf between the North parts of Newfoundland and the country lately called by her Majesty Meta Incognita."

It is impossible to turn from this Expedition without adverting, in terms of indignation, to those who, instead of looking into the evidence which strikingly evinces the earnest and continued exertions of Henry VIII. in reference to this project, prefer the easier task of stringing together such paragraphs as the following:—

"Neither was the turbulent, voluptuous, proud, and cruel disposition of Henry VIII. any great encouragement to men of abilities and enterprise to undertake voyages of discovery, and thereby expose themselves to the king's fickle and tyrannical temper in case of miscarriage."*

"But it is more difficult to discover what prevented this scheme of Henry VII. from being resumed during the reigns of his son and grandson, and to give any reason why no attempt was made either to explore the Northern Continent of America more fully, or to settle in it. Henry VIII. was frequently at open enmity with Spain: the value of the Spanish acquisitions in America had become so well known, as might have excited his desire to obtain some footing in those opulent regions; and during a considerable part of his reign, the prohibitions in a papal bull would not have restrained him from making encroachments upon the Spanish dominions. But *the reign of Henry was not favourable to the progress of discovery.* During one period of it, the active part which he took in the affairs of the Continent, and the vigour with which he engaged in the contest between the two mighty rivals, Charles V. and Francis I. gave *full occupation* to the enterprising spirit both of the King and his Nobility. During another period of his administration, his famous controversy with the Court of Rome kept the nation in perpetual agitation and suspense: *engrossed by those objects,* neither the King nor the Nobles had *inclination or leisure to turn their attention to new pursuits;* and without their patronage and aid, the commercial part of the nation was too inconsiderable to make any effort of consequence."†

"That prince, (Henry VIII.) full of bustle, needy of money, and not devoid of intelligence, might have been supposed rather prompt to embark in such enterprises: but involved in so many disputes, domestic and theological, and studying, though with little skill, to hold the balance between the two great continental rivals, Charles and Francis, he was *insensible to the glory and advantages to be derived from Maritime Expeditions.*"‡

* Forster, Northern Voyages, p. 268.

† Dr Robertson's America, book ix.

‡ Edinburgh Cabinet Library (vol. i. p. 98), by Professors Leslie and Jameson, and Hugh Murray, Esq.

CHAP. X.

VOYAGE FROM ENGLAND IN 1536.

It has been thought unnecessary to speak in detail of the Expedition of Verrazani in 1524, or of that of Cartier in 1534, as they did not advance beyond the points which former Navigators had rendered quite familiar. Of a subsequent voyage from England, in 1536, our information, derived altogether from Hakluyt, is quite meagre, but there was evidently contemplated a more adventurous range of search. The scheme originated with "one Master Hore of London, a man of goodly stature and of great courage, and given to studie of cosmography."* Amongst the company, it is stated, were "*many gentlemen of the Inns of Court, and of the Chancerie.*" One of the persons particularly spoken of, is "M. Rastall, Sergeant Rastall's brother," a name familiar in the Law, from the well-known "Entries" of the brother here alluded to. After a tedious passage, the gentlemen reached Cape Breton and proceeded Northward, but seem to have made little progress when they were arrested by famine, which became so pinching that one individual killed his companion "while he stooped to take up a root for his relief,"† and having appeased the pangs of hunger, hid the body for his own future use. It being ascertained that he had somewhere a concealed store of animal food, he was reproached for his base selfishness, "and this matter growing to cruel *speeches*,"‡ he stated plainly what he had done. The Chief of the Expedition was greatly shocked at this horrible discovery, "and made a notable oration, containing how much these dealings offended the Almightie, and vouched the Scrip-

* Hakluyt, vol. iii. p. 129. † Ibid. vol. iii. p. 130. ‡ Ib.

tures from first to last what God had in cases of distresse done for them that called upon Him, and told them that the power of the Almighty was then no lesse than in all former time it had bene. And added, that if it had not pleased God to have holpen them in that distresse, that it had bene better to have perished in body, and to have lived everlastingly, than to have relieved for a poore time their mortal bodyes, and to be condemned everlastingly both body and soul to the unquenchable fire of hell."* But in vain did this good man, who was not himself of the Profession, entreat his associates to combat the unhappy tendency to prey on their fellow-creatures; and they were about to cast lots to ascertain who should be killed, when a French vessel unexpectedly arrived "well furnished with vittaile." Notwithstanding the amity of the two nations, it was decided, in the multitude of Counsellors, to consult their own safety at the expense of the new comers. The case being one of plain necessity, they resolved to act on the familiar maxim which permits the law to slumber in such emergencies, and to get possession of the French vessel, viewing it, doubtless, if any argument was had, in the light of the *tabula in naufragio* spoken of in the books.

The thing would seem to have been managed with fair words and characteristic adroitness. Hakluyt got his information from Mr Thomas Buts, of Norfolk, whom he rode two hundred miles to see, "as being the only man now alive that was in this discoverie." Buts must have been very young at the time of the Expedition—probably in London as a student of law or articled to an attorney—and it can hardly be supposed that he was trusted with a prominent part at this interesting crisis, when there were on board men of the experience of Rastall and the others. Yet there was evidently a touch of vain-glory about his narrative to Hakluyt—something of the "pars fui"—and the old man, though long retired from business, kindled up at the reminiscence: "Such was the *policie* of the English that they became masters of the same, and

* Hakluyt, vol. iii. p. 130.

changing Ships and vittailing them they set sayle to come into England!"* The despoiled Frenchmen followed these harpies of the law, and made complaint to Henry VIII.

"The King causing the matter to be examined and finding the great distresse of his subjects, and the causes of the dealing with the French, was so moved with pitie that he punished not his subjects, but of his own purse made full and royal recompense unto the French."†

It had been stated at the outset that the adventurers were "assisted by the King's favour and good countenance," which, with his subsequent clemency and generosity, may furnish a suitable answer to the silly tirade of Forster.

* Hakluyt, vol. iii. p. 131.

† Ib.

CHAP. XI.

EXPEDITION OF CORTEREAL IN 1574, AND RETROSPECT TO A PRETENDED VOYAGE BY A PERSON OF THE SAME NAME IN 1464.

THE long interval between the voyage of 1536 and that of Frobisher supplies nothing worthy of particular notice. One incident, however, may be glanced at, because it is probably connected with a misconception as to a pretended expedition of much earlier date.

In the work of Hakluyt published in 1582, we find the following passage:—

"A verie late and great probabilitie of a passage by the North-West part of America in 58 degrees of Northerly latitude. An excellent learned Man of Portugal of singular gravety, authoritie and experience tolde me very lately that one *Anus Cortereal Captayne of the yle of Tercera* about the yeare 1574 which is not above *eight years past* sent a shippe to discover the North West Passage of America and that the same shippe arriving on the Coast of the said America in fiftie eyghte degrees of Latitude found a great entrance exceeding deepe without all impediment of ice, into which they passed above twentie leagues and found it alwaies to trende towards the South the lande lying low and plain on either side. And that they persuaded themselves verily that there was a way open into the South Sea. But their victuals fayling them and they beeing but one Shippe they returned backe agayne with joy."

Nothing further is heard on the subject.

One of the idlest of the numerous efforts to detract from the fame of those who led the way in the career of discovery, is the assertion that Newfoundland was discovered by a person named Cortereal as early as 1464, twenty-eight years before the enterprise of Columbus. The following passage on the subject is found in Mr Barrow's Chronological History of Voyages (p. 37).

"The first Navigator of the name of Cortereal, who engaged in this enterprise, was John Vaz Costa Cortereal, a Gentleman of the Household of the Infanta Don Fernando—who, accompanied by Alvaro Martens Hornea, explored the northern seas, by order of King Alfonso the Fifth, and discovered the *Terra de Baccalhaos* (the land of Cod Fish) afterwards called Newfoundland.

"This voyage is mentioned by Cordeiro, (Historia Insulana Cordeiro 1 vol. fol.) but he does not state the exact date, which however is ascertained to have been in 1463 or 1464; for on their return from the discovery of Newfoundland, or Terra Nova, they touched at the Island of Terceira, the Captaincy of which Island having become vacant by the death of Jacome Bruges, they solicited the appointment, and in *reward for their services* the request was granted, their patent commission being dated in Evora, 2nd April 1464.

"Notwithstanding this early date of a voyage across the Atlantic, there exists no document to prove that any thing further was done by the Portuguese, in the way of discovery, till towards the close of the fifteenth century; and if the evidence of that in question rested on this single testimony of Cordeiro, and on the fact of the Patent, it would scarcely be considered as sufficiently strong to deprive Cabotas of the honour of being the first who discovered Newfoundland; at the same time *if the Patent should* specify the service for which it was granted, *and that service is stated to be the discovery of Newfoundland*, the evidence would *go far* in favour of the elder Cortereal."

Supposing, for a moment, the statement here made to be correct, it must doubtless be received with astonishment. In all the eager controversies between Spain and Portugal, growing out of the discovery of America by the former power, not the slightest reference is made to this antecedent voyage, although we are apprised, by the letter of Thorne, of a resort even to the falsification of maps. Is it possible that Portugal, during the most stirring period of her history, would not attempt to follow up a discovery which was yet deemed worthy of a signal reward? The younger Cortereal, moreover, we have seen, speaks of the country visited by him in 1501 as before altogether unknown, and of that lying further north as discovered only the year before. Would such language have been used by him, or endured by his countrymen, if he had merely revisited a region discovered thirty-seven years before by a member of the same family?

We have in the work of the Portuguese writer Galvano, translated by Hakluyt, a minute and copious History of Maritime Discovery, in which, though the voyage of Gaspar Cortereal is particularly described, not the slightest allusion is found to this earlier enterprise.

It will probably be considered, also, rather remarkable that when Columbus, twenty years after this discovery, submitted to the Court of Portugal his project for seeking land in the West, it was referred to a learned Junto, who pronounced it extravagant and visionary, and that on appeal to the Council this decision was affirmed. To remove all doubt a Caravel was secretly sent to sea, provided with the instructions of Columbus, and her return, not long after, without success, was considered to establish, conclusively, the impracticable character of the scheme.

But it happens that Mr Barrow, in putting forth the statement, has not looked even into the work which he professes to cite as his authority. The volume of Cordeyro was published in 1717, and is entitled "Historia Insulana das Ilhas a Portugal sugeytas no Oceano Occidental." Of it, and of its author so little is known that his name does not find a place even in the Biographie Universelle. A greater part is occupied with adulation of some of the principal families of the different islands; yet there is supplied the very Document at full length, to whose possible language Mr Barrow hypothetically attaches so much importance. A copy of the work is found in the Library of the British Museum. The Commission of Cortereal, as Governor of Terceira, bears date (p. 246), Evora, 12 April, 1464, and in the consideration recited for the grant not the slightest reference is made to any such discovery.*

Thus does the evidence in support of this preposterous claim disappear. The whole story had probably its origin in some confused tradition which reached Cordeyro as to the voyage of 1574. Yet mark how Error, "like to an entered tide, rushes by and leaves" even Mr Barrow hindmost

"There seems little reason to doubt that a Portuguese navigator had discovered Newfoundland *long before the time of Cabot*. John Vaz Casta Cortereal, a gentleman of the Royal Household, had explored the Northern Seas by order of Alphonso

---

* "E considerando en de outra parte os servicos que Joao Vas Cortereal, fidalgo da casa do dito Senhor meu filho, tem feyto ao Infante meu Senhor seu padre que Deos haja, & depois a mim & a elle, confiando em a sua bondade, & lealdade, & vendo a sua disposicao, a qual he para poder servir o dito Senhor & manter seu direyto, & justica, em galardao dos ditos servicos lhe fiz merce de Capitania da Ilha Terceyra."

the V. about the year 1463, and discovered the *Terra de Baccalhaos* or land of Cod-fish, afterwards called Newfoundland."*

As authority for these assertions, Mr Barrow is cited! Again:

"This house was that of Cortereal: for a member of which, John Vaz Cortereal, claims are advanced as having discovered Newfoundland *nearly a century* (!) before the celebrated voyages of Columbus or Cabot."†

---

* Dr Lardner's Cyclopædia, History of Maritime and Inland discovery, vol. ii. p. 138.

† Edinburgh Cabinet Library, by Professors Leslie and Jameson, and Hugh Murray, Esq. vol. i. p. 158.

CHAP. XII.

SIR MARTIN FROBISHER.

To exhibit a just estimate of the merits of this navigator, is one of the gravest portions of the duty that remains to be performed. There will here be found, probably, the most striking proof yet presented of injustice to the fame of Sebastian Cabot.

Had Frobisher seen the tract of Sir Humphrey Gilbert? The question may not, perhaps, be deemed one of essential importance, when we know that Ramusio, twenty-two years before, had furnished a statement, which it is impossible to misunderstand, of the course pursued, and of the point attained, by Cabot, and that there was suspended in the Queen's Gallery the Map, exhibiting his discoveries, referred to in that tract. Yet the evidence happens to be so singularly conclusive as to invite the inquiry.

A doubt, indeed, on the subject has arisen only from the conduct of Hakluyt, who in giving a place to the work of Sir Humphrey Gilbert has suppressed the very curious and interesting explanation of its history; and, owing to the blind confidence in that compiler, no one has since thought of going beyond his volumes. There is, fortunately, a copy of the original publication in the Library of the British Museum (title in catalogue *Gilbert*).

The tract was published on the 12 April 1576, and is preceded by an Address to the reader from *George Gascoigne*, who thus explains the manner in which it came into his possession:

"Now it happened that myself being one (amongst many) beholden to the said Sir Humphrey Gilbert for sundry courtesies, did come to visit him in the winter last past, at his house in Limehouse, and being very bold to demand of him, how he spent his time in this loitering vacation from martial stratagems, he courteously took me into his study, and there shewed me sundry profitable and very commendable exercises which he had perfected painfully with his own pen, and amongst the rest this present discovery. The which, as well because it was not long, *as also*, because I understood *that M. Forboiser, a kinsman of mine, did pretend to travel in the same discovery*, I craved it at the said Sir Humphrey's hand for two or three days."

Gascoigne retained possession of the tract, and subsequently published it.

Frobisher (or Forboiser as he is more commonly called in the old accounts) sailed from Gravesend, on his first voyage, 12 June, 1576. We thus find that the tract was obtained by a kinsman, for his use, the preceding winter, and that it even appeared in print two months before Frobisher left the Thames. The following is an extract from it (Hakluyt, vol. iii. p. 16).

"Sebastian Cabota by his *personal experience* and travel hath *set forth and described this passage* in his Charts, which are yet to be seen in the Queen's Majesty's Privy Gallery at Whitehall, who was sent to make this discovery by King Henry VII. and *entered the same fret*: affirming that he sailed very far westward with a quarter of the North on the North side of Terra de Labrador the 11th of June. until he came to the Septentrional latitude of 67° and-a-half, and finding the sea still open said, that he might and would have gone to Cataia if the mutiny of the master and mariners had not been."

There is another tract in Hakluyt (vol. iii. p. 24) already referred to, entitled "Certain other reasons or arguments to prove a passage by the North-West, learnedly written by *Mr Richard Willes*, Gentleman." Here, also, a perilous discretion has been exercised in the way of curtailment. The Essay appeared originally in a new edition of Richard Eden's Decades, published by Willes, in 1577.* The tract is addressed to the Countess of Warwick whose husband was the patron of Frobisher, and is headed "For M. Captayne Frobisher, passage by the North-West" (fol. 230). That Willes had been solicited to prepare it is apparent from the conclusion (fol. 236).

"Thus much, Right Honorable, my very good Lady, of your question concerning your servant's voyage. If not so skilfully as I would, and was desirous fully to do, at the least as I could and leisure suffered me, for the little knowledge God

---

* "The History of Travayle in the West and East Indies, &c. by Richard Eden. Newly set in order, augmented and finished by Richarde Willes. London, 1577."

hath lent me, if it be any at all, in cosmography and philosophy, and the small experience I have in travaile. Chosing rather in the clear judgment of your honourable mind to appear rude and ignorant, and so to be seene unto the multitude, than to be found unthankful and careless in anything your Honour should commande me. God preserve your Honor. At the Court the 20 of March, your Honor's most humbly at commandment *Richard Willes.*"

This Tract was prepared after the first voyage of Frobisher, and reference is made in it to a document now lost, viz., the Chart drawn by Frobisher to exhibit the course he had pursued. The account given by Willes of Cabot's description of the Strait corresponds with that supplied by Sir Humphrey Gilbert, but it is, as has been shown on a former occasion, more explicit.

"Cabota was not only a Skilful Seaman but a long travailer, and such a one as *entered personally* that *Strait* sent by King Henry VII. to make the aforesaid discovery, as in his own Discourse of Navigation you may read in his Card drawn with his own hand; the mouth of the North-Western Strait lieth near the 318 meridian [60° W. Long. from Greenwich] between 61 and 64° in elevation continuing the same breadth about ten degrees West where it openeth Southerly more and more" (fol. 233).

That Frobisher was considered as having done nothing more, on his first voyage, than to act on the suggestions of Cabot, *and as far as he went to confirm them,* may be inferred from another passage. It was plain that he had not penetrated to the extent mentioned by Cabot, yet he had followed the instructions as to the quarter where the Strait was to be found, and his partial success inspired a hope that he might, in a second attempt, urge his way through. That this was the extent of the merit claimed for the recent voyage is plain from the language which Willes addresses to a lady whose influence had been mainly instrumental in setting it forth. After representing the Strait to be "betwixt the 61st and 64th degrees North," he adds, "So left by our countryman Sebastian Cabote in his Table, the which my good Lord your father [The Earl of Bedford] hath at Cheynies and *so tried* this last year by your Honor's Servant as he reported and his Card and Compass do witness" (fol. 232).

The very history of the voyages themselves is stripped by Hakluyt of the evidence they furnish as to a knowledge of

Cabot's previous enterprise. Thus we have (vol. iii. p. 47) the account of three voyages "penned by Master George Best, a gentleman employed in the same voyage," and find (p. 60) that this gentleman was the Lieutenant of the Admiral's ship. There is a copy in the King's Library (title in catalogue *Frobisher*) of his work as originally published in 1578; and prefixed to it is a long and interesting Dedication to Sir Christopher Hatton, of which no part is found in Hakluyt. Amongst other things he says, "And Sebastian Cabote being an Englishman and born in Brystowe, after he had discovered sundry parts of Newfoundland and attempted the passage to Cataya by the North-West for the King of England, for lack of entertainment here (notwithstanding his good desert) was forced to seek to the King of Spain."

There was another work published during the same year, entitled "A Prayse and Reporte of Master Martin Forbaisher's voyage to Meta Incognita by Thomas Churchyard" (Library of British Museum, title in catalogue *Churchyard*), in which the writer says, "Gabotha was the first in King Henry VII.'s days that discovered this frozen land, or Seas *from Sixty-seven towards the North*, and from thence towards the South along the Coast of America to 36° and-a-half, &c. But this Gabotha's labor *robs no piece of prayse from Master Forboisher*, for Gabotha made *but a simple rehearsal* of such a soil, but Master Forboisher makes a perfect proof of the *mines* and *profit* of the country." It is curious to note, thus early, a disposition on the part of Frobisher's admirers to cast into the shade the enterprise of Cabot. The claim put forth to superior merit—sufficiently idle in itself—must have appeared utterly ridiculous after the worthlessness of the ore had been ascertained, and it seems to have been subsequently thought safer to waive any allusion whatever to him who had gloriously led the way in the career of discovery.

Thus, then, we have the most conclusive evidence of a knowledge of what Cabot had done, and of its direct influence on Frobisher's enterprise. Let us now see what the latter actually accomplished.

The *First* Expedition left Gravesend, as has been said, on the 12th June, 1576. No interest attaches to its movements until the 11th of August, at which point we take up the narrative of the Master of the Gabriel, Christopher Hall (Hakluyt, vol. iii. p. 30)—

"The 11 we found our Latitude to be 63 degr. and 8 minutes, and this day we entered THE STREIGHT.

"The 12 wee set saile towardes an Island, called the *Gabriel's* Island, which was 10 leagues then from us.

"We espied a Sound, and bare with it, and came to a Sandie Baye where we came to an anker, the land bearing East-South-east off us, and there we rode at night in 8 fathome water. It floweth there at the South-east Moone. We called at *Prior's* sownd, being from *Gabriel's* Island, tenne leagues.

"The 14 we waied, and ranne into another sownd, where we ankered in 8 fathome water, faire sande and black oaze, and there calked our ship, being weake from the wales upward and took in fresh water.

"The 15 day we waied, and sailed to *Prior's* Bay, being a mile from thence.

"The 16 day was calme and rode still without yce, but presently within two houres it was frozen round about the ship, a quarter of an ynch thicke and that day very faire and calme.

"The 17 day we waied, and came to *Thomas Williams* Island.

"The 18 day we sailed North North West, and ankered again in 23 fathome, and tough oaze, vnder *Burchers* Island, which is from the former Island, ten leagues.

"The 19 day in the morning, being calme, and no winde, the Captaine and I tooke our boate, with eight men in her, to row us ashore, to see if there were there any people, or no, and going to the top of the Island, we had sight of seven boates, which came rowing from the East side, toward that Island: whereupon we returned aboored againe: at length we sent our boate with five men in her, to see whither they rowed, and so with a white cloth brought one of their boates with their men along the shoare, rowing after our boate, till such time as they sawe our Ship, and then they rowed ashoare: then I went on shoare myself, and gave every of them a threadden point, and brought one of them aboored of me, where he did eate and drinke, and then carried him ashore againe. Whereupon all the rest came aboored with their boates, being nineteen persons, and they spake, but we understoode them not. They be like to Tartars, with long blacke haire, broad faces, and flatte noses, and tawnie in color, wearing seale skins, and so doe the women, not differing in the fashion, but the women are marked in the face with blewe streekes downe the cheekes, and round about the eyes. Their boates are made all of seales skinnes, with a keele of wood within the skin: the proportion of them is like a Spanish Shallop, save only they be flat in the bottome, and sharpe at both ends.

"The twentieth day we waied, and went to the East side of this Island, and I and the Captaine, with foure men more went on shoare, and there we sawe their houses, and the people espying vs, came rowing towards our boate: whereupon we plied toward our boate; and wee being in our boate and they ashore, they called to us, and we rowed to them, and one of their company came into our boate, and we carried him aboard, and gave him a Bell and a knife: so the Captaine and I willed five of our men to set him a shoare at a rocke, and not among the company, which they came from, but their wilfulness was such, that they would goe to them, and so were taken themselves, and our boate lost.

"The next day in the morning, we stoode in neere the shoare, and shotte off a fanconet, and sounded our Trumpet, but we could heare nothing of our men: this Sound we called the Five Men Sound, and plyed out of it, but ankered againe in thirtie fathome, and oaze, and riding there all night, in the morning, the snowe lay a foote thicke upon our hatches.

"The 22 day in the morning we wayed, and went againe to the place where we lost our men, and our boate. We had sight of fourteen boates, and some came neere to us, but we could learne nothing of our men: among the rest, we enticed, one boate to our ships side, with a Bell, and in giving him the Bell, we tooke him, and his boate, and so kept him, and so rowed down to *Thomas Williams* Island, and there ankered all night.

"The 26 day we waied, to *come homeward* and by 12 of the clocke at noone, we were thwart of *Trumpets Island.*"

Such was the result of Frobisher's *Only* Voyage, having in view the discovery of a North-West Passage!

It is seen, at once, that he got entangled with the land by keeping, at the outset, too far North. Cabot had said, that the Strait was between the 61st and 64th degree of latitude; and Ramusio tells us, from the navigator's Letter, and Sir Humphrey Gilbert and Lord Bacon from his card, that the course he took was "very far *Westward, with a quarter of the North on the North side of Terra de Labrador.*" Frobisher's reasons for disregarding facts which *must* have been known to him, can only be conjectured. One motive may have been a puerile ambition to strike out a new route. We learn from Best, (Hakluyt, vol. iii. p. 58) "This place he named after his name, *Frobisher's Strait,* like as Magellanus at the South-West end of the World, having discovered the passage to the South Sea, and called the same Straits Magellan's Straits." A more indulgent explanation is suggested by recollecting the account which he gave (Hakluyt, vol. iii. p. 129) of the fate of one of the English ships engaged in the attempt at discovery in 1527. Frobisher understood that the vessel had been "cast away as it entered into a *dangerous gulf* about the *great opening* between the *North parts of Newfoundland* and the country lately called by her Majesty Meta Incognita." (Ib.) It is not improbable that he may have been induced by a dread of the fate of his predecessor absurdly to commence his examination on the very verge of the limit fixed by Cabot, without the least reference to the course pursued by that Navigator which had conducted him from 61° at the commencement of the Strait to 64° at its termination. The precise extent to which Frobisher threaded his way amongst rocks and islands is not given by Hall, but is stated by Best, (Hakluyt, p. 58) at fifty leagues, and again (p. 59) at sixty leagues.

The *Second* Voyage was prompted by mere cupidity. The incident which stimulated the hopes of the adventurers is thus related, (Hakluyt, vol. iii. p. 59)

" Some of his company brought floures, some greene grasse: and one brought a piece of blacke stone much like a sea cole in colour, which by the waight seemed to be some kinde of metall or minerall. This was a thing of no account in the judgment of the Captaine at the first sight, and yet for novelty it was kept in respect of the place from whence it came. After his arrival in London being demanded of sundry of his friends what thing he had brought them home out of that country, he had nothing left to present them withal but a piece of this blacke stone, and it fortuned a gentlewoman one of the adventurers wives to have a piece thereof, which by chance she threw and burned in the fire, so long that at the length being taken forth, and quenched in a little vinegar, it glistered with a bright marquesset of Golde. Whereupon the matter being called in some question, it was brought to certaine Goldfiners in London to make assay thereof, who gave out that it held Golde, and that very richly for the quantity. Afterwards the same Goldfiners promised great matters thereof if there were any store to be found, and offered themselves to adventure for the searching of those parts from whence the same was brought. Some that had great hope of the matter sought secretly to have a lease at her Majesty's hands of those places, whereby to enjoy the masse of so great a public profit vnto their own private gaines.

" In conclusion, *the hope of more of the same Golde ore* to be found kindled a greater opinion in the hearts of many to advance the voyage againe. Whereupon preparation was made for a new voyage against the yere following, and the Captaine more especially directed by commission for the searching more of this Golde ore than for the searching any further discovery of the passage."

All the movements of the Expedition had exclusive reference to this new object of pursuit.

" Now had the Generall altered his determination for going any further into the Streites at this time for any further discovery of the passage having taken a man and a woman of that country, which he thought sufficient for the use of language. and also having met with these people here which intercepted his men the last yere (as the apparell and English furniture which was found in their tents, very well declared) he knew it was but a labor lost to seeke them further off, when he had found them there at hand. And considering also the short time he had in hand, he thought it best to bend his whole endeavour for the getting of myne, and to *leave the passage further to be discovered hereafter*." (Hakluyt, vol. iii. p. 70.)

On the 22nd August, having collected upwards of two hundred tons of ore, they left the Island, whence it had been principally obtained, on their return to England. "We gave a volley of shot for a farewell in honour of the Right Honourable Lady Anne Countess of Warwick, whose name it beareth, and so departed aboard." (Hakluyt, vol. iii. p. 72.) They reached Bristol in October.

The *Third* Voyage had the same objects in view with the preceding, and we find it remarked at the close, (3 Hakluyt, p. 96) "The people are now become so wary and so circumspect by reason of their former losses, that by no means we can apprehend any of them, although we attempted often in this last voyage. But to say truth *we could not bestow any great time* in pursuing them because of our great business in *lading* and other things."

There is little interest in pursuing the details of such an expedition. But one part of the account is too curious not to be noticed. By stress of weather, Frobisher was actually driven to the southward into Hudson's Strait, and yet abandoned the route which he saw plainly before him in order to resume the search for ore.

"The seventh of July as men nothing yet dismayed, we cast about towards the inward, and had sight of land, which rose in form like the Northerland of the Straits, which some of the fleetes, and those not the worst mariners, judged to be the North foreland: however other some were of contrary opinion. But the matter was not well to be discerned by reason of thicke fogge which a long time hung upon the Coast, and the new falling snow which yeerely altereth the shape of the land, and taketh away oftentimes the Mariners markes. And by reason of the darke mists which continued by the space of twentie days together, this doubt grew the greater and the longer perilous. For whereas indeed we thought ourselves to be upon the Northeast side of Frobisher's Straits we were now carried to the *Southwestwards of the Queens Foreland,* and being deceived by a swift current coming from the Northeast were *brought to the Southwestwards of our said course many miles more than we did think possible* could come to passe. The cause whereof we have since found, and it shall be at large hereafter declared." (3 Hakl. 79.)

"The tenth of July the weather still continuing thicke and darke, some of the ships in the fogge lost sight of the Admirall, and the rest of the Fleete, and wondering to and fro with doubtful opinion whether it were best to seeke backe againe to seaward through the great store of yce, or to follow on a doubtful course in a Seas Bay or Straights they knew not, or along a coast, whereof by reason of the darke mistes they could not discerne the dangers if by chance any rocke or broken ground should lie off the place, as commonly in those parts it doth" (p. 80).

"The General, albeit, with the first, perchance, he found out the error, and that this was not the olde straights, yet he persuaded the Fleete alwayes that they were in their right course, and knowen straights. Howbeit, I suppose, he rather dissembled his course." "And as some of the companie reported, *he has since confessed that if it had not beene for the charge and care he had of the fleete and freighted ships, he both would and could have gone through to the South Sea, called Mar del Sur, and dissolved the long doubt of the passage which we seeke to finde to the rich country of Cataya*" (p. 80).

Having taken in a vast quantity of ore the vessels returned, and it proving, on examination, utterly worthless, no further attempt was made by Frobisher.

The preceding detail, while it has enabled us to draw some facts from the rare and curious volumes in which they have long slumbered, has effected incidentally, it is hoped, the purpose which connects them with these pages. It is evident, that nothing but Frobisher's departure from the plain Instructions laid down for his government, prevented his doing what was achieved by Cabot so long before, and by Hudson in the next century. But after his first blind experiment he was intent on another object. We find him actually driven into the true Strait and confessing that he saw his way quite clear. At this very moment he had in his Cabin the Instructions drawn up, at the instance of his patrons, by Willes, describing the Strait in a manner not to be misunderstood, and strengthening all the hopes suggested by his own observation. That paper, as actually printed in England the year before he sailed on the Third Expedition, urges to this day its testimony against him. The tract of Sir Humphrey Gilbert, procured in MS. for his use, and printed two years before, offered the same cheering confirmation. It is difficult to screen Frobisher altogether from reproach, for the discovery of the passage evidently continued a leading object with those who had set forth the Expedition. When, therefore, he voluntarily abandoned the route which he was convinced would conduct him through the Strait, we see that his own eager sympathies were with the more sordid objects of pursuit, and induced him to turn away from the peril, and the glory, of the onward course.

What must be thought, under such circumstances, of a writer who refuses a place to the name of Cabot in a list of those who had engaged in the enterprise?

"The reign of George III. will stand conspicuous and proudly pre-eminent in future history, for the spirit with which discoveries were prosecuted and the objects of science promoted; and a dawn of hope appears that ere its close the interesting problem of a North-West passage will be solved, and this great discovery, to which *the Frobishers,* the Hudsons, &c., so successfully *opened the way*, be accomplished. Little, if any thing, has been added to the discoveries of these extraordinary men, who, in the *early periods* of navigation, had every difficulty to struggle against," &c. (Quarterly Review, vol. xviii. p. 213.)

CHAP. XIII.

VOYAGE OF HUDSON.

After what has been said of the evidence that lay open as to the success of Cabot, the task may be a superfluous one of tracing a familiarity with it to each succeeding Navigator. Yet with regard to Hudson, his acquaintance is apparent even with the volumes which collect and arrange the knowledge on the subject existing at the time of that Expedition of 1610 which has given to his name so much celebrity. In the voyage made by him two years before, he is found conferring amongst other designations that of "*Hakluyt's* Headland" (Purchas, vol. iii. p. 464). It would be absurd, then, to suppose him ignorant of the Volumes, published in London eight years before, which constitute that writer's claim to the gratitude of Seamen; nor can we suppose that in undertaking a voyage in search of the North-West passage he would overlook the information which they supplied as to his predecessors in the enterprise. He would find at p. 16, of the third vol. the Treatise of Sir Humphrey Gilbert, in which it is said, "Furthermore, Sebastian Caboto, by his personal experience and travel, hath set forth and described this passage in his charts, which are yet to be seen in the Queen's Majesty's Privy Gallery at Whitehall, who was sent to make the discovery by King Henry VII., and entered the same fret, affirming that he sailed very far westward with a quarter of the North on the North side of Terra de Labrador the 11th of June, until he came to the Septentrional latitude of 67° and-a-half." He would find at p. 26, of the same volume, the yet more pointed statement of Willes, that Cabot represented the strait through which he penetrated to commence at about a longitude equivalent to 60° west from Greenwich and between 61° and 64°

of latitude, "continuing the same breadth about ten degrees West, where it openeth southerly more and more." It could hardly fail to arrest his attention at p. 80, that Frobisher, in his last voyage, being driven by stress of weather into the very Strait thus described, "confessed that if it had not been for the charge and care he had of the Fleet and fraughted Ships he both would and could have gone through to the South Sea." In the same volume, p. 9, is the passage from Gomara, which represents Cabot to have proceeded by the route of Iceland. At page 441 of the first volume occurs a special recommendation of "Ortelius' Book of Maps." It has already been stated that in this work the Bay is plainly exhibited, and that the author had Cabot's Map before him. When, therefore, it appears that Hudson, in 1610, touched at Iceland on his way out, and finally penetrated into the Bay by following the Instructions so distinctly laid down, we cannot but suppose him aware that he was merely attempting to retrace the course taken, a century before, by Sebastian Cabot.

APPENDIX.

APPENDIX.

(A.)

(*See page* 42.)

FABYAN'S CHRONICLE—ALLUSION TO THE VOYAGE OF CABOT.

FABYAN died, according to Stow, in 1511. Five years after, his Chronicle was published by Pynson, but it then reached only to the tenth year of Henry VII.'s reign, that is 1495. A new edition of the work was published by Rastall, in 1533, with the Continuation. It is here, of course, that we look for the paragraphs referred to by Stow; yet, there is not to be found the slightest allusion to the expedition or to either of the Cabots. Mr Ellis, who gave to the public, some years ago, an edition of Fabyan with notes, and has even furnished a copy of Fabyan's Will occupying seven folio pages, does not seem to have been aware of the importance of inquiry on this point. Stow, in the collections which he made for his Survey, speaks of a Continuation by Fabyan himself, as low as the third year of Henry VIII. which book, he adds, "I have in written hand" (Harleian MS. 538). Mr Ellis, in his Preface to Fabyan (p. xvii.), supposes that the MS. thus referred to may be the one now in the Cotton Manuscripts (Nero C, no. xi.), but this comes down only to the beginning of the reign of Henry VII., and though some of the last pages have been destroyed, yet it would seem from an examination of the copious Index which fortunately *precedes* it, and is evidently contemporary with the body of the work, that it did not reach the period in question. Assuming, however, the correctness of Mr Ellis's conjecture, the question would still remain open as to the authenticity of the ordinary version. Mr E. refers (ib.) to another MS. copy which he had heard of, but had not, as it would seem, consulted. The point is worthy of attentive examination. Stow, of course, in making the assertion, knew of the printed work of Fabyan. The Stow MS. could be instantly recognised by its allusion, under the year 1502, to the exhibition of the savages. We must strike out the reference to Fabyan in Stow, Speed, and Purchas, or deny that any part of the Continuation can be by him, for it is difficult to believe that he would prepare *two* works relative to the incidents of the same reign differing essentially from each other. It forms a presumption in favour of the Stow MS., and against the Continuation by Rastall, that while the worthy Alderman, noting from time to time what fell under his observation, would be likely to advert to the incident in question, it might readily escape a compiler endeavouring to recall the leading events of the era after curiosity about the Newfoundland had passed away.

It is remarkable, that the original edition of Fabyan, published by Pynson, is accompanied by a single leaf, on which are noted the death of Henry VII. and the accession of his son. As Mr Ellis republishes this (see his edition, p. 678) without any attempt to account for the disappearance of the intermediate matter, a conjecture may be hazarded. Bale, in his "Scriptorum Illustrium Magni Brytanniæ, &c." (Bas. Ed. of 1557, fol. 642), states that Cardinal Wolsey had caused some copies of Fabyan's work to be burned, because it exposed the enormous revenues of the priesthood, "Ejus Chronicorum exemplaria nonnulla Cardinalis Wolsius in suo furore comburi fecit quod cleri proventus pingues plus satis detexerit." Mr Ellis is of opinion (Preface, xviii.) that the obnoxious passage "must" have been that in which an abstract is given of the Bill projected by the House of Commons in the 11th Henry IV.; but this seems to furnish a very inadequate motive for the vehement indignation of the Cardinal. A more perilous epoch to the Chronicler was that in which he had to record the death (in 1500) of Cardinal and Chancellor Morton. Of this personage, Bacon says, in his History of Henry VII., "This year also died John Morton, Archbishop of Canterbury, Chancellor of England and Cardinal. He was a wise man, and an eloquent, but in his nature harsh and haughty; much accepted by the King, but envied by the nobility, and *hated of the people.*" "He (Henry VII.) kept a strait hand on his nobility, and chose rather to advance clergymen and lawyers which were more obsequious to him, but had less interest in the people."

It is highly probable, that the popular sentiment would be reflected from the page of Fabyan, and give umbrage to Wolsey, who may be supposed anxious that Henry VIII. should pursue the very policy attributed by Bacon to his Father. At this precise point, then, occurs a chasm in the copies extant of Pynson's edition. Was not this part sacrificed to the resentment of Wolsey, or suppressed from a dread of his displeasure, and was it not afterwards supplied by Rastall? The MS. which had, meanwhile, been lost sight of, could not elude so indefatigable a collector as Stow. The single leaf referred to, of Pynson's edition, may be either part of the original work, or a hasty substitute, got up on the withdrawal of the obnoxious matter, so as to give to the work the appearance of being brought down to the latest period.

(B.)

(*See page* 95.)

ENGLISH EXPEDITION SAID TO HAVE BEEN FOUND BY HOJEDA AT CAQUIBACOA.

The claims of Truth are so paramount to those of any Hypothesis, however convenient and apparently well sustained, that a caution must here be interposed. It might be presumed that Navarette (tom. iii. p. 41) would not lightly hazard the unqualified assertion alluded to; yet this consideration will, perhaps, occur with most force to those who have not examined his volumes. He adduces no authority in support of the position, and the Document which seems, at a hasty glance, to countenance it, will be found, on examination, to suggest an opposite conclusion.

Cabot had discovered a vast Continent along the coast of which he proceeded to the South as far as Florida without reaching its termination. Of this fact the Spanish Government was, of course, fully aware in July 1500, the date of the agreement with Hojeda in which allusion is made to the English, for we find (Navarette, tom. iii. p. 77) a Letter from the Sovereigns dated 6th May, 1500, which Navarette himself (ib. p. 42) connects with an intention to follow up the discoveries of Cabot. The conduct of England was of course regarded by the Court of Spain with indignation and alarm, as involving a violation of the Papal Bull. Cabot followed the main land no further only because his provisions were exhausted. When the Spaniards, then, subsequently discovered Terra Firma, nothing was more natural, or correct, than to suppose it connected with the Great Continent coasted by the English, and in resolving to take possession, their policy, and pretended exclusive rights, would lead them to watch and repel all foreign competition. It was as if, in after times, the Spanish commander at Pensacola or St Augustine had been advised of the colonization of Virginia by the English.

On turning to the agreement with Hojeda it is found that he is enjoined to continue his examination of the region he had discovered on the former voyage, and which seemed to run East and West, as it must lead *towards* (hacia) the place where it was known the English were making discoveries. He is directed to set up marks as he proceeds with the Royal Arms, so that it might be known he had taken possession for Spain, and the English be thereby prevented from making discoveries in that direction (Navarette, tom. iii. p. 86).

"Item: que vaes é sigais aquella costa que descubristes que se corre leste—vuest, segun parece, per razon que *va hacia la parte* donde *se ha sabido* que descubrian los Ingleses é vais poniendo las marcas con las armas de SS. A. A. ó con otras senales que sean conocidas, cuales vos pareciere porque se conozca como vos habes descubierto aquella tierra, para que atages el descubrir de los Ingleses por aquella via."

A Grant of Land is made to Hojeda in consideration prospectively of his active exertions to prosecute discoveries and to check those of the English (ib. p. 88).

"Para que labrees, é fagaes labrar, é vos aprovecheis é podais aprovechar de alli, para lo que habees de descubrir é en la costa de la tierra firme para el atajo de los Ingleses."

The general direction of the region visited by Hojeda is correctly described, and it is certain that had Cabot not been stopped by a failure of provisions, but turned the Cape of Florida and followed the coast, he must have reached Caquibacoa. The vast interval occasioned by the Gulf of Mexico was then unknown.

It is quite plain that the injunction contained in Hojeda's instructions, so far from assuming the identity of the spots visited by him and the English, involves a conjecture as to their relative position towards each other. It was by *following up* his discoveries that Hojeda was to meet and check intrusion. The phraseology, too, discountenances the idea that the person addressed had conveyed the information as to the danger; it seems rather communicated to him in the way of caution. Nor would the setting up of marks to let the English know, on reaching them, of the Spanish claim be probably so much insisted on, if, long before, Hojeda had personally given notice of it. The allusion seems to be not so much to any one expedition of the English as to a particular quarter from which their encroachment was to be apprehended; and Hojeda is, therefore, enjoined to spread out his party, as soon as possible, over the intermediate region, so that it might be found preoccupied. If Caquibacoa had been the scene of common discovery, and of actual encounter, it is strange that Hojeda should now be told by others of the direction which led *towards* the English.

Hojeda was examined on oath, at great length, in the law proceedings between Don Diego Columbus and the Crown, and the very question at issue was as to originality of discovery. He makes not the slightest allusion to such a meeting, and yet, in the course of a trial before a domestic tribunal, there would seem to have been no motive for omitting to state what, if true, must have been known to so many. Nor is this all. If Hojeda really found a party of Englishmen in that quarter he can hardly escape the charge of perjury. He swears positively (Navarette, tom. iii. p. 544) that he was the first who attempted to follow up the discovery of Columbus ("el primero hombre que vino a descubrir despues que el Almirante"). After speaking of his having found the marks of Columbus he proceeds to detail his own discoveries, mentioning particularly Caquibacoa; and he swears that no part of this had ever been discovered or visited either by Columbus or any one else ("nunca nadie lo habia descubierto ni tocado en ello asi el Almirante como otra persona"). The statement is repeated in another part of his testimony (p. 546), "e que toda esta costa y la tierra-firme, y el Golfo de Uraba y el Darien el Almirante ni otra persona no lo habia descubierto."

One other forcible consideration will occur to those apprised of the character of Hojeda. That fiery and daring adventurer would have regarded the rival party as impudent trespassers on the dominions of the King of Spain, and as setting at defiance the Papal Bull. A man who gravely quotes this instrument in his manifesto to the poor Indians as sufficient authority for subjugating them, would hardly have exacted less deference to it from Christians. He was the last person in the world to come home quietly with a report of the intrusion—not knowing when he should return—and to throw on his Sovereign the necessity of giving that direct authority for expulsion which it might be more agreeable to find the officer taking for granted. Hojeda would have known his cue without a prompter.

In a recent volume (Lardner's Cyclopædia, History of Maritime and Inland discovery, vol. ii. p. 35), the assertion is made that

" Hojeda *met with* English navigators near the Gulf of Maracaibo," and a sufficient authority is supposed to be found for it in the language of the Document already quoted. Without repeating what has been said on that point, it may be remarked that the writer in the Cyclopædia does not deal fairly with the original. He represents Hojeda as ordered " to follow and examine *the coast which he had already discovered*, and *which* appears to run East and West, as *that is* the part *which* the English are known to be exploring," &c. It is obvious that the most important words are here left unnoticed. The expression " por razon que va *hacia* la parte donde se ha sabido que descubrian las Ingleses" will not bear the translation of the Cyclopædia without the substitution indicated by brackets, " as that *is* [goes towards] the part where the English are known to be exploring."

Should it appear, in the end, that the assertion has no better foundation than the document in question, what a melancholy proof have we of the perils to which Truth is subject when a writer like Navarette, who was to clear up all difficulties, is found rashly starting new errors to run their course through successive volumes!

It must be acknowledged that the remarks now submitted rather take from the force of what appears, in the text, a plausible case. But a frequent observation of the diffusive consequences of a single error suggests that there is something of moral guilt in pressing too earnestly a statement the truth of which is not sincerely confided in.

If deprived of the happy coincidence suggested by the assertion of Navarette, it must be left to conjecture to determine in what quarter the active and enterprising spirit of Cabot was employed during the long interval between his undoubted voyages from England and the time of his entering the service of Spain.

Another motive has its weight. The curious and important Documents at the Rolls Chapel will probably one day be arranged and made available to the purposes of history. Evidence may then come forth, and it is desirable that no erroneous hypothesis should be found in the way of Truth. Until that period we must be content to remain in the dark. Where the records are in such a state of confusion as to warrant the charge which has been before mentioned for *finding* a specific paper of which the exact date—the name of the party—the purpose and general tenor—are given, it is obvious that no private fortune would be adequate to meet the expense of a general search.

(C.)

(*See page* 174.)

WAS CABOT APPOINTED GRAND PILOT?

A DOUBT on this point is expressed in the text. Nothing is said on the subject in the grant of the pension, and the circumstantial evidence seems to negative the existence of such an office in his time. There is preserved in the Lansdowne MSS. (No. 116, art. 3) a Memorial presented by Stephen Burrough, an English seaman of considerable note, the object of which is to enforce the necessity of appointing such an officer. It appears by an accompanying document that Burrough himself was forthwith appointed "Cheyffe Pylot" for life, and also "one of the foure masters that shall have the keepyng and oversight of our shipps, &c." It is declared the duty of the Chief Pilot to "have the examination and appointing of all such mariners as shall from this time forward take the charge of a Pilot or Master upon him in any ship within this our realm." This is the duty supposed to have been assigned to Cabot, but it seems difficult to reconcile the language of Burrough with the previous existence of any such office. His memorial recites "Three especial causes and considerations amongst others, wherefore the office of Pilot-Major is allowed and esteemed in Spain, Portugal, and other places where navigation flourisheth." Had any such duties ever been exercised in England, he would of course have referred to the fact, and insisted on the advantages which had resulted, more particularly as he was educated in the school of Cabot, and expressly names "*the good olde and famuse man Master Sebastian Cabota.*"

(D.)

(*See page* 224.)

LETTERS PATENT NOW FIRST PUBLISHED DATED 19 MARCH 1501, FROM HENRY VII. TO RICHARD WARDE, THOMAS ASHEHURST, AND JOHN THOMAS, OF BRISTOL, AND JOHN FERNANDUS, FRANCIS FERNANDUS, AND JOHN GUNSOLUS OF PORTUGAL.

MEMORANDUM quod XIX die Marcii, anno regni Regis Henrici Septimi XVI, ista Billa delibata fuit Domino Custodi Magni Sigilli Angliæ apud Westmonasterium exequenda.

TO THE KYNG OUR SOVEREYNE LORD.

Please it your Highness of your most noble and habundaunt Grace to graunt unto your welbeloved subjects Richard Warde, Thomas Asshehurst and John Thomas, merchants of your Towne of Bristowe, and to John Fernandus, Francis Fernandus, and John Gunsolus, Squyers, borne in the Isle of Surrys under the obeisaunce of the Kynge of Portingale your gracious Lettres Patentis under your Greate Seale in due forme to be made according to the tenour hereafter ensuying, and that this Byll sygned with your gracious hand may be to the Reverend Fader in God Henry Byshop of Salesbury, Keeper of your Greate Seale, sufficient and immediate warrant for the making, sealying, accomplysshyng of your said Lettres Patentes, and they shall duryng ther lyves pray to God for the prosperous contynuance of your most noble and ryall astate.

H. R.

Rex universis et singulis ad quos præsentes Literæ Nostræ pervenerint Salutem: Notum sit vobis et manifestum quod ex certis considerationibus nos moventibus de advisamento Consilii Nostri, concessimus et Licentiam dedimus, prout per Præsentes Concedimus et Licentiam damus, pro Nobis et Hæredibus Nostris quantum in Nobis est, dilectis subditis nostro Ricardo Warde, Thomæ Asshurst, et Johanni Thomas, mercatoribus Villæ Nostræ Bristolliæ ac dilectis nobis Johanni Fernandus, Francisco Fernandus et Johanni Gunsolus, armigeris in Insulis de Surrys sub obediencia Regis Portugaliæ oriundis, et eorum cuilibet ac cujuslibet eorum hæredibus, attornatis, factoribus, seu deputatis ac eis et eorum cuilibet plenam ac liberam auctoritatem, facultatem et potestatem committimus navigandi et se transferendi ad omnes partes, regiones et fines Maris Orientalis Occidentalis, Australis, Borealis et Septentrionalis, sub Banneris, et Insigniis nostris cum tot et tantis et talibus Navibus sive Batellis quot sibi placuerint et necessariæ fuerint, cujuscunque portagii quilibet Navis sive Batella extiterit, cum Magistris, contromagistris, marinariis pagettis aliisque hominibus pro gubernatione, salva custodia et defensione Navium et Batellarum prædictarum competentibus requisitis et necessariis, ad custus et onera dicti Ricardi et aliorum prædictorum et pro hujusmodi salariis vadiis et stipendiis prout inter eos poterunt concordare ad inveniendum, recuperandum, descoperiendum et investigandum Insulas, patrias, Regiones sive provincias quascunque Gentilium et Infidelium in quacunque Mundi parte positas quæ Christianis omnibus ante hæc tempora fuerunt et in præsenti sunt incognita.

Ac hujusmodi Banneras et insignia nostra in quacunque villa, oppido, Castro insula seu terra-firma a se sic noviter inventis affigendi, ipsasque villas, oppida, castra, insulas et terras firmas pro nobis et nomine nostro intrandi et capiendi et ea tanquam Vasalli nostri ac Gubernatores Locatenentes et Deputati nostri, eorumque dominio, titulo, dignitate et præeminencia eorundem nobis semper reservatis, occupandi possidendi et subjugandi.

Et insuper quandocumque, imposterum, hujusmodi Insulæ Patriæ, Terræ et Provinciæ per præfatos Ricardum et alios prævocatos adeptæ recuperatæ et inventæ fuerint, tunc volumus et per præsentes concedimus quod omnes et singuli tam viri quam fœminæ hujus regni nostri cœterique subditi nostri et insulas hujusmodi sic noviter inventas visitare et in eisdem inhabitare cupientes et desiderantes, possint et valiant licite et impune ad ipsas patrias, insulas et loca cum eorum navibus, hominibus et servientibus, rebus et bonis suis universis transire et in eisdem sub protectione et regimine dictorum Ricardi et aliorum prænominatorum morari et inhabitare, divitiasque, fructus et emolumenta patriarum, terrarum et locorum prædictorum adquierere et obtinere.

Dantes insuper et concedentes præfatis Ricardo, Thomæ et Johanni, Francisco et Johanni et eorum cuilibet plenam tenore Præsentium potestatem et auctoritatem omnes et singulos homines marinarios cæterasque personas ad Insulas, Patrias, Provincias terras firmas et loca prædicta ex causa prædicta se divertentes et confluentes tam in comitiva dictorum Ricardi et aliorum prænominatorum quam in comitiva aliorum illuc imposterum recursum habere contingentium tam supra Mare quam in Insulis, patriis, terris-firmis et locis hujusmodi post quam inventa et recuperata fuerint regendi et gubernandi Legesque Ordinationes, Statuta et Proclamationes pro bono et quieto regimine et gubernatione dictorum hominum, magistrorum, marinariorum, et aliarum personarum prædictarum faciendi, stabiliendi, ordinandi et constituendi et superinde proclamationes faciendi ac omnes et singulos quos in hac parte contrarios et rebelles ac Legibus, Statutis et Ordinacionibus prædictis inobedientes invenerint ac omnes illos qui furtum, homicidia, rapinas commiserint et perpetrariunt aut aliquas mulieres Insularum seu Patriarum prædictarum, contra eorum voluntatem aut aliter, rapuerint et violaverint juxta leges et statuta per ipsos in hac parte ordinata castigandi et puniendi. Ac etiam concessimus præfatis Ricardo, Thomæ, Johanni, Johanni, Francisco et Johanni hæredibus et assignatis suis quod postquam aliquæ insulæ, provinciæ, Terræ-firmæ, regio seu provincia imposterum per ipsum Ricardum et alios prænominatos inventa fuerint tunc non licebit alicui seu aliquibus subdito seu subditis nostris durante termino decem annos proximo et immediate sequentes ad ipsas villas Provincias, Insulas, Terras-firmas et Loca causa mercandisandi ac bona acquirendi *absque licentia nostra regia et* [the words in *italics* illegible but supplied conjecturally from the corresponding paragraph in the subsequent patent of 9th Dec. 1502] dictorum Rieardi et aliorum prænominatorum hæredum et assignatorum suorum cum suis navibus frequentare aut se divertere aut in eadem ingredi seu in eisdem pro aliquibus bonis acquirendi intromittere.

Et post terminum dictorum decem annorum quod nullus ex nostris subditis ad aliquam Terram-firmam, insulam, patriam seu loca per ipsos Ricardum et Thomam et alios prædictos sic noviter inventa navigare et frequentare præsumat absque *licentia nostra prædicta et* [the words in *italics* supplied as before] prædictorum Ricardi et cœterorum sub pœna amissionis et forisfacturæ omnium Bonarum, mercandisarum, rerum et navium quarumcunque ad ea loca sic noviter inventa navigare et in eadem ingredi præsumentium (videlicet) una medietas inde erit ad opus nostrum et alia medietas ad opus dictorum Ricardi et aliorum prænominatorum et hæredum suorum.

Et ultius ex abundanti gratia nostra concessimus et per Præsentes concedimus pro nobis et hæredibus nostris quantam in nobis est præfatis Ricardo, Thomæ, Johanni, Johanni, Francisco et Johanni et eorum cuilibet hæredibus et assignatis suis quod ipsi et eorum quilibet mercandisas, mercimonia, aurum et argentum in massa, lapides preciosa et alia bona quæcumque de crescentia patriarum, insularumque et locorum prædictorum per ipsos sic recuperandorum et inveniendorum tam in dictis navibus et batellis quam aliis quibuscunque navibus exteris a dictis patriis insulis, terris-firmis et locis in hoc regnum nostrum Angliæ ad quemcunque portum seu alium locum ejusdem adducere et cariare et adduci seu cariari facere possit et valeat, eaque vendere et distribuere ad eorum proficium et advantagium aliquo Statuto actu ordinatione seu provisione inde in contrarium factis sive ordinatis nonobstantibus.

Ac nos intime considerantes grandia custus et onera quæ circa præmissa facienda et perimplendo requiruntur volentes igitur præfatis Ricardo, Thomæ et aliis memoratis personis gratiam provide facere specialem Concessimus (*prout*) per Præsentes concedimus eisdem, hæredibus et assignatis suis quod ipsi et eorum quilibet h redes et assignati sui prædicti de tempore in tempus durante termino quatuor annorum a tempore recuperationis et inventionis Insularum, et provinciarum prædictarum proximo et immediate sequentes, mercandisas, mercimonia cæteraque bona in uno navi tantum cujuscunque portagii fuerit eskippata et onustata ac in hoc regnum nostrum Angliæ adducenda et transportanda in portu seu loco prædicto ad terram ponere, eaque vendere, exponere et pro libito suo distribuere possint de tempore in tempus, qualibet viaggio, durante termino, dictorum quatuor annorum absque aliquibus custumis, subsidiis, seu aliis deveriis pro eisdem bonis mercimoniis et cæteris præmissis in dicta unica navi tantum contentis et eskippatis nobis aut hæredibus nostris infra dictum regnum nostrum Angliæ aliqualiter solvendis.

Proviso tamen quod nobis de custumis, subsidiis pondagiis et aliis deveriis Nobis pro cæteris mercandisis, mercimoniis et bonis in omnibus aliis navibus contentis debitis juxta consuetudinem in hoc regno nostro Angliæ hactenus usitatam fideliter respondeatur ut est justum. Et Insuper volumus et concedimus per Præsentes quod quilibet Capitalis Magister, contra magister et Marinarius cujuslibet Navis ad aliquam Terram-firmam Insulam, patriam, provinciam et locum prædictum frequentantis et navigantis habeant gaudeant et percipiant de bonis et mercimoniis a dictis Insulis, Terris-firmis et Provinciis in hoc regnum Angliæ adducendis custumas et subsidia sequentia, videlicet.

Quod quilibet Magister habeat gaudeat et precipiat subsidia et custumas, quolibet viagio, quatuor doliorum.

Et quilibet Contramagister vel Quarter-Magister custumas et subsidia duorum Doliorum.

Ac quilibet Marinarius custumas et subsidia unius Dolii.

Licet *sint caveata et eskippata* [the words in *italics* supplied as befor] ut bona sua propria aut ut bona alicujus alterius personæ cujuscunque et hoc absque aliquibus custumis, subditis debitis seu deveriis infra hoc regnum nostrum Angliæ ad opus nostrum aut hæredum nostrorum pro eisdem doliis aliqualiter solvendis seu petendis.

Et si contingat aliquem vel aliquos mercatorem seu mercatores hujus regni nostri ad dictas Insulas Patrias et Loca sub licencia dictorum subdictorum nostrorum aut absque licencia causa habendi mercandisas et mercimonia adventare et laborare ad bona et mercimonia ab eisdem partibus in hoc regnum nostrum adducere tunc volumus et concedimus, per præsentes, præfatis, Ricardo, Thomæ, Johanni, Johanni, Francisco, Johanni hæredibus et assignatis suis quod ipsi durante termino decem annorum antedicto habeant de quolibet hujusmodi mercatore, solutis nobis custumis, subsidiis et aliis deveriis nobis in hac parte debitis et consuetis, vicesimum partem omnium hujusmodi bonarum et mercimoniarum per ipsos a dictis Insulis, patriis et Locis quolibet viagio durante dicto termino decem annorum in hoc regnum nostrum Angliæ traducendorum et cariandorum habendam et capiendam hujusmodi vicesimam partem in portu ubi contigerit dicta bona discarcari et exonerari.

Proviso Semper quod prædicti Ricardus et alii prædicti, hæredes et assignati sui et non alii omnino imposterum durante dicto termino decem annorum sint Factores et Attornati in dictis Insulis Terris-firmis et Patriis pro quibuscunque hujusmodi mercatoribus aliisque personis illuc ex causa prædicta confluentibus in et pro eorum Factis mercatoriis in eisdem.

Proviso etiam quod nulla navis cum bonis et mercandisis a dictis partibus sic noviter inventis carcata et onusta *postquam in aliquam portum hujus* [the words in *italics* supplied as before] Regni nostri adducta fuerint non exoneratur de eisdem bonis et mercandisis nisi in præsentia præfatorum Ricardi et aliorum prædictorum eorumve hæredum seu deputatorum ad hoc assignandum sub pœna forisfacturæ eorumdem bonarum et mercandisiarum; unde una medietas ad opus nostrum et alia medietas præfatis Ricardo et aliis prænominatis et hæredibus suis applicentur

Et si imposterum aliqui extran*ei aut aliæ* [the part in *italics* supplied as before] personæ ad ipsas partes contra voluntatem ipsorum Ricardi et aliorum prænominatorum causa habendi divitias navigare et ea vi et armis ingredi ac dictos Ricardum et alios prædictos aut hæredes suos ibidem insultare ac eos expellere et debellare aut alias inquietare presumpserint quod tunc volumus ac eisdem subditis tenore Præsentium damus et committimus ipsos extraneos licet sint subditi et vasalli alicujus Principis Nobiscum in liga et amicitia totis suis veribus tam per terram quam per mare et aquas dulces expugnandi resistendi et Gueriam contra eos levandi et faciendi easque capiendi, subpeditandi et incarcerandi ibidem quousque Fines et Redemptiones eisdem subditis nostris fecerint moratur aut alias secundum sanam discretionem ipsorum subditorum nostrorum et hæredum suorum castigandi et puniendi.

At etiam præfatis subditis nostris cæterisque personis prædictis plenam tenore Præsentium potestatem damus et committimus sub se quoscunque Capitaneos, Locatenentes et Deputatos in singulis Civitatibus, villis, Oppidis et Locis dictarum Insularum Provinciarum, Patriarum et Locorum prædictorum ad regendum et gubernandum omnes et singulas personas in eisdem partibus sub regimine et gubernatione dictorum subdictorum nostrorum ibidem commorantium ac ad justitiam eisdem secundum tenorem et effectum Ordinationum Statutorum et Proclamationum prædictorum debite exequendum et administrandum per Literas suas Patentes sigillis eorum sigillandas, faciendi, constituendi nominandi et substituendi. Et insuper concessimus et per Præsentes concedimus præfatis Ricardo, Thomæ, Johanni, Johanni, Francisco et Johanni ad terminum vitæ suæ et cujuslibet eorum diutius viventis officium Admiralli supra Mare in quibuscunque locis, patriis, et provinciis a se sic noviter inventis et imposterum inveniendis et recuperandis, ipsosque Ricardum, Thomam, Johannem, Johannem, Franciscum, Johannem et eorum quemlibet conjunctim et divisim Admirallos nostros in eisdem partibus facimus, constituimus, ordinamus et deputamus, per Præsentes dantes et concedentes eisdem et eorum cuilibet plenam tenore Præsentiarum potestatem et auctoritatem ea omnia et singula quæ ad officium Admirallitatis pertinent faciendi exercendi et exequendi secundum legem et consuetudinem maritimam in hoc regno nostro Angliæ usitatam.

Ac etiam postquam præfati Ricardus Warde, Thomas Ashhurst et Johannes Thomas, ac Johannes Fernandus, Franciscus Fernandus et Johannes Gunsolus aliquas terras-firmas, insulas, patrias et provincias, oppida, castra, civitates et villas per assistentiam nostram sic invenerint, obtinuerint, et subjugaverint tunc volumus et per Præsentes concedimus eisdem, hæredibus et assignatis suis quod ipsi et hæredes sui habeant, teneant et possideant sibi hæredibus et assignatis suis omnia et singula talia et tanta, terras-firmas, insulas, patrias, provincias, castra, oppida, fortallicia, civitates et villas qualia et quanta ipsi et homines tenentes et servientes sui possunt inhabitare, custodire sustinere et manutere: Habenda et Tenenda eadem Terras Insulas et loca prædicta sibi, hæredibus et assignatis suis et cujuslibet eorem de nobis et hæredibus nostris imperpetuum per Fidelitatem tantum absque aliquo Compoto seu aliquo alio nobis aut hæredibus nostris proinde reddendo seu faciendo, Dignitate Dominio, Regalitate, Jurisdictione, et pre-eminentia in eisdem nobis semper salvis et omnino reservatis.

Et ultius concessimus præfatis Ricardo, Thomæ, Johanni, Johanni, Francisco, Johanni quod ipsi hæredes et assignati sui prædicti dictas terras-firmas, insulas et provincias ipsis et hæredibus suis prædictis ut præmittitur sic concessas, postquam inventæ et recuperatæ sint, ac cum in plena possessione earundem fuerint teneant possideant et gaudeant libere, quiete, et pacifice absque impedimento aliquali nostri aut hæredum nostrorum quarumcunque. Et quod nullus ex subditis nostris eos eorum aliquem de et super possessione et titulo suis de et in dictis terris-firmis, insulis et provinciis se aliqualiter contra voluntatem suam expellat quovis modo *seu aliquis extraneus aut aliqui extranei virtute aut colore alicujus concessionis nostræ sibi Magno Sigillo Nostro per antea factæ aut imposterum faciendæ cum aliquibus aliis locis et insulis . . . . et contiguis ac membris et Parcellis præfatis Insulis Terris-firmis Provinciis et locis . . . . . . absque licentia . . . . subditorum nostrorum et aliorum prænominatorum aliquo modo intromittat nec intromittant* [Through the words in *italics* the pen is drawn in the original, and a space then occurs, from which the writing has been carefully and completely erased].

Promittentes bona-fide et in verbo regio Nos ratum gratum et firmum habituros totum et quicquid præfati Ricardus, Thomas, Johannes, Johannes Franciscus et Johannes et eorum quilibet pro præmissorum complemento fecerint fierique procuraverint in hac parte. Et quod Nos aut hæredes nostri nullo unquam tempore in futuro ipsos aut eorum aliquam hæredes et assignatos suos in jure, titulo et possessione suis inquietabimus, impediemus aut molestium eis faciemus nec per alios nostros subditos aut alios quoscunque quantum in nobis fuerit fieri seu procurari permittemus seu procurabimus, nec ipsos hæredes et assignatos suos pro aliqua causa imposterum emergente seu contingente ab eisdem Terris-firmis, provinciis et locis nullo modo amovebimus aut amoveri seu expelli per subditos nostros procurabimus. Et ultius ex uberiori gratia nostra et mero motu nostro concessimus et per Præsentes concedimus pro Nobis et hæredibus quantum in nobis est Johanni Johanni Fernandus, Francisco Fernandus et Johanni Gunsalos, Armigeris de Insulis de S[illegible] [illegible] Regis Portugall[illegible] et eorum cuilibet quod ipsi et eorum quilibet ac omnes liberi sui tam procreati quam procreandi in perpetuam sint indigeni et ligei nostri et hæredum nostrorum et in omnibus causis, querelis, rebus et materiis quibuscumque habeantur pertractarentur teneantur, reputentur et gubernentur tanquam veri et fideles Ligei Nostri infra Regnum nostrum Angliæ oriundi et non aliter nec alio modo. Et quod ipsi et omnes liberi sui prædicti omnimodo actiones reales personales et mixtas in omnibus Curiis, locis et jurisdictionibus nostris quibuscunque habere exercere eisque uti et gaudere ac eas in eisdem placitare et implacitari respondere et responderi, defendere ac defendi possint et eorum quilibet possit in omnibus sicuti veri et fideles Ligei nostri infra Regnum nostrum prædictum oriundi. Et quod ipsi et eorum quilibet Terras, Tenementa, reditus, reversiones, servitia et alios possessiones quæcunque tam in dominio quam in reversione infra dictum regnum nostrum Angliæ ac alia dominia et loca sub obedientia nostra perquirere, capere, recipere, habere tenere possidere et hæreditare sibi, hæredibus et assignatis sui imperpetuum vel alio modo quocunque ac ea dare, vendere, alienare et legare cuicunque personæ sive quibus cunque personiis sibi placuerit libere, quiete, licite et impune possint et quilibet eorum possit ad libitum suum adeo libere integre et pacifice sicut possit et valeat aliquis Ligeorum nostrorum infra regnum nostrum Angliæ oriundus. Ita tamen quod prædicti Johannes Fernandus, Franciscus et Johannes Gunsolus et omnes liberi sui prædicti solvant aut solvi faciant et eorum quilibet solvat seu solvi faciat talia custumas subsidia et alia demandia pro bonis, mercibus, mercandisis et mercimoniis suis in Regnum nostrum Angliæ adducendis vel extra idem Regnum educendis qualia alienigeni nobis solvant aut solvere deberent vel consueverunt. Et quod idem Johannes Fernandus, Franciscus et Johannes Gunsolus et omnes liberi sui prædicti de cætero in futuro colore seu vigore alicujus Statuti, Ordinacionis sive concessionis in Parliamento nostro aut extra Parliamentum nostrum facti vel fiendi non arcteantur seu compellantur nec eorum aliquis arcteneatur teneatur seu compellatur ad solvendum, dandum vel supportandum nobis vel alicui hæredum nostrorum seu cuicunque alteri aliqua Taxas, Tallagia seu alia onera quæcunque pro terris, tenementis, bonis vel personis suis præterquam talia et tanta qualia et quanta alii fideles Ligei nostri infra dictum Regnum nostrum oriundi pro bonis, terris tenementis seu personis suis solvunt dant faciunt vel supportant aut solvere, dare, facere vel supportare consueverunt et teneantur sed quod prædicti Johannes Fernandus, Franciscus et Johannes Gunsolus et omnes liberi sui prædicti habere et possidere valeant et possint et eorum quilibet valeat et possit omnia et omnimodo alia Libertates, privilegia, franchesias et custumas ac eis uti et gaudere possint et eorum quilibet possit infra dictum Regnum nostrum Angliæ, jurisdictiones et dominia nostra quæcunque adeo plene libere, quiete, integre et pacifice sicut cœteri Ligei nostri infra idem Regnum nostrum oriundi habent utunt et gaudent aut habere, possidere, uti et gaudere debeantet valeant aliquo statuto, acto, ordinacione vel aliqua alia causa, re, vel materia quacunque nonobstante.

Proviso semper quod præfati Johannes Fernandus, Franciscus et Johannes Gunsolus homagium ligcum nobis faciunt et eorum quilibet faciat ac Lotto et Scotto et aliis oneribus in Regno nostro prædicto debitis et consuetis contribuant et eorum quilibet contribuat sicut alii ligei nostri infra dictum regnum nostrum oriundi faciunt.

Proviso etiam quod iidem Johannes Fernandus, Franciscus et Johannes Gunsolus solvant et eorum quilibet solvat nobis et hæredibus nostris tot et tanta custumas subsidia et alia deveria pro bonis et mercandisis suis prout alienigeni nobis solvere et reddere teneantur.

Et ulterius ex uberiori gratia nostra concessimus præfatis Ricardo, Thomæ, Johanni, Johanni, Francisco, et Johanni quod ipsi habeant Præsentes Literas Nostras in Cancellaria nostra absque aliquo fine seu feodo aut aliquibus finibus seu feodis pro eisdem Literis nostris aut aliqua parte eorundem aut pro Magno Sigillo nostro ad opus nostrum in Hannaperio dictæ Cancellariæ nostræ aliqualiter solvendis.

Et volumus et concedimus per Præsentes quod Reverendissimus in Christo Pater Henricus Episcopus Salisb. Custos Magni Sigilli nostri auctoritate præsentis Concessionis nostræ fieri faciat et sigillari tot et talia Brevia sub Magno Sigillo nostro sigillanda Custodi sive clerico Hanaperii nostri dirigenda pro exoneratione dictorum Finium et Feodorum quot et qualia in hac parte necessaria fuerint et requisita, absque aliquo alio Warranto aut prosecutione penes Nos in hac parte faciendis.

In cujus, &c.

(E.)

(*See page* 276.)

CONJECTURE AS TO THE NAME "DOMINIS VOBISCUM" ERRONEOUSLY ASSOCIATED WITH THE VOYAGE OF 1527—FORSTER'S MISTAKE AS TO NORUMBEGA—NAVARETTE, &C., AS TO THE PERIOD AT WHICH NEWFOUNDLAND WAS FIRST FREQUENTED FOR FISHING.

WHENCE could have arisen the misconception of Frobisher as to the words *Dominus Vobiscum* associated with this enterprise? Assured that he was wrong, a conjecture may be hazarded. Were they the final adieu and benediction of Wolsey to his ecclesiastical protegé and correspondent—perhaps as the vessel passed Greenwich? Such an exclamation would linger on the popular ear. One of the ships was never heard of, but all hopes of her could not have been abandoned for many years, and the fate of those on board must have long been a subject of painful speculation, and to their relatives of agonizing suspense. The invocation of the odious Cardinal may have been recalled as little likely to propitiate Heaven—in fact of evil omen—and the impression, coloured highly at the time by the imagination, might be confusedly traced by Frobisher, half a century afterwards, amidst the faded reminiscences of the Expedition.

Forster (p. 436, note) is very much puzzled at the name of *Norumbega,* which occurs in the heading of Hakluyt's account of the voyage, and supposes "that some of the toys which were presented to the savages, consisting of looking-glasses, bells, &c., were of *Nuremberg* manufacture, and that by the name given to the country they meant to preserve the memory of this fact!" The name is found distinguishing the country immediately to the southward of Newfoundland on the maps or descriptions of Ortelius, De Laet, Bertius, and Cluverius. In another passage of Hakluyt, (vol. iii. p. 163) reference is made to the same Norumbega in connexion with the enterprise of Sir Humphrey Gilbert, and in a way not to be misunderstood. As to the origin of the name, it might have occurred to Forster, from the termination Hochlega, &c. and the usual custom of the French of preserving Indian names, that it was aboriginal.

He has not only overlooked these considerations, but something else of which his ignorance is less excusable. The article which immediately follows the account of Verrazani's voyage of 1524, in Ramusio, (tom. iii. fol. 423, F.) is "a Discourse by a great Sea Captain of France," relative to these regions, written fifteen years after the time of Verrazani. He describes the "terra di Norumbega" as lying where we have stated, and expressly states it to be so called by the natives, "la terra é detta *da pæsani suai* Norembega." So, too, *Thevet*, in his Cosmographie Universelle, (Paris ed. of 1575, tom. ii. fol. 1010) says of this region, "que aucuns ont appelee Terre Francayse *et ceux du pays Norumbeque.*"

There is one incidental point which the Letter of Rut conclusively settles. Navarette has a long dissertation to prove that the Newfoundland fishery was not pursued at so early a period as has been usually supposed. This opinion is adopted by a recent writer, (Dr Lardner's Cyclopædia, History of Maritime and Inland discovery, vol. ii. p. 24) who says "Don M. de Navarette, whose *authority* on this point seems *conclusive*, is disposed to think that the Biscayans did not discover Newfoundland till 1526, and *he shews* that they did not frequent the Banks *till* 1540." Now we have the positive statement of the English Commander to Henry VIII. that on entering St John's on the 3rd of August, 1527, he found "eleven sail of Normans, and one Brittaine, and two Portugall Barkes, and all a fishing." Herrera (Dec. ii. lib. v. cap. iii.) gives this same report by an English vessel which had touched in the West-Indies, as to her having been at the Baccalaos, and found there engaged in fishing fifty vessels, Spanish, French, and Portuguese. The misfortune of Don M. Navarette is that with no firm hold of the History of the New World, even as found in the works of his own countrymen, he attaches an importance altogether exaggerated, and sometimes absurd, to the Documents over which he is incumbent, and when he finds a scrap of manuscript exhibits it with a sort of triumph and as quite decisive, when, in a majority of cases, it owes its origin to ignorance or fraud. Thus, on this point, he gravely cites the negative testimony of half-a-dozen masters of vessels taken on a trial of which he has a MS. account. These persons, it seems, were unable to carry back further the history of the fishery. Infinite discretion is necessary on the part of a writer circumstanced like Don M. Navarette. The eye quickly becomes diseased unless the microscope be often withdrawn, and a healthy look taken round the natural horizon

PORTRAIT OF SEBASTIAN CABOT BY HOLBEIN.

Reference has already been made (page 179) to the Portrait of Sebastian Cabot in considering the singular misconception as to the meaning of the epithet "*Militis* aurati." The statement of Purchas (vol. iv. p. 1812) is as follows:—

"Sir Seb. Cabota; his Picture in the Privie Gallerie at White-Hall hath these words, *Effigies Seb. Caboti Angli, filii Joannis Caboti Veneti militis aurati, &c.*; he was born at Venice, and serving Henry VII., Henry VIII., Edward VI. was *accounted* English—Galpano saith he was borne at Bristol."

This Picture now belongs to the Representatives of the late Charles Joseph Harford, Esq. of Bristol. The inscription which Purchas curtails by an "&c." is this:—

"Effigies Seb. Caboti Angli, filii Johannis Cabòti Veneti Militis Aurati, *Primi Inventoris Terræ Novæ sub Henrico VII. Angliæ Rege.*"

The manner in which the Portrait came to the knowledge of Mr Harford, and finally into his possession, is very minutely stated in a Memoir prepared by him and left with his family. Without needlessly introducing names it may suffice to state that whilst travelling in Scotland, in 1792, he saw it for the first time at the seat of a nobleman; and, many years afterwards, his friend the late Sir Frederick Eden was enabled to gratify his anxious wishes by procuring it for him.

The work of Purchas was published in 1625, at the close of the reign of James I. That the picture was not in the Gallery in the time of Charles II., would appear from the following circumstances:—

There is a tract by Evelyn, the celebrated author of *Sylva*, &c., entitled "Navigation and Commerce, their Original and Progress, containing a succinct account of traffic in general, its benefits and improvements; of discoveries, wars, and conflicts at sea, from the original of Navigation to this day; with special regard to the English nation; their several voyages and Expeditions to the beginning of our late differences with Holland; in which his Majesty's Title to the

Dominion of the Sea is asserted against the novel and later pretenders, by J. Evelyn, Esq. S.R.S. London, 1674." It is dedicated to Charles II., to whom the author expresses his gratitude for an appointment to the Council of Commerce and Plantations. The object of it, as may be inferred from the title, is to shew the early and diffusive influence of England at sea. Referring to the triumphant conflicts with France in the time of Henry VIII. he says, (p. 73) "see also that rare piece of Holbein's in his Majesty's Gallery at White-Hall." He adverts (p. 57) to Sebastian Cabot, "born with us at Bristol," and hazards a conjecture as to his having, with his father, "discovered Florida and the shoars of Virginia with that whole tract as far as Newfoundland before the bold Genoese." Had the portrait in question been in the Gallery at White-Hall in Evelyn's time, he would not have omitted to notice the remarkable assertion which its inscription conveys.

The disappearance of the picture, therefore, from White-Hall, and its getting into private hands, may be referred to the intermediate period. It was, probably, bought at the Sales which took place after the death of Charles I., and of which the following account is found in Walpole's Anecdotes of Painting in England:—

"Immediately after the death of the King, several votes were passed for sale of his goods, pictures, statues, &c.

"Feb. 20, 1648. It was referred to the Committee of the Navy to raise money by sale of the crown jewels, hangings, and other goods of the late King.

"In the ensuing month the House proceeded to vote, that the personal estate of the late King, Queen, and Prince should be inventoried, appraised, and sold. This vote, in which they seem to have acted honestly, not allowing their own members to be concerned in the sale, was the cause that the collections fell into a variety of low hands, and were dispersed among the painters and officers of the late King's household; where many of them remained on sale with low prices affixed.

"All other furniture from all the King's Palaces was brought up and exposed to sale; there are specified, particularly, Denmark or Somerset-house, Greenwich, *Whitehall*, Nonsuch, Oatlands, Windsor, Wimbleton-house, St James's, Hampton-court, Richmond, Theobalds, Ludlow, Carisbrook, and Kenilworth Castles; Bewdley-house, Holdenby-house, Royston, Newmarket, and Woodstock manor-house. One may easily imagine that such a collection of pictures, with the remains of jewels and plate, and the furniture of *nineteen* palaces, ought to have amounted to a far greater sum than *one hundred and eighteen thousand pounds*.

"The sale continued to August 9, 1653. The prices were fixed, but if more was offered, the highest bidder purchased; this happened in some instances, not in many. Part of the goods were sold by inch of candle. The buyers called contractors, signing a writing for the several sums. If they disliked the bargain, they were at liberty to be discharged from the agreement on paying one fourth of the sum stipulated. Among the purchasers of statues and pictures were several painters, as Decritz, Wright, Baptist Van Leemput, Sir Balthazar Gerbier, &c. The Cartoons of Raphael were bought by his Highness (Cromwell) for 300*l*."

The circumstances which refer this Portrait to Holbein seem to be conclusive. Cabot is represented as in extreme age. Now he had not been in England from 1517 until his return in 1548. The Portrait, therefore, must have been taken after the last-mentioned date. Holbein enjoyed the continued patronage of Henry VIII. after Sir Thomas More had introduced his works to the King's notice in the manner so familiarly known. He lived through the reign of Edward VI., and died at Whitehall of the plague, in 1554. It is not probable, under such circumstances, that a Portrait of Cabot, destined for the King's Gallery, would have been taken by any other hand.

Such seems to be the curious history of a Picture in itself so interesting. Painted for Edward VI., in compliment to this great seaman and national benefactor, and the property, in succession, of two Queens, and two Kings of England, its retirement to private life may probably be dated from a Sale at which Oliver Cromwell was a bidder.

Cabot was evidently, as has been said, at a very advanced age when the Portrait was taken. His stature, though somewhat lost in a slight stoop, must have been commanding. Holbein would seem to have wished to catch the habitual, unpremeditated expression which he had doubtless, from engagements about the Court, had frequent opportunities of remarking. It is that of profound, and even painful, thought; and in the deeply-marked lines, and dark hazel eye, there yet linger tokens of the force and ardour of character of this extraordinary man. The right hand exhibits an admirable specimen of the painter's minute, elaborate finish. Of the compasses which it holds one foot is placed on a great globe resting on a table on which are an hour-glass and writing materials. The rich robe, and massy gold chain, are probably badges of his office as Governor of the Society of Merchant-Adventurers. It is impossible not to gaze with deep interest on this memorial, heightened, perhaps, by a reflection on its present humble position—emblematic, indeed, of the slight on the closing years of the great original.*

---

* A Catalogue of the Pictures, &c., belonging to Charles I., drawn up in his lifetime, and apparently for his use, is found amongst the Harleian MSS. No. 4718. Amongst those enumerated as then in the Privy Gallery at White-Hall that of Cabot is not mentioned. This might lead to the inference that it had got into private hands sooner than is above suggested, particularly as it appears by

(G.)

ERROR IN ATTRIBUTING TO CABOT THE WORK ENTITLED "NAVIGATIONE NELLE PARTE SETTENTRIONALE," PUBLISHED AT VENICE IN 1583.

THERE has been universally referred to Sebastian Cabot a work entitled "Navigatione nelle parte settentrionale," published at Venice in 1583; and in the Catalogue of the Bodleian Library, it is actually announced under the title "*Cabot.*" The Biographie Universelle, adverting to this circumstance, says, in seeming despair, that this work, unknown to all the Biographers who had been consulted on the subject, is perhaps imaginary.* An explanation may be given, though somewhat at the expense of the Biographie Universelle, and of the Bodleian Catalogue.

The work in question will be found in the second volume of Ramusio (ed. of 1583 and of 1606, fol. 212). In the Memoir of Camus on the Collection of De Bry and Thevenot, he takes occasion to furnish a list of the contents of Ramusio, and in his account (p. 10) of the second volume this tract is noticed as the 17th article. The Biographie Universelle cites this Memoir (art. Ramusio), but of

---

the Catalogue that some of the Pictures had been recently obtained in the way of exchange. Again, it may have been sent, or taken, away by the King. In the MS. work of Richard Symonds (Harleian MSS. No. 991), it is said, "The Committee at Somerset-house valued the King's pictures and other movable goods at 200,000*l.*, *notwithstanding that both himself and the Queen had carried away abundance.*" The painting in question is not specially mentioned in a List of the Sales during the Protectorate, found in the Harleian MSS. No. 7352, though this is by no means decisive, as several of the entries are mere charges against individuals for "a Picture," "two pictures," "three pictures," &c. (fol. 222, et seq.). Cabot's Portrait has recently been seen, in London, by the most eminent artists, and instantly recognised as a Holbein. However we may balance between probabilities as to its intermediate history, a doubt as to its identity with the picture referred to by Purchas, seems to involve not only the necessity of accounting for the disappearance of the latter, but also the extravagant supposition that *two* Portraits of Cabot, bearing the same remarkable inscription, were executed by the great Artist of his day.

* "Ce livre inconnu a tous les Bibliographes que nous avons consultés est peutetre imaginaire" (art. Cabot).

course it could not have been read attentively, or we should not have heard of the ineffectual inquiries amongst the bibliographers. The authenticity of the work, wholly unknown to the bibliographers consulted by the Biographie Universelle, is discussed by *Foscarini* in his Literatura Veneziana, and by *Tiraboschi* in the Storia Della Literatura Italiana. They denounce the error of attributing it to Cabot, though not aware of its real history. Tiraboschi supposes it a translation of some work now lost.

The truth happens to be, that it is nothing more than the Journal of Stephen Burrough during his two voyages to the North-East, with an absurd introduction from some anonymous writer at Venice! The account of the incident at Gravesend which probably suggested to the Italian the name of Cabot is omitted, and the whole is disfigured, but the identity may at once be detected by comparing the closing paragraph of the article in Ramusio as to the first voyage (fol. 216) with the corresponding paragraph of the Journal of Stephen Burrough (Hakluyt, vol. i. p. 283); and, again, the concluding paragraph of the second voyage (fol. 219) with the corresponding part in Hakluyt, vol. i. p. 295.

It is proper to remark that in the work of Ramusio, as published by himself, this tract is not to be found, but has been interpolated in the subsequent editions. The voyage, indeed, was not completed until after Ramusio's death. Yet this circumstance rather aggravates the charge against the Biographie Universelle. That work (art. Ramusio) earnestly advises the reader to consult *Camus** in selecting a copy of Ramusio, and Camus, following the Books on

* An instance of the carelessness of this writer ought to be mentioned in justice to the Abbe Prevost. In the "Histoire et Description Generale de la Nouvelle France," by Charlevoix (Ed. of 1744, tom. i. p. 100), an account is given of the memorable expedition of Dominique de Gourgue to Florida, and use is made of a history of the expedition in the possession of the family of de Gourgue, drawn up by the chivalrous Commander himself. This statement is repeated by the Abbe Prevost (Histoire Generale des Voyages, vol. xiv. p. 448, Paris ed. in 4to), with a reference, such as he had before given, to Charlevoix as the Historian of New France. Camus (p. 46) falls into the error of supposing that the reference of Prevost is to the old work of Lescarbot, and remarks, "Il cite pour garant de ce fait l'auteur de l'Histoire de la Nouvelle France; je n'ai pu l'y trouver au moins dans l'edition de 1609!" The document referred to by Charlevoix is yet in the possession of the Family, and the Viscount Gourgue was good enough recently, at the author's request, to permit the collation of it with a copy of the MS. Narrative in the King's Library at Paris, supposed to have been transmitted by Dominique de Gourgue to Charles IX.

Bibliography, specially recommends the perfidious editions. It is plain, therefore, that the remarks of the Biographie Universelle were made without consulting the guide which is recommended to the reader.

A remark cannot be forborne on the utter folly which has consented to repeat the advice referred to as to the selection of a Ramusio. It is obvious that the great value of such a work resides in the assurance felt by the reader that the articles found there were subjected, at an early period, to the honest judgment of the compiler, and that before admitting them he satisfied himself that they had a fair claim to authenticity. The discrimination which Ramusio exercised has become an important item of evidence. Thus he rejects the first and second of the alleged voyages of Amerigo Vespucci, but republishes the two last.* Though he speaks in respectful terms of Vespucci, we may fairly infer that he considered the first voyage as a fiction, and the account of the second as suspicious on account of the unwarrantable importance assumed by Vespucci for himself at a time when he was known to have been acting under the orders of Hojeda. Now what can be more obviously absurd than to recommend an edition where this valuable characteristic is completely lost sight of and new matter is interpolated, on no avowed responsibility, yet in such a manner as to have misled some of the most learned individuals and societies of the day, and of course fatally deceptive to those who make only an occasional hurried reference to the work?

One example of the pernicious consequence of this proceeding is too remarkable to be passed over. It relates to that memorable fraud, the pretended voyage of Nicholas and Antonio Zeno.

The Dedication of this work, as originally published by Marcolini, bears date December, 1558. Ramusio died in July 1557; and of course it is impossible that it could have been published by him, or that he could have marked it for insertion. It does not appear in the Ramusio of 1559, but was interpolated into the second volume in 1574, seventeen years after his death. This circumstance is decisive against its authenticity. Ramusio, a native of Venice, was not only a diligent and anxious collector of voyages, but, it appears by his work, was familiar with the family of the Zeno of that

* "In questo volume non si fa mentione delle navigationi fatte da Amerigo Vespucci all' Indie Occidentali per ordine de gli Re de Castiglia, ma solamente di quelle due che el fece di Commissionie del Re di Portogallo" (tom. i. fol. 130).

city, and he speaks with pride (Ed. of 1559, tom. ii. fol. 65, D.) of the adventurous travels of Caterino Zeno in Persia. Had the materials for such a narrative existed he would have eagerly seized the opportunity of embodying them, and it is plain that the imposture dared not make its appearance in his lifetime. Yet, from the subsequent interpolation, this tract, by almost unanimous consent, has been considered to bear the high sanction of Ramusio's name.

"This," says Forster (p. 180), "is the account given of the affair *by Ramusio.*" The Biographie Universelle (art. Zeno) says "Cette Relation a été reimprimé *par Ramusio.*" And the Quarterly Review (vol. xvi. p. 165, *note*) speaks of certain things known "before *Ramusio published* the Letters of the two Zeni." In short, the misconception has been universal.

Nor is it merely from the silence of Ramusio that an inference is drawn against this pretended voyage.

He declares in the Preface to the Third Volume, that he considers it not only proper, but in the nature of a duty, to vindicate the truth in the behalf of Columbus, who was the first to discover and bring to light the New World.*

He answers in detail the calumny that the project was suggested to Columbus by a Pilot who died in his house, and refers for a refutation of the idle tale to persons *yet living in Italy*, who were present at the Spanish Court when Columbus departed. He recites the circumstances which had conducted the mind of Columbus, as an able and experienced mariner and Cosmographer, to the conclusion that his project was practicable.

"Such," he declares in conclusion, "were the circumstances that led to his anxiety to undertake the voyage, having fixed it in his mind that by going directly West the Eastern extremity of the Indies would be discovered."†

He breaks into an apostrophe to the rival city of Genoa which had given birth to Columbus, a fact so much more glorious than that about which seven of the greatest cities of Greece contended.‡

---

* "No pure é convenevole, ma par mi anco di essere obligato a dire alquate parole accompagnate dalla verità per diffesa del Signor Christoforo Colombo, ilqual fu *il primo inventore di discoprire et far venire in luce questa meta del mondo.*"

† "Tutte queste cose lo inducevano á voler far questo viaggio, havendo fisso nell' animo che andando a dritto per Ponente esso troverebbe le parti di Levanti ove sono l'Indie."

‡ "Genoua si vanti et glorii di cosi excellente huomo cittadin suo et mettasi á paragone di quatunque altra citta percioche costui non fu Poeta, come Homero

The full force of this evidence cannot be understood without adverting to the strength of Ramusio's prejudices in favour of his native City. He honestly acknowledges that their influence may mislead him when he is disposed to rank the enterprize of Marco Polo, of Venice, by land, as more memorable than even that of the great Genoese by sea.*

Yet this is the writer who is said to have given to the world undeniable evidence not only that the Venetian Zeno knew of these regions upwards of a century before the time of Columbus, but that traces had been discovered proving that the Venetians had visited them long before the time of Zeno. And in a work of the present day we have these monstrous assertions:

They [the Zeni] "added a Relation which, whether true or false, contained the positive assertion of a continent existing to the West of the Atlantic Ocean. *This Relation was unquestionably known to Columbus.*"†

The professed author of the book, Marcolini, was a bookseller and publisher of Venice. It bears his well-known device, of which Dr Dibdin‡ has given a fac-simile. The motive for getting it up is pretty well disclosed in the concluding remarks which allude to the prevailing appetite of the public for such works. It is stated that

---

del qual sette citta dell maggiori che havesse la Grecia contesero insieme affermando ciascuna che egli era su Cittadino, ma fu un huomo il quale *ha fatto nascer al mondo un altro mondo* che é effetto incomparabilment molto maggiore del detto di sopra." The terms in which he denounces the effort to disparage Columbus, on the ground of pretended hints from the Pilot, assure us of the manner in which he would have treated the subsequent imposture absurdly attributed to himself; "questa favola laqual malitiosamente dopo suo ritorno fu per invidia finta dalla gente bassa et ignorante." Again: "una favola pieno di malignita et di tristitia." He loftily denounces the baseness with which a low envy had seized on and dressed up this tale, "ad approvar la detta favola et dipingerla con mille colori."

* "Et se l'affettione della patria non m'inganna, mi par che per ragion probabile si possa affermare che questo fatto per terra debba esser anteposto à quello di mare," Pref. tom. ii.

† Dr Lardner's Cabinet Cyclopædia, History of Maritime and Inland Discovery, vol. i. p. 225.

‡ Bibliographical Decameron, vol. ii. p. 244–5. In Singer's learned "Researches into the History of Playing Cards, with Illustrations of the origin of Printing and Engraving on Wood," is an account (p. 64–65) of Marcolini's beautiful volume, entitled *Le Sorti*. "The decorative woodcuts are very numerous, and many of them very beautiful; great numbers of them afterwards served to decorate the *Capriccios* of that odd genius Doni, who seems to have been employed by Marcolini to write some of his whimsical productions as vehicles for these Woodcuts."

the slight materials extant had been put together that they might not be altogether lost at a period "most [illegible] narratives, and of the discoveries of strange countries, made by the bold and indefatigable exertions of our ancestors" ("studiosissima delle *Narrationi nuovi* et delle discoperte de paesi non conosciuti fatte dal grande animo et grande industria de i nostri maggiori").

A full exhibition of the evidence which establishes this production to be a rank imposture would require more space than can here be justifiably devoted to a topic purely incidental. As it is likely to engage attention, anew, in connexion with the rumoured discoveries in East or Lost Greenland, such a degree of interest may be thrown round it as to warrant, hereafter, in a different form, a detailed examination.

Reverting to the immediate subject under consideration—the alterations of Ramusio in recent editions—an example occurs in reference to this voyage of the Zeni, which shews not only that new matter has been unwarrantably introduced, but that the text has been corrupted, without hesitation, to suit the purposes of the moment.

It has been made a charge against Hakluyt, that in translating the work of Marcolini, he has interpolated a passage representing *Estotiland*, the Northern part of the new Region, as abounding in gold and other metals:

"In Hakluyt's Collection of Voyages, it is added, they have mines of all manner of metals, but especially they abound in gold. This passage, however, is not to be found in the Italian original of Ramusio."*

The English Translator of Forster, referring (p. 189) to the alleged infidelity of Hakluyt, says,

"From many circumstances, it appears, that Hakluyt's collection was made principally with a view to excite his countrymen to prosecute new discoveries in America, and to promote the trade to that quarter of the globe. Considering it in this light, and that hardly any thing was thought worthy of notice in that age but mines of silver and mountains of gold, *we need not wonder at the interpolation!*"

Thus has Hakluyt been made, alternately, the theme of extravagant eulogium and groundless denunciation! The passage about gold *is* in the original (fol. 52) precisely as he translates it: "Hanno lingua et lettere separate et cavano *Metalli d'ogni sorte et sopra tutto abondano d'Oro et le lor pratiche sono in Engroneland* di dove traggono pellerecie, &c." The misconception of later writers

* Forster's Northern Voyages, p. 189, note

is due to a complex piece of roguery running through the several editions of Ramusio.

The story of Nicolo and Antonio Zeno gains a footing, for the first time, in the second volume of the Venice edition of 1574, of which there is a copy in the Library of the British Museum The passage of the original representing Estotiland to abound in Gold is found there (fol. 224 A.). But before the next edition came out, the well-known result of Frobisher's magnificent hopes was calculated to throw ridicule on such representations. The passage, therefore, disappears from the editions of 1583 and 1606 (fol. 232 A.). The suppression is executed in rather an awkward manner. On turning to the passage indicated of the more recent editions, there will be discovered, at the eleventh line from the top of the page, a chasm in the sense between "cavano" and "di dove." The suppression of the intermediate words, which are marked in *italics* in our quotation from the original, constitutes the fraud, and renders what remains unintelligible. Hakluyt made his translation from the Ramusio of 1574, and not from the original work of Marcolini. This is evident from the fact, that in his translation (vol. iii. p. 124) immediately after the death of Nicolo Zeno, there follows a deduction of descent from him to "the other Zenos that are living at this day," of which there is not a syllable in the original (fol. 51), but it is interpolated into the Ramusio of 1574. He escaped the falsification of the edition of 1583, because his translation was made prior to that time, it having appeared in his early work "Divers Voyages, &c." published in 1582. The matter, then, stands thus. Hakluyt followed a vicious copy, but one which had reached only the first stage of depravation. Those who denounce him merely happen to have got hold of a subsequent edition which has been further tampered with. Neither party went back to the Original, though by no means a rare book; and it is curious that the critics of Hakluyt, while talking of the "original," had before them neither the original Marcolini, nor the original Ramusio, nor even, if the expression may be used, the original counterfeit of Ramusio. In this last particular Hakluyt has the advantage over them.

It has been ascertained from Oxford that the tract which figures in the Catalogue of the Bodleian Library is not to be found in a separate form, but only as an item of the second volume of Ramusio. The person who prepared the Catalogue was doubtless caught by the attractive name of Cabot, and unfortunately gave to it this deceptive prominence.

The erroneous citation by Hakluyt (vol. iii. p. 6) of the *second* volume of Ramusio, instead of the *first*, was probably occasioned by this tract. [illegible] had said that the passage containing the Conversation of Butrigarius was to be found in the Italian History of Navigations. Hakluyt, in looking over the first and third volumes of Ramusio, found no leading title to catch his attention, whilst the spurious article in the second volume has the name of Cabot running ostentatiously at the top of the page. He probably conjectured that it was to be found there. *Purchas* (Pilgrims, vol. iii. p. 807) implicitly follows Hakluyt, and repeats the citation of the second volume.

It is remarkable that in "The History of Navigation," found in Churchill's Collection (vol. i. p. lxxiv.) and usually attributed to Locke, there is an account of the contents of Ramusio, and this item of the second volume is represented as a description of Cabot's Voyage "to The *North-West!*"

Another instance of unwarrantable liberty taken with the text of Ramusio, occurs in a passage which has already been cited. In that Conversation, usually connected with the name of *Butrigarius*, the speaker is described in the edition of 1554 (vol. i. fol. 413, A.) merely as a gentleman, "un gentil'huomo," but in the editions of 1583, 1606, and 1613 (fol. 373), the expression is altered to "un gentil'huomo *Mantovano*," doubtless from mere conjecture.

The fact is remarkable, that owing to the deceptive instructions given for the purchase of this work, there is rarely found in the most carefully selected Libraries an uncorrupted copy—one which can be taken up without peril to the reader, at every turn, of being the dupe of rash, or fraudulent, alteration by an unknown editor.

Additional matter appearing in 2nd London Edition at Pages 77–78 and mentioned in Preface. To paragraph in Text ending "was first discovered by an expedition commissioned to 'set up the banner' of England." The following Note is appended:

"A passage in the Interlude of the Nature of the Four Elements" given in Mr. Collier's recent 'Annals of the Stage,' supplies a curious allusion to this fact. The Interlude is by some antiquarians referred to the year 1510, and by others to 1517:

"And also what an honorable thynge,
Both to the Realme and to the Kynge,
To have had his domnynyon extendynge
There into so far a grounde
Whiche the noble Kynge of late memory,
The most wyse prynce, the VII Herry
Caused furst for to bee founde".